HARRY BLUMENTHAL, M.A., M.F.C.C.
Washington-Whittier Medical Building
12468 East Washington Blvd.
Whittier, California 90602

INTERNATIONAL JOURNAL OF
PSYCHOANALYTIC PSYCHOTHERAPY

International Journal of Psychoanalytic Psychotherapy

Edited by ROBERT LANGS, M.D.
and the Editorial Board

Volume Eight
1980–81

NEW YORK • JASON ARONSON • LONDON

JOURNAL POLICY

All manuscripts should be submitted in triplicate and double-spaced on white bond paper. The title page of each article must contain the author's full name and address, academic affiliation, date of submission, and a 150-page word summary of the article's contents. Charts and tables must be on separate pages, keyed to the manuscript. Headings, which should be brief, follow the style used in this journal. Footnotes and references, also following the style of the Journal, should be listed separately triple-spaced at the end of the article.

Submit all manuscripts to Robert J. Langs, M.D., 425 East 58th Street, New York, New York 10022.

ISBN: 0-87668-428-2

Library of Congress Catalog Number: 75-648853

Contributors

Reprint request addresses are in italics.

FARIBORZ AMINI, M.D. is Associate Clinical Professor of Psychiatry at the University of California, San Francisco, where he is Director of the outpatient department, Department of Psychiatry, and also Director of Residency Training. He is on the faculty of the San Francisco Psychoanalytic Institute and is a practicing analyst and child psychiatrist.

STUART ASCH, M.D. is Clinical Professor of Psychiatry, Cornell University Medical College, and a faculty member of the New York Psychoanalytic Institute and the Columbia University Psychoanalytic Institute. *New York Hospital/525 East 68th Street/New York, New York 10021*

GORDON BAUMBACHER, M.D. is Assistant Professor of Psychiatry at the University of California, San Francisco. He is Assistant Director of Residency Training, Department of Psychiatry, a candidate in adult and child analysis at the San Francisco Psychoanalytic Institute, and is in private practice. *University of California/San Francisco, California 94143*

MARK J. BLOTCKY, M.D. is Director, Children's Unit, Department of Child and Adolescent Psychiatry, Timberlawn Psychiatric Hospital and Clinical Instructor of Psychiatry, Southwestern Medical School, University of Texas Health Science Center, Dallas, Texas. He teaches in the residency training programs at Timberlawn and at Southwestern Medical School. *Timberlawn Psychiatric Hospital/P.O. Box 11288/Dallas, Texas 75223*

DANIEL B. BORENSTEIN, M.D. is on the teaching faculty of the Los Angeles Psychoanalytic Society and Institute and the UCLA Neuropsychiatric Institute. He is the current President of the Southern California Psychiatric Society. He practices psychoanalysis and psychotherapy privately in West Los Angeles. *151 North Canyon View Drive/Los Angeles, California 90049*

RONALD D. BROWN, M.D., F.R.C.P. (C) is a member of the Canadian Psychoanalytic Society. He is in charge of psychoanalytically oriented psychotherapy training programs at the Hòpital Général Juif Sir Mortimer B. Davis, a McGill University teaching hospital.

J. ALEXIS BURLAND, M.D. is Clinical Professor of Psychiatry and Human Behavior at Jefferson Medical College, current President of the Philadelphia Psychoanalytic Society, on the faculty of the Philadelphia Psychoanalytic Institute, and on the editorial board of *The International Journal for Psychoanalytic Psychotherapy*. *15 Colwyn Lane/Bala Cynwyd, Pennsylvania 19004*

THEODORE L. DORPAT, M.D. is Clinical Professor of the Department of Psychiatry and Behavioral Sciences at the University of Washington School of Medicine and a training analyst at the Seattle Psychoanalytic Institute. *2271 N.E. 51st Street/Seattle, Washington 98015*

SUSANNA ISAACS ELMHURST, F.R.C.P. is on the faculty at the University of Southern California, and the staffs of the Reiss-Davis Child Study Center and the Mt. Sinai Child Residency Program, Los Angeles. *9606 Arby Drive/Beverly Hills, California 90210*

ROBERT T. FINTZY, M.D. is on the faculty of UCLA and teaches residents and child fellows in the Cedars-Sinai training program. He is currently in private practice in West Los Angeles.

JUDITH H. FORGOTSON, M.D. is Chief, Division of Child Psychiatry and Assistant Professor of Psychiatry, Southwestern Medical School, University of Texas Health Science Center, Dallas, Texas. She is the Director of Child Psychiatry Training for both medical students and residents and has a special interest in the use of videotapes in teaching child psychiatry.

ELEANOR GALENSON, M.D. is Clinical Professor of Psychiatry at Mt. Sinai School of Medicine, and at Albert Einstein College of Medicine. She is also Director of the therapeutic nursery at the Lexington School for the Deaf. *9 East 96th Street/New York, New York 10028*

MERTON GILL, M.D. is Professor of Psychiatry at Abraham Lincoln School of Medicine, University of Illinois (Chicago), and Supervising Analyst at the Chicago Institute for Psychoanalysis. *P.O. Box 6998/912 South Wood Street/Chicago, Illinois 60680*

ROBERT A. GLICK, M.D. is Physician-in-Charge of emergency psychiatric services at Columbia Presbyterian Medical Service. He is Assistant Clinical Professor of Psychiatry at Columbia University College of Physicians and Surgeons. *40 East 89th Street/New York, New York 10028*

ARNOLD GOLDBERG, M.D. is Attending Psychiatrist and Director of Psychiatry, Residents Supervision at Michael Reese Hospital, Chicago, Illinois. He is Clinical Associate Professor of Psychiatry at the Pritzker School of Medicine, University of Chicago, and a Training and Supervising analyst on the faculty of the Chicago Institute for Psychoanalysis. *180 North Michigan Avenue/Suite 2407/Chicago, Illinois 60601*

ANDRE GREEN, M.D. is a Training Analyst at the Paris Psychoanalytic Institute and a former Vice President of the International Psychoanalytic Association. *6, Rue du Val de Grace/75006 Paris/France*

LESLIE S. GROH, Ph.D. has concentrated on the treatment of borderline and psychotic children, adolescents, and adults. He served on the faculty of the Menninger School of Psychiatry as a psychotherapy supervisor for six years. He is currently in private practice in Los Angeles. *8111 Beverly Boulevard/Los Angeles, California 90048*

JAMES GROTSTEIN, M.D. is a Training and Supervising Analyst with the Los Angeles Psychoanalytic Institute. He is Associate Clinical Professor at the UCLA Department of Psychiatry, and Director of the Group for Advanced Studies in Schizophrenia and Allied Conditions. *9777 Wilshire Boulevard/Beverly Hills, California 90212*

BETTY JOSEPH is a member of the British Psycho-Analytical Society. *36 Clifton Hall/London NW8 OQG/England*

CECILIA KAROL, M.D. is Clinical Instructor in Psychoanalysis at New York University and president-elect of the New Jersey Psychoanalytic Society. *79 Sherwood Road/Tenafly, New Jersey 07670*

M. MASUD R. KHAN is a member of the Institute of Psychoanalysis, London, Director of the Sigmund Freud Copyrights, and Foreign Editor of the *Nouvelle Revue de Psychoanalyse*. He is a former editor of the International Psycho-Analytical Library. *Flat 7/24 Palace Court/London W2 4HU/England*

ALAN KROHN, Ph.D. is on the faculty of the Department of Psychiatry at the University of Michigan, on the senior staff of the University of

Michigan Psychological Clinic, and in private practice in Ann Arbor. *University of Michigan/Department of Psychiatry/900 Wall St./Ann Arbor, Michigan 48104*

ROBERT LANGS, M.D. is editor of this journal and Program Director of the Lenox Hill Hospital Psychotherapy Program in New York. *30 East 60th Street/Room 409/New York, New York 10022*

MELVIN R. LANSKY, M.D. is Adjunct Associate Professor of Psychiatry at UCLA Medical School, and Chief, Family Treatment Program, Brentwood V.A. Medical Center, Los Angeles. He is a graduate of the Los Angeles Psychoanalytic Institute, and his paper "On Blame" was co-winner of the Jaques Brien Award for the best paper by a member of the Institute in 1978. *1100 Glendon Avenue/Suite 1527/Los Angeles, California 90024*

MORTON LEVITT, Ph.D. was, until his recent death, Executive Associate Dean and Professor of Psychiatry at the University of California, Davis, School of Medicine, and an affiliate member of the San Francisco Psychoanalytic Society and Institute.

JOSHUA LEVY, Ph.D. is a Training Analyst at the Canadian Institute of Psychoanalysis. He is Director of Psychotherapy programs and Assistant Professor of Psychiatry at the University of Ottawa Medical School. *Royal Ottawa Hospital/1145 Carling Avenue/Ottawa, Ontario K12 7K4/Canada*

DAVID LIBERMAN, M.D. is former President of the APA. former Secretary of the IPA. and former Professor of Psychopathology at the University of Buenos Aires. A training analyst of the Institute of Psychoanalysis of the Buenos Aires Psychoanalytic Society he has contributed papers on communication and linguistics in the analytic process to international congresses. *Santa Fe 2829/1429 Buenos Aires/Argentina*

JOSEPH D. LICHTENBERG, M.D. is a practicing psychoanalyst in Washington, D.C. He is a Training Analyst in the Baltimore-Washinton, D.C. Institute for Psychoanalysis, and he chairs a seminar and workshop on psychobiography and Henry James. *1616 Eighteenth Street, N.W./Washington, D.C. 20009*

NATHANIEL J. LONDON, M:D. is Director of the Minnesota Psychoanalytic Foundation, Geographic Training analyst and Faculty Member of the Chicago Institute for Psychoanalysis, and Clinical Professor at the Department of Psychiatry, University of Minnesota. He is also a Lecturer at the University of Minnesota School of Social Work. *1837 Medical Arts Building/Minneapolis, Minnesota 55402*

JOHN E. MEEKS, M.D. is Director of Child and Adolescent Services for the Psychiatric Institute of Washington, D.C. He is the author of *The Fragile Alliance: An Orientation to the Outpatient Psychotherapy of Adolescents. 4460 McArthur Boulevard N.W./Washington, D.C. 20037*

W.W. MEISSNER, S.J., M.D. is Associate Clinical Professor of Psychiatry at the Harvard Medical School and a member of the faculty of the Boston Psychoanalytic Institute. He has coauthored a basic psychoanalytic text with Dr. Elizabeth Zetzel and has recently published *The Paranoid Process.* I le has been actively involved in the study of aspects of clinical psychoanalysis and has maintained an interest in various areas of applied psychoanalyis, including psychohistory, for several years. *6 Somner Road/ Cambridge, Massachusetts 02138*

ARTHUR T. MEYERSON, M.D. is an associate professor of clinical psychiatry at the Mount Sinai School of Medicine and director of the Psychiatric Acute Care Services at the Mount Sinai Hospital. He is an Associate member of American Psychoanalytic Association, a Fellow of the American Psychiatric Association, and an associate editor of *The Journal of Psychiatry and Law. Mount Sinai Hospital/Mount Sinai School of Medicine/New York, New York 10029*

IRA L. MINTZ, M.D. is a child psychoanalyst and is a member of the faculty of the Columbia University Psychoanalytic Training Center, and a member of the American Psychoanalytic Association, and a Fellow of the American Psychiatric Association. *39 Park Place/Englewood, New Jersey 07631*

WAYNE A. MYERS, M.D. is Clinical Associate Professor in the Cornell University Medical Center. He is a member of the New York Psychoanalytic Society and Institute, the American Psychoanalytic Association, and the International Psycho-Analytic Association. He is on the faculty of the Columbia University Psychoanalytic Clinic for Training and Research. *1385 York Avenue (Apt. 17G)/New York, New York 10021*

ANNA ORNSTEIN, M. D. is Professor of Child Psychiatry, University of Cincinnati College of Medicine, and a faculty member, Cincinnati Institute for Psychoanalysis. *4177 Rose Hill Avenue/Cincinnati, Ohio 45229*

EDNA O'SHAUGHNESSY is a psychoanalyst of children and adults, and a member of the British Institute of Psycho-Analysis. *6 Oakhill Avenue/London NW3/England*

THOMAS A. PETTY, M.D. is Clinical Professor of Psychiatry at Wayne State University School of Medicine and Lecturer at the Michigan Psychoanalytic Institute. He is in the private practice of psychoanalysis and psychiatry in Grosse Point, Michigan. *17300 East Jefferson Avenue/Grosse Point, Michigan 48230*

LEO RANGELL, M.D. is Clinical Professor of Psychiatry, University of California, Los Angeles and Clinical Professor of Psychiatry (Psychoanalysis), University of California, San Francisco. He is also Past President of the American Psychoanalytic Association and Past President of the International Psychoanalytic Association. *456 North Carmelina Avenue/Los Angeles, California 90049*

RUTH RIESENBERG MALCOLM is Lecturer at the Tavistock Clinic and a Supervising and Training analyst at the British Institute of Psychoanalysis. *33 Greenhill/Hampstead High Street/London NW3 5UA/England*

BEN RUBENSTEIN, Ph.D. is Adjunct Clinical Professor of Psychiatry at the Dartmouth Medical School. He is an affiliate member of the Boston Psychoanalytic Society and Institute. *Route 3/Brattleboro, Vermont 05304*

KURT A. SCHLESINGER, M.D. is Associate Clinical Professor of Psychiatry at the University of California, San Francisco, and Associate Chief of Psychiatry at Mt. Zion Hospital. He is on the faculty of the San Francisco Psychoanalytic Institute, and a member of GAP. *1920 Scott Street/San Francisco, California 94115*

MARC SHEINBEIN, Ph. D. is a Clinical Child and Family Psychologist in private practice in Dallas, Texas. He is Assistant Professor, Department of Psychiatry, University of Texas Health Science Center at Dallas, and Chief Psychologist, Children's Medical Center, Dallas, Texas.

JOHN A. TALBOTT, M.D. is Professor of Psychiatry at Cornell University Medical College and Associate Medical Director at the Payne Whitney Psychiatric Clinic. He is on the faculty of the Columbia Psychoanalytic Center and a member of the American Psychoanalytic Association. *New York Hospital, PWC163/525 East 68th Street/New York, New York 10021*

ROBERT S. WALLERSTEIN, M.D. is Chairman of the Department of

Psychiatry, University of California San Francisco School of Medicine and Director of the Langley Porter Institute. He is a Training and Supervising Analyst in the San Francisco Psychoanalytic Institute, a former President of the American Psychoanalytic Association, and currently a Vice-President of the International Psychoanalytic Association. *Department of Psychiatry, University of California, San Francisco/San Francisco, California 94143*

KENNETH M. WIGGINS, M.D. is Director, Children's Psychiatric Inpatient Unit, Children's Medical Center and Associate Professor of Psychiatry, Southwestern Medical School, University of Texas Health Science Center, Dallas, Texas. He teaches in the residency training program at Southwestern Medical School and serves as consultant to school districts and a wide number of social agencies.

C. PHILIP WILSON, M.D. is a psychoanalyst specializing in psychosomatics. A member of the faculties of the Columbia and New York University Psychoanalytic Institutes, he also lectures and teaches at St. Luke's Hospital Center, Columbia's College of Physicians and Surgeons and the Downstate Medical School, where he is an Assistant Clinical Professor of Psychiatry. Formerly Chief of Psychosomatics at Brookdale Hospital Center, he is Chairman of the Psychosomatic Workshop of the Psychoanalytic Association of New York, Inc. *1148 Fifth Avenue/New York, New York 10028*

LEON WURMSER, M.D. is Director of the Alcohol and Drug Abuse Program and Professor of Psychiatry at the University of Maryland School of Medicine. *721 West Redwood Street/Baltimore, Maryland 21201*

LYMAN C. WYNNE, M.D., Ph.D. is Professor of Psychiatry and Director, Division of Family Programs, University of Rochester School of Medicine and Dentistry. *University of Rochester/School of Medicine and Dentistry/300 Crittenden Boulevard/Rochester, New York 14642*

Table of Contents
International Journal of
Psychoanalytic Psychotherapy
Volume 8

CONTRIBUTORS

The Therapeutic and Analytic Interaction

CONTENTS

Basic Clinical Issues

Contents

INTERNATIONAL JOURNAL OF
PSYCHOANALYTIC PSYCHOTHERAPY

Truth Therapy/Lie Therapy

ROBERT LANGS, M.D.

In this paper an attempt is made to conceptualize a basic dimension of various psycho-therapeutic treatment modalities, especially psychoanalysis and psychoanalytically oriented psychotherapy. The central variable under consideration is the extent to which each endeavors to approach the truth within both patient and therapist as it exists dynamically in terms of their spiraling unconscious communicative interaction. That treatment modality which takes into account every possible dimension of such truths is termed *truth therapy*. Treatment modalities that make no attempt to arrive at these truths or that deliberately or inadvertently falsify their nature are termed *lie or barrier therapies*. Extensive consideration is given to truth therapy and the truth system on which it is based. The basis for the need for lie therapies is explored, and lie systems, which may arise from either patient or therapist, or both, are identified. A classification of common types of lie patients and lie therapists (and their main techniques) is offered. The implications of this delineation for our understanding of the dynamic therapies are discussed, and a number of new clinical issues arising from this perspective are addressed.

There have been many efforts of late to characterize and distinguish what has become an enormous variety of therapeutic modalities—psychoanalysis, analytic psychotherapy, supportive therapy, gestalt and existential therapies, behavior modification, and so on. These have been classified along various lines: exploratory versus supportive, breaking down defenses versus reinforcing them, interpersonal versus intrapsychic, individual versus group, individual versus family, etc. There remains, however, a sense of dissatisfaction regarding these distinctions and considerable question in respect to their empirical validity and specific implications for patient-therapist interactions.

The inconclusive status of these distinctions is reflected, too, in a multiplicity of related topics. Issues stand unresolved in respect to the conscious and unconscious motivations within patients as they approach a treatment situation; there is also the question of the conscious and unconscious motives of the therapist who offers such help, as well as of the underlying factors that determine the choice and explication of the therapeutic modality he will use. This touches upon the problem of fundamental resistances within patients in response to a given treatment format, as well as on the issue of counterresistances within therapists. It also suggests the complicated issue of the process "cure" or symptom alleviation (a term used in its broadest sense to include all types of characterological, behavioral, and symptomatic change) as well as the broader question of the essential nature of the therapeutic interaction itself.

This paper is an effort to elaborate a *selected fact* (Bion 1962)—a realization that provides a new meaning and synthesis to previously unclarified and disparate clinical observations. This fact crystallized for me, in my clinical and supervisory work, in the opposition (or continuum) that lends this paper its title: truth therapy/lie therapy. With this as our framework, let us turn to a reconsideration of certain selected concepts pertinent to the therapeutic situation.

SOME BASIC DEFINITIONS

Patient

Let us begin by considering the term *patient*, a term whose meaning is too often taken for granted. Almost without thinking, we could readily state that a patient is an individual who seeks out (or is directed to) and engages a professional—a therapist—in an effort designed for relief of mental suffering and its consequences (neurosis, as I will later term it).

It seems evident, however, that this generally accepted characterization is not only naive but lacks substantial and functional meaning. For example, it would provide no basis for distinguishing a stated wish for help from actual participation in a manner conducive to symptom alleviation. It would allow no room for the differentiation between the conscious wish for cure and unconscious wishes that may contradict this manifest intention.

Similarly, this definition would provide little reason to explore the patient's conscious and unconscious motives for seeking therapy, his expectations as to how it will be carried out, or the implications of his efforts to actually shape the therapy along particular lines. Finally, it would preclude an important distinction that has been largely overlooked: that between the *designated patient* (the person seeking or pushed toward help) and the *functional patient* (the person within the therapeutic dyad who, at a given juncture, is consciously or unconsciously expressing a need for help, that is, for a curative response from the other member of the dyad).

We need a definition of the term, then, that will take into account both stated and unstated—unconsciously expressed—needs and functions. The latter involve factors beyond the formal delineation of the patient's role and requisites (e.g., his position vis-à-vis the therapist, his responsibility for the fee and hours, the fundamental rule of free association, etc.). It becomes a matter of defining the characteristics of the functional patient, the range of behaviors and attitudes that characterize a meaningful and workable quest for psychological and emotional help. Beyond the simplistic definition of the designated patient, we must consider whether the designated patient is at any particular point also a functional patient. Similarly, we need criteria to determine when a designated therapist is, for long or short periods, operating as a functional patient. The final delineation depends on our definition of a number of related terms.

Therapist

The prevailing definition of the term *therapist* is based on his manifest roles and functions; it is actually a definition of what I would term more specifically the *designated therapist*. So defined, the therapist is an individual who, it is supposed, has the expertise to provide symptom relief to the neurotic patient. This definition encompasses the entire range of therapeutic approaches, analytic or not. But if we choose to go deeper, we are faced with the need to define the *functional therapist*. Here we must identify a set of conscious and unconscious behaviors and functions that characterize therapeutic endeavors. On this basis, we could then empirically decide, in examining a particular therapeutic interlude, whether the designated therapist or the designated patient is at that moment serving as the functional therapist, and whether he is doing so consciously or unconsciously.

Therapy

The term *therapy* encompasses, in common parlance, any endeavor to provide symptom relief to the neurotic patient. As such, it embraces many divergent modalities. Here the specific nature of the curative process comes into question. Such issues as effectiveness, durability of outcome, detrimental consequences, and the actual basis for change come under scrutiny. Here it would be particularly helpful if we could identify the actual healing transactions in a given treatment situation. Their surface and underlying aspects must be delineated, including the nature of the spiraling communicative unconscious interaction between patient and therapist, as well as all that it touches upon, both past and present.

In this way, we can shift from the superficially descriptive definition of therapy to one more in keeping with the actuality of unconscious processes. We can then delineate the standards or practices, stated with full sensitivity to both direct and indirect expression, conscious and unconscious meaning and function, that define the various treatment forms.

Neurosis

I propose that we use the term *neurosis* to refer to any symptomatic or characterological disturbance—somatic, psychic, or behavioral—that derives to some significant degree from inner mental conflict and dysfunction. A neurosis, then, is a maladaptive response, one that is inappropriate to consensually validated reality. It is a reaction based largely on pathological unconscious fantasies, memories, and introjects, as well as on dysfunctions and disturbances in each of the macrostructures: id, ego, and superego. At the core of every neurosis lies the most primitive and psychotic part of the personality: major separation and bodily anxieties, internal structural conflicts, pathological identifications, and fears of highly disruptive mental configurations and elements (see Grotstein 1977a,b). This constellation is built up through the years and therefore involves important genetic factors.

Neurotic responses are maladaptations evoked by current realities and their manifest and latent implications. For patients in therapy or analysis, these *adaptive contexts* occur primarily in the realm of the therapeutic interaction; they derive from the behaviors and verbalizations of the therapist or analyst. Traumatic contexts stemming from relationships outside of treatment are secondary. The discovery, analysis, working through and resolution-modification of the unconscious factors in a neurosis is one important means of providing a patient the opportunity for an insightful, lasting revision of his maladaptive responses and their replacement with relatively nonsymptomatic, adaptive resources and reactions founded on genuine structural change.

Truth

We require for our purposes a definition of truth relevant to the patient and his neurosis, and to the therapist and his interventions—relevant, in short, to the nature of therapy. It must therefore be a definition that encompasses the immediate unconscious therapeutic communicative interaction as this pertains to the patient's illness. This implies that there can be but one truth system in this context, though patient or therapist can deal with it in a variety of ways. Truths must be formulated as hypotheses through an in-depth evaluation of an activated adaptive context and derivative response, and must then be confirmed through an unanticipated Type Two derivative expression.

The search for the truth begins with the surface relationship and transactions between patient and therapist, however the two participants are defined. It then extends into the conscious and unconscious implications—meanings and functions—of these transactions, specifically as they pertain to factors underlying the development and maintenance of the patient's neurosis and activated in the patient-therapist interaction.

This definition has many implications. First, it indicates that the most basic truths in psychotherapy pertain to the designated patient's illness. It therefore implies that the neurosis of the designated therapist is secondary and has meaning only as it relates to the emotional difficulties of the patient. However, it does leave room for the recognition that under certain conditions the neurosis of the therapist may take center stage—at which point he becomes, by the definitions developed here, the functional patient.

Second, this conception places the spiraling unconscious communicative interactions between patient and therapist at the very heart of the treatment situation. It encompasses the surface and depths of this interaction, its manifest and latent dimensions, and suggests that the truth about the patient's neurosis can be known only by taking this interaction as the starting point and tracing out its constituents from there—intrapsychically, interactionally, dynamically, and genetically.

Third, this definition permits the understanding of truth in terms of both reality and fantasy. It allows consideration of both accurate and erroneous perceptions of actuality, of both realistic and unrealistic forms of imagination. It accommodates both the introjective and the projective aspects of the patient's experiences within the therapeutic interaction, and fosters the understanding of the patient's illness in terms of sources in both the present and the past, within the therapeutic situation as well as outside it. Empirically, however, it stresses the overriding primacy of the former.

Truth, as defined here, can be stated in terms related to psychoanalytic validation within the clinical situation. The formulation of such truths requires a maximal degree of self-knowledge within the therapist, who must be capable of generating validatable assessments of his own mental state, his conscious and unconscious communications to the patient, the nature of the conscious and unconscious therapeutic interaction, and the full scope of the communications from the patient. The ultimate test for the truth of an interpretation is whether, when imparted to the patient, it meets with interactional and cognitive validation. Interactional validation

occurs through *derivative* representations of positive introjective identifications with a therapist considered capable of understanding the truth.
Cognitive validation is afforded the therapist by the revelation of indirect,
surprising, and unique Type Two derivatives (i.e., disguised material
which organizes meaningfully around an immediate adaptive context
related to therapy), often in the form of the emergence of a *selected fact*.

   In the actual development of this definition, it was the search for
postulates for which Type Two derivative validation could be consistently
obtained that led to the selection of truth as it pertains to the patient's
neurosis as a key dimension of the therapeutic experience. It is therefore
possible to propose that therapeutic modalities can be defined in terms of
their approach to and handling of this particular form of truth in the
treatment situation. Before doing so, it will be necessary for us to define
the opposite of truth, the lie.

Lie

   We may define the term *lie* free of any pejorative implications (see Bion
1970). In our context, it may be defined as any communication or behavior, conscious or unconscious, designed on some level to avoid, falsify,
break the link to, or create a barrier against the dynamically cogent
meanings and functions of the patient's neurosis within the therapeutic
interaction. In short, a lie is any effort to seal off or destroy awareness of
the truth—the actual factors and expressions of the patient's neurosis. As
we shall see, most lies in therapy are expressed unconsciously. Our
definition does not refer to conscious and deliberate lies, since these may
either express or obliterate the truth of the patient's illness.

   While the term *lie* has a penumbra of meanings that might adversely
affect its scientific usage, it serves remarkably well as a selected fact.
Attempts to develop a different term, such as barrier, fiction, or falsification, proved unsuccessful. None of these were able to convey the essential
implications of the term *lie*.

   Empirically, a lie is revealed when the material from the patient fails to
permit a meaningful interpretation—an assessment that must be subjected carefully to validation. In addition, whenever an interpretation or
management of the framework is met with a nonvalidating response, we
may suspect the presence of lie communication in patient or therapist.

   The implications of the term *lie* may be made somewhat clearer by
recognizing that defenses and resistances may be expressed as potential
truths or functional lies. If their manifestations can be organized around a
specific adaptive context to yield Type Two derivative meaning, they have
truthful qualities. I have previously described their presence in the Type

A communicative field, in which the use of symbols and illusion prevails (Langs 1978–1979). In this instance, the communicative expressions of defense and resistance contain within them derivative (unconscious) elements of truth and meaning. Therefore, even though they function for purposes of defense, they also serve to search for and express the truth of the patient's neurosis.

On the other hand, there is another constellation of defenses and resistances which have rather different communicative qualities in respect to truth and lie. They serve to destroy meaning, rather than to reveal it in disguised form. They deal with truth by creating lies and barriers to its expression. They are functional falsifications quite divorced from any derivative expression of the prevailing truth about the therapeutic interaction and the patient's neurosis. The lie-defense is a barrier to the truth, rather than a disguised expression of it. This is a form of communication that I attempted to delineate in describing the static Type C communicative field, characterized by barrier formations and falsifications and in which relatedness and meaning are destroyed (Bion 1977, Langs 1978–1979).

This is a specific definition of the lie, one based on the unconscious functions of a communication. A conscious lie in these terms may serve to either express or obliterate underlying truths; it may be a derivative of the truth or a barrier to it. If the former, it is not a lie as defined here. If the latter, it is the most flagrant and pervasive form of the lie-barrier that we know of.

To my knowledge, these distinctions have not been specified in the prior literature. They are, however, foreshadowed by Bion's discussion (1977) of the Column Two function of the grid. This column represents statements known by the speaker to be false on one level of discourse (however truthful on another), statements that serve as barriers to underlying chaotic truths. Bion has also given unique consideration to the conscious liar and the lie system (1970), and his comments on –K, efforts to destroy knowledge and understanding (1962), are also relevant. The key concept is that of two distinctive types of defensive formation: (1) those based on derivatives which upon analysis reveal both their own unconscious meanings and functions and that which is defended against (the usual psychoanalytic conception); and (2) those based on impervious barriers which do not reflect or reveal upon analysis either their underlying meanings and functions or that which is thereby sealed off.

In the clinical situation this distinction can be made by identifying the prevailing adaptive context within the therapeutic interaction. If the material organizes meaningfully as Type Two derivatives in response to that context, in terms of unconscious fantasies and perceptions, we have an expression of some underlying truth. If, on the other hand, there is either a distinct absence of any representation of the adaptive context, or if there is an evident context without a meaningful derivative constellation, we have evidence for the presence of lies and barriers.

While there is only one constellation of truth, there are many lies and barriers. Some serve as intrapsychic walls and as a means of rupturing interpersonal ties (links) between patient and therapist. Others function primarily as projective identifications and as a means of action-discharge through which disturbing falsifications are placed into the object either in the service of riddance or as evocation-of-proxy responses (Wangh 1962).

Some projective identifications express and impart truths, while others entail lies. This suggests a distinction regarding Type B communicators, who make extensive use of action-discharge mechanisms and projective identification, that had never previously been delineated: some patients use these mechanisms in the service of a search for the truth, while others use them in order to destroy the truth and maintain the lie. Interpretations of the underlying meanings and functions of the projective identification prove feasible with the first group, though not with the second, with whom interventions must center on the nature and functions of the prevailing lie and barrier.

THE POLARIZATION OF TWO BASIC THERAPEUTIC MODALITIES

With these definitions in mind, let us now take our concepts of patient, therapist, and therapy and superimpose each on the axis connecting (and separating) our concepts of truth and lie. Such a process will in all likelihood allow us to provide a more specific content for each of the concepts involved. Several avenues of approach suggest themselves here, of which I shall choose but one: a discussion of psychoanalysis and psychoanalytically oriented psychotherapy. I choose these modalities because of their avowed intention to seek out, identify and analyze the truth of the patient's neurosis. Many noninterpretative therapeutic approaches would accept readily the characterization if not the appellation of lie-barrier therapy outlined here. They do not profess to approach psychoanalytic truth, sometimes not acknowledging it at all. Their self-understanding is that they effect their therapeutic results in some other manner. I will return to this subject in my final discussion, since I hope to offer a point of view that will foster a sympathetic understanding of the nature of these therapeutic modalities and of the patients and therapists who turn to them.

Truth Therapy

We can distinguish two extreme types of patients, therapists, and therapies. With respect to truth or lie communication, a number of combinations of patients and therapists are possible. However, truth therapy can exist and be perpetuated only in the presence of a patient and a therapist who are both of them truth-receiving (listening) and truth-telling (associating and intervening). While this is the ideal model for insight-oriented therapy and is taken for granted in most analytic writings, once we define the relevant attributes we will be in a position to discover just how rare this type of treatment actually is.

In brief, truth therapy is a treatment situation in which the conditions are created that permit the patient to express analyzable derivatives, the therapist to impart sound interpretations, and the patient to receive and meaningfully utilize the proffered understanding. If we focus first on the patient, it can be readily seen that our considerations go well beyond his surface announcement that he wishes to understand himself or, more vaguely, to be relieved of his symptoms. It is also insufficient to state that the truth-seeking patient is capable of free associating and of tolerating the deprivations and limited gratifications of a sound analytic setting and interpretive approach. Similarly, it is inadequate to suggest that such a patient is capable of forming a manifest therapeutic alliance with the therapist based on apparent cooperative efforts directed toward insight and understanding.

The criteria for a truth-seeking patient involve the manner in which he expresses himself and receives and processes the interventions from the therapist. In regard to the former, the truth patient utilizes the Type A communicative mode. Over brief sequences of sessions, these patients represent directly or through relatively undisguised derivatives the prevailing adaptive context within the therapeutic interaction. They provide as well a coalescing derivative network in which meaningful unconscious perceptions, fantasies, memories, and introjects are available. Their material leads to a validated interpretative intervention related to a pertinent therapeutic context or indicator that touches ultimately upon the patient's symptomatology and its genetic and current underpinnings.

Quite unconsciously, then, truth patients express their genuine wish to understand by becoming engaged in meaningful *derivative communication*, viable indirect communications organizable around an adaptive context derived from the therapist's interventions. This is the hallmark of a truth-telling patient. And while ultimately his search is directed toward the truth about his own inner mental world and neurosis, he is also prepared to touch upon the true meanings of the therapist's communications as they reflect both the latter's neurosis and his sound functioning. The patient seeks ultimately to know and understand both his unconscious fantasies and his unconscious perceptions of the therapist. These are consistently developed in response to their spiraling communicative interaction, an ongoing reality filled with unconscious implications. All other adaptive contexts and communications, however meaningful, will accrue specific pertinence through linkages to this communicative inter-action. In fact, the absence of any such link implies a departure from the search for the ultimate truth about the patient and a shift toward lie-barrier therapy. Thus, while the truths which must be dealt with in the therapeutic situation are layered hierarchically, a sine qua non is the link to the central adaptive context within the therapeutic interaction. Only interpretations that take into account the main adaptive contexts within the interaction, and the patient's unconscious responses to them, receive Type Two derivative validation.

Next, we can consider the therapist, who has been attending to the patient's associations. Let's assume a truth-seeking patient who has represented the main adaptive context and his derivative responses. For the therapist to be in a position to comprehend and interpret such material, and to have his intervention experienced by the patient as a statement of truth, there must exist a secure and stable therapeutic environment. While a patient may express truth-seeking derivatives in a modified frame (almost always, these are references to the deviation itself), he will have major difficulties in experiencing the therapist's interventions as similarly truth-seeking unless the framework is secured or in the process of being rectified. This is the case largely because deviations in the basic ground rules and therapeutic contract serve as barriers to the truth; they convey a valid image of the therapist as lying and lie-seeking. For a patient to experience the therapist's interventions as an entirely symbolic effort directed toward understanding the truth, there must be no contradictory communications. Alterations in the framework, for example, usually belie such efforts.

The truth therapist, then, is capable of securing and maintaining a stable and consistent therapeutic environment, of adhering to the frame in the face of nonemergency efforts by the patient to evoke deviations, and of responding interpretively to such pressures as well. In the presence of an inadvertent or patient-evoked alteration of the framework, such a therapist is capable of both rectifying the frame and interpreting the patient's responsive unconscious fantasies and perceptions. When the frame is stable, he is able to offer sound interpretations based on an integrated approach that involves the prevailing indicators and adaptive context, as well as the most meaningful aspects of the derivative complex.

The capacity of a therapist to effect truth therapy is by no means a simply cognitive accomplishment. In order to generate an interpretation or reconstruction that will receive Type Two derivative validation, he must first be capable of appreciating the unconscious implications of his interventions—silences, interpretations, reconstructions, and managements of the framework. This requires a capacity for self-analysis and an ability to organize the material from the patient as a Type Two derivative commentary on the adaptive context of each of his interventions, including their manifest and latent implications. This requires a great deal of the therapist: a capacity for frustration tolerance and for delay; an ability to renounce the gratification of pathological instinctual drives and the use of pathological defenses; a healthy and secure superego and ego ideal system; the capacity to tolerate and contain projective identifications and role and image evocations; and a relative mastery of his own pathological tendencies. It seems likely, then, that an unanalyzed therapist can only hope to approximate truth therapy and that only a truth analysis can enable a therapist to develop fully the use of this treatment modality.

While there are many additional requisites the therapist must meet in order to do truth therapy, I would add but one, a factor that applies equally to patient and therapist. Stating it in terms of the therapist, I am referring to a set of interrelated capacities to tolerate and analyze the emergence of a therapeutic regression in the patient (the expression of primitive and sometimes terrifying derivatives of his inner mental world), to experience disruptive and pathological pressures and projective identifications, and to tolerate some degree of parallel regression and primitive expression within himself. The search for truth always entails such regression, as well as significant pain. On the positive side, to the extent that the therapist experiences a limited and appropriate regression, he can grow in personal insight. It is, however, essential to delineate the positive and negative attributes of truth therapy, or of any truth system, and to recognize both its pain and its adaptive rewards. We will return to this issue once we have further clarified the patient's contribution to truth therapy.

We now turn to the truth-seeking patient once he has received a correct interpretation (i.e., an understanding of a segment of the truth in respect to the most active and pertinent neurotic manifestations within the therapeutic bipersonal field at a given moment, be it in the patient or therapist). In my earlier investigations (Langs 1978a,b, 1979), I had assumed that truth-seeking patients (and actually, virtually all patients) respond to a correct interpretation with two forms of validation: (1) derivatives reflecting an inevitable positive introjective identification with the understanding therapist (the interactional and relationship spheres); and (2) Type Two derivative validation with the report of surprising new material that not only confirms the interpretation in an unexpected manner but that also functions quite often as a *selected fact*, giving new meaning to previously disparate material. The latter is a cognitive validation.

My more recent studies, however, have indicated that this dual validation does not in itself suffice as a means of identifying the truth seeker. There are actually three attributes to the truth patient: (1) the expression of analyzable derivatives stemming from an adaptive context within therapy; (2) a response with Type Two derivative validation to correct interpretation or management of the frame by the therapist; and (3) his actual utilization of the insights derived in this way to achieve conscious understanding, the development and use of new adaptive resources, conflict resolution, and the modification of ego dysfunctions and maladaptive responses. Thus the patient's validating response takes place primarily on an unconscious level. He may then react in one of several ways to his experience of a correct interpretation and his responsive associations. Continued truth seeking is only one of several possibilities.

The patient who is fully accepting of truth therapy is both a *truth sender* and *truth receiver*. He will therefore process his cognitive insights and introjective experiences in a way that leads him to consciously recognize at least some fragment of the truth as it had not previously been known to him. He is able to broaden his self-understanding and to link other realizations to this new truth. He makes use of his direct insight into himself—and the therapist—in effecting new and more constructive adaptive responses. When such responses, founded upon conscious insight and unconscious conflict resolution, become durable, we speak of insightful structural change.

Truth-seeking patients make use of these insights in a manner that constructively influences their behavior. They soon embark upon new adaptive behaviors and offer fresh communications unconsciously designed to reach out toward additional repressed, denied, or split-off truths. This thrust toward growth, however gratifying, is studded with periods of defense-resistance, anxiety, regression, and suffering. Eventually, however, come new resolution and relative peace.

There is another kind of patient, who communicates truth-containing derivatives, who then obtains a truthful interpretive response from the therapist, who next provides almost immediate cognitive and interactional validation, and who yet proves incapable of processing this understanding toward adaptive structural change. At the very last moment, so to speak, they turn away from the truth and prove refractory. They do not work through the insights they have indirectly validated and acknowledged. Their maladaptive behavior and symptoms remain unchanged. They may be characterized as *truth senders* and as *lie receivers (obliterators)*.

Implicit to this conception of truth therapy is the understanding that the neuroses develop through two interrelated factors: (1) pathological and distorting intrapsychic fantasies, introjects, and memories; and (2) pathological behaviors and attitudes in external objects (in particular, the maternal figure and the therapist), which form the basis for disruptive introjects and distortions in id, ego, and superego functioning. Because of this, truth therapy requires an understanding of the unconscious implications of the therapist's actual behaviors and interactions, as well as of the patient's inner mental world. While all truths related to the therapeutic interaction must ultimately be traced out to those within the patient, it remains critical to understand that important truths within the bipersonal field may stem from the therapist as well.

Truth therapy may be considered a commensal relationship (Bion 1970) in which the patient is able to benefit and grow, as is the therapist, but secondarily. And while it entails a frightening disequilibrium, it is optimally nondestructive and devoid of any degree of pathological symbiosis or parasitism (Bion 1970). In general, available surface insights and understanding are in keeping with the underlying unconscious truths, so that there is a sense of consistency and integrity that is relatively lacking in lie therapy. A major motivation for truth therapy lies in the wish within both patient and therapist to cope through understanding, active mastery, knowledge, and integrity—whatever their temporary cost. By no means do all patients and therapists prefer this particular adaptive mode.

There are many motives within both patient and therapist that prompt them to depart from truth therapy. In structural terms, these motives involve defensiveness, superego corruption, and the wish for pathological instinctual drive gratifications. On an object relationship level, they entail wishes for inappropriate fusion and merger. In terms of affects, they involve active wishes to immediately and maladaptively obliterate anxiety, depression, guilt, and the like. Intrapsychically, the hope is to submerge and bypass inner conflict and to create rigid barriers against the influence of pathological unconscious fantasies, memories, and introjects. In terms of the therapeutic process and the role of necessary but temporary therapeutic regression, the wish is to avoid such experiences and the more primitive parts of the personality that would find expression in its course. There are needs as well to deny the necessary degree of separateness between patient and therapist. More broadly, the wish is to deny dreaded anticipations of nonexistence and death.

When the search for truth exists in only one of the two participants to

the therapeutic dyad, destructive envy is mobilized in the other participant. A truth-seeking therapist is experienced at times by all patients, and
in particular by lie patients, as persecutory and attacking, since he
threatens to unleash the painful affects and contents related to their most
disturbing inner constellations. In this light, we can begin to appreciate
the extent to which psychoanalysts and others have failed, despite the
intensity of their quest, to develop a validated, truth-seeking treatment
modality, and the pervasive struggle among individual therapists against
work of this kind.

Lie Therapy

   While there is but one form of truth therapy, there are many types of lie
therapy, and of lie patients and lie therapists. In this context, it is well to be
reminded that the term *lie* as used here implies ultimately an unconsciously determined falsification and the development of impenetrable
barriers to underlying truths, accompanied as a rule by significant breaks
in interpersonal relatedness. The lie is a form of nonrepresentation, of
nonderivative communication. Functionally, it serves to obliterate and seal off
expressions of the patient's neurosis and his valid unconscious perceptions of disturbances in the therapist. The hallmark of the lie patient can
be found in the clinical validation of the impossibility of meaningfully
organizing his material around an adaptive context known to the therapist and derived from the therapeutic interaction.
   Lie patients range from those who tell deliberate, obliterating untruths
to those who use surface truths as barriers to unconscious truths. A lie
patient may consciously believe in the veracity of a particular communication, despite its essential function as an untruth vis-à-vis the actively
mobilized neurotic constellation within the bipersonal field, primarily
within the patient, though secondarily within the therapist as well.
Unconsciously, then, lie patients often use apparent truths as barriers to
more catastrophic truths connected to the most pressing manifestations
of neurosis within the therapeutic interaction (Bion 1977).
   Lies, then, are designed to substitute either falsifications or superficial
truths for more disturbing and compelling underlying truths, and to
create impenetrable barriers to these inner and outer actualities. It is here
that the difference in the defenses of the truth seeker and the lie patient
can be identified: the truthful patient will defend himself with communications designed to cover underlying fantasies, conflict, and disturbance; nonetheless, he ultimately reveals in some derivative form the
hidden unconscious meanings and functions of both the defense and the
underlying neurotic disturbance. On the other hand, the lie patient does

not communicate such derivative meaning; his expressions are designed essentially for the destruction and concealment of meaning.

On another level, the truth seeker maintains a significant degree of relatedness with the therapist even as he defends himself, while the lie patient attempts to destroy meaningful interpersonal links. His goal is the destruction of meaning and the creation of nonmeaning and defensive chaos; he is a negative rather than a positive communicator. The truth seeker intends to create understanding, however disguised, and to seek it out, while the lie patient has no such purpose; he wishes instead to obliterate the possibility of any emergence of meaning and truth. (These considerations are comparable to, but extend, my recent discussion of the Type A and Type C patient; see Langs 1978–1979.)

It has been remarkably difficult for psychoanalysts to recognize the existence of lie patients. This blind spot appears based in part on a lack of insight into the attitude and propensities of many analysts in regard to the search for meaning or its destruction. A lie therapist is inconceivable to most analysts. Nonetheless, in the specific clinical situation, both patient and therapist may operate under the influence of lie systems. These may be based on shared premises, which will tend to make the two participants quite compatible, or they may be founded on distinctly different assumptions (falsifications and barriers), creating distinct clashes. The latter situation can be thought of as an unrecognized version of what Bion (1963) has termed *reversing perspective:* therapist and patient experience the same sensory cues—verbal and nonverbal—though each makes use of the material for a different lie system.

With a lie patient, a truth therapist will focus his therapeutic efforts on the unconscious meanings and functions of the patient's lie-barrier needs and propensities. Any other effort is bound to be hollow, and is tantamount to joining in the patient's lie system and maintaining a pretense of therapy, a false illusion that will function on some level as a neurotic (open to reality testing) or psychotic (closed to reality testing) delusion.

If we define the lie therapist as communicating in a way that avoids the critical unconscious communicative interaction, that is, the prevailing adaptive context and the patient's unconscious responses, then the literature suggests that lie therapists and lie patients are extremely common in both the psychotherapeutic and the psychoanalytic situations. It appears, in fact, that lie patients are the rule. It is therefore essential to understand the nature of the symptom alleviation that may occur in a lie therapy setting.

The essence of lie therapy is the creation of falsifications and barriers to the truth of the patient's neurosis, and secondarily that of the therapist, as activated within the therapeutic interaction. There is considerable evidence that some degree of symptom relief can take place on this basis, entirely without true understanding. This entails the commonly referred to reinforcement of the patient's defenses, many of which are pathological, and the gratification as well of pathological conscious and unconscious needs and fantasies. It also involves the offer of new lie systems to the patient. Unconsciously, the lie therapist proposes new types of impenetrable barriers to the underlying truths within the bipersonal field and new means of rupturing meaningful interpersonal links to the point where these formations may seal off an active pathological core within the patient, providing him temporary symptom relief.

The situation is, as a rule, even more complex than this initial description would imply. The lie therapist generates a series of unconscious perceptions, projections, and projective identifications which are by and large introjected by the patient. These may have very complicated effects, including a reinforcement of the patient's own lie system, his defensively obliterating functions and his Type C barriers. This also exacerbates the patient's unconscious need to protect himself from the therapist's neurosis.

While lie-based introjects may prove to be symptom alleviating, they also entail distinctly detrimental elements. As Bion (1970) has noted, the relationship between the overt liar and his audience is essentially parasitic and unconsciously designed to destroy both participants; the same holds true for the unwitting liar, whether patient or therapist. Whatever other mechanisms of symptom alleviation are available in lie therapy, it seems evident that there is little development of unencumbered adaptive resources, little possibility for true growth, and the creation instead of a need for relatively rigid and fixed barriers and systems of falsification. In addition, the interactions in the lie therapy are at bottom destructive, weak, uninsightful, and envious. Nonetheless, the lie is for many an attractive barrier against underlying catastrophic truths and is frequently put to such use by both members of the therapeutic dyad.

Thus, lie systems and therapy involve the development of usually brittle and rigid Type C barriers and falsifications that require endless reinforcement and repetition, though they may very well succeed in temporarily sealing off the most primitive and disturbing parts of the patient's or therapist's personality, as well as of their interaction. The lie offers an immediate sense of relief at the expense of a full definition of inner and outer reality, and leads to the formation of illusory and delusional phenomena. In this light, many symptomatic acts and slips of the tongue can be understood as what I would call neurotic hallucinations and delusions, in that such false impressions and beliefs occur in otherwise nonpsychotic persons and yield readily to reality testing while nonetheless being unconsciously maintained. Yet despite these liabilities, the lie system offers immediate protection, a quick means of modifying anxiety and frustration, and a potential barrier to underlying disturbance. It is a system and form of therapy, then, with its own assets and liabilities: it may sometimes lead to rather stable and nondisruptive symptom alleviation, though quite often this proves to be a fragile equilibrium vulnerable to deterioration.

CLASSIFYING PATIENTS AND THERAPISTS

Lie Patients

It is possible tentatively to clinically identify some relatively common types of lie patients.

The overt liar. This type of patient is, as a rule, diagnosed as either schizophrenic or psychopathic, and has proven resistant or refractory to most treatment modalities. While the psychopath is usually always a lie patient, the schizophrenic is infrequently so, even if he does use lies. Much depends on the extent to which these lies function unconsciously as derivative and therefore revealing communications. In general, these patients are extremely vulnerable to frustration or hurt. They respond with lies and barriers, and often with action, flight, or a rupture of personal relatedness.

The deliberate, nonderivative liar epitomizes certain characteristics of all individuals inclined toward the use of unconscious lie systems: an inability to tolerate frustrating realities, a need to evade such actualities through direct falsifications rather than deal with them, and a strong sense of underlying destructiveness and sometimes seductiveness.

Interventions built upon the contents of a falsification are absurdities; they demean and ridicule the therapist. This quality demonstrates the parasitic effects of the liar in his relationship with his audience—here, the therapist. It must be stressed that even though seemingly meaningful derivatives may be contained in surface lie communications, the very presence of the deliberate lie tends to undermine their deeper truthful implications.

In intervening, the therapist must keep in mind that this communicative style involving the blatant lie must first be modified interpretively before any other type of therapeutic work can be undertaken. The therapist must be quite certain he has not unconsciously contributed to the liar's propensity. He must recognize that therapeutic modification of this style, as well as of any unconscious lie system, must be founded upon development of a secure therapeutic framework and on an essentially truth-seeking interpretive approach. Both insight and inevitable introjective identifications serve as vehicles for the shift from deliberate lying to a more truthful communicative style.

This touches upon the basic issue of whether it is possible to modify a patient's use of lie systems to the extent that he becomes, in the main, a truth-seeker. While a definitive answer to this question would require extensive empirical investigation, my general impression is that such a change would be, at the very least, extremely difficult to accomplish. In general, the more blatant and pervasive the need to consciously lie, the more difficult it is to develop such a transformation. Unconscious lie systems and patients are more amenable to analytic change. Much depends on the extent to which the patient's use of deliberate and covert lies alternates with truth-seeking communication, since it is the latter that will reveal the unconscious meanings, functions, and genetics of the patient's need to lie.

The mindless patient. This type of lie patient is usually diagnosed as schizophrenic or borderline. He tends to be under intense pressure from the psychotic part of his personality, which is both quite active and quite primitive. By obliterating the presence of thoughts, this type of lie patient attempts to create impervious barriers to the catastrophic qualities of his most immediate fantasies and perceptions.

There are degrees of mindlessness, the most extensive of which is the obliteration of any awareness of thought, feeling, or the like. Next are patients who permit isolated, fragmented contents to register, though they obliterate all intrapsychic connections and interpersonal links. As some of these fragments begin to coalesce, this type of patient may disown them and experience them as arising either through the influence of someone else or involuntarily from within. They tend to respond with other distancing devices, endeavoring to destroy or obliterate any thoughts or affects that manage to emerge. In verbalizing, they are hollow and repetitious. They place themselves outside of their conscious fantasies and talk about such neutral issues as how they should indeed get around to exploring and dealing with what is on their mind—though they seldom do so. Much of this pathology may be described as a failure in adequate containing functions (Bion 1977).

These patients may be silent in therapy for long periods. At best they offer fragmented and terse associations using a single image or lacking imagery entirely. Even the single-image associations are generally stated in an empty and barren way, without specificity and with little nuance. Only rarely is an adaptive context represented and linked to a derivative complex, and even then it tends to be greatly disguised. The links between other actual and potential thoughts are severed, and in addition the basic interrelatedness with the therapist is restricted or seemingly absent. Should thoughts appear, they are usually so disturbing and evidently psychotic—often intensely paranoid and depressive—that the patient makes strong secondary efforts to obliterate their existence or to take physical flight from the situation in which the thoughts occurred.

Despite these restrictions, some of these patients are in part truth-seeking. From time to time they communicate a represented adaptive context and a fragmented derivative network, thereby producing unconscious meanings which can then be interpreted to them. Often, however, the therapist is restricted technically to the playback of representations of this type of lie-barrier defensiveness, since the underlying anxieties, fantasies, memories, and introjects are nowhere in evidence. A great deal of patient holding and containing is called for, though care must be taken to not miss opportunities for interpretive comments and to mistakenly remain fixated with unhelpful confronting and noninterpretive interventions.

The lie narrator. This type of patient, whom I have described elsewhere (Langs 1978–1979) as the Type C narrator, is often richly imaginative and superficially appealing. He engages in long and sometimes dramatic narrative tales filled with deceptively attractive imagery. However, the failure of this material to organize meaningfully around an adaptive context betrays its primary function as an unconscious lie-barrier to underlying chaotic truths. On other occasions, these patients will go on in endless detail about a particular adaptive context, reporting flat direct thoughts and fantasies about the therapist or analyst, but without offering meaningful indirect derivatives. When they display imagination in elaborating their conscious fantasies about the analyst, it is always in the absence of any representation of a significant adaptive context.

The unwary therapist will tend to treat such material in terms of its surface meanings, or as Type One derivatives without an adaptive context, and so will offer functionally meaningless lie-interventions involving purported unconscious meanings and genetic sources. Such interventions do not receive Type Two derivative validation but instead evoke continued rumination and surface elaborations. Under such conditions the therapist has joined the patient in his lie system. The therapeutic work takes place entirely in terms of content that is either manifest or hollowly latent; the underlying chaos within patient, therapist, and their interaction is entirely avoided. It seems likely that many false analyses have taken place with patients of this kind in treatment with analysts who have understood the basic function neither of these communications nor of their own interventions.

The frame changer. Largely on an unconscious level, patients sense that the very existence of truth therapy can be undermined by modifications in the ideal or standard framework of the therapeutic and analytic situations (Langs 1979). As a result these patients will attempt in both gross and subtle ways, sometimes repeatedly, to engage the therapist in alterations of the therapeutic environment. These are attempts not only to create a lie-dominated bipersonal field but also to provide intrapsychic and inter-personal barriers to underlying truths. In addition, they usually involve efforts at pathological projective identification.

Two distinct types of frame changers can be identified: (1) those who attempt to modify the frame in order to express their own propensities toward lie communication and to destroy any possibility of truth therapy; and (2) those who generate thrusts toward lie therapy in the hope of establishing a truth therapy situation. With the first group, efforts to secure the frame and to interpret the implications of the patient's efforts at deviation will prove difficult, since the patient seldom provides a meaningful communicative network—a represented adaptive context and a coalescing derivative complex. These are patients in whom lying and projective identification are deeply ingrained. They wish only for a lie therapy and will obliterate virtually every meaningful interpretation from the therapist, as also every genuine effort on his part to create a secure and truthful bipersonal field. Such patients are reminiscent of those described by Balint (1968) in terms of regression in search of gratification rather than in search of adaptive change. The second type of patient is more inclined toward truth seeking, and attempts to provide, for himself and the therapist, an opportunity to analyze and modify their propensities for lying. His efforts at modifying the framework will be accompanied by meaningful derivative communication, and he will re-spond favorably both to the therapist's interpretations and to his sound management of the framework.

It is in this context that we may stress the extent to which a secure framework is necessary for truth therapy. Lie patients attempt to modify the basic conditions of treatment by altering the framework and hope to achieve *framework deviation cures* and *therapeutic misalliances* through establish-ment of falsifications and Type C barriers designed to seal off all access to the psychotic and other disturbing parts of their personalities.

The somatizer. There is some indication that the somatization of uncon-scious fantasies, memories, and introjects is a form of lie communication. Somatizers tend to make frequent use of unconscious lies and barriers; there is reason to postulate that this type of somatization tends to occur in a Type C field. More rarely, there may be a meaningful derivative network associated with such symptoms.

This list is by no means exhaustive. It emphasizes the expressive side of this communicative style and leaves the receptive side untouched. Those who obliterate, falsify, or destroy the meaning and implications of what they see, hear, and momentarily understand must receive attention as well. These patients are *lie receivers* or *obliterators of truth*, and their responses to the analyst's interventions are greatly influenced by this factor.

Lie Therapists and Analysts

The lie therapist can be identified through the nature of his interventions, which reflect his receptive and expressive communicative propensities. All noninterpretive therapists may be classified as lie therapists, while interpretive therapists and analysts may be categorized along several lines. I will offer two such classifications.

The first is based on the identification of what appear to be the basic false premises of clinical psychoanalysis. These are passed on from analyst to analyst through their own personal analyses and the formal teaching they receive. They contribute to their functioning as lie therapists and analysts. Space permits the listing of only two of these false premises— one regarding the analyst, the other the patient—and a true premise regarding each of these.

False premise. The analyst is a participant-observer whose main function is to create a flexible, relatively safe background and relationship for the patient's pathological projections and transferences. These transferences are distortions based on displacements from past relationships. In general, the analyst functions well and is effective. His interventions are to be understood primarily in terms of their intended, conscious meanings and functions. They should be largely interpretive, though noninterpretive interventions have their place, often as preliminary to interpretation and reconstruction. Management of the ground rules relies on common sense and requires flexibility.

The analyst's countertransferences—his pathological responses—are relatively rare and isolated. Though based on unconscious fantasies, they are usually gross, self-evident, and limited. Only rarely do they significantly influence the course of an analysis.

True premise. The analyst is in a continuous unconscious communicative interaction with the patient. His behaviors, silences, interventions, and managements of the ground rules or framework convey not only their consciously intended implications but also crucial unconscious communications. The patient consistently adapts to these stimuli, which prove to be the primary source of his associations and behaviors, whether conscious or unconscious; outside stimuli are secondary and exert their effects through their influence on the continuing communicative interaction. The analyst has two major functions—interpreting-reconstructing and managing the framework—and all departures from an interpretive stance and the maintenance of a steady and secure frame are filled with pathological unconscious communications to which the patient is exquisitely sensitive.

As a dimension of the ever-present communicative interaction, the influence of unconscious countertransference fantasies, memories, introjects, and the like is always present to some degree. In addition to these inevitable countertransferences, which exert a low-level continuous influence, there may be interludes in which preponderant countertransference is the central feature of the therapeutic interaction. As a rule, the therapist or analyst becomes the functional patient at such times, and the designated patient may respond by becoming the functional therapist.

In sum, the false premise tends to isolate the therapist from the patient, and to imply that the two are involved in a static relationship in which the therapist's communications are given only surface consideration, while those from the patient are sometimes viewed in depth. The true premise sees the patient and therapist in an extensive and continuous unconscious communicative interaction; every nuance of the therapist's work has a strong unconscious influence on the patient and vice versa.

False premise. The patient is emotionally ill. Because of this, he largely distorts his relationship with the therapist or analyst so that his associations and behaviors are based primarily on pathological fantasies and on displacements from the past and projections—transferences. In the main, the patient's free associations are derived from intrapsychic conflicts and derivatives, which tend to be viewed as isolated mental products. In the face of occasional empathic failures or inevitable separations, the therapist's behaviors are evocative of material from the patient, which nonetheless can best be understood intrapsychically and in terms of displacements from past significant relationships.

In the main, transference expressions are conveyed through direct allusions to the therapist, or through evident displacement figures. While healthy functioning is acknowledged in the patient, much of it is confined to his rational capability to maintain a cooperative relationship with the therapist—the therapeutic alliance. Little attention is paid to other valid (nontransference) capacities, and the patient's sound unconscious perceptiveness, especially as it pertains to the analyst's conscious and unconscious communications, is virtually ignored. Resistances are intrapsychically based and are to be interpreted as such.

True premise. The patient is indeed ill, likely to project and distort, and bound to express his pathological mental world through projections and transferences. Nonetheless, these reactions are consistently stimulated by aspects of the immediate relationship with the therapist, and by the latter's conscious and unconscious communications. The patient's reactions to the therapist are always a mixture of transference and nontransference, unconscious distortion and valid perceptiveness. The transference component, which is represented in every communication from the patient, can be identified only after the valid elements in the patient's communications are identified. Every interpretation from the therapist should, in principle, account for both the distorted and the veridical aspects of the patient's associations and behaviors.

The patient, then, is capable of extensive areas of valid functioning and communication, much of it unconscious. When faced with expressions of illness—countertransference—in the therapist, he has the ability to unconsciously perceive many latent aspects of this disturbance and to respond with usually unconscious therapeutic efforts, thereby serving as the functional therapist. Such unconscious valid functioning will eventually be extended into distorted and inappropriate responses and communications, the contributions of the patient's unconscious transferences.

In sum, the patient's behaviors and communications are always a mixture of transference and nontransference, that is, transversal communications (Langs 1978a). He is engaged in an unconscious communicative interaction with the therapist, and everything he imparts has some bearing on that interaction. His associations and behaviors do not reflect isolated contents, but derive their most immediate meaning and their genetic implications from the ongoing therapeutic interaction.

Many techniques and therapeutic practices have arisen on the basis of these false premises, creating the conditions for lie therapy. Perhaps the primary motive for these erroneous assumptions resides in the needs of therapists and analysts to deny the presence and influence of their own unconscious countertransferences and to defend themselves ultimately against the most primitive and disturbed parts of their own personalities. Many additional motives contribute, including the fear of the patient's most regressed communications and fears of separateness and loss. The dread and anxiety are such that these false premises are almost rigidly maintained, thereby revealing their brittle but self-protective qualities.

In principle, every therapist is a mixture of lie therapist and truth therapist. It seems that at this point in psychoanalytic history the former predominates in most individual practitioners. This observation, which is unfortunately both realistic and harsh, will be better understood if we turn now to some common types of lie therapists and lie analysts. These will be identified in terms of their behaviors in the therapeutic interaction, that is, the nature of their interventions. In general, the therapist in whom the lie modality predominates will make use of a mixture of these techniques, often without significant awareness of the unconscious implications of his interventions. Following are the common techniques of lie therapists.

The framework changer. Analysts and therapists in this group—and the literature bears witness to few exceptions—tend to take a very lax attitude toward the ground rules of psychotherapy and psychoanalysis. Most believe that psychotherapy is a distinctly different treatment modality from psychoanalysis, implying in part that in the former situation alterations in the basic ground rules and the use of noninterpretive interventions are more than justified. More broadly, these therapists tend to modify the standard framework quite readily, cancelling sessions, changing hours, intervening noninterpretively, modifying total confidentiality through such measures as signing insurance forms, and so on. Some will attempt to explore the patient's material after such a deviation, though few will do so in advance. Even fewer will take the material from the patient in advance of such a deviation as a commentary on the proposal and as reflecting in part the patient's unconscious, valid awareness of the actual consequences of the proposed deviation. Without exception, these alterations in the standard frame create the conditions for lie therapy. They are themselves unconscious lie communications—falsifications and barriers—even in those rare emergencies in which such steps are justified.

In general, there is a tendency among frame-changing therapists to deploy the naive rationalization of the need for flexibility and humanity as justification for deviations. This is an attitude that is itself a lie and a falsification, since it cannot be validated in Type Two derivative form by the material from a patient subsequent to the invocation of such a technical measure. Instead, such material unfailingly indicates the patient's need for a therapeutic environment, based on a secure frame, that provides a full openness to the communicative relationship and properties of the bipersonal field, and the opportunity for unconscious and analyzable expressions from the patient.

A therapist who deviates gratifies some aspects of his unconscious countertransferences, conveys some type of pathological projective identification, and offers the patient Type C barriers against prevailing and disturbing adaptive contexts that impinge upon the necessary separateness and disturbed parts of the personality of both participants. It is for these reasons that patients consciously accept such deviations, while universally indicating in derivative form their unconscious awareness of their inherent destructiveness. Deviations reflect a need for Type C barriers and lies within the therapist and invite the patient to move away from or seal off the truth about his own neurosis and that of the therapist. Because truth therapy can take place only within a secure therapeutic environment, we must realize the frequency with which therapists turn from truth to lie therapy in current practice.

The genetic reconstructionist. This type of lie therapist epitomizes the therapist or analyst who utilizes Type One derivatives isolated from adaptive contexts related to the immediate therapeutic interaction. The patient's associations are treated as isolated contents without immediate interactional pertinence and are interpreted in terms of isolated unconscious fantasies and memories within the patient himself. Their derivative roots are consistently traced to past genetic figures; in particular, unconscious perceptions of the analyst are thereby denied.

Such an attitude is, of course, based on the premise that the patient is expressing himself primarily through transferences—distortions derived from past relationships. His associations are therefore interpreted in terms of their roots in earlier relationships (or as having isolated unconscious meanings and fantasied contents). Often the manifest content is addressed and simply translated into terms involving genetic antecedents. Implicit to this approach is the assumption that the analyst has in no way actually behaved like the earlier figure (Little 1951) or otherwise stimulated the patient's communications.

Another aspect of such work is the extent to which it lacks any effort at Type Two derivative, psychoanalytic validation. Instead, direct and conscious elaboration, and the repetition of familiar memories, are often viewed as confirming the analyst's interpretation or reconstruction; such work is characteristically linear and flat. It lacks both the convoluted, coalescing, and truly unique qualities of sound interpretive efforts and the originality of unanticipated validation.

Under these conditions the patient's material is consistently formulated as inappropriately defensive and resistant, as well as distorted and pathological, based primarily on early pathogenic experiences. The patient is viewed as caught up in his own intrapsychic fantasies to which the analyst has essentially made no contribution and which refer only rarely to the ongoing analytic interaction. When conscious fantasies and impressions about the analyst emerge, they are treated as transferences per se, rather than as derivatives which may well contain not only disguised unconscious fantasies and memories but unconscious perceptions as well. The latter type of functioning in response to the analyst's conscious and unconscious communications is virtually never considered.

The total effect is the development of a lie therapy in which the analyst's own unconscious communications, both valid and distorted, are not consistently taken into account. As a result, the treatment situation serves in large measure as a barrier and falsification in respect to the analyst's own inner disturbances. In addition, the patient's pathology is often misconstrued, in that many of his nonpathological and nontransference-based communications, which are in fact validly related to unconscious perceptions of the therapist, are treated as distortions.

The patient is therefore offered a lie system that stems largely from the therapist's pathological (mainly defensive) needs. At the heart of this lie system is the substitute of a genetic explanation for an understanding of the immediate unconscious communicative interaction, with its pathological and nonpathological elements to which ultimately the patient makes genetic links. Functionally it is irrelevant whether these genetic interpretations are true or false; they serve in either case as barriers to the unconscious truths within the bipersonal field. Sometimes these truths involve aspects of the patient's pathology other than those interpreted, and, very often, contributions from the analyst's unconscious countertransferences. As a result, this type of lie system (with its strong sadistic component) may or may not interdigitate with the patient's own falsifications and barriers (if these are present), which make up his own particular lie system. This often takes the form of strong masochistic trends. If concordant, there may be symptom relief based on a shared lie system. If discordant, the patient may incorporate the analyst's lie system and thereby gain temporary symptom alleviation, or he may, consciously or unconsciously, violently oppose the lie system, leading to therapeutic chaos, stalemate, and sudden, unexplained termination. These are major resistances whose unconscious sources are not understood by the therapist. Much of the outcome depends on the extent to which the patient is able to incorporate the therapist's lie system as a means of sealing off underlying and disturbing truths related to expressions of his own and the therapist's most disruptive psychopathology.

Genetic reconstructionists intervene in a manner entirely divorced from the prevailing adaptive context within the therapeutic interaction. Often this entails erroneous interpretations and mismanagements of the framework. Since attention is directed to the past, however, conscious awareness of these present errors is split off and denied by both patient and analyst—sealed off and falsified. The concept of genetic and projected transferences serves here as a lie system. This is reflected in the finding that many responses from the patient that the analyst identifies as transference-based are in actuality nontransference-based. Genetic interpretations are used as barriers to the truths of the immediate analytic situation and interaction, and to the central neurotic expressions of both participants. Freud's dedicated quest for the truth, which brought mankind far closer to the inner and outer actuality of neuroses than ever before, nevertheless provided a model of lie therapy that prevails to this day. In this context, it is well to recall my own discussion (1976a,b) and, earlier, those of Szasz (1963) and Chertok (1968). Using different approaches, we have suggested that despite the undeniable brilliance of his insights, Freud's discovery of transference served in part as a defensive means of denying his countertransference-based contributions to the therapeutic interactions in which he participated. This remarkable fact shows how treacherous the search for the truth within the therapeutic interaction may be, and how conscious integrity cannot protect the therapist from his own unconscious need for lies and barriers.

The interpreter of outside relationships. This is another common type of lie therapist. Here, purported dynamic interpretations and genetic derivations are developed in terms of the patient's relationships with figures outside the treatment situation, without any correlation being drawn to the patient-therapist interaction. Such interventions virtually never receive Type Two derivative validation. Functionally, they serve to create lies and barriers to the compelling and relatively chaotic truths within the therapeutic interaction. They serve mainly to generate a lie system which is often shared by patient and therapist, and which is elaborated in a flat and linear fashion.

The user of the psychoanalytic cliché. This type of lie therapist uses a technique which overlaps with those discussed earlier. Because of its prevalence, however, it deserves separate mention. As in other forms of lie therapy, the material from the patient is treated in isolated fashion, considered on a manifest or readily inferential level, and viewed largely in terms of intrapsychic dynamics and distortions. A large number of psychoanalytic clichés are thereby introduced through the therapist's interventions. At times these are highly intellectualized and abstract: allusions to the patient's dependency, hostility, symbiotic needs, and the like. At other times they draw upon well-worn psychoanalytic hypotheses such as those related to the oedipus complex, preoedipal disturbances, and such. It is the absence of dynamic specificity, of unconscious links to the therapeutic interaction, and of derivative meaning that transforms these overt truths into functional lies.

As with other forms of lie interventions, there is total disregard for the crucial adaptive contexts within the therapeutic interaction. The psychoanalytic cliché offers powerful Type C barriers to psychic truths, and patients willingly accept them on the surface. They then weave elaborate though essentially falsified responsive tales as a means of avoiding their own inner disturbance and their disturbed unconscious perceptions of the therapist.

Who then among us does not recognize some aspect of his psychoanalytic and psychotherapeutic techniques among these characterizations of lie therapy? It seems quite evident that lie therapy and lie therapists are the rule rather than the exception. From this we may infer that there is a powerful attraction in falsifications and barriers and among us all an enormous dread of the chaotic and terrible truths of our neuroses and those of our patients. Immediate safety is sought at the expense of both growth and the development of adaptive resources. It seems evident that the consistent utilization of truth therapy techniques requires of the therapist a considerable degree of self-understanding, self-scrutiny, and tolerance of anxiety and psychic pain.

DISCUSSION

This delineation of truth and lie therapy raises a number of unique clinical issues, while offering substantially new perspectives on timeworn clinical debates. Perhaps the most important suggestion in this discussion is that psychoanalysis and psychoanalytically oriented psychotherapy, as usually practiced, are forms of lie therapy. While these treatment modalities differ from other types of lie therapies in a number of ways, they share in common with virtually every form of therapeutic endeavor practiced today the existence of significant lie systems inherent in its clinical methodology and practice. This understanding reflects the universal need in all human beings, patients and therapists alike, for lie therapy and lie systems. Corollary to this is the recognition that the adoption of truth systems by truth patients and truth therapists is an accomplishment not easily won.

This realization could provide dynamically oriented therapists new perspectives on the noninterpretive treatment modalities and on therapeutic approaches that propose to seek out the truth but that include in their basic assumptions such evident flaws as the implicit acceptance of lie fictions and lie barriers. Perhaps the most important judgment we can make of a therapeutic modality is whether it is committed to the full search for the truth. Modalities so inclined would allow the revision in clinical observation, theory, and practice that ultimately characterizes the truth therapy modality.

It is in this context that we can recognize that classical psychoanalysis is distinguished by its total commitment to the truth, despite its failing to have as yet attained this goal clinically. Other dynamic therapies have built into their theoretical edifices significant lie-barrier systems that pose major obstacles to their own avowed search for the truth. It is in fact precisely the classical psychoanalytic viewpoint that permits the discovery of lie systems, whether in its own practice or within other treatment modalities. This implies that this particular approach is most open to the modifications in understanding and technique called for by this presentation.

Paradoxically, though no longer unexpectedly, the discovery and application of truth therapy lead to the realization that until now, the perpetuation of a given therapeutic approach has relied heavily on its lie propensities, the lie systems it offers its patients. The growth and development of truth therapy will be arduous, and initially one can expect only a small number of truth patients and truth therapists. Yet despite the emphasis here on the universal need for lies there is also part of every human being that wishes to know and deal with the truth, however painful. As truth systems are accorded greater value by both individuals and groups (professional and lay), truth therapy should establish itself as a significant form of therapeutic practice.

A number of pressing clinical issues arise. One important question is how a truth therapist can best develop the treatment setting and approach for the lie patient. We are now aware of the nature of certain resistances that prompt patients initially to be refractory to truth therapy. Perhaps the best approach is one in which the therapist establishes truth conditions and quite naturally concentrates his interpretations on the patient's responses (efforts to modify the framework, to obtain noninterpretative interventions, etc.), in the expectation that the insights developed in this way will provide the patient a first important step toward becoming a truth patient. But how then should we approach the lie patient who envies the truth therapist, and who self-protectively, unconsciously feels that he must destroy any possibility of truthful unconscious commmunication? Is it possible to knowingly deviate and offer relatively well-understood and well-modulated sectors of lie communication to such patients, as an initial effort to permit their involvement in the therapeutic situation, in the hope that subsequently there can be a gradual shift toward definitive truth therapy? It may well be that such compromises leave lasting and relatively unmodifiable unconscious images of the therapist as a lie communicator, and the therapeutic outcome would thereby be significantly affected. And yet this may nonetheless be the most optimal treatment setting and outcome possible for these patients, given their own pathological needs and propensities.

Similar questions arise regarding therapists and analysts. It seems inconceivable that any therapist would compromise his commitment to knowing the truth about both his patient and himself within a therapeutic interaction, whatever its structure and nature might be. A therapist with unconscious needs for lie communication is an inherently destructive and parasitic figure; even his utilization of the lie therapy modality is bound to suffer. But what then of the lie therapist who knowingly utilizes a lie-barrier system *as the basis* for his therapeutic work? Is it possible for a therapist, once he knows the truth, to effectively function as a lie therapist? And is today's patient population such that we need knowledgeable lie therapists who, while practicing a given form of lie therapy, are at least aware of its presence and some of the prevailing unconscious dynamics? Such may be the overriding practical necessity, though a serious danger lies in accepting such pragmatic needs as a basis for turning away from the truth. These considerations should in no way lessen the pursuit of establishing truth therapy as a basic and important treatment modality for emotional ills. Nor should we abandon the hope that this approach, with its great pain and yet its enormous promise, could someday become the prevailing form of psychotherapy.

Along somewhat different lines, the recognition of truth and lie systems provides a means of viewing the conscious and unconscious therapeutic communicative interaction in a new light. There is much to be learned in defining the truth or lie system being offered by a therapist to a particular patient, while simultaneously identifying the prevailing truth or lie system in the latter's communications. Lie systems function as barriers, fictions, unconscious communications, and projective identifications, much of this infused with massive defensiveness, parasitism, and destructiveness, however self-protective. However, a lie system relies in substance upon a particular constellation of elements which must exclude all other possibilities lest it be damaged or collapse. Because of this, rival lie systems or any truth system poses a threat to its maintenance. All psychopathology entails the use of some type of lie system, permeable or not. Truth systems serve to modify pathological defenses, and function essentially as constructive unconscious communications and projective identifications, however much they may threaten a particular lie patient (or lie therapist) and his system.

Finally, having made repeated use of the extremes of this continuum—truth tellers and lie communicators—for the purposes of exposition, I must remind the reader that neither type exists in pure form, whether patient or therapist. Sectors of lie within the truth patient inevitably reflect significant aspects of his psychopathology and its genetics, and therefore provide meaningful opportunities for interpretive work. On the other hand, it is the nucleus of truth expression and seeking in the lie patient that offers a viable potential for the analytic modification of his lie system (and his need for it) to the point where his truthful tendencies can predominate. Much analytic work, however, must be done to develop a capacity within patients to tolerate the truth, to work with it and grow by it.

For the therapist, matters are somewhat different. The lie therapist will generally express his truthful propensities quite unconsciously, and while they may generate isolated positive introjects within the patient, they will not provide him the cognitive insights and adaptive resources necessary for sound structural change. The kernels of truth conveyed by such a therapist will provide the truth-seeking patient with islands of hope which tend, in the long run, not to be fulfilled, since the therapist's lie tendencies inevitably predominate.

The truth therapist will also express himself from time to time through lies, and these involve his inevitable countertransferences. While the patient may respond to these communications in a manner that proves analyzable and even growth-promoting, sound interpretive work requires that the therapist must become aware of his lie and resolve these propensities. While such interludes usually replicate aspects of the patient's earlier pathological interactions, their rectification and interpretation prove constructive for the patient—and for the therapist.

In conclusion, it is my hope that this paper will be seen as an effort to break down our current, fixed, somewhat stale, and apparently lie-infused conceptualizations of the therapeutic interaction. Such ideas have taken us as far as they can; it is time now to discover their flaws and untruths. On this basis a new and clinically validated system of truth can be developed. And of course this must be done with the recognition that, as was true of our predecessors, we can generate only the best truths available to us for the moment. Eventually flaws must be discovered even in our new system, and psychoanalysis will prepare for yet another step in its progress as a science.

REFERENCES

Balint, M. (1968). *The Basic Fault: Therapeutic Aspects of Regression.* London: Tavistock.

Baranger, W., and Baranger, M. (1966). Insight in the analytic situation. In *Psychoanalysis in the Americas.* ed. R. Litman, pp. 56–72. New York: International Universities Press.

Bion, W. (1962). *Learning from Experience.* In W. Bion, *Seven Servants.* New York: Jason Aronson.

——— (1963). *Elements of Psycho-Analysis.* In W. Bion, *Seven Servants.* New York: Jason Aronson.

——— (1970). *Attention and Interpretation.* In W. Bion, *Seven Servants.* New York: Jason Aronson.

——— (1977). *Seven Servants.* New York: Jason Aronson.

Chertok, L. (1968). The discovery of the transference: toward an epistemological interpretation. *International Journal of Psycho-Analysis* 49:560–576.

Grotstein, J. (1977a). The psychoanalytic concept of schizophrenia: I. The dilemma. *International Journal of Psycho-Analysis* 58:403–426.

——— (1977b). The psychoanalytic concept of schizophrenia: II. Reconciliation. *International Journal of Psycho-Analysis* 58:427–452.

Langs, R. (1975a). Therapeutic misalliances. *International Journal of Psychoanalytic Psychotherapy* 4:77–105.

———— (1975b). The therapeutic relationship and deviations in technique. *International Journal of Psychoanalytic Psychotherapy* 4:106–141.

———— (1976a). *The Bipersonal Field.* New York: Jason Aronson.

———— (1976b). *The Therapeutic Interaction,* Vols. 1 and 2. New York: Jason Aronson.

———— (1978a). *The Listening Process.* New York: Jason Aronson.

———— (1978b). *Technique in Transition.* New York: Jason Aronson.

———— (1978–1979) Some communicative properties of the bipersonal field. *International Journal of Psychoanalytic Psychotherapy* 7:89–161.

———— (1979). *The Therapeutic Environment.* New York: Jason Aronson.

Little, M. (1951). Counter-transference and the patient's response to it. *International Journal of Psycho-Analysis* 32:32–40.

Szasz, T. (1963). The concept of transference. *International Journal of Psycho-Analysis* 44:432–443.

Wangh, M. (1962). The "Evocation of a Proxy": a psychological maneuver, its use as a defense, it purposes and genesis. *Psychoanalytic Study of the Child* 17:451–469.

Developmental Perspectives on the Bipersonal Field

J. ALEXIS BURLAND, M.D.

A discussion of "Truth Therapy/Lie Therapy," by *Robert Langs, M.D.* Certain parallels are drawn between those aspects of the psychotherapeutic situation of which Langs writes and the developmental situation between the young child and his or her primary objects. Infantile issues are replayed in therapy, most clearly in the content of neurotic structures. But also, the capacity for "truth therapy," or the limitations which impose "lie therapy," either for the patient or for the therapist, reflect the outcome of developmental challenges, i.e., in character structure in particular. A developmentally conceived explication of Langs's typology of "lie patients" and "lie therapists" is offered. Questions are posed as to how to conceptualize the therapeutic situation as a developmental process.

For almost a decade Langs has been attempting to identify and characterize a particular dimension of the psychotherapeutic situation. Starting from Freud's concept of the role of the day residue in dream formation, he has evolved an approach to the understanding of psychoanalytic psychotherapy centered upon his observation that what the therapist says or does can act just as do "real" events in the dreamer's previous day; that is, certain unconscious mental contents of the patient can become attached to the actions—verbal and non-verbal, conscious and unconscious—of the therapist. In a manner similar to that occurring in dreams, a complex bipersonal interactional dynamism evolves with manifest and latent content that can best be understood when the contributions of each participant are taken into account. Langs has described and catalogued instances in which errors, technical and personal, on the therapist's part work together with certain aspects of the patient's psyche to create obstacles to a psychotherapeutic process whose goal is structural change through insight. Langs's concept of the importance of the proper psychotherapeutic "frame" is his prescription for at least minimizing such occurrences.

He has also endeavored to describe how the interactional processes of the psychotherapeutic situation work to further change through insight. Patient and therapist interact through a communications system that is itself complex, conscious and unconscious, verbal and nonverbal. This has been Langs's focus of attention in his more recent writings, including "Truth Therapy, Lie Therapy."

Langs's searches have led him to explore subverbal and subcognitive dimensions of the psychotherapeutic encounter, a realm where, as he describes it, self-object phenomena, primary process thinking, and the pleasure principle would seem to prevail. He has also placed the psyche of the therapist alongside that of the patient at the center of the process, perhaps his most controversial proposition. Although his writings say little that psychoanalysts should find surprising—after all, the concepts of transference and countertransference imply unconscious and therefore infantile communication between patient and analyst—there are those who are not as comfortable as Langs with the exploration of interactional mental processes quite so far removed from the preconscious and conscious verbal derivatives of primarily oedipal material. The writers of the Kleinian school, whose viewpoint Langs finds compatible, are equally controversial in their assumptions concerning unconscious mental processes.

Langs's writings thus far have omitted developmental theory and data. For almost half a century now certain analysts have been involved in a related pursuit, that of attempting to penetrate the primary repression barrier, that is, to find ways of exploring those early and crucial life experiences that because of infantile amnesia seem to defy direct expression in verbal derivative form. These efforts have proceeded in two directions. In clinical work with patients whose psychological problems relate to these earliest months of life, methods have been proposed to identify, conceptualize, reconstruct, and influence derivatives of psychogenetically significant preoedipal experiences. Although the clinical data studied thus far often closely resemble the data that interest Langs, his focus has been on the current interactional expression of the derivatives of early experiences rather than on any information they may give us about the patient's early life experiences or the psychogenesis of either his resistance to the analytic encounter or, conversely, his capacity to enter into and profit from it. Langs's approach has been psychodynamic-interactional, and accordingly he has proposed a phenomenological classification. His technical suggestions have focused upon interpretation via the transference and countertransference and the technical management of the frame that encloses them. The developmentalist's interest has been in the reconstructive aspects of interpretation, and upon the improved understanding of early experiences, and analysis has been examined as a developmental process.

The second approach to the exploration of the "unforgettable but unrememberable" (Frank 1969) years of life has been the direct observation of infantile development. With both approaches, communication has been a central issue, just as it has been of late for Langs. And, as with Langs's work, there has been much controversy on the subject. Psychoanalysis has long acknowledged the use of the analyzing instrument in understanding what lies beneath the surface. But there is disagreement as to how deeply it can penetrate and to what extent at least some introspectively explicit verbal participation on the part of the subject is necessary. For some, true psychoanalytic work with children, or even young adolescents, is considered impossible because their verbal participation seems too unreliable; to someone holding this point of view, infant observation would be viewed, of course, as fruitless. Similarly, this view would also question the feasibility of the therapeutic intrapsychic exploration of the psychotic or borderline patient. Psychoanalysis would be seen as limited to the treatment of those whose psychogenetically significant experiences occurred after the age of three, when memories become more verbal. At the other end of the spectrum are those who believe themselves fully conversant with the mental life of the infant from birth, both in infancy and as the infantile persists throughout life. In all likelihood most analysts are situated between the two extremes, acknowledging the capacity, in some instances, for intuitive-empathic communication with the unconscious but timeless remnants of events from the second year of life—perhaps even, with caution, the second half of the first year of life. Those who have applied their analyzing instrument in attempts at communicating with infants claim, rather convincingly, at least partial success at identifying with the subjective experiences of the young. Here too, however, the majority prudently acknowledge that their success is limited. The infantile, both past and present, can be elusive to the adult ego.

Langs has not commented on the connection between the developmental and pathogenic significance of infantile experiences and the dimensions of the therapeutic interaction of which he writes. As a psychoanalyst he is obviously conversant with the psychogenetic aspects of symptom formation. This is implied in his references to the infantile nature of the inappropriate gratifications the patient or therapist obtains in a pathological bipersonal field. But the developmental perspective is interested also in the evolution of nonsymptomatic mental life, including the development of precisely those ego skills necessary for the kind of communication essential to insight therapy. Langs in describing Bion's concepts of alpha and beta elements and functions has stated that these are phenomena expressive of developmental experiences, but he has not enlarged upon that aspect of it.

There are areas of common interest between Langs and the psychoanalytic developmentalist. The first and most obvious is the parallel between the patient-therapist and the mother-infant interaction. Spitz (1956) and Winnicott (1956) are well-known spokesmen for this view. They saw the psychoanalytic situation, because of its regressive nature, as uniquely capable of invoking memory-traces and affects of the original mother-infant relationship; in fact, an adequate relationship with the mother can be viewed as requisite to later analyzability. It is to state the obvious to refer to the similarities between the empathic, nonjudgmental, hovering attentiveness of the analyst and *certain* aspects of the adequate mother. Langs's concept, after Bion, of the analyst as container makes even more evident this similarity, for this is a function vital to good mothering. Perhaps this is also reflected in Langs's usual emphasis upon the errors and inadequacies of the therapist as opposed to those of the patient, although "Truth Therapy/Lie Therapy" is an exception to this. As in the mother-child relationship, more is expected of the caregiver.

Other writers have written of the later ramifications of the mother-infant relationship. Although the empathic, nonverbal communication between mother and infant (and patient and therapist) is by no means a new concept in psychoanalysis, Kohut (1971, 1977) has most recently placed particular emphasis on it. Spitz (1965) termed it the "dialogue." Clearly these writers are referring to the developmental history of what in the end would become a capacity for "truth therapy," either as patient or therapist. And is not the "lie therapist" like the insensitive, unempathic mother who, for whatever reason, cannot tune in on her child's "truth," especially including the child's "truth" that may be concealed behind the child's "lie"? Winnicott's concept of the false (as opposed to the true) self (1960) touches directly on this issue; he, too, relates the development of a false self to unempathic mothering.

It is in his agreement with Kleinian concepts that Langs speaks to the later expressions of the more destructive aspects of the mother-infant interaction—to oral aggression, oral rage, envy, and pathological symbiosis, to the developmental outcome of the "bad" mother introject. That these negative infantile forces can be evoked in therapy and can act as powerful resistances, some analyzable and others not, is well known to those who work with the borderline and psychotic (like Klein herself) and is reflected in the literature on that subject.

The infantile persists throughout life in the timeless unconscious, in psychic structure, in neurotic symptom formation, and in character structure. Although a technical article dealing with technical issues, is not

"Truth Therapy/Lie Therapy" also an article about character structure? One can take the varieties of "lie patients" and "lie therapists" and identify them diagnostically and developmentally. The "overt liar," for instance, is a psychopath who, as Greenacre has well described (1945, 1950), seeks actualization of fantasy as an expression of infantile grandiosity over the acknowledgment of reality. For such an individual the overriding principle in life is the illusion of the persistence of a compliant self-object world. Morality, as an expression of socialization and reality relatedness in their broadest ego-developmental sense, is given very low priority.

Langs's term *mindless patient* is of interest, as it is the term I used in referring to the most striking characteristic of severely maternally deprived children of all ages (Burland 1979). When, as a result of grossly inadequate mothering, there is a failure to establish the libidinal object (Spitz 1965), behavior looks as if the child were characterologically fixated in the normal autistic phase of development. Without an affective tie to the mother (and therefore to the external world), hatching, secondary process thinking, and reality relatedness fail to adequately develop. "Mindless" hedonism results. Such children are found most commonly (but not exclusively) in the poverty sector of the community, where their frenetic, joyless, nonstop seeking for instant gratification has a scattered and fragmented quality and leaves them asocial, ineducable, narcissistically infantile, and destructive.

The "lie narrator" brings to mind images of the narcissistically vulnerable child, "entertaining Mommy" in order to bask in her approval. Kohut's description of the mirror transference (1971) would seem applicable here.

The "frame changer" can be understood as one intent upon controlling the self-object, one who had failed to cope effectively with the rapprochement discovery of separateness (Lax, Bach, and Burland 1980) and so plays out in relationships the dynamics of the tale of Aladdin and his magic lamp, that is, the genie is omnipotent, but Aladdin has the genie.

"Lie patients" as a group can be viewed as character disordered people who seek from their therapist part-object gratification rather than insight; as is almost definitional for character pathology, it is expressed within and contaminates the working alliance. The true neurotic, with his firm sense of inside versus outside, projects onto the analyst whole object representations, more or less outside of the working alliance. The self-object related patient, on the other hand, operates on the basis of the assumption that his needs create his reality, an illusion to which he clings in order to deny separateness. This would seem to fit Langs's description of the "lie patient."

The character typology of the "lie therapist" can also be viewed in developmental terms. Most broadly speaking, and as is the case with mothers, unempathic therapists most likely did not themselves experience sensitive parenting (or a sensitive analysis, Langs, I'm sure, would add). But there are also variations between therapists as to what extent their personal infantile past is relinquished or rejected, the degree to which, for purposes of characterological stability, they need to over-emphasize the logical, rational, more secondary-process aspects of their inner, and therefore their interpersonal, lives. Such aspects of character may not necessarily relate to issues of "pathology" versus "normalcy," and therefore may not call attention to themselves in the course of an analysis. Langs's rather strongly phrased criticism of the training analysis, in which he sees blind spots being passed on to the next generation of analysts, may be understood in this light; that is, this is not just a matter of an inadequate analysis but also a question of "finding the right person for the right job." But then, character analysis has not been given sufficient attention since Reich's defection from the mainstream of psychoanalysis, and probably nowhere is this as critical an issue as it is for training analyses.

A second character trait implicity identified by Langs in his description of the "lie therapist" can be understood in terms of current concepts of narcissism. I refer to the capacity—or the lack of capacity—to identify with the patient, to follow the patient's associations, and to understand them from the patient's perspective. Developmentally, this requires first the establishment of a good sense of inside versus outside and of true self- and object-differentiation. From the position of a firm sense of identity and of self, a therapist can then relax his or her ego boundaries and be open to experiencing the patient's subjectivity. This is different from a self-object or merger experience, in which the therapist's needs are assumed to have shaped the "subjectivity" of the patient. Though a certain kind of "closeness" or nonverbal communication may be felt, in fact grandiose projections are being experienced instead.

To merely identify the parallels between certain infantile experiences and the patient-therapist interaction is insufficient to address the questions implicit in Langs's article. It may add another dimension to his taxonomical efforts—a psychogenetic one to add to his dynamic-economic ones—but a good psychoanalytic explanation should offer also technical clinical direction. Lampl–de Groot (1967) has written that the understanding of early psychological development and its manifestations in the clinical setting has progressed faster than our understanding of how to deal effectively with such manifestations. The concept of psychoanalysis as a developmental as well as an insight-generating process is an effort to bridge that gap. Such authors as Fleming and Altschul (1963), Fleming (1972), Burland (1975), Shane (1979), and Settlage (1980) have written on the subject.

The resolution of the infantile neurosis by means of analytic intervention can be viewed as a developmental process in which fixation upon oedipal objects, appropriate to early childhood, is at last relinquished. But the more recent problematic concepts on the subject refer to developmental phases that precede and in fact make possible the establishment of age-adequate oedipal relationships in the first place.

As might already have been gathered, "lie patients" and "lie therapists" do not seem to fall into the category of "normal neurotics." Transference and countertransference resistances of a primarily oedipal nature do not lead to such devastating breakdowns in communication. Neurotic resistances are analyzable; in fact, their analysis is at the core of the analytic process. Character resistances on the other hand block communications as they disrupt the working alliance. The developmental issues they reflect involve such very basic issues as the relinquishment of infantile grandiosity and the development of the capacity for object relationships.

Where there is a problem in establishing object relationships in the first place, due to inadequate interactions with the primary objects in infancy, the therapist as a new and better object takes on a unique importance. Langs's concept of the bipersonal field and the importance of the frame can be viewed as a prescription for maintaining a very specific and limited "new" and "better" object role: patient, tolerant, empathic, altruistic, nondestructive. The "truth therapist," particularly for the "lie patient," offers a different model for identification. Here I refer to the concept of the therapist as a "real object," although I would qualify that expression. Just as the "good mother" is to a considerable extent a projection based upon the pleasurable sensations of gratification, so the "good therapist," no matter how "good" he or she may "really" be, still must gratify the specific needs of the patient—or must seem to do so—in order to be perceived as "good." As Langs implies, the "lie patient" can respond to the "truth therapist" only if some yearning for a "good" or "better" object exists and seems to be gratified. It is not always easy to draw the line between real and fantasied gratification, of course.

One cannot argue, even a decade later, with Lampl–de Groot's statement (1967) that developmental theory has moved further than the elaboration of its technical ramifications, even though progress has been made in devising usable concepts. The controversy that surrounds the issue, though at times overly strident, is at least an indication that efforts are under way to confront and resolve the questions. Object relations theory offers a vocabulary and a conceptual system that negotiates well the distance between past and present relationships. It is therefore a most promising tool in this venture.

I would view Langs's contributions in this and other papers as potentially a most significant part of that adventure. In his microscopic scrutiny of the formal aspects of the therapeutic process he has formulated a useful vocabulary and taxonomy that relates specifically to the vicissitudes, within the clinical setting, of the development of narcissism and the capacity for object relationships. I do not think it is by coincidence that he finds useful the developmental theories of a child analyst—i.e., Klein—even though those theories are themselves at the center of a seemingly never-ending conflict of their own. There are other developmental theorists to whom he could also turn.

It remains, of course, work in progress. Therapeutic effectiveness remains elusive to those who have attempted to delimit it. Insight, making conscious the unconscious, replacing id with ego, the mutative interpretation within the transference, "working through," identification with the therapist/analyst, bringing defenses under greater conscious ego control, mourning lost infantile ideals and objects, the enhancement of interrupted ego development, the restoration of the self—all are probably apt, and each is surely insufficient as an explanation of the effects of treatment. The interactional dimension is a part of all of them, as treatment is a two-party system; in this, Langs's approach holds promise for what it can illuminate. Psychological development is another dimension cutting across all of these partial explanations. It is precisely the developmentally significant past that is replayed within the therapeutic interaction, for better or for worse, on the part of both patient and therapist. How best to understand and conceptualize, and to manage, this bitemporal as well as bipersonal field would seem to be the joint search for both Langs and the developmentalists.

REFERENCES

Bach, S. (1976). Some notes on perspective. Unpublished manuscript.

Burland, J. A. (1975). Separation-individuation and reconstructions in psychoanalysis. *International Journal of Psychoanalytic Psychotherapy*, 4:303–335.

Burland, J. A., and Cohen, T. (1979). Psychoanalytic perspectives on vulnerable and high risk children. In *Treatment of Emotional Disorders in Children and Adolescents*, ed. Sholevar, Denson, and Blinder. New York: Spectrum Publications.

Fleming, J. (1972). Early object deprivation and transference phenomena: the working alliance. *Psychoanalytic Quarterly* 41:23–49.

Fleming, J., and Altschul, S. (1963). Activation of mourning and growth by psychoanalysis. *International Journal of Psycho-Analysis* 44:419–431.

Frank, A. (1969). The unrememberable and the unforgetable: passive primal repression. *Psychoanalytic Study of the Child* 24:48–77.

Greenacre, P. (1945). Conscience in the psychopath. In P. Greenacre, *Trauma, Growth and Personality*, pp. 165–187, New York: International Universities Press, 1952.

——— (1950). General problems of acting out. In P. Greenacre, *Trauma, Growth and Personality*, pp. 224–236. New York: International Universities Press, 1952.

Kohut, H. (1971). *The Analysis of the Self*. New York: International Universities Press.

——— (1977). *The Restoration of the Self*. New York: International Universities Press.

Lax, R., Bach, S. and Burland, J. A. (1980). *Rapproachement*. New York: Jason Aronson.

Lampl-de Groot, J. (1967). On obstacles standing in the way of psychoanalytic cure. *Psychoanalytic Study of the Child* 22:20–35.

Settlage, C. (1980). The psychoanalytic understanding of narcissistic and borderline personality disorders: advances in developmental theory. In *Rapprochement*, ed. R. Lax, S. Bach, and J. Burland. New York: Jason Aronson.

Shane, Morton (1979). The developmental approach to "working through" in the analytic process. *International Journal of Psycho-Analysis* 60:375–382.

Spitz, R. (1956). Transference: the analytic setting and its prototype. *International Journal of Psycho-Analysis* 37:380–385.

——— (1965). *The First Year of Life*. New York: International Universities Press.

Winnicott, D. W. (1956). On transference. *International Journal of Psycho-Analysis* 37:386–388.

——— (1960). Ego distortion in terms of true and false self. In D. W. Winnicott, *The Maturational Process and the Facilitating Environment*, pp. 140–152. New York: International Universities Press.

The Analysis of Transference: A Critique of Fenichel's *Problems of Psychoanalytic Technique*

MERTON GILL, M.D.

Three principles of the analysis of transference are proposed: first, that transference is encouraged to expand within the analytic situation; second, that the principal technique for doing so is the interpretation of disguised allusions to transference in the patient's manifest associations; and, third, that transference is primarily resolved by its interpretation in the here and now of the therapeutic situation. This third principle includes three major considerations: (1) all transference is related to something in the actual therapeutic situation; (2) the analysis of transference requires an examination of the extent to which the actual therapeutic situation does and does not account for the patient's experience of the relationship; and (3) in this examination the patient simultaneously has a new experience and acquires insight into how that experience differs from his predetermined expectations. The extent to which these principles are derived from Freud's writings is briefly discussed. Finally, Fenichel's monograph is examined and shown to fall short due to failure to employ these principles.

This paper is a slightly revised and expanded version of my contribution to a symposium at the December 1978 meeting of the American Psychoanalytic Association. This contribution was entitled "Classics Revisited: Fenichel's 'Problems of Psychoanalytic Technique.'" The symposium, chaired and introduced by Dr. Arnold Cooper, included presentations by Drs. Arthur Valenstein and Leo Rangell.

Although the title of Fenichel's monograph, "Problems in Psychoanalytic Technique" (1941), makes clear that Fenichel did not represent it as a comprehensive and integrated account of analytic technique, the relatively small role that discussion of the transference plays in the monograph is noteworthy in the light of the centrality usually ascribed to the analysis of the transference. Remarks about transference are scattered through the monograph, but the section specifically labeled "Comments on the Analysis of Transference" occupies less than five pages out of a total of ninety-seven, exclusive of the review of the literature.

I am of the opinion that Fenichel's monograph fails to make an adequate statement of the principles of the analysis of the transference as these were proposed by Freud. I will attempt to justify this conclusion by first outlining these principles. I must, however, make clear that I will make explicit several major points that Freud left implicit; I therefore anticipate some disagreement as to whether my emphases are in fact consistent with Freud's intentions. I will then assess the monograph in the light of these principles. I emphasize that this assessment must be evaluated in light of the fact that Fenichel presumably was not writing a systematic account even of the transference, let alone of technique. Nevertheless, Fenichel does present what he calls a general account of the theory of therapy, and the many remarks he makes in passing—which I believe hint at the principles I will state—suggest to me that if these principles had been sharply clear in his mind he would have stated them. I anticipate some disagreement on this point too. I must also say that there are many indications in the monograph that Fenichel's actual practice came much closer to the principles I will state than one might conclude from the theory he proposes. This is a general problem in our field. One cannot be sure how an analyst practices from the theory he espouses, and this difficulty exists as well in our evaluation of Freud's practice. Freud's case reports were all designed to demonstrate the yield of the analyses for the structure and function of the psyche, not the technique by which this yield was acquired.

THE PRINCIPLES

My statement of the analysis of the transference is organized into three principles. The first is that the analyst encourages the transference to expand as much as possible within the analytic situation. Second, the chief technique for doing so is by interpretation of resistances to awareness of the transference within the analytic situation. These interpretations are of allusions to the transference in associations that do not manifestly pertain to the transference. The third principle involves the resolution of the transference. This takes place primarily by way of work with the transference in the here and now. This includes first the demonstration that the patient's experience of the events of the actual analytic situation is determined in part by preexisting expectations; second, in the course of this demonstration the patient has a new interpersonal experience which differs from his biased expectation. These two features comprise a combined experiential and cognitive resolution of the transference. This resolution may be further consolidated by the recovery of the experiences of the past which gave rise to the bias.

The first principle is that the analyst encourages the transference to expand as much as possible in the analytic situation. Freud made clear that resistance is primarily expressed in repetition. This repetition takes place in transference both outside and inside the analytic situation. The principal way in which the repetition can be made amenable to influence is by encouraging its expression inside the analytic situation. The more thoroughly this is possible the more fully will a transference neurosis supplant the manifestations of the neurosis in the patient's contemporary life outside the treatment. The repetition may take place in either the motor or the psychic sphere both without and within the analytic situation. The analyst encourages its manifestation in the psychic sphere and within the analytic situation as much as possible.

The reason it is desirable for the analysis that the transference expand as much as possible within the analytic situation is that it can be dealt with best there because it is the most completely and accurately known there. As Freud (1916–1917) said, since the analyst is at the very center of the analytic situation, he is able to observe the transference from its initiation and throughout its development.

To repeat, the chief technique for encouraging the transference to expand as much as possible within the analytic situation is interpretation of allusions to the transference in the associations which are not manifestly about the transference. There are important resistances, on the part of both patient and analyst, to awareness of the transference. On the patient's part this is because of the difficulty of recognizing erotic and hostile impulses toward the very person to whom they have to be disclosed. On the analyst's part this is because the patient is likely to attribute the very attitudes to the analyst which are most likely to cause him discomfort. It is for this reason that the analyst must be alert not only to the attitudes the patient has toward him but also to the attitudes the patient believes he has. The resistances to the awareness of these attitudes is responsible for their appearing in various disguises in the patient's manifest associations. The most commonly recognized disguise is by displacement, but identification is equally important (Lipton 1977). In displacement the patient's attitudes are narrated as directed toward a third party. In identification the patient attributes to himself attitudes he believes the analyst harbors toward him.

There are controversies in our literature as to how early transference appears in the analytic situation, how pervasive it is, and how soon it becomes a resistance. An important reason that the controversy remains unresolved is the failure to distinguish implicit and disguised transference from spontaneously explicit transference. Freud (1913) laid down the dictum that transference should not be interpreted until it becomes a resistance. But Freud was mistaken in believing that the apparently freely associating patient might not be simultaneously showing resistance to awareness of the transference. The analyst should interpret transference wherever he suspects it, from the beginning and throughout the analysis. It is through such interpretation that the transference is encouraged to expand within the analytic situation, however pervasive it may or may not implicitly be. As Freud (1912) said, resistance accompanies the treatment step by step. This is not to dispute the desirability of learning as much as one can about the patient and therefore not interfering with a free production, whether early or later, unless some transference threatens the continuation of the analysis so that its interpretation is mandatory rather than optional.

The resolution of the transference takes place primarily by way of work with the transference in the here and now. This includes first the demonstration that the patient's experience of the relationship is only partially determined by the events of the analytic situation.

To clarify this point, it must first be pointed out that every manifestation of the transference takes place in relation to something in the actual analytic situation, something that has actually taken place. There is no such thing as a pure transference. In general terms, this is an illustration of the principle that an unconscious wish cannot be expressed as such but only as it attaches to a preconscious content, which is Freud's original general definition of the concept of transference in *The Interpretation of Dreams* (1900–1901). This current stimulus for the transference can be called a transference residue in analogy to the dream day residue. It may be difficult to find because it may seem so trivial in comparison to the repercussions in the transference or because the patient so quickly disavows it. It is always present and it is important to find because of its role in the resolution of transference. Langs (1978) has discussed this issue extensively. What I have called "transference residue" he calls "adaptive context."

The second step in the resolution of the transference in the here and now is that when the point of departure for the transference in the current analytic situation can be found, it is examined in relation to whether it can plausibly account for the attitude woven around it. If it cannot adequately account for the attitude, the way is open to a search for the determinant within the patient which led him to experience the analytic situation as he did rather than in some other possible way—that is, to the "transference-component," as Fenichel called it, of the attitude. The discovery of this component is a necessary step toward its alteration.

When the analyst seeks what may to the patient have been as plausible a conclusion as he can form in the light of his limited cues, he is respecting the patient's attempt to be realistic rather than seeing him as concocting a transference out of whole cloth. This is an aspect of a third important consideration in the resolution of the transference by work within the analytic situation. For in the examination of the patient's attitude the analyst behaves in a way different from what the patient's preexisting bias had led him to anticipate. The analyst does not deliberately behave differently with technical intent. It is rather that his stance as an analyst must inevitably differ from the patient's transference expectations. In the examination of the relationship between attitudes and current cues the patient simultaneously has a new experience and gains insight into how this experience differs from his expectations. This point is important to stress because emphasis on work in the transference in the here and now is sometimes mistaken for an overemphasis on experiencing and an underemphasis on insight and working through. On the contrary, what is being described is a process in which working through takes place in the affectively meaningful present and in which experience and insight take place in an intrinsic unity.

The question arises of the role of remembering the past in the resolution of transference. The usual formulation is that the aim of the analytic process is to recall the past, with the implication that it is through such recall that the transference is resolved. Such recall can play a role in consolidating the resolution, but if the resistance is overcome in the transference in the here and now the memories of the past appear relatively easily, more or less spontaneously. Kris (1956) described a reciprocal relation between resolution in the present and recall of the past.

FREUD'S MODEL

Before turning to how Fenichel's model looks when assessed in the light of these principles, I will establish a perspective by relating them to Freud's discussions of technique. I believe that Freud's model of the analytic process—despite some evidence of vacillation—was that the analytic process is essentially carried out on the transference in the analytic situation. He said analysis could be divided into two phases: "In the first all the libido is forced from the symptoms into the transference and concentrated there; in the second the struggle is waged around this new object and the libido is liberated from it" (1916–1917, p. 455). This formulation explicitly states the principle of the expansion of the transference in the analytic situation but fails to state how this is to be effected.

This statement, I believe, implies that the resolution takes place primarily by work within the analytic situation, though I expect that those challenging my opinion will point out the great emphasis Freud laid on recovery of the past, presumably to resolve the transference. I offer the following quotation from Freud (1914) in support of my inference that his primary emphasis falls on the present: "From the repetitive reactions which are exhibited in the transference we are led along the familiar paths to the awakening of the memories, which appear without difficulty, as it were, after the resistance has been overcome" (p. 155). The resistance has been overcome then *before* the memories appear, that is, through work with the transference in the here and now.

FENICHEL'S VIEWS

As for the principle of the expansion of the transference in the analytic situation, one could easily come away from Fenichel's monograph with the contrary conclusion that the analysis of the transference is an important but ancillary part of the process and that the process could take place primarily in the repetition *outside* the analytic situation.

That his actual practice may have looked very different from this is suggested by several remarks he makes in passing. He says that "the concentration of the whole analysis in transference analysis if possible naturally has definite advantages" but then goes on to say that "there are also situations (for example certain transferences) which if left to our choice, we prefer to analyze on the basis of the material of the 'life outside'" (p. 96). He also says that "the interpretation of a symptom is especially impressive when it comes about in connection with a new edition of the symptom in the transference" (p. 43).

Of course, if Fenichel does not stress the need for encouraging the transference to expand as much as possible within the analytic situation, he will say little or nothing explicitly regarding the techniques necessary to bring this about. And it is true that we find nothing concerning what I described as my second point, namely the importance of bringing the transference within the analytic situation to awareness by interpreting allusions to the transference in the associations not manifestly about the transference.

Fenichel's failure to make this point is best demonstrated by the fact that instead of emphasizing the priority to be given to interpretations of the transference, his leading principle for determining priority of interpretation is that it should go to what is most superficial in the patient's material. Indeed this principle, which he mentions repeatedly, is one of the major arguments of the monograph.

But Fenichel fails to specify just how one recognizes what is most superficial in the patient's associations. He does say that resistance should be interpreted before content, ego before id, and defense before instinct. None of these formulations specifies content in terms of a particular context, such as inside or outside the transference, but only in terms of relative depth. That no specific context is implied becomes apparent further in Fenichel's statement that any content is defense relative to a deeper layer but is what is warded off relative to a more superficial layer.

The stipulation that one should always interpret the more superficial of the two parties to a conflict is therefore difficult to put into practice. How can one tell what is resistance and what is content, what is ego and what is id, what is defense and what is instinct in the concrete associations the patient offers? And is it not furthermore true that in any actual analytic material the two parties unite in a compromise formation? Is the standard injunction to interpret the resistance first a clinically meaningful and usable principle?

Fenichel makes other efforts to specify priority of interpretation. The first priority, even though it is casually introduced, is that "we must operate at that point where the affect is actually situated at the moment" (p. 45). Fenichel introduces this criterion in connection with the rule that the "patient determines the subject matter of the analytic hour" (p. 44), but he soon adds that the patient does not know where the affect is situated at the moment and that the analyst must seek it out (p. 45). He says that the patient determines the subject matter of the hour not only by what he says but frequently also by what he does *not* talk about, or by *how* he speaks, or what he does. Clearly the analyst has a job to do. He cannot simply rely on what the patient spontaneously talks about. Fenichel's insistence throughout the monograph on the active role the analyst must play in conducting an analysis is to me an important point, one that needs to be reaffirmed in the face of recurrent theoretical trends that would inhibit the analyst from playing an active role for fear of interfering with the spontaneous development of the transference. I believe the analyst's job to be work with the transference in the here and now, bringing it to awareness and resolution.

There are hints in the monograph that on some level Fenichel senses that the principle of priority to the more superficial should be replaced by the principle of priority to the interpretation of the transference in the here and now. For example, despite his emphasis on interpreting the superficial, he points out that an interpretation can be *too* superficial. In close association to that insight he speaks of the "bitter retribution" that can follow from the neglect of sufficiently definite transference interpretations.

An illustration he offers of a dream of incest at the beginning of an analysis is again a hint of priority to the transference in the here and now. He writes that such a dream may mean such things as that if the patient admits this the analyst will leave him in peace, that perhaps he is being obliging in the transference or, on the contrary, is ridiculing the analyst (pp. 57–58). Thus Fenichel's illustrations include an important aspect of the third principle I proposed, namely the relating of a transference attitude to something in the actual current analytic situation, though he does not discuss it as a general principle.

That manifestations of the transference *sometimes* take place in relation to the actual events in the analytic situation is of course known to all analysts. Here are some instances from Fenichel's monograph: dream interpretation can afford the patient libidinal satisfaction (p. 51); the rule against major decisions may be heard as a parental prohibition (p. 29); a too deep interpretation can act as a seduction (pp. 38, 46); to call the analyst a mirror is misleading because the personality and other characteristics of the analyst (such as his sex) may even be decisive for the transference (p. 72). Furthermore, Fenichel writes that one is constantly surprised at the relative insignificance of the actual occurrences in the analytic situation to which there are repercussions in the transference (pp. 72–73), that the danger of active technique in Ferenczi's sense is its influence on the transference (p. 86), and that he agrees with Ferenczi that such transference repercussions should be analyzed as soon as possible after the action has been undertaken (p. 88).

More generally, Fenichel says that the analyst's attitudes are continually taking part in the process (p. 87). But Fenichel does not elevate the relation between transference and the actual analytic situation to a general principle except in some remarks about human behavior generally. He suggests, for example, that all human actions are a mixture of transference and realistic responses (p. 72) and that actions, impulses, and associations are always fed by both present realities and the past, though the past predominates in neurotics (p. 31).

The second consideration I advanced for the resolution of the transference in the here and now—namely, the examination of the relation between the patient's experience of the relationship and the actual analytic situation—is not made explicit, presumably because Fenichel accepts the usual formulation that resolution takes place primarily by way of genetic transference interpretations, that is, through interpretations aimed at connecting the transference to the past. But, in keeping with the general absence of any detailed discussion of the analysis of the transference, neither are genetic transference interpretations emphasized. While Fenichel neither explicitly distinguishes the two kinds of interpretation nor specifies their respective roles, there is again an indication that his practice might well have taken account of the distinction. It lies in his description of what he calls a "reverse transference interpretation." He gives as an example: "You are not aroused at this moment about your father, but about me" (p. 61). This illustration in the transference clearly parallels Loewenstein's description (1951) of an interpretation "upwards."

As for the new experience accompanying the interpretation of the transference, it is not to be found in Fenichel either, though it is progressively appearing in current literature on technique (Kanzer and Blum 1967, Dewald 1976). I suspect it will be chiefly in regard to this point of a new experience that I will be said to be going beyond even what Freud *implied*. This may be true. I suspect also that this point will be taken as an indication that I have fallen prey to an overemphasis on experiencing and an underemphasis on insight. Here I disagree. I believe the importance of new experience in analysis as a factor in change is often underestimated for fear that to grant it opens the gate to manipulation and corrective emotional experience in Alexander's sense (1946). The importance of experience in the transference is generally granted as in Freud's repeated statements that the transference does us "the inestimable service of making the patient's hidden and forgotten . . . impulses immediate and manifest" (1912, p. 108). I believe it should be possible to recognize that the experience of being treated otherwise than one expected provides the inestimable service of making immediate and manifest the fact that people can be different from what one has come to expect. One can grant experience its role without having to belittle the importance of insight into these experiences, both expected and new, in consolidating them into permanent new acquisitions.

TWO ILLUSTRATIONS

However extensively one may discuss issues of technique in general terms, the real test of a technical principle lies in its application to a concrete instance. In defense of my argument that in interpreting the transference Fenichel fails to give appropriate attention to the actual situation as a determinant in the present, I shall first discuss a clinical vignette offered by Fenichel himself. I recognize that it is risky to assume that one really knows what was said in a reported vignette, but I believe one has a right to conclude that if something is not stated, it is at the least not considered important. The illustration has the disadvantage of being a rather subtle one, but it is unreasonable to suppose that Fenichel would overlook a gross indication of a determinant of the transference in the present.

Fenichel describes a patient who proposed his own interpretation in intellectual terms. Fenichel then interpreted this as the patient's attempt to protect himself against feelings he feared. The patient held it against Fenichel that he exposed his resistance, instead of cooperating with his apparent readiness to analyze. Fenichel quotes the patient as saying: "But that is exactly my sickness, the fact that I cannot admit such feelings. You should cure me of that. And you demand as a prerequisite for the cure that I should be able to feel in the analysis." Fenichel then describes his own response thus: "Thereupon I tried to make it clear that I did not make such a demand but that he should search within himself and see that this not-having-feelings was really a wish-not-to-have-feelings actively put into play by himself" (pp. 7–8).

Fenichel's statement that he tried to make clear that he was not making such a demand is at least an implied transference interpretation. It suggests that the patient's view that the analyst was making such a demand is determined by his past. And surely there is a determinant in the past.

But is it not also true that Fenichel's interpretation that the patient was trying to protect himself against feelings he feared is plausibly understood by the patient as a demand that he should stop doing so? Would the patient not have been more receptive to the possibility that his hearing the interpretation as a demand had an important determinant in the past if Fenichel had acknowledged this very interpretation as the determinant in the present instead of saying that he tried to make it clear that he did not make such a demand? Is not Fenichel's repetition of his interpretation (that the patient was trying to protect himself against feelings he feared) a subtle rejection of the patient's complaint rather than an analysis of its meaning? Is the repetition of the interpretation not a deflection from dealing with the transference?

As a second illustration suggesting a failure to give enough importance to the transference I take Fenichel's description of the stages of insight a woman patient went through in the course of arriving at a conviction that she envied a penis. First she described a fear of going insane, then a doubt of her own perceptions and a fear that something she believed she had seen had only been imagined, then a fear of losing control of motility so that she would do something without wanting to. I omit a series of additional steps leading to compulsive thoughts of what kind of writing instrument the author of the book she was reading had worked with, then curiousity about the methods used by men in productive work, then a reference to infantile masturbation rendered intolerable by the feeling of not being able to perform it the way men do and so finally to penis envy as a psychic reality. One cannot fail to be impressed with the extraordinarily elaborate steps in the analytic work; but is it not equally extraordinary that not once is a manifestation in the transference mentioned? Doubtless they were there, and probably some were interpreted. But what does it mean that they are not mentioned in the discussion (pp. 9–11)?

On the other hand, Fenichel's recognition of the role of the actual situation is stressed in another illustration in which a treatment was making no progress. Fenichel says that in such a circumstance the patient has a right to ask for information, and until this right is admitted and an answer given, the transference—by which he clearly means the determinant in the past—cannot be demonstrated (pp. 38–39). By "an answer given" I understand no more than accepting the plausibility of the patient's complaint in contrast to an affirmation or denial of the validity of the complaint.

I have discussed Fenichel's monograph only from the point of view of an explicit statement of the principles of the analysis of the transference. I have made no attempt to set these remarks into the broader perspective of the monograph as a whole.

I repeat that I suspect that Fenichel's actual work conformed to those principles more than the formulations in his monograph do. On the other hand, although I argued that Freud's model conformed to the one I espouse in this paper, I suspect that his actual work often underplayed the analysis of the transference. To what extent work by analysts in general conforms to the principles I have stated, one can only guess. In the view of some of my colleagues I have overemphasized the analysis of the transference and of the here and now. I do not think so, but in any case the explicit and systematic statement of these principles is a step toward resolving controversy about the role of transference interpretation in technique. For the discussion to be useful it should be in terms of concrete clinical data. I plan to offer some in another context.

REFERENCES

Alexander, F., and French, T. (1946). *Psychoanalytic Therapy*. New York: Ronald Press.

Dewald, P. (1976). Transference regression and real experience in the psychoanalytic process. *Psychoanalytic Quarterly* 43:213–230.

Fenichel, O. (1938–1939). *Problems of Psychoanalytical Technique*. Albany, N.Y.: Psychoanalytic Quarterly, 1941.

Freud, S. (1900–1901). The interpretation of dreams II. *Standard Edition* 5:339–610.

——— (1912). The dynamics of transference. *Standard Edition* 12.

——— (1913). On beginning the treatment (further recommendations on the technique of psycho-analysis). *Standard Edition* 12.

——— (1914). Remembering, repeating, and working-through. *Standard Edition* 12,

56   MERTON GILL

——— (1916-1917). Introductory lectures on psycho-analysis. *Standard Edition 16.*

Kanzer, M., and Blum, H. (1967). Classical psychoanalysis since 1939. In *Psychoanalytic Techniques: A Handbook for the Practicing Psychoanalyst,* ed. B. Wolman, pp. 93–146. New York: Basic Books.

Kris, E. (1956). The recovery of childhood memories in psychoanalysis. *Psychoanalytic Study of the Child* 11:54–88.

Langs, R. (1978). *Technique in Transition.* New York: Jason Aronson.

Lipton, S. (1977). Clinical observations on resistance to the transference. *International Journal of Psycho-Analysis* 58:463–472.

Loewenstein, R. (1951). The problem of interpretation. *Psychoanalytic Quarterly* 20:1–14.

Self Psychology and the Distinctiveness of Psychotherapy

ARNOLD GOLDBERG, M.D.

After a brief review of some major theoretical points of the psychology of the self, psychotherapy is delineated from psychoanalysis via this perspective. The suggestion is made that the difference lies less in the method than in the goal. Clinical examples illustrate that the goal of psychotherapy consists of a repair of the self. This is in contrast to the goal of psychoanalysis which is a reorganization of the self. An accurate diagnostic assessment of the nature of the individual psychopathology enables one to recommend either reparative (that is, psychotherapeutic in the narrow sense) or reconstructive (psychoanalytic) treatment.

The issue of psychotherapy as a distinctive and separate endeavor has been a subject of controversy and discussion ever since psychoanalysis entered the arena for the treatment of mental illness. Although Sigmund Freud (1919) cautioned against diluting the pure gold of analysis, many others (Alexander and French 1969, Langs 1977) consider all psychotherapy as in the general realm of psychological treatment which, in turn, claims psychoanalysis as its most intensive and prolonged representative. There have been numerous classifications of treatment, based upon methods as well as goals. One common division separates supportive treatment from the more intensive efforts, while another equally popular one lumps all psychotherapy together and delineates it from analysis. There is no doubt that the answer to the dilemma is not available through administrative fiat but more properly belongs to the efforts of scientific scrutiny. Every advance in depth psychology should offer itself to an examination of its usefulness in areas outside its immediate clinical

A different version of this paper was presented as the Franz Alexander Memorial Lecture, April 1977, in Los Angeles, California.

relevance. Even though self psychology derived from specific psycho-analytic studies, its yield goes beyond analysis to the investigation of all psychotherapeutic work. The new insights gleaned from self psychology would seem to present another opportunity to resolve the problem of whether psychotherapy is a distinctive pursuit.

SELF PSYCHOLOGY AS A NEW PERSPECTIVE

A brief review of the work of self psychology is in order. It derives, of course, primarily from the research of one man, Heinz Kohut (1971, 1977), and from the analysis of a particular class of patient—the narcissistic personality disorders. Unfortunately, the original work was so couched in classical analytic jargon (a word that I do not use depreciatingly) and was so clearly about a supposed rare type of patient, that it was not readily recognized for its far-reaching implications. Only gradually has the yield for psychotherapy, per se, as well as a call for a fundamental shift in our perception of an enormous field of psychological data, become evident.

When Kohut talked of the self, he talked of something that is eminently clear to all of us, yet something that gets quite confounded in scientific explanation and examination. The self is the developing and shifting picture, perhaps we should say symbol or system, of the individual in depth. It is easy but unfortunately erroneous to lump it with other such tags as *identity* or *personality*, or to confuse it with the social sphere of selves in interaction. The psychoanalytic meaning of *the self* is one that encompasses the unconscious and infantile symbols of this entity. To keep it within the psychoanalytic framework, Kohut offered it as a content of the ego, but one close to experience. This definition implies varied levels of analytic theory and would posit *ego* as a rather abstract term and *self* as a more immediate one. My colleague, John Gedo, and I (1973) were never too happy with this distinction and chose to consider the term solely in terms of its clinical relevance, and thus to fairly closely follow Hartmann's suggestion (1965) of the self being significant in relation to, and as opposed to, objects. Probably these are trivial distinctions as long as we are consistent in considering the vertical axis of the self, as long as we pursue its meaning as part of a depth psychology. The self must be seen as a complex system with roots in the unconscious and with varied pre-conscious and conscious manifestations.

Kohut's concentration on the self was hardly unique or original, but his analysis of the self was. His first book demonstrated that individuals who seemingly were so self involved as to prevent ordinary object libidinal transference formation, were quite analyzable as long as one appreciated the formation of a different kind of transference: one where the analyst was experienced as a part of the self or as a selfobject. The occurrence of this form of transference, which later became classified into two major and several minor forms, became of great significance in making a distinction between object relations and object love. The former has to do with the social sphere of people interacting and includes both those objects that serve as functional aspects of the self as well as the latter: those seen as distinct centers of initiative. Objects of love and hate are independent of the self; selfobjects are felt as co-terminous with the self. But this distinction should be made with a clear lack of value judgment because neither is better nor more mature; rather, these can be seen to develop separately and independently.

The growth of the self via the use of others and the growth of the self in loving and hating others often are formulated as separate lines of development—narcissism and object love. As in all of our science, this is only a suggested way to look at things. It is a theory and not a law. No one denies the interdependence of narcissism and object love. Everything in normal growth is interdependent, but that should not prevent us from focusing and concentrating on singular developmental lines. As with any new theory, one must use it in order to see and appreciate its value. To those clinicians who claim never to have seen either transferences of this variety or evidence of narcissistic maturation, it must be realized that not until you know *what* to see are you able to achieve a perception (much like first visualizing bacteria under a microscope). Theories such as these are enabling devices and should lend a new perspective to our clinical data.

In focusing on how the person experiences another, on the particular functional relationships of others, this perspective of the self brings us inside that person's psyche and causes us to take up our position as empathic observers. This is a stance equally familiar, and applicable, to both psychoanalysis and psychotherapy. The psychotherapist has learned that selfobject transferences are quite common outside the psychoanalytic situation and indeed become readily established in a variety of therapeutic settings. Thus, the task for psychotherapy reverts to a familiar and formidable one—that of claiming its own boundaries. This task may be simplified in part by asking how the person experiences his or her self. The psychology of the self directs attention to the self experience vis-à-vis others and focuses on the affective reactions in that experience. It adds the specifics of the therapist's role in that experience (Goldberg 1972, 1973, 1975).

PSYCHOTHERAPY VS. PSYCHOANALYSIS

Many theories of psychotherapy derive so fundamentally from analytic theory that almost all the work of treatment is erroneously based upon a deficiency model: we repair ego deficits, we strengthen defenses, we become available objects for instinctual discharge. Using the particular conceptualization of a mature, adult psyche as an endpoint, one directs the efforts of treatment to approximate that ideal state of harmony between ego, id, and superego. I often think of this as the continuum theory of treatment which has as a basic premise the thesis that all good psychotherapy is but a smaller or limited form of psychoanalysis and that more of it, done almost daily, would be an analysis. This theory also regards the active participation of the therapist as necessitated by the patient's inability to utilize a purely analytic approach. Using or needing one's therapist in a role other than that of an interpreter of the unconscious is seen as evidence of severe trauma in infancy and childhood and,therefore, of the existence of pathologic immaturity. The patient's needs may thus be seen pejoratively, and their gratification as something improper that hopefully can be stopped as soon as possible. Psychotherapy is a stepchild disowned by its natural parents.

One reconciliation of the separation of pure psychoanalysis from psychotherapy has been to suggest abbreviated forms of analysis. This has its theoretical basis in the tenet that the treatment be based on interpretation and resolution of the transference neurosis, regardless of frequence of contact. This is not the place to discuss such departures from classical technique. Rather, my aim is to differentiate psychological interventions on the basis of change in the self-symbol as a goal. As such, this is an ideal differentiation and subject to a host of qualifications. Psychotherapy defined as any psychological intervention designed to alleviate emotional difficulties, covers and includes psychoanalysis. However, a further subdivision of psychotherapy defines it as nonanalytic psychological intervention. It includes all the talking therapies and none of the somatic treatments.

The somewhat prevalent view of psychotherapy as a continuum of quantity—one which has led clinicians to feel that the spectrum involves more and deeper of whatever they do—has naturally led to the endpoint of psychoanalysis which usually is considered to be the most and deepest. Bibring (1954) and others attempted to classify the nature of the interventions to be made in therapy and analysis. Too often, however, we find ourselves "interpreting" in supportive therapy and "confronting" in psychoanalysis, thereby confounding Bibring's classification. To claim a continuum from supportive psychotherapy to intensive psychotherapy to psychoanalysis may be repeating in the psychological field what often is seen in other areas, i.e., imposing a continuum to make better sense of observables where, in fact, none exists. Schroedinger (1943) long ago demonstrated that many perceptions of things as continuous result simply from the inner ordering devices of the observer. This is a common and by no means erroneous activity unless it tends to blur major breaks or distinctions of quality or kind in favor of those of quantity. Thus, the continuum theory has a built-in value judgment that occurs at that mysterious point of pure interpretation without contamination.

Psychotherapy more and more is seen as palliative first aid, with no clear guidelines for what to do or when to do it, save for the general rules regarding what should be avoided. Psychotherapy had no rationale; it was defined by what it was not—psychoanalysis. Hence, what we need is not more apology for psychotherapy but a reasonable theory of psychotherapy.

A first step in delineating psychotherapy is to separate it from the variety of active therapeutic maneuvers engaged in by psychiatrists or others whose aims are primarily to alleviate suffering, but which in themselves do not involve a prerequisite of increased understanding on the part of the patient. Drugs, hospitalization, changed settings, group or individual discussions—all are therapeutic, of course, but they would not qualify here as psychotherapy. This is not to be considered as any sort of value judgment, since removing all treatment from a continuum makes it more specific in its application and, therefore, no longer a matter of more and deeper is better.

The next step would be to allow a vast area of overlap in practice but not necessarily in theory (which, as stated, can be seen as ideal). In *Models of the Mind* (1973), Gedo and I delineated the various modes of therapy and noted how they may all be present to some extent in every treatment. What is crucial and essential about psychoanalysis may be seen in psychotherapy; certainly the reverse is true. The search for pure forms is a worthwhile scientific endeavor even though not a fact of everyday life. Whereas psychoanalysts may feel that the establishment and resolution of the transference neurosis accurately spells out their essential work they might also argue that this does not always happen, need not happen, or happens only occasionally in psychotherapy. This would still, however, fit the criterion for delineation regardless of the exceptions and qualifications. Anything short of or less than that which employs all or some of the theory and technique therefore becomes the proper arena of psychotherapy. Although it is a clear and concise definition, it still may do little more than shift the problem to a new vocabulary.

For the answer to what is crucial and particular to psychotherapy, we seek neither that which is ameliorative because of some active, basically nonpsychological involvement, nor that which is but a portion of psychoanalysis. It should consist of learning about one's self; some increased comprehension and expanded vision of one's make-up. But more importantly, I would stress that the difference between psychotherapy and psychoanalysis lies *less in the method than in the goal.*

It is suggested that we move toward a view of the psyche as a multi-leveled organization, that we see the psychotherapist as fitting into the organization in an effective manner. The changes brought about by psychotherapy are those which enlarge or broaden one's concepts to include psychologic material (action or images or symbols) that has remained outside the total system. However, the inclusion of such material need not involve a fundamental new and/or distinct symbol. This is more properly the business of psychoanalysis. For psychotherapy, we see modifications, enlargements, or filling in of defects of the symbol of the self. This is a discrete change in a basically unchanged self: a repair.

The self is an evanescent concept and we can never hope to clearly demarcate it. Clear pictures of the self are the self-representations commonly considered in analytic theory. However, these are essentially similar to computer printouts and are but momentary reflections of the complexity of the self. We use the term *self-symbol* or *self-system* to indicate that the self is a system of interdigitating pictures, actions, and words that come together to deliver a conceptual idea. We obtain but glimpses of this complexity. Let me present a rather typical case to illustrate this thesis.

CASE HISTORY

Mrs. Cunningham was in her fifties, married, and the mother of two grown sons. She came to see a therapist because of a fairly long-standing depression. Her sadness was accompanied by binges of overeating, short periods of insomnia, long episodes of tearfulness, and much overt anger. She was able to date the onset of her depression to the time of her youngest son's marriage, about one year subsequent to his older brother's marriage. Mrs. Cunningham was unhappy with both sons and their marriages; she was particularly displeased with her daughters-in-law, each of whom she resented openly but in rather different ways. The first was deceitful, insincere, and theatrical; the second was smug, self-sufficient, and condescending. Mrs. Cunningham was able and willing to describe each of these frustrating relationships in some detail, punctuating her description with sighs, tears, and an occasional overt wish for a severe misfortune to be visited upon one or the other of these hateful relatives. Sometimes she would apologize for her malicious wishes but never would she disown them.

Mrs. Cunningham had not been a chronically depressed person through the years, but she does recall a severe and profound experience when she was age fourteen: her eighteen-year-old brother was killed in an accident. She was overwhelmed with grief when this bright, handsome, and very promising member of the family was struck down. She was one of four children; all of the girls survived while the only son became the victim of tragedy. She said a pall settled over the house after her brother's death and this took years to dissipate.

Mrs. Cunningham was a poor historian of her early childhood, given as she was to the denunciations of her children, her praise of her grandchildren, and the elucidation of the misfortune of her present circumstances. However, she did sketch an uneventful childhood, a rather successful marriage, and an active work career until about ten years previous, when her husband became more successful and thereby raised their standard of living appreciably. She retired from work soon thereafter. She described her parents in matter-of-fact but distant terms, but did tell of a quite intimate relationship with one sister. Mrs. Cunningham's husband was pleasant, tolerant, but firmly unable and unwilling to share her discontent with their children. For the most part, Mrs. Cunningham no longer talked to her husband about the issue, which had now become an old and settled one. An arrangement of pleasant visits had been worked out with an absence of all surface animosity.

When this patient began treatment with me she had only recently left another psychiatrist whom she felt had failed to help her. She had no ill feeling toward him and confessed that she enjoyed their talks, but gained little of lasting value from him. She had a brief experience with antidepressant drugs, which had seemed primarily to increase her irritability and anxiety. Her referral was via an internist who was concerned about her weight.

Mrs. Cunningham was a fooler. Initially it seemed that rapid relief would be effected by a catharsis of her vast supply of feelings of maltreatment, self-pity, and rage. This procedure was equivalent to draining an abscess that had an easy source of replenishment (her manner of describing what she felt had happened with her previous therapist); one could see the addicting propensity of this form of treatment. The classical psychoanalytic assemblage of ingredients for depression involving anger at an object which, once internalized, allowed the hostility to be vented subsequently upon the self, was perhaps right but at best inadequate. She was relieved but not better. As a matter of fact, she was not very happy with this picture of herself as a raging and miserable mother-in-law, and the shift from bitterness to self-chastisement and personal condemnation was a ready and profound one.

As the treatment continued, the discussions ranged from descriptions of interactions with her husband to events of the day to episodes of the past that seemed most meaningful. It was my feeling that this was not an empty and desolate woman bitterly awaiting a fate of increasing despair but rather a very unhappy woman who was in great pain when angry. It was clear that anger was readily and easily available to her but that, in itself, anger was an ordeal for her to experience.

The detailed abreactions of whatever feelings Mrs. Cunningham had toward her husband, sons, daughters-in-law, grandchildren, sister, etc., continued to have a salutary but evanescent effect. She could see herself as a resentful and unfulfilled person, and she was quite capable of humor about and toward herself. At one point in the treatment, I took the position of trying to explain how people might feel toward her and about her; in particular, the hateful wives of her sons. The effort was made to have her consider them and to help or instruct or educate her to be empathic with these women, who may have been frightened or awed or intimidated by her. This exercise was a dismal failure and the patient became more depressed than before. I grew frustrated and exasperated as I found the weekly routine of futile talks, so familiar to the other therapist, now beckoning to myself. I thought of new drugs, of group therapy, of encouraging participation in a variety of activities; I even suggested that her husband enter treatment. In brief, Mrs. Cunningham and I were seeing her in the same way: a pathetic woman with nothing to do and nowhere to go. As common as such perceptions may be, the sharing of them by patient and therapist, often listed as a problem in countertransference or just as often urged as merely the facing of reality, also are valuable clues to psychotherapeutic efforts which can be ameliorative for both participants.

Of course, the experience of futility that was mine was also the patient's, as were the associated anger and search for solutions. My description to her of the need for her to be empathic with those around her whom most disappointed her was a prescription to me to get on the ball, or to push myself somehow to be in touch and understand her dilemma and depression. The impasse at which we had arrived was obvious but just as clear was the lack of change in things.

The patient appeared to be brighter one day, as she told of a visit with her grandchildren which was enjoyed by all. The picture of her struggling with the desire to do so much more than she felt able to do seemed eminently clear, and I pursued the details of the rift with the daughters-in-law. Each, for her own different reasons, had become unavailable to her as a source of contact and feeling, but this was not for the patient's lack of trying, or at least that seemed to have been the case. The first son's wife had repeatedly manipulated and used her relationship with Mrs. Cunningham, who soon became convinced that this kind of situation could not be endured and so had reduced their contacts to a minimum.

The second daughter-in-law simply had no use for Mrs. Cunningham because she was surrounded by her own family and friends and had no need to call upon her mother-in-law.

I then heard of a recent incident when a clear opportunity was presented for Mrs. Cunningham's usefulness and she had demured. She insisted that she knew better, was wiser because of repeated efforts which had failed. The event concerned the illness of one of the daughters-in-law, who had asked casually for something during a telephone conversation and then repeated the request on the following day. My patient said she had heard the request and had considered an immediate response but could not bring herself to do so. She recalled all of the efforts she had made in the beginning to this woman, and how she had felt so deflated by her. I told her that she was describing herself as one who had looked forward to having these women for daughters and now was so unfulfilled. She was a picture of good intentions, good resources, loads of energy, and no outlet. We thereby put into words what she had been feeling.

This perception reverberated in her with the image of the brother who had been struck down in his prime. Here, too, was a person of marvelous potential never realized. Here was a tragedy of unfulfillment that Mrs. Cunningham had witnessed, lived, and taken into her own self as a pathologic identification. She was the amalgam of the family picture of loss, bereavement, and bitter resentment over an unfinished life. This patient, in a way, was a reenactment of unfinished business and incompleted opportunity, so much had been the pride of her family before his life was aborted. Confrontation plus interpretation allowed a new set of feelings and images to emerge.

There is no doubt that the added ingredients of survivor-guilt based upon competitive feelings toward the only son also were significant features in this depression. There also is no doubt that alternative dynamics, explanations, and even descriptions of the treatment are available and possible, and even true. But Mrs. Cunningham got better as she put this new concept of her self into words; as she began to see and talk of a different picture of her self. She had only momentary glimpses of the past influences on her present life, but she did have an expanded vision of her immediate set of relationships. In almost every area of her existence she was portraying a wasted life. She changed and soon overcame her depression.

In brief, Mrs. Cunningham did establish a narcissistic relationship with her therapist in that she was mirrored. This is one illustration of the self-object. All of the old, hidden, and denied feelings of specialness, pride in performance, eagerness to shine, and so forth, were allowed to surface and be properly confirmed and responded to. I served her as a very necessary and meaningful extension of her self. Now she could allow some of her exhibitionistic and boastful feelings to emerge. She began dressing up, taking courses, being firm and diplomatic with her husband and friends, and shortly thereafter she terminated therapy. What had been isolated from the totality of her self because of a narcissistic injury due to rebuffs now joined in the repaired self-symbol.

CLINICAL THEORY

As this and other patients need a verbal contribution to gain a grasp of their selves, so, too, do many other people use a host of methods to gain new perceptions. Some would say that, in effect, we offer patients new theories as to what they are and how they become so. Not always are these efforts able to yield dramatic symptom relief but, for the most part, the work of psychotherapy is to gather together events, ideas, images, and whatever else may be offered for a new such construction. The act really is one of creation, pursued by patient and therapist to form an expanded or altered self-concept for the patient. Exposure of defenses, abreaction of emotion, reexamination of distortions of reality, are all contributions to this new and more elaborate picture. All of the tried and true techniques of psychotherapy aim at this work of construction. All we claim here is a reasonable description of the end product—a change in the self-concept, be it from a disavowed aspect, as in some, or from one that seemingly overtakes the entire personality, as with Mrs. Cunningham. The work of the changed concept is traditional and familiar to all therapists, although some patients need new ideas of action, new images, or new language, but always in terms of a new perception of their selves.

You may feel some verbal sleight of hand is being attempted when an explanation for treatment is offered by way of the simple statement that one sees things differently. This can easily be but a circular definition of improvement. However, the way in which one sees things differently is part of the explanation and this requires a more detailed description of the manner in which our psychotherapeutic efforts do manage such alterations. Behind the feeling of deceptive simplicity with such an explanation there often lies the wish for some weighty scientific terms to lend credibility and authority. They would add nothing of value to this theme of an altered vision of one's self, but one easily could employ such terms to say the same thing.

New perceptions are built up and organized according to individual modes of vision. In treatment we alter, modify, add to, or rearrange such self-perceptions, and from this, a change in the emotional state results. At times the therapeutic relationship yields a feeling of difference by virtue of the therapist's reflecting a specific image to the patient—sometimes, merely one of acceptance. There are times when a relationship needs a complex set of transactions which require specific activity on the part of the patient in order to conceptualize the self differently; at times, the concept must be symbolized verbally to achieve a new self-perception.

One cannot say what were decisive steps for improvement in the treatment outlined above. The technical maneuvers are not of primary concern so much as our attempting a theoretical stance for the results. I do not mean to disparage these maneuvers nor to make light of the interpretation of defenses and/or the recognition of unconscious phenomena. Rather, I hope to present the reader with a different orientation to the problem.

Mrs. Cunningham discovered the words and concepts to fit and alter the self that had resulted initially from her brother's death and which was reenacted in her new experience of nonfulfillment. The treatment assisted these new or renewed or reactivated configurations, and the result must be seen in terms of the context of patient and therapist together.

PSYCHOANALYSIS COMPARED

The essential distinction between psychotherapy and psychoanalysis involves a change or transformation within the latter that does not take place in the former. The essentials of psychotherapy involve the integration of a self-concept. The techniques of achieving this are quite variable and range from confrontation to interpretation. The results of the techniques are in the direction of a new meaning about one's self arising vis-à-vis the therapist and others. In analysis we reorganize the self, or perhaps more often we restore a self to its more fundamental state from one of disorganization or faulty organization. At a certain point in every effort to line things up according to quantity, a qualitative change does take place. The old argument about how many hairs make a beard is answered by knowing a beard emerges when you see it as such; it is a question of perception. Just as simply, we can distinguish psychoanalysis in its task of reorganizing the self from psychotherapy and its job of repairing a segment of the self.

Let me briefly sketch an analysis of a woman who entered analysis as a bitter and depressed person and, like Mrs. Cunningham, described a life of missing out and being short-changed. Her early childhood had been disrupted when her environment changed from one of comfort and content to one of struggle and poverty. This real deprivation coincided with her experience of a similar deprivation of a mother who was disappointed in her daughter's appearance and with a father who preferred a son to this daughter. The deprived quality often was manifested in the form of envy—of penises, wealth, intelligence—but also in the form of depression, inhibition, and ultimately of resignation.

Analysis evoked a series of angry reactions to the reawakened wish for acceptance and admiration, and the recurring presentation of herself as dirty, smelly, dumb, and unlovable. This woman had married a man in whom she felt deeply disappointed because he was so inadequate and unfulfilled; he had never reached his potential and always fell short of his aspirations. To her, he seemed inadequate and incomplete—a living mirror of herself. The analysis concentrated on the self-image but she continually invoked the reality of her life as a limitation to any kind of genuine self-fulfillment. She posed the question of divorcing this inadequate man and facing a life of painful loneliness or staying with him and enduring a life of dissatisfaction.

The crucial point in this analysis was the construction of a new self-picture that demonstrated a reordered reality which could exist without the nagging conflict of childhood and neurosis. This patient could always see her deficit everywhere and anywhere, especially in her (to her) castrated mate. For a long time she felt that only a change in her husband (sending him off to analysis) would help her. Slowly she improved as a sense of admiration in her own self and her accomplishments grew. Thereupon she was less troubled about her spouse's problems, insofar as she differentiated him from herself and his deficiency from her sufficiency. Her new reality was a clear picture of her husband, with acceptance and without sad resignation. This was due essentially to her working through, in the analysis, a developmental stage of desiring admiration, primarily from her father. As a result she no longer felt unloved and deficient. She now saw herself and her husband differently; she proclaimed that her analysis should not be related to her husband's problems but to her own self. Her termination was more joyful than resigned, in spite of her supposedly unchanged world. Her old reality or world vision had been a variable overwhelmingly determined by unconscious needs and her picture of a hateful self; this primarily emerged in her distinguishing and delimiting others as pictures of inadequacy. Whether one chooses to speak of self-object differentiation or stages of separation or mirroring, the essential step was one of constructing a new symbol. The outside observer may see no change. The patient sees change everywhere. How we think about the world changes it for us.

Though superficially alike, the two women were different. Mrs. Cunningham utilized therapy to repair and regain a self-symbol of vitality which had been achieved in her normal development and then subsequently damaged by a narcissistic injury. The second woman had organized herself around a developmentally inadequate process wherein the necessary response from her parents was faulty. For her, a new organization was needed. Both were depressed, both suffered chronic narcissistic rage, and both suffered from their anger. But anger was not the core of their pathology as much as was their common inability to have a meaningful picture of themselves confirmed. Most importantly, they had different needs from treatment and it is suggested that the proper therapeutic effort can be differentiated on the basis of treatment goal: repair versus reorganization. This stance claims that the techniques used in both therapy and analysis are similar, and it reminds me of Franz Alexander's answer to the question of whether one should analyze dreams in psychotherapy. He said, "Only if you know how to." On the other hand, it is a position that does demarcate therapy and analysis rather sharply and likewise supports all the conditions for the conduct of an analysis, such as frequency of appointments, etc. A task like reorganizing a faulty self-symbol needs everything going for it, and making such an effort with less frequent contact adds a probably insurmountable burden.

The distinctiveness of psychotherapy can be seen in terms of one's goal and can be approached utilizing a self psychology. Of course this is just a suggested theory and is only useful until it is proven wrong. But one should not mind, since all theories are wrong and better ones always lie ahead. The most significant thing is that we continue to search.

CONCLUSION

New theories should be used in a variety of ways to see if they offer solutions for old problems and that is the aim of this point of view. The idea of repairing the self as the essential of psychotherapy is one possible result of using the new perspective of self psychology to reexamine the results of psychological intervention.

In order to test the efficacy of this suggestion, one must examine cases of psychotherapy (used in the narrow sense) to see if the concept of a repaired self-symbol is helpful. This is in sharp contrast to a totally new configuration of the self, or reorganization, which psychoanalysis seems to serve. Of course, this by no means says that one patient is sicker than the other, only that there are different needs. The distinction between repair and reorganization also demands a break in the continuum theory of treatment and this forces us to consider the self in assessing treatment. Do we return to an earlier state of equilibrium or do we aim to achieve a new equilibrium? That our interventions may be similar need not prevent our saying that a new symbol has come about. This is a conceptual decision that each must make. The point that a collection of hairs becomes a beard or a much repaired sofa becomes a new couch is one that repeatedly presents itself to us in our perceptions of the world, and so it may be with psychological treatment.

REFERENCES

Alexander, F., and French, T. (1946). *Psychoanalytic Therapy*. New York: Ronald.

Bibring, E. (1954). Psychoanalysis and dynamic psychotherapy: similarities and differences. *Journal of the American Psychoanalytic Association* 2:745–770.

Freud, S. (1919). Lines of advance in psycho-analytic therapy. *Standard Edition* 17:157–168.

Gedo, J.E., and Goldberg, A. (1973). *Models of the Mind: A Psychoanalytic Theory*. Chicago: University of Chicago Press.

Goldberg, A. (1972). On the incapacity to love: a psychotherapeutic approach to the problem in adolescence. *Archives of General Psychiatry* 26:3–7.

——— (1973). Psychotherapy of narcissistic injuries. *Archives of General Psychiatry* 28:722–726.

——— (1975). Narcissism and the readiness for psychotherapy termination. *Archives of General Psychiatry* 32:695–699.

Hartmann, H. (1965). Contributions to the metapsychology of schizophrenia. In *Essays on Ego Psychology*. New York: International Universities Press.

Kohut, H. (1971). *The Analysis of the Self*. New York: International Universities Press.

——— (1977). *The Restoration of the Self*. New York: International Universities Press.

Langs, R. (1977). *The Bipersonal Field*. New York: Jason Aronson.

Schroedinger, E. (1943). *Science and Humanism*. London: Cambridge University Press.

Toward a Further Definition of Psychoanalytic Psychotherapy

NATHANIEL J. LONDON, M.D.

A discussion of "Self Psychology and the Distinctiveness of Psychotherapy," by Arnold Goldberg, M.D. Arnold Goldberg's applications of self psychology to psychotherapy help conceptualize psychoanalytic psychotherapy, contribute to technique, and provide new goals. Self psychology is formulated in terms of an intrapsychic focus and other psychoanalytic considerations of clinical process, is consistent with advances in the psychoanalytic study of object relations, and advances the clinical theory of psychoanalysis. Two concepts of self psychology are discussed and illustrated: separate lines of development for object relations and object love, and a supraordinate position for self psychology. Goldberg's distinction between psychotherapy and psychoanalysis on the basis of their respective goals helps decide the choice of treatment. However, a formal distinction between the modalities does not lie in their goals but rather in the qualities of the treatment relationship and the nature of the treatment process.

Arnold Goldberg has elaborated on the application of self psychology, as formulated by Heinz Kohut (1971, 1977), to the practice of psychoanalytic psychotherapy. He has also asserted that psychoanalytic psychotherapy may be qualitatively distinguished from psychoanalytic treatment by its goals: in the view of self psychology, psychotherapy is directed toward repair of the self while psychoanalytic treatment aims for reorganization of the self. The main purpose of this discussion is to recognize and further explicate Dr. Goldberg's contribution to psychotherapy.

Dr. Goldberg has conceptualized and illustrated the application of self psychology to psychotherapy in a series of outstanding papers (1972, 1973, 1975), and his present publication is a continuation of that effort.

My appreciation to Suzanne Albrecht, M.D., Ronald Brazman, M.S.W., and Keith Hartman, M.D., for their contributions.

His brief review of self psychology theory is not only a model of clarity and conciseness but is also a more refined formulation. His designation of object relations and object love as separate lines of development has clarified Kohut's earlier distinction of narcissism and object love as separate lines of development. Of the many contributions to psychoanalytic psychotherapy advanced in the past five years, Goldberg's work has provided something new of a definitive and substantive nature. This does not mean that the contributions of self psychology are sufficient in themselves to bring clarity and organization to the practice of psychoanalytic psychotherapy but rather that these contributions may provide an additional theoretical framework particularly suited to help conceptualize and order considerations of process and technique for a range of psychotherapeutic situations.

Dr. Goldberg views goal-limited psychoanalytic psychotherapy as deserving its own definition rather than being considered an attenuated form or something "less than" psychoanalytic treatment. In full agreement with Dr. Goldberg's position, I have consistently admired his published clinical illustrations and formulations. But in conceptualizing the "distinctiveness" of psychotherapy, I have approached the subject from a somewhat different vantage point. While this point of view will not be fully developed in this discussion, it merits some explication.

A PROCESS ORIENTATION

There are important differences between psychoanalytic psychotherapy and psychoanalysis, but they should not rest on any a priori considerations of what one should or should not do in psychotherapy or psychoanalysis. Concern for a spontaneously unfolding clinical process, particularly as it pertains to the interaction of analyst and patient, is central to all psychoanalytic approaches to treatment. The activity of the psychoanalyst is directed toward facilitating and organizing the process and, together with the patient, bringing it to a point of resolution. The analyst's attunement to the ongoing process is decisive as to whether it becomes accelerated, controlled or uncontrolled, interrupted, stagnated, or resolved. The concept of resistance is crucial. Different situations arise in psychotherapy as compared to psychoanalysis because of differences in the formal arrangements for the treatment, such as a conversational mode rather than free association and once-weekly sessions rather than four a week. Such factors influence the unfolding clinical process in many ways, including the extent of the therapeutic regression and the emergence of observable and analyzable transference manifestations. In addition, different situations arise in psychotherapy because a wider range of patients with differing personality organizations and a wider range of presenting problems may be selected. A clinician's response to each situation must be assessed on its own merits. In other words, a process orientation avoids any prescriptive notions of conducting psychotherapy in favor of empirical considerations. For example, the timing of an interpretation should not be influenced by whether the treatment is psychotherapy or psychoanalysis, but rather by considerations intrinsic to the unique clinical situation. Prescriptive notions about conducting psychotherapy tend to lead to excessive caution or excessive boldness, either of which disrupts the developing process and confuses a focus on critical issues and limitation of goals.

THE FOCUS OF PSYCHOANALYTIC PSYCHOTHERAPY

The psychoanalytic orientation to the study of man and its clinical applications rest on its "intrapsychic focus." This focus, so difficult to define and yet so necessary to grasp, converges on the individual's integration of his life experiences, as they are consciously and unconsciously organized and elaborated and as past integrations and future anticipations converge on the immediate present.

Personal motives (Loewald 1971), as understood in terms of conflicting drives and defenses in relation to object love, frequently emerge as significant determinants of human behavior (such as the vicissitudes of the oedipus complex). This very core of the clinical theory of psychoanalysis, the varieties of intrapsychic conflict as considered from the psychodynamic and genetic points of view, come into focus in the crucible of the psychoanalytic situation and the transference neurosis. But even when core motivational conflicts are crucial determinants of the clinical problem, they are hard to approach in psychotherapy. Their derivatives, as Dewald (1977) recently noted, may be fruitfully dealt with in a goal-limited psychotherapy in suitable cases. For the broader range of patients and clinical problems for which psychotherapy is indicated, psychodynamic conflicts may not be pertinent or even marginally relevant to the clinical goals. The problem of psychoanalytic reductionism is pertinent when psychoanalysts or psychoanalytically oriented psychotherapists impose the interpretation of core conflicts in unsuitable situations or without proper regard for the development of the treatment process.

The problem of psychoanalytic reductionism is pertinent to the "culturalist" critique of Freudian psychoanalysis. Self psychologies are more congenial to "culturalists" than are the messy fears, fantasies, loves, hates, and bodily concerns that are so prominent in psychoanalytic data. In fact, the concepts of identity and self are particularly well suited to make connections between subjective experience and social involvement. That is why Kohut's self psychology seems so familiar to the advocates of, let us say, Karen Horney or Harry Stack Sullivan. To them it is as if the Freudian analysts are finally coming around to accepting the findings of these bold dissidents from "psychoanalytic orthodoxy." There is some truth to that conclusion, just as there is truth to the charge that the psychoanalytic vision of man in the 1930s was one-sided in its preoccupation with core conflicts. The merits and deficiencies of the contributions of Horney and Sullivan are beyond the scope of this discussion. Suffice it to say that these contributions contained concepts and clinical observations pertinent to a contemporary self psychology; yet they offered little to advance psychoanalysis. They blurred the distinction between the intrapsychic focus of psychoanalysis and social interaction. The neo-Freudian definition of psychoanalytic psychotherapy, which has been very influential, remains vague with regard to focus, process, and goals. The scope of psychoanalysis was not widened but rather diffused.

Just as self psychology, as described by Goldberg, has a familiar ring to neo-Freudians, Freudian psychoanalysts like myself are also prone to react with a sense of "so what else is new?" Far from being guilty as charged of psychoanalytic reductionism, we have always been sensitive to the needs and aspirations of the "self" in clinical work—just as we have been sensitive to sociocultural influences in patients' lives. Yet, the working self psychology of the practicing psychoanalyst has been implicit and has lacked an explicit theory. The lack of an explicit self psychology is one of the factors that explains the wide divergencies among psychoanalysts in their practice of psychoanalytic psychotherapy, in contrast to psychoanalysis per se. If the neo-Freudian version of psychotherapy appears bland and vague, the overall impression of psychotherapy as practiced by Freudian psychoanalysts is too often erratic and inconsistent.

The main lines of psychoanalytic investigation have for many years pointed toward a psychoanalytic self psychology. In facilitating the hierarchic development of mental functions and psychic organization, psychoanalytic structural theory, or ego psychology, has provided a firm basis for the development of the self. I refer particularly to the contributions of Hartmann (1964) and Rapaport (1967). Psychoanalytic object relations theory, as exemplified by the contributions of Mahler (1968), encompasses an extensive body of knowledge of the organization of self and objects. Kohut's self psychology is consistent with these lines of psychoanalytic inquiry and adds a new dimension from an experiential-interactional point of view (London 1978).

THE SELFOBJECT IN SELF PSYCHOLOGY

The concept of the selfobject is essential to such an experiential-interactional viewpoint. In the treatment situation, the "selfobject" refers to the actual presence of the analyst, as experienced by the patient in manifold ways, which aids or deters sustaining and consolidating his self. The clinician tracks the patient through the clinical process in terms of this interaction. That is to say, levels of differentiation and organization of the patient's self are considered over time in relation to the selfobject: to the "contextual unit" (Schwaber 1978) of patient and analyst. Perhaps this view of the patient's self in interaction with the selfobject is an application of systems theory to the psychoanalytic clinical process. If that is the case, it is an application consistent with the intrapsychic focus and the process criteria of psychoanalysis. Similarly, the self–selfobject contextual unit allows consideration of its developmental antecedents as repeated in the transference.

In Goldberg's clinical example of the case of Mrs. Cunningham, the clinical turning point involved understanding a pathological identification. Self psychology is not required to reach such an understanding. However, the discovery of the pathological identification and its subsequent partial resolution took place in the ongoing treatment interaction by means of a focus on the patient's self and her sense of unfulfillment. Goldberg's challenge is to be accurately attuned to the emerging clinical process and to shifts in the nature of the treatment relationship. This challenge is familiar in terms of attunement to the nature of the resistance, working alliance, transference, and working through. Self psychology adds a further dimension in calling attention to the self–self-object context, which provided a guide to Dr. Goldberg as Mrs. Cunningham proceeded to free herself from her identification with her dead brother.

FURTHER COMMENTS ON SELF PSYCHOLOGY

Self psychology is a developing field subject to considerable ambiguity and controversy. Two concepts are particular sources of difficulty: (a) separate lines of development for object relations and object love, and (b) a supraordinate position for self psychology. Goldberg has described object relations and object love as separate lines of development. Such a concept at first appears to defy common sense. The sense of one's self and of others is inextricably linked in subjective experience to the drives and contrasts with a concept of the development of object relations as separation of object relations and object love is made by the clinician in the clinical setting by means of vicarious introspection. "We learn what another person *means* to someone via empathy and *then* we assign this meaning to the area of selfobject (part of the self), someone who is an obstacle (hate), or someone we love" (Goldberg 1978).

A view of a separate line of development for the self–selfobject contextual unit helps the clinician formulate more mature levels of object relations as well as to recognize and respond to more archaic levels. This contrasts with a concept of the development of object relations as confined to preodipal development. Also, pathology of the self, formulated as narcissistic resistances, has tended to be respected but to be viewed as either immutable deficiencies or regrettable obstacles to be somehow overcome in order to get to the "real thing." Self psychology provides a means to consider such resistances as necessarily appropriate for focus in treatment and analyzable. It should be noted, of course, that the distinction between analyzable and unanalyzable deficiencies in the development of the self remains an unsettled matter.

CASE ILLUSTRATIONS

The following clinical vignette, drawn from supervision of a once-weekly psychotherapy, illustrates the usefulness of distinguishing object relations from object love in a goal-limited psychotherapy.

Alice M was an attractive, intelligent but depressed and conflicted young woman. Having been jilted by her fiancé, she moved to another city where her social circle was limited to fellow workers. The members of the social circle, of both sexes, appeared to border on homosexuality in various degree and she had little in common with them other than her work. Alice showed no evidence of an incapacity to love (Goldberg 1972). Her complaint was a fear that she lacked the capacity to attract someone worthy of her love. That is to say, her depleted self-esteem did not derive from an early arrest of the development of the self but rather from disturbances at more mature levels of object relations. While this concise report cannot detail the evidence for such a conclusion, a correct diagnostic assessment is crucial. Suffice it to say, evidence for a mature level of object relations derived not only from her history and present functioning but from the nature of the developing relationship with the therapist.

A diagnostic assessment that the patient has the capacity to love does not necessarily mean that the focus of the treatment will be on conflicts involving object love. In this case, a solid working alliance was easily established because the therapist was well attuned to Alice's level of object relations. In the opening phase, Alice was preoccupied with defining herself and her life situation. She did not turn to the therapist to gratify her unfulfilled yearnings (an erotic transference) but rather used him as an auxiliary to herself (a mature level of selfobject) to confirm her capacities and to take distance from the social circle with which she was enmeshed—to see herself as different from them. The activity of the therapist was nonintrusive and clarifying, with little interpretation and no advice or other "parameters."

The early phase of psychotherapy showed little overt change in Alice's life experience, but there was a progression in her involvement and openness in the treatment situation. A striking change did occur after the eighteenth session, when Alice visited her parental home on vacation. She had a chance to observe a harsh demonstration of her mother's repeated devaluations of the father she idolized. Her recognition and integration of this observation was new for her, no doubt prepared by a heightened capacity for objective reflection and self-observation as a result of the treatment. She recognized her mother's devaluation not only of her father but of herself, and she confronted her mother in a manner new for her. By the twentieth session, Alice's depression had lifted and she was bubbling with reports of significant changes. She became more assertive and began to see herself not only as capable of loving but as worthy of being loved. More suitable partners suddenly appeared. At this point there were hints of an inhibition of sexual intimacy related to the line of object love at the level of oedipal conflicts.

To formulate the treatment so far, Alice had recovered from a wounded self after being jilted. The pathology of the self that emerged in the psychotherapy centered on her assessments of her self in relation to others—to her mother, her fiancé, and her present social group. That she became enmeshed in a social group unsuitable for her appeared immediately related to her low self-esteem and fear of another disappointment rather than a defensive behavior related to sexual conflicts. Yet there were indications of core conflicts, at an oedipal level, that had not come into focus. It remains to be seen whether such conflicts will, indeed, interfere with intimacy. If not, this treatment will be an example of "repair of the self." But it is not unusual that such a repair of the self allows the patient to define long-standing conflicts and their complexity in a way that provides a sound basis for seeking an analysis. The clinical situation to this date has been appropriate to a focus on object relations, whereas an effort to focus on the conflicting motives involved in object love would have been ill-timed and off the mark.

A supraordinate position for self psychology is implicit in Dr. Goldberg's paper (see Kohut 1977). This view envisages all psychoanalytic clinical theory subsumed under self psychology and is yet to be fully tested or accepted among psychoanalysts. It asserts that the overall integrity and organization of the self is conceptually a higher order consideration than specific clinical problems such as core or derivative conflicts. Such a theoretical framework, rather than dismissing the interpretation of core or derivative conflicts, actually sharpens such an interpretive focus under appropriate circumstances. Interpretations are better timed and more complete.

The following vignette, also drawn from the supervision of a once-weekly psychotherapy, illustrates the emergence of derivative conflicts. Mary C, a schoolteacher, exemplified altruism as a defense. Her devotion to her students, as it subsequently turned out, served to protect her from her fears of intimacy. The psychotherapist was initially confronted with a patient wounded and outraged when her students or colleagues failed to meet her selfless high expectations. The grandiosity implicit in these expectations did emerge. As the therapist helped her to explore and understand her vulnerability in this area, a solid though equally altruistic working alliance developed.

The patient was in a state of turmoil as a vacation approached. Everyone around her appeared preoccupied with the impending vacation, while she was burdened and harassed in her devotion to getting the work done. She had no vacation plans. The therapist called attention to his own impending vacation as a factor in her turmoil. As Mary considered the implications of her reacting to the therapist's vacation, she had a flash of insight regarding the pupils she loved: "My God, I'm going to miss those kids!" She immediately recognized how she was avoiding life and intimacy by her devotion to the therapist and her students. After the vacation it was clear that a new aspect of the self had emerged. She appeared enthusiastic, obviously delighted with the progress of her treatment, and there were indications of an idealization of the therapist quite different from the earlier altruistic devotion. The content of the treatment sessions showed a dramatic shift. She spoke of her concern about dressing attractively for fear of being considered "seductive" by other women. She began to question why she always selected unsuitable partners for her brief and disappointing love affairs. There were connections in both instances to the image of a mother forbidding expressions of femininity and sexuality. Considerations of technique with respect to an "analysis of the self" were hardly required at this point. Indeed, through a partial resolution of her altruistic defense, Mary appeared to have achieved a "repaired self" and to be ready, willing, and able to explore her sexual conflicts. What was now indicated was "old fashioned" defense analysis. There is little reason to think that any interpretation of the altruistic defense early in the treatment would have fostered the impressive progress of this patient. Rather, it is my impression that early attention to Mary's wounded-self made possible the remarkable shift in the defensive process that ensued.

Another vignette drawn from supervision, this time of a twice weekly psychotherapy, illustrates the supraordinate position of self psychology. Claire T suffered from a chronic severe conversion hysteria with a number of medical complications. Her conversion symptoms had led to her being invalided with severe contractures. The woman resident psychiatrist had her first contact with Claire in a context of psychiatric management in a hospital setting. With skillful care and a sound use of other medical and rehabilitative services, she developed a good relationship with Miss T and continued to care for her following discharge from the hospital. At this point she and Miss T began a formal psychotherapy.

The treatment process quickly became repetitious and stagnant with a seemingly unending series of complications involving the other medical services. One theme, however, emerged with unmistakable clarity. Miss T repeatedly sought—often in highly exhibitionistic and inappropriate ways—to get someone, anyone, to recognize her professional competence and devotion to her work. In point of fact, Miss T had a record of impressive achievements. The therapist, however, in common with many others who had contact with Miss T, understood her symptoms in terms of secondary gain: that she fell ill to avoid work.

Could the clinical impasse be resolved if the therapist only understood that Miss T probably fell ill as a way of dealing with intrapsychic conflicts? That would not be sufficient, nor would it clarify the nature of the resistance. The therapist, as a result of supervision, reconsidered the evidence and became convinced that the patient was indeed committed and able in her work. She conveyed this recognition to Miss T in a simple and unobtrusive fashion. The result was dramatic. The working alliance was quickly reestablished, the patient's social functioning improved, and the flow of the treatment moved toward significant sexual fantasies and conflicts in the context of a manageable regressive transference.

Miss T seemed to have sensed in myriad subtle ways the criticisms implicit in the formulation of secondary gain directed toward the one area of her life in which she functioned well. The result was a wounded self with regressively activated aggressive and exhibitionistic behaviors; she was incapable of joining a working alliance. The problem had to be resolved for the treatment to proceed; the needs of the self were supraordinate in the clinical setting to the core conflicts determining the neurosis. Nor was this dramatic improvement the end of the matter. Miss T's vulnerability to feeling devalued and accused of exploiting her symptoms became a major transference resistance that had to be confronted. Such a confrontation elicited some developmental origins for this vulnerability. Essentially, the developmental problem, reawakened in the transference, was that of a mother trying to make empathic contact with a daughter who not only exploited her symptoms but whose capabilities and purposes were confused and confounded by derivatives of unrecognized core conflicts. At this point, more than simple recognition of Miss T's competence was required. Interpretation of her outraged reaction to such empathic failures, now directed toward the therapist, became a focus of the treatment. This predominant resistance had its own developmental history understandable in terms of self psychology.

After a little more than a year of treatment, the patient was functioning well in her work and had made dramatic strides in overcoming the contractures and the conversion symptoms that had produced them. The core conflicts, which had surfaced from time to time—always following the resolution of a transference resistance—were not really dealt with, nor were her problems involving intimacy resolved. Nevertheless, the patient was pleased with her progress and insisted on ending the treatment. A six-month follow-up indicates that she remains confident and works productively. Considering the difficulties in the treatment of such a severe hysterical neurosis, this case is presented not only as an example of a supraordinate position for self psychology but also as an example of a successful goal-limited psychotherapy.

REPAIR OF THE SELF AND REORGANIZATION OF THE SELF

Dr. Goldberg has invoked a supraordinate position for self psychology to distinguish psychoanalytic treatment from psychoanalytic psychotherapy. His distinction between analysis and therapy on the basis of goals contains "something new" significant to the choice of treatment.

The choice of psychoanalytic treatment is based on the conclusion that a situation evoking a transference neurosis is required in order to achieve a major reorganization of the self. If the goal is a more modest repair of the self, as in the case of Dr. Goldberg's patient, Mrs. Cunningham, psychotherapy is the treatment of choice. The impact of a successful goal-limited psychotherapy on the life of someone like Mrs. Cunningham deserves serious consideration, so that my term *modest repair* should not be misunderstood to minimize the value of the results.

Goal-limited psychotherapy has been considered in terms of shifting a state of psychological disequilibrium to one of equilibrium. Patients presenting with long-standing character problems have proved difficult in this regard. Clinicians have been prone to be pessimistic about any intervention short of an extensive "reorganization." Yet Mrs. Cunningham could have been viewed in such terms and Dr. Goldberg's application of self psychology did lead to a reasonably successful "repair." In his "On the Incapacity to Love" (1972), Dr. Goldberg reported a number of examples of successful goal-limited psychotherapy with adolescents showing characterologic problems. My own experience is consistent with Dr. Goldberg's reports. No panacea is implied with respect to the application of self psychology to such difficult problems, but neither should a major shift in the organization of the self be viewed with disdain. The techniques involved are quite different from Alexander's "corrective emotional experience" (1954), a point that cannot be pursued here but merits further elaboration.

Promising results from the application of self psychology are found with sufficient frequency to suggest that we take a new look at successful brief treatments that were formerly dismissed as "transference cures." "Transference cures" refer to transient identifications with the therapist or idealizations of the therapist in the service of resistance. They should be distinguished from situations where the transient identification or idealization is not or is not only in the service of resistance but leads to a repair of the self. If the clinician is able to recognize the happy occurrence of the latter situation, he has an opportunity to conduct the treatment in a way that consolidates a successful goal-limited psychotherapy. Without such consolidation, the patient is more likely to leave treatment with a "transference cure" of questionable value or an unsuccessful treatment experience.

The following case of a once-weekly psychotherapy is offered as an example of a "repair of the self" which to my view could be misinterpreted as a "transference cure." This report is highly condensed and simplified for the purposes of concise exposition. Robert F sought treatment in his mid-thirties when he appeared blocked in any career advancement. He seemed tight, inhibited, sullen, irritable, and utterly frustrated in a sense of inability to realize his potentials in his personal and professional life. This mental state had persisted, essentially unchanged, at least since he was sent to boarding school at age ten. Yet, he was a thoughtful, intelligent man with sound values, many assets, and some considerable achievements. He had made a good marriage and his children were developing well in spite of the depressive pall that hung over the family. It was hard to test his capacities for self-observation because he was so utterly preoccupied with a sense of failure.

The psychotherapy tended to be strained and frustrating, as were all aspects of his life. Gains were made but they were hard won. An in-depth grasp of his present and past life was achieved but had little impact on his sense of disappointment. He was able to play an effective role in his family when his father developed a terminal illness. After his father's death, as is so often the case, he seemed to take hold of his life somewhat better. At this point, after a year of psychotherapy, we agreed that maximum benefit had been obtained and so discontinued treatment. It seemed a partial success but there were no decisive victories.

Mr. F returned to treatment several years later. There were impressive

gains in his external life situation. He had changed his job to a position
with more opportunities and he was actively involved in community
affairs. While obviously more content than before, the same sense of
frustration and disappointment prevailed. After several months I had
good reason to make the following observation to him: I understood very
well that his mother was a very difficult woman, a source of disappointment and embarrassment to him now as well as in his childhood. Yet I
failed to understand why this painful state of affairs made it inevitable
that he wreck his life.

What I had said had a profound impact on Mr. F. He had assumed that
he was doomed by his mother's lack of empathy. My statement opened up
new vistas. I don't believe that the import of my statement was the crucial
factor; any number of other observations may have had the same impact.
It came at a particular point in time in the developing treatment process
and all that had led to that point was decisive. Nevertheless, the statement
was earthshaking to Mr. F and changed his life. He became euphoric as he
began to become freer, assertive, and quite creative in forging a new life
style. What was a source of delight to me, however, was to a significant
degree a source of apprehension to Mr. F. Perhaps, he suggested, we were
"creating a monster." He feared with each expression of a healthy
assertiveness that he risked becoming inconsiderate or tyrannical toward
others. Much of the work in this phase involved defenses against emerging aggression. Fortunately, those he feared he was tyrannizing, such as
his wife, responded very favorably to the changes. It is important to note
that Mr. F first idealized my observation and quickly turned to idealize me
and the treatment process. Links to old and thwarted yearnings to idealize
his father were very much part of the work. In contrast to the earlier
psychotherapy, a decisive change did occur as a concealed part of the self
emerged. This was characterized by humor, resourcefulness, and aggressiveness. We seriously considered undertaking an analysis. After
thorough deliberation Mr. F decided that he was satisfied with his
impressive progress and was not prepared to undertake psychoanalytic
treatment at that time. The treatment was brought to a close, again, after
a little more than a year.

Dr. Goldberg has overstated his point in using the opposition *repair of the
self/reorganization of the self* as a broad concept for distinguishing psycho-
analysis from psychotherapy. Once the treatment is selected, it is difficult
and, I believe, disadvantageous to distinguish psychoanalysis from psychotherapy by its goals. Once the decision is made, the task of the clinician
is to develop the treatment situation to the best of his ability. Of course
goals need to be limited, but the limitation of goals should be determined

by process criteria rather than by whether one is conducting psychotherapy or analysis.

Generally speaking, the formal constraints of a psychotherapeutic
situation (such as the lesser frequency of interviews as compared to an
analysis) will necessarily limit the goals to a repair of the self. However,
these concepts—repair of the self, reorganization of the self—are rather
abstract and lack clear-cut observational referrents. One can determine
whether a therapeutic regression or a transference neurosis has or has
not taken place, but how is one to determine after successful treatment
whether the self is repaired or reorganized? There is no theoretical reason
why reorganization of the self cannot occur in a successful psychotherapy, and I believe that this does occur at times.

To reduce my argument to an absurdity, should a psychotherapy be
converted to an analysis if the patient appears to become involved in a
reorganization of the self? Surely this would be a disservice to a successful
psychotherapy, unless certain process considerations were fulfilled. If the
patient, in the course of psychotherapy, were to progress to a fruitful
opening-up wherein the complexities of his life become clarified and the
need for a psychoanalytic situation is clearly demonstrated, then one
should convert the psychotherapy into an analysis. Alternatively, should
one consider an analysis to be unsuccessful if it appears that the self was
only repaired rather than reorganized? This would be the wrong question, because it is not stated in terms suited to the clinical process. The
correct question, in assessing such an analysis, is whether the goals
achieved by the analysis could have been met by psychotherapy. This is an
important and difficult question, but one that can be approached by
observable process criteria. The Task Force on Criteria for the Psychoanalytic Process of the American Psychoanalytic Association is currently
developing such criteria (Peer Review Committee, 1976). In summary, the
indications for one modality or the other requires serious consideration of
goals. But a distinction between psychoanalysis and psychotherapy does
not lie in their goals but in the formal qualities of the treatment process.
Once the treatment is under way, whether it be analysis or psychotherapy, the question of the limitation of goals no longer lies in the
realm of abstract goals but in an optimal development of the treatment
situation.

Thus, the value of self psychology, as advanced by Goldberg, is best
demonstrated in the clinical setting. It is an approach carefully attuned to
the process criteria and focus of psychoanalysis. I have increasingly
turned to its concepts for teaching psychotherapy. It is particularly useful
for helping the beginning student gain an empathic as well as an objective

grasp of the realities of his patients' lives. Self psychology can be misused or misinterpreted. Goldberg (1975) has noted that its technical concepts have in some circles been reduced to "being nice" to patients, as if the therapist panders to narcissism and avoids any confrontation, particularly with respect to matters of aggression. The value of self psychology is also limited if insulated from a broad knowledge of psychoanalysis. It cannot stand as an independent discipline and its promise lies as an addition to, and an advance of, psychoanalysis.

Self psychology, in contrast to a psychotherapy based on Sullivan's "interpersonal relations," advances the clinical theory of psychoanalysis rather than diverging from its core. Can a focus on self psychology as a supraordinate concept distract a clinician from a proper focus on motivational conflicts? Conversely, can a concentration on motivational conflicts lead to treatment failures because problems crucial to self psychology have been neglected? The answer to both questions is affirmative as well as beside the point for the further development of psychoanalytic psychotherapy. What is required is that both frames of reference be explored further by empirical study in a wide range of treatment situations.

REFERENCES

Alexander, F. (1954). Some quantitative aspects of psychoanalytic technique. *Journal of the American Psychoanalytic Association* 2:685–701.
Dewald, P. (1977). The process of change in psychoanalytic psychotherapy. Presented to the Fall Meeting, American Psychoanalytic Association, December 17, 1977.
Goldberg, A. (1972). On the incapacity to love: a psychotherapeutic approach to the problem in adolescence. *Archives of General Psychiatry* 26:3–7.
——— (1973). Psychotherapy of narcissistic injuries. *Archives of General Psychiatry* 28:722–726.
——— (1975). Narcissism and the readiness for psychotherapy termination. *Archives of General Psychiatry* 32:695–699.
Hartmann, H. (1964). *Essays on Ego Psychology*. New York: International Universities Press.
Kohut, H. (1971). *The Analysis of the Self*. New York: International Universities Press.
——— (1977). *The Restoration of the Self*. New York: International Universities Press.
Loewald, H. (1971). On motivation and instinct theory. *Psychoanalytic Study of the Child* 26:91–128.
London, N. (1978). Discussion of "Psychoanalysis of the Self and Psychotherapy" by J. Palaci. Presented to the Chicago Conference on Psychology of the Self, October 15, 1978.
Mahler, M. (1968). *On Human Symbiosis and the Vicissitudes of Individuation: Infantile Psychosis*. New York: International Universities Press.
Peer Review Committee of the American Psychiatric Association (1976). *Manual of Psychiatric Peer Review*. Washington, D.C.: American Psychiatric Association.
Rapaport, D. (1967). *The Collected Papers of David Rapaport*, ed. M. Gill. New York: Basic Books.
Schwaber, E. (1979). On the "self" within the matrix of analytic theory. *International Journal of Psycho-Analysis:* 60:467–480.

Clinical Application of the Concept of a Cohesive Sense of Self

JOSEPH D. LICHTENBERG, M.D.

Recent psychoanalytic studies have contributed significantly to our understanding of how the formation of self-image groupings (the body self, the self experienced as individuated, and the grandiose self) integrate to form a cohesive sense of self. In addition to our increased knowledge of the normal development, we have a richer understanding of vulnerability to fragmentation of the sense of self. Knowledge of the development of the sense of a cohesive self and its vulnerability to fragmentation are applied to illnesses familiar to psychoanalysts. During normal adjustment reactions different aspects of the self predominate. In most such instances, images of the self can be balanced so that self-cohesion is retained. In the conflicts of the psychoneurotic, aspects of the self may be defensively segregated. Psychoanalysis must enable these aspects of the self to come into awareness and be blended into the general experiencing of the self; rarely does the threat of loss of self-cohesion present a special problem in working on this with a psychoneurotic patient. In contrast, the narcissistic personality and borderline personality disorders present specific problems centering on the potential of the patients to experience fragmentation of their sense of self. Clinical vignettes and theoretical formulations contrast these with the familiar problems that arise in the treatment of the psychoneuroses. The therapist's full empathic contact and a correct strategy of interventions arise from the appreciation of the presence or absence in the patient of threatened fragmentation of the cohesive sense of self.

In a previous publication (Lichtenberg 1975), I presented an account of the development of sense of self from infancy through early childhood. After the infantile period of fragmentary moments of awareness of a sense of self, the child begins to experience himself as a cohesive entity with some unity and continuity. The maintenance of that sense of cohesion is subject to the vicissitudes of intrapsychic conflict at every subsequent developmental phase. Stating this more broadly, each disequilibrium of the psychic state—from the normal transitions of daily life (waking to asleep, fed to hungry, studying to dating) to the disequilibria of major pathologic states—constitutes some potential disruption of self-

cohesion. Most disequilibria, even those involving relatively severe fluctuations of sense of self, may occur without the sense of cohesion
becoming fragmented. In some instances, in patients with narcissistic
personality disorders, borderline disorders, and psychoses, disequilibria
in the psychic state reflect an impairment, subtle or gross, in which
fragmentation occurs. The concept of whether a cohesive sense of self is
maintained or fragmented is of considerable diagnostic and therapeutic
importance. For the therapist to achieve an appropriate empathic understanding of his patient he must be able to recognize both those instances
in which self-cohesion is maintained and those in which it is lost. This
paper relates concepts of self-cohesion—its development, its normal and
pathological alterations, and its pathological fragmentation—to familiar
clinical problems.

I approach the psychoanalytic concept of the self by maintaining a strict
distinction between the experiential realm, in which the sense of self can
be understood empathically, and the nonexperiential realm, which refers
to functioning of the psychic structures id, ego, and superego. In this way,
sense of self can be seen as arising during the infantile stage as islands of
experience that are then, bit by bit, formed into more ordered groupings
of images.

One grouping of images, *the body self*, forms as the psychic correlates to
the child's full range of experiences that center on his body (its surface, its
interior, and all the body-centered sensations and feelings, see Lichtenberg 1977). A second group of images making up the self, those of *the self as
separate and individuated*, originate from the differentiation of the self and
the object as discrete experiential entities. This line of development leads
from dependency to emotional self-reliance and adult object relations
(A. Freud 1968, p. 64). A third component group of images comprising the
self, *the grandiose self*, develops from the infant's archaic assumption of
perfection and omnipotence. These grandiose images originate in the line
of development that begins with archaic fantasies derived from infantile
experiences of total mother-infant merging. From these archaic fantasies,
two sets of images form in childhood: grandiose omnipotent images of the
self and idealized images of the parents. The latter are experienced as
retaining self- as well as object-qualities. In adult life, this line of development leads to self-images with feeling qualities of heightened self-esteem
and to idealized images reflecting superego and ego-ideal representations
(Kohut 1971, 1977, Gedo and Goldberg 1973).

Each grouping of images is comprised of individual images that may be
conscious or unconscious. In the nonexperiential realm, representations
that comprise each component of the self can be regarded as having id,
ego, and/or superego aspects. In the course of maturation and develop-

ment, bodily self-images, self-images in relation with objects perceived as distinctly separate, and images of the grandiose self associated with idealized self-objects become blended together. Subsequently, in normal development, changes can be experienced within the balance between these broad clusters of self-images, while the overall sense of the self retains an essential feeling of sameness (Lichtenberg 1975).

During the period in which the integration of component self-images takes place, self-experience achieves a continuity in time: I am the same me, the same member of my family, whether it is a time when I am alone and stroking my body before sleep or when I am with mother, agreeing or opposing or when I am showing off my skills. The continuity in time is paralleled by continuity in space: my body, my mind, my name are all contained in the self as place. There is continuity of state—active or passive, asleep or awake. Cohesion of the self is the experiential sum of these continuities in time, space, and state. The experience of self-cohesion is not either cognitive or affective; it is invariably both (Schur 1969). In the adult, the affective-cognitive sense of cohesion of self is most often taken for granted; it is most apt to be noted when its loss is threatened or when fragmentation has occurred.

The first section of this paper describes normal and pathological alterations in the sense of self that can occur as a result of shifts in the balance of the three component groups comprising the self without cohesion becoming fragmented. The second section describes fragmentation of the sense of self that occurs in the narcissistic personality disorders and the borderline disorders.

NONFRAGMENTING SHIFTS WITHIN THE SENSE OF SELF

Oscillations in which one component grouping may come to dominate self-experience without there being a loss of a sense of cohesion occur throughout all periods of life. During a physical illness or a training period for an athletic event, the body image component may predominate. When falling in love or involved in an infinite variety of other experiences of interpersonal relations, images of the self as it interacts with discretely separate objects may occupy the center of self-experience. When making a speech or involved in any matter that touches on self-esteem enhancement or diminution, images of the grandiose self as it interacts with idealized self-objects are apt to be the focal point. Self-experiences that reflect the major restructurings of psychic functioning in adolescence can be cited to illustrate dramatic shifts in the balance between the component groups without loss of sense of cohesion. Commonly, even in the turbulence of adolescence, the relatively mature ego can regulate those pursuits which oscillate between high and low tension states and make smooth enough transitions between conflictual situations and problem-solving challenges. The adolescent thus can experience a marked fluidity of self-experience and still generally retain an essential intactness of self. For example, the adolescent commonly alternates between states of self-centered preoccupation and periods of intense cramming for an examination.

Mr. R, an eighteen year-old college freshman, was interviewed twice weekly in the college mental health center as a normal control in a research project.

Tuesday: I haven't been studying too good. I get started and I start thinking about my chemistry exam next Monday and I wonder if I'm going to be able to really ace it. I remember high school and the awards I got and worry about getting the grades I want in college. Then I tried to get back to studying and the next thing I knew I was thinking about my date last Saturday: Did she go for me? or think I'm not with it? Finally I hung it up and went to the commons room to see what was happening.

Preoccupied with grandiose fantasies fired by libidinal and aggressive drive derivatives, the adolescent may be so diverted into narcissistic tension states as to have difficulty concentrating or studying. It might be said that the grandiose self-images dominate to a degree that this component has swallowed up all those body self-images and all object related self-images which are not intimately connected to grandiose aims. Since alterego sharing within peer relations, often in a setting of musical cacophony that mirrors the internal turbulence, protects the dominant self-grandiosity against threats of deflation, the adolescent's ego functioning is centered on achieving these narcissistic object relations.

Friday: Last night I got my act together and hit the books. I'm into chemistry now and it's work all the way. I'm pretty sure I'm OK for Monday. I've got the time all planned out. Bob and I will quiz each other Sunday afternoon and I'll knock off at supper time and relax, if I can.

As the time draws near for a specific reality challenge such as an examination, anxiety about the specific demand calls for a reordering of priorities within the defensive organization. The adolescent may then erect a stringent defense against his narcissistic preoccupations; the full force of the capacity to repress, isolate, and split off images of the grandiose self will silence the narcissistic demands. Self-images based more on a discrete appreciation of objects, work requirements, and superego-guided goals will predominate in the overall sense of the self, and the full capacity for perceptual-cognitive processing will be directed to the problem-solving task.

> Tuesday: Have I got big plans for the weekend. My chick from back home is coming. I wonder if she'll be looking good. If my friends will dig her. (The exam?) Oh, the exam. I almost forgot all about it. Put it this way. Nothing to worry about. When I came out I started thinking about med school and getting in and my parents being pleased.

Cramming is of course of a limited duration. When the examination period is completed, an instant rebound of the dominance of the grandiose self is often observed in success-failure mirroring fantasies and in stimulus cravings for further exhibitionistic excitement.

The psychic disequilibrium described above illustrates a shift in the balance of self-experience that occurs when one cluster of images becomes predominant as a *temporary reversible adaptational response*. In contrast, in the disequilibria of the psychoneuroses, as in all instances of emotional illness, a persisting disturbance occurs because of a prior failure in the infantile ego's capacity to deal with conflict. The effect at the experiential level is that a portion of self-experience (and the complex motivations associated with that portion) is rendered inaccessible to the remainder of the cohesively experienced self. Unlike the patients to be discussed in the next section, despite his deficit in specific areas of experiences of the self, the psychoneurotic patient, except under the severest regressive occurrences, does not evidence a fragmentation of his sense of self-cohesion.

Mr. S, a bright capable lawyer in his early thirties, entered analysis because of concerns about his potency and fears he would not be made a full partner in his law firm. His father was a successful builder who came from a military family. To others the father appeared a fair-minded if stern man. To Mr. S, the only son, his father seemed a forbidding martinet. This view was in part the consequence of Mr. S's closeness to his mother, a rather spoiled woman who complained to her son about her husband's harshness and presumed neglect. She generally pampered him, often making excuses for him, letting him sleep late against the father's wishes. During the analysis, Mr. S. described repeated experiences at work in which he would feel as though he were immobilized and unable to concentrate whenever he was criticized by one of the full partners under whom he occasionally worked. Analysis had already revealed that the repression of his physical and mental assertiveness and the isolation of his anger was an automatic unconscious response to the threat of retaliation were he to react aggressively to his critical father or father substitute. It is this aspect of his problem that I shall illustrate selectively, omitting, therefore, the direct rivalry over sexual urges toward his mother and their particular focus in primal scene exposure.

Excerpt from hour 270: I could hardly drag myself out of bed today. The first thought I had was I have to work with Dick James today, and I groaned. He's the only senior partner I feel that way about. I wanted to pull the covers up and go back to sleep. (Silence). *Analyst: Do you want to pull the cover over your feelings with silence now?* Yeah. I feel something but I don't know what. Restless, I guess, and I can't concentrate. My head feels useless. That's how I get when Dick James just looks at me. Even before he's said anything. *Analyst: You're feeling restless now here with me and frightened?* Ah—your bill. I started to write the check and it went clear out of my head. So I'm late again. It reminds me of when I was late mowing the lawn. My father would look at me for a day or two and say nothing. Finally he'd erupt and tell me in no uncertain terms what an empty-headed kid I was and how I'd never amount to anything. I'd feel crushed.

In this excerpt, the patient refers to himself as feeling immobilized, useless, unable to concentrate and crushed. In an excerpt to follow from hour 620, he speaks of how a part of himself wanted to be assertive while another part looked on and laughed. I have chosen this example because this patient used the language of fragmentation of the self as a metaphoric expression of his awareness of discrepancies between his self-feeling at a time of stress and his normal or ideal self-feeling. Neither, however, in his functioning (except in a very limited degree) nor in his essential sensing of himself was he experiencing a true disturbance of his self-cohesion. The analyst was not confronted with the technical problems that arise when loss of cohesion of the sense of self is threatened. Unlike treating patients with narcissistic and borderline personality disorders, the analyst could count on a clear sense of separateness between the patient's self and his object, a continuity in the patient's sense of himself and his object, and an awareness of the transitions between experiential states.

In the psychoneurotic patient, as defenses are worked with and set aside, the ease and flow of affective-cognitive free-association is the best indicator of the patient's ability to tolerate without fragmentation the experiencing of dystonic symptoms and inconsistent character traits. This is the result of two major developments the relatively undamaged preoedipal child is able to achieve during the oedipal period. First is the capacity to feel intensely and varyingly toward two separate distinct parents of opposite sex and to structure representations of the self- and object-images involved in these complex experiences. For the analyst, in listening to the associations of a psychoneurotic patient, it is evident that his father and mother were distinctly perceived people. Each was different from himself, from each other, and from aspects of themselves at different times. It is usually far easier for the analyst to come to "know them" as whole people through the patient's transferences than it is when working with a patient with a narcissistic or borderline disorder. Second is the experiential changes that reflect completion of the process of internalizing a group of prohibiting/encouraging, approving/disapproving idealized representations that comprise the superego and ego ideal. "The superego introduces a safety device of the highest order, which protects the self from dangerous internal instinctual stimuli, from dangerous external stimuli, and hence from narcissistic harm" (Jacobson 1964, p. 133). Thus, from the standpoint of the maintenance of self-cohesion, it is important that the individual has undergone, to a full and rich degree, these triangular experiences with his parents and the guidances and prohibitions attendant upon them. For a sense of cohesion, it is not necessary that the stress of these experiences be resolved without lasting conflict; the retained sense of self-cohesion reflects the capacity of the ego to organize the common conflictual components without a basic disturbance of integration occurring.

Excerpt from hour 332: The member's meeting is in three days and I can't get my mind off of it. If I don't make member this year I probably never will. I think I have a good chance. I even think I deserve to, and I never would have been able to say that before. I may have thought it, but I couldn't risk saying it; I'd expect you to put me down or sarcastically jolly me along. *Analyst: Your fear of my putting you down if you assert yourself isn't so automatic anymore?* Not with you, but I wish I could say the same for Dick James. Whenever I picture the member's meeting, I can hear his voice saying "well we know he tries but." Then I hear Tom coming to my defense, but it doesn't help. I know I'm too hung up on Dick James. Obsessed you'd call it. *Analyst: Do you find it easier to tell me about your picture of the meeting than about your feelings?* I'm not sure how I feel. I know when I hear Dick's voice something inside me churns up. I know you'd say it's my anger and I guess it is. I feel like defending myself, not waiting for Tom to do it, but doing it myself. Then I stop—I don't know why. *Analyst: Are you afraid of being like the black man in your dream of the night before last, the one who started shooting his automatic rifle and couldn't stop?* You mean I'd want to rat-a-tat-tat at Dick James and never stop? Man is that a scary thought.

Excerpt from hour 620: I had the feeling you were laughing at me yesterday when I told you my plan to stop the analysis in June. I know you weren't (at least I think I do), but when I felt it, I'd see the inside and want to tell you off. *Analyst: Is it easier to experience yourself seething at me and telling me off if you think of yourself outside the hour?* Yeah —I don't feel it so much now. *Analyst: Is it like the difference between how you felt when you were outside the bedroom listening to father and mother argue and how you felt in direct contact with your father?* Exactly. Outside I'd tell him: shut up, stop yelling at her, you bastard. Go away and let us alone. Oh, in my imagination I was a brave one outside—real big deal, independent big boy. It makes me laugh. Then he'd say something to me—anything— and I'd be Momma's good little boy again—with him—with her— with you—with anybody. No matter how brave I was (or am) I always knew I was Mother's good boy and I'd laugh, laugh at myself and laugh to make myself brave, too. Come on you sissy, do it. Like when I beat up on my friend Charley. But I felt bad then too (always feel bad about that). But sometimes a boy has to be a boy and a man has to be a man even if it hurts somebody. I can accept that now.

Joseph Slap and I (Lichtenberg and Slap 1972, 1973) have described the process by which the conflictual elements of psychoneuroses are organized as the forming of *intersystemic suborganizations*—discrete, persistent groupings of a specific drive with an ego apparatus and with a superego component. Where psychic conflict is of low intensity, the drive will be coupled with an ego-facilitative function compatible with superego dictates. The self-representations associated with the drive-discharge patterns and those associated with moral and ethical guidances will seem to operate in unison. Such intersystemic groupings are flexible in their organization and function, and utilize a broad range of cognitive controls and self-representational aspects. These subunits are easily subjected to synthesizing operations which blend them together with other functional groupings. In the adult, they become structured into large groupings organized to facilitate the individual's functioning in terms of his predominant interests and object relations.

Two such low intensity conflicts for Mr. S were his toilet training struggles with his mother and his rivalry experiences with his peers. His mother was patient with him and took pride in his toiletting and intellectual accomplishments. She tolerated rather well his infantile aggressions so that he drew on these more accepted and, for him, syntonic modes of anger to compensate for the repression of his rivalrous oedipal urges toward his father. Thus intellectually and in athletic games, he could compete with his peers with adequate although somewhat blunted assertiveness. As an adult he could work well with Tom who was like his mother, and could compete well enough with his peers in the firm.

Where psychic conflict is of a greater intensity, manifestations of defensive activity become connected with a specific drive and with superego strictures. In those intersystemic suborganizations in which defensive functioning predominates, the adaptive effort is restricted to warding off painful affects.

A suborganization typical of the psychoneuroses had formed in the oedipal period. This suborganization was comprised of Mr. S's urge to challenge his father, his defense against the urge, and the superego prohibition against his "murderous" desire; it then remained separated off from the dominant grouping of representations of self-reactions to nonconflictual situations. The organizing capacity of the ego, however, was capable of rationalizing the discrepancy and/or tolerating the ambiguity.

The experiential correlate to the structural processes is that no fragmentation of the sense of self-cohesion occurred; instead what was disturbed was the *balance* within the self. A significant group of self-images involving assertiveness, those that would have contributed to effectiveness in certain specific rivalrous situations, instead aroused anxiety and were defended against, restricting the fullest possible range of self-experience. Also separated off were self- and object-images that reflect the mature capacity of the ego-ideal and superego to tolerate and give guidance to assertive actions; what were active were archaic images of assertiveness prohibitors (the castrating, sarcastic, ridiculing, retaliative father). The result was an internal, relatively unmodified self-punitiveness (self-castration, -ridicule and -punishing). In analysis, the slow process of making conscious these separated-off images reflecting ego and superego representations, and the drives related to them, allowed their integration with the other self- and object-images with a no more than gradual awareness of the imbalance and its restoration.

An arresting hypothesis concerning the rate of analytic progress presents itself here. Is one factor in the length of treatment the psychic apparatus's degree of tolerance to recognition of imbalances in the self-images? That is, as hitherto dystonic self-images become accessible to awareness with the analytic dissolution of a psychoneurotic intersystemic suborganization, are there individual variations in the degree to which they can be blended with the other self-images without cohesion being sacrificed? Is it possible that on some occasions the analyst may fail to consider the patient's need for time to integrate new self-image potentials? If so the analyst's resulting lack of understanding of this intra-analytic problem may be the cause of some negative therapeutic reactions.

In a pioneering effort to apply the concept of perceptual pooling to the ego capacity to integrate varying self-images, Spiegel (1959) categorized the disruptive pressure on constancy of self-feeling exerted by differing occurrences and hypothesized that "perceptions having to do with self-feeling result from the ego's relating of a single or small number of self-representations to the self considered as framework" (p. 96). He described three conditions that might disturb a constant feeling of self: (1) those in which a small group of self-images are at marked variance with the self as a whole, such as the young adolescent's being startled by the force of his genital excitement; (2) those in which the sense of self is threatened by variance within a small group of self-images, such as when a lack of clarity exists between self and object as exemplified by a tendency to regard an undesirable self-trait or painful body part as outside the self and by mergings of self and object in masturbatory fantasies and narcissistic preoccupations; and (3) those in whom the basic framework of the self as a whole is threatened, as depersonalization in concentration camp victims which has resulted from the shattering effect of the discrepancy between a familiar, established self-feeling and commitment to widely disparate regressive aims appropriate to the totally altered situation (Jacobson 1959).

Using Spiegel's three factors, it can be said that the classical theory of the analysis of the psychoneuroses applies to the first factor: that small groups of self-images at variance with the self as a whole and defended against because of prior conflict are brought into awareness and gradually integrated. The second factor, in which a marked variance exists within a group of self-images due to a lack of clarity between self and object, has come under increased focus in the studies of Kohut (1971, 1977). These studies demonstrate in the narcissistic personality disorders the blurring of self-object boundaries, the need for the object to sustain the grandiose strivings of the self, and the seeking in the object of idealized aspects for mirroring and identification, and the fragmentation that occurs when the object is unavailable.

It is increasingly apparent, however, that many patients who come for psychoanalysis and who have problems that center on self-esteem regulation involving idealizing transferences (Gedo 1975) do not experience fragmentation of their self-cohesion. Their capacity to deal with their conflicts in the course of a classical psychoanalytic treatment is similar to that of Mr. S. Thus it is important to distinguish between narcissistic personality disorders in which the clinical problem may center on the danger of fragmentation of the sense of self-cohesion and psychoneurotic reactions laden with conflicts over self-esteem regulation in which serious danger of disturbed cohesion does not occur. For those psychoneurotic patients with problems in self-esteem, the "central psychopathology does not *primarily* reside either in the self or in the *archaic* narcissistic self-objects. The central psychopathology concerns structural conflicts over (incestuous) libidinal and aggressive strivings which emanate from a well-delimited, cohesive self and are directed toward childhood objects which have in essence become fully differentiated from the self" (Kohut 1971, p. 19; italics mine).

During their oedipal period, these patients, especially the bright and gifted ones, often displace the urgency of their drive investment from the arena of the sexual conquest of the parent to a precocious conquest of learning and a mastery of the nursery school and kindergarten environment. "As a result, phase specific anxieties are apt to be minimized and the unrealizable nature of oedipal fantasies can more easily be denied" (Tartakoff 1966, p. 245). However, the struggle over replacing the oedipal rival is only partially finessed; castration anxiety and guilt, while not consciously well integrated, are often intense. Experiences that reflect the whole intersystemic suborganization of direct oedipal drive urges, defenses mobilized in response to signal guilt, and prohibiting superego internalizations will remain relatively unintegrated. These may appear in full force only toward the later stages of psychoanalysis.

The task this kind of patient carries into adolescence is not the modification of superego-derived taboos against sexual pursuits subsequent to the decathexis of the parent as a prime target. Rather it is the testing out of the fantasy of oedipal success. Adolescent point scoring in the dating game may reconfirm the unchallenged oedipal fantasy; Don Juan or femme fatale fantasies will congeal with a sense of entitlement which circumvents guilt. Or adolescent failure will lead to severe disappointment. The bitterness that results from failure is more apt to be directed against fate or the sexual partner than toward a questioning of the self.

The transference constellation that carries the weight of these patients' significant oedipal experiences is their effort to win the mirroring romanticized approval of the analyst-parent for their displays either of mental health or of analytic prowess in presenting interesting symptoms. A sense of success brings with it a feeling of expansiveness; a feeling of failure leads to complaints of deflation and recriminations. The imbalance in the sense of self is revealed in the following ways: (1) an impoverishment of those self-images associated with comfort and pleasure in human contact with an object experienced as separate and discrete and a shallow closeness, ardor, and sensitivity in love relationships; (2) an impoverishment of those self-images associated with the "efficacy" pleasure of bodily and mental functioning for its own sake so that work and play are performed for exhibitionistic purposes and to obtain omnipotent control; (3) a predominance of self-images concerned with the enhancement of feelings of grandiosity and omnipotence and symptoms that reflect humiliation-laden fantasies—small penis or physical ugliness, feelings of inadequacy even in the face of accomplishment, inhibition of self-display; and (4) a predominance of feelings of embarrassment, humiliation and shame, a relative absence of guilt, and a reliance on external rather than internal approval.

Spiegel's third factor, a disturbance in the basic framework of the self as a whole, occurs infrequently in the psychoneurotic patient. However, when the basic framework is shattered a temporary fragmentation of the self may occur. I can cite a serious loss of cohesion occurring in three patients with psychoneuroes. The first was confronted with the unexpected death of a parent toward whom ambivalent feelings were at a height. The mourning, for a brief period, was like a rent in the total fabric of the self, and the patient's well-established cohesive sense of self was temporarily shattered. The second patient had had a dramatic transitory traumatic wartime experience in late adolescence. As he dealt with this experience during the course of his analysis, he had a period of reliving (abreacting) the traumatic event in which he reexperienced the fragmentation of his self-cohesion and developed a state of frozen panic. The third patient, an adolescent male, experienced puzzling episodes of fragmentation that were eventually traced to his identification with his mother who had had a short psychotic episode during his fourth year.

The disturbance of the basic framework of the self as a whole can also be considered a factor in the problems of many adolescents and young adults who experienced a temporary or more lasting fragmentation of their preexisting sense of self during the disruption of the Viet Nam War and the upsurge of the drug culture. Lichtenstein (1973) has theorized that "there can never be an 'objective sense of reality,' only one selectively chosen by 'unconscious content'—one which excludes other aspects of reality experience and defines identities in its own specific way" (p. 166). For the individual who comes to adolescence in times of radical social and political upheaval, it is particularly difficult to redefine his childhood sense of reality in the light of a markedly altered world. He may confront areas of reality experience previously excluded by the influence of held values and be left with an anxiety-producing discrepancy in his sense of self and an isolation based on loss of the sense of oneness with others, particularly those previously closest to him. If he cannot redefine his reality in the light of the altered external world, he may experience a constricting defensive rigidity. In either case, the self is apt to be experienced as having radically disparate elements. The process of blending discrepant self-images is thus made far more difficult than in less turbulent times.

FRAGMENTING SHIFTS WITHIN THE SENSE OF SELF

What does the concept of cohesiveness of the sense of the self and its pathological fragmentation add to the concept of the vicissitudes of drive derivatives and their conflicts? The answer lies in the necessity to achieve the empathy needed to treat patients who suffer from narcissistic personality and borderline disorders. In these illnesses, unlike in the neuroses, the patient struggles with a constant tendency to experience a disturbance in self-cohesiveness. If the analyst cannot properly recognize and feel empathy for the internal state of disconnectedness and potential fragmentation of these patients, he will be able neither to establish a working relationship with the patient nor to understand his own disquieting responses. The difference between working with a patient whose sense of self is intact and a narcissistic or borderline patient can be illustrated by considering the implications of a correct interpretation of drive vicissitudes for a neurotic patient.

The Neurotic Patient

The patient, a thirty-year-old woman in her fourth year of psychoanalysis, had been in a state of negative transference for several days. During this period she brought up a number of grievances against the analyst without any clear focus. She began the hour under consideration in a gay flirtatious mood. The analyst recognized the resurgence of an erotized transference and asked her about her switch in mood. She acknowledged that her mood had changed, that she had been sad and angry after the hour the day before. She had begun to read a romantic novel and lost herself in erotic daydreams about the analyst. The analyst suggested the upsurgence of her romantic wishes toward him might have been her way to protect herself against the anger she had been feeling and against coming closer to understanding its source. She replied irritably that she knew the analyst would think that. She added that before she lost herself in the novel, she had been looking at her calendar and realized that the analyst's summer vacation was only three and one-half weeks off. She had not wanted to think about it. The analyst interpreted her prior anger as connected to her unrecognized anticipation of his being away. He noted the relationship of her present feelings and her emotional reaction in childhood when her father would leave for an extended business trip. The patient began to associate to the hurt she had felt when, in spite of her pleas, her father would leave. In her further associations, she added information about her lifelong use of daydreams to relieve her loneliness.

What did the analyst understand and feel empathy for in the psychoneurotic patient that led his interpretations to be accurate and successful? Traditionally the answer would be that he recognized that (1) she mobilized her libidinal wishes as a defense against her aggressive wishes, (2) the latter were in response to a fear of feeling lonely and abandoned, (3) the anticipation of a current source of loneliness during the analyst's vacation had been repressed, and (4) the repression was the result of a primary process displacement from an intensely felt sense of loss during the absence of her beloved father during her oedipal years. However, the analyst correctly understood and felt empathy for a great deal more. He recognized that (1) the patient could easily connect the flirtatious self of the current hour with the angry self of the prior hours, (2) she could actively seek to understand for herself and for the analyst the cause of her mood change, feeling no discontinuity in the sense of self that would be anxiety arousing, (3) she would easily carry a temporal frame of reference—the past, yesterday's anger; the present, today's erotic feelings; the future, the loneliness of anticipated vacation—and relate the whole present sequence to memories of the distant past, (4) she would regard herself both as working with the analyst to understand and resolve problems (the therapeutic alliance) and as having intense emotions toward the analyst that felt both real in the present and simultaneously reflective of past experiences.

A patient suffering from a narcissistic personality disorder might present similar associative content, but the experience of the patient would be different. She would not experience her eroticized transference as a defense against anger, but as a restoration of an expansive, sexually attractive self after a period of low self-esteem. She would regard herself as now free of the danger of fragmentation and deflation of her sense of worth. Thus she would not be pleased to connect the two emotional states; rather she would be glad to be rid of the one and resent and fear any effort on the analyst's part to remind her of it. She might fear that her erotic excitement would spiral into overintense exhibitionistic urges and thus lead to embarrassment and shame. She would then want the analyst to intervene by acknowledging her desire for mirroring approval and her fear of overstimulation. Since for her the image of herself as beautiful and loving and of the idealized father-lover-analyst as an approving, appreciative responder would be the source of a reinstated self-worth, she would be acutely resistive to the interpretation given the neurotic patient. She would be apt to hear herself depicted in the analyst's eyes as not loving, but as harboring hidden aggressive wishes. She would feel the analyst did not understand or appreciate her, was inflicting unnecessary hurt on her and contributing to the total fragmentation of her sense of self. Rather than responding as did the patient in the example who irritably said that she knew the analyst would think that and then was able to tolerate the mild hurt and rebuff, the narcissistic personality disorder patient would be deeply deflated. The remainder of the hour would be quite different: it would revolve around the patient's response to the faulty empathy of the analyst. The central core of the analyst's faulty empathy would be his misappraisal of the manner in which the patient experienced her self-image and the image of the analyst. Unlike the neurotic patient who regarded herself as a separate person having wishes of a sexual nature for a distinctly separate other person, the narcissistic personality patient would regard the analyst as an idealized extension of herself. Just as in her self-image she would regard herself as beautiful, she would regard the analyst as the idealized mirroring responder—a necessary component to the maintenance of her self-esteem. His vacation and its effect must be understood in this context; for the patient it would be like the loss of a part of herself.

A borderline disorder patient might also present associative content of a similar eroticized transference. The analyst's problems in establishing empathic contact and responding to the borderline patient would be different from those both with the neurotic and the narcissistic personality disorder patient. The analyst's first comment, noting a change in mood, might fall on deaf ears or be actively resisted. Indeed the angry self of the previous hours would not seem to the borderline patient to have any integral connection or continuity with the present flirtatious self. The borderline patient is not only actively disinclined to understand disparate feeling states and disparate self-images, she (or he) is indeed very threatened by the recognition of their existence. The borderline patient loses effective time discrimination: the past angry self is not connected to the present loving self, and the future self on its own during the vacation is not to be anticipated at all because of the arousal of anxiety and the immediate danger of reactivating the angry, even murderous, self. The threat seems so grave to the patient that during the period of positive erotic feelings, an interpretation of the presence of underlying aggressive wishes often leads the patient to temporarily lose contact with the therapeutic purpose. The unconscious past, and overwhelmingly conscious present, sense of frustration prevents any degree of self-reflectiveness. The central core of any faulty empathy by the analyst would be his misappraisal of the manner in which the patient experiences the self-image and the image of the analyst. Unlike the neurotic patient who regarded herself as a separate person having changing feelings— anger and loving—toward a distinctly separate other person, the borderline patient experiences a fragmentation of the continuity between the angry and loving selves. The angry self is involved in a specific struggle with a dangerous powerful figure, the analyst, and the angry feelings and thoughts often are projected or denied. The anger is sometimes an effort to maintain distance as a separate self, as the child does in employing his aggression to buttress his individuation. The borderline patient regards agreement with the therapist as submission. The deep unconscious fear is that, rather than retain individuation, the loving self will be absorbed into the protective orbit of the object as a passive clinging satellite. Thus, for the loving self, the analyst's impending vacation is often the stimulus for wishes to be included in a symbiotic closeness of affectionate, sensual, mutual interdependence. For the angry self, it is often the stimulus for violent and self-defeating flights into pseudoindependence that risk destroying the internal representation of the therapist. This is further complicated by the intense envy the patient feels for the analyst's parting without doubt and torment. The two states, with the separate pairings of loving and angry self and object, are split. The transitional experiences, recoverable in the neurotic patient who described the shift from her anger and loneliness to her novel reading and erotic daydreaming, are for long periods of the treatment totally fragmented and lost to therapeutic focus.

The Narcissistic Personality Disorder Patient

Clearly a more serious disturbance of self-cohesion than that described as an imbalance in the component groups exists in narcissistic personality disorders. In some patients, overt manifestations of fragmented self-cohesion are apparent. Other patients with narcissistic personality disorders may succeed in disguising, to themselves and others, the nature of their disturbance by creating a veneer of success in some spheres of endeavor. However, whether superficially apparent or not, the fragmented cohesiveness of self-experience—what Bach (1975, 1976) calls the narcissistic state of consciousness—will become apparent in the transference, and the patient's fear of it will be a central position in their treatment. For the analyst, the occurrence of these disturbances in self-cohesion is often puzzling and unsettling. The patient's prolonged periods of deflation and of relating to the analyst as a depersonalized extension of the self (a self-object) present the analyst with a frequently tedious task requiring considerable empathy. The development of the cohesive self-sense and the vicissitudes of self-experience centering on the grandiose self and the idealized parental images, as a frame of reference, provide background knowledge valuable for maintaining needed empathy and introspection (Kohut 1966, 1971, 1977, Kernberg 1975, Lichtenberg 1975, Modell 1976).

Mr. T, an unmarried consulting engineer in his mid-thirties, entered psychoanalysis with a variety of diffuse complaints including no sense of purpose, boredom, and generalized discontent. His most prevalent self-image was that of a person compelled to work, to maintain a schedule as had his father, and to comply with "the same ridiculous demands as slobs who work from nine to five." When he pictured himself this way, he saw the analyst as similarly oppressed and showered contempt on himself and the analyst. The origin of this contempt lay in his mother's decidedly psychopathic view of the world: everybody takes advantage of everyone else; the smart guy is the most successful cheat; her husband didn't and wasn't. When his dominent self-image was that of the trapped-into-earning-a-living, put-upon slob, he would pour out a litany of ever-shifting bodily complaints. The analyst was tilted toward sharing the patient's feeling that time dragged on unendingly and that he too was trapped in an activity devoid of meaning or value. The analyst's best safeguard against an overwhelming ennui was persistantly to use his empathy with the patient's blah feelings as the basis for interpreting the patient's fear of completely succumbing to a sense of depleted self-resources, of staying in bed, or of inviting an operation and long hospital stay. Mr. T was also continually provocative in respect to the analyst's "middle class values and work ethic." The first breakthrough to Mr. T's questioning his psychopathic stance came when he acknowledged that the analyst seemed to enjoy his work and that, while he felt envious, he also hoped to be able to feel the same way.

At times Mr. T's grandiose image totally dominated his self-experience. He would then regard himself as the smartest engineer in the firm, not only because he had come up with a solution no one else had, but also because while the slobs worked at their presentations he had done little preparation and put it over on everyone. In the midst of this grandiosity, he was also anxious. If the analyst said nothing he was afraid lest the patient spiral so in his excitement as to lose control and become insufferably arrogant enough to invite retaliative humiliation. If the analyst questioned the patient's need to sacrifice a good feeling of accomplishment based on actual ability in order to achieve the pleasure of exaggerating his brilliance, he would feel less internal spiraling of excitement. However, questioning any aspect of this inflated self-esteem carried with it the danger of deflating the good feeling entirely.

In addition to the grandiose self-image of the intellectual was another—the handsome exhibitionistic stud dressed in the latest fashion and dominating the social scene. Here his anxiety had a very specific source. After attracting the richest, best looking girl, he would then be totally impotent. Just when he was flying high, he would be brought abruptly to earth. This represented his most dystonic symptom and the place for the most welcomed interpretations. He was ready to consider the factors in his many sexually overstimulating childhood experiences as a source of his problem and was grateful as his sexual potency improved.

His grandiose self-image took other unintegrated forms—the athlete doing daredevil stunts, the fighter fired up by righteous indignation suddenly physically attacking other men or threatening the analyst, and the big investor risking his financial stability. His image of himself as deflated contained opposite representations—the cowardly passive avoider of any controversy, the physically damaged little boy with an inferior genital, and the miser who mooched nickels and dimes from friends and family.

The oscillations of these affective-behavioral states were rapid, and, for a long time during the initial phase of the analysis, the source or stimuli for the changing states was puzzling. The sense of disconnectedness and inexplicable changes in the patient was intensified by Mr. T's limited awareness of the radical polarity of his self-experience. When I speak of a rapid, dramatic affective-behavior change, I am speaking as an outside observer. From the patient's point of view, self-image was sufficiently fragmentary that when he was behaviorally the put-upon slob this was more than a feeling state, it was an identity. The relationship between this self-image and, for example, that of the brilliant, exhibitionistic, professional engineer showed little continuity, balancing, and blending. The analyst could only make headway with the patient when he could empathically sense the degree of disconnectedness and work within the framework of the self-image operant during the hour. Only in the course of time did Mr. T begin to recognize the existance of his differing self-images and to evidence an interest in the transitions and their causes.

By his third year of analysis the pattern that bore on the dream to be reported had become well established and consciously recognized. With even a day's disruption in the analytic continuity and whenever he had had much contact with his parents, fragmentation of the sense of himself as an integrated, feeling, and functioning human being occurred. He would appear disheveled and sickly and complain of feeling blah, totally devoid of energy. His only wish was to sleep—for hours and days. He would whine about any demand on him, especially the demands of the analysis. If he tried to associate, his thoughts would quickly become fragmentary; he would verbalize a disjointed, unintelligible mix of incidents, fantasies, and hypnagogic imagery. At these times he would describe a strong hyperawareness of certain body parts—such as the position of his hands or knots in his stomach. "I'm falling apart, I can't think, I can't feel anything about anyone," were common expressions.

On the night of his dream, he was anticipating a holiday weekend during which the analyst was to be away for a day and Mr. T had planned a trip to his parents' home. A specific day residue came from his analytic hour. He had described positive feelings toward the analyst with unusual directness and dropped for the moment his usual litany of complaints about his own coldness and the analyst's mechanical "computer-mindedness." Instead, he stated he had bought a plant. He wanted to have something alive to care for. He then said, "Oh, you know, it just occurred to me—it's like your plant—I've noticed how it grows in here."

In his dream he was in a doctor's office. The doctor didn't look like the analyst, but like Harry, a friend of his. Both he and the doctor were naked from the waist up. The doctor examined him and said he was all right: everything was A-OK. Then they walked to the front of the building together. The doctor said he would have to go back to his office; he had to examine someone with liver trouble and would be in his office very late. As they were parting, there was an accident. A young man was hit by a truck and dragged along under it; his neck was twisted so that his head was turned around. Inside his neck there were wires like a telephone connection. The doctor went to examine the young man and Mr. T went along to see and to help. The young man was gray and dead looking.

His associations were that Harry was a person who was meticulously careful at his work (the opposite of the patient). However, he was careless with clothing articles, and because Harry had left a handsome tie pin lying about, Mr. T had "borrowed" it. The analyst suggested the Mr. T wanted to take something from somebody he admired just as he had wanted a plant like the analyst's, but following his own childlike inclinations buttressed by his mother's advice, he found it easier to "borrow" the tie pin than to work for something—to raise a plant, for example. The analyst's suggestion reminded him that his parents were on his back to visit his Uncle Paul to be sure he stayed in his will. He'd like the money so he could pay for analysis and quit his job. He knows the analyst doesn't approve of that. The analyst noted that in his dream, Mr. T had the doctor stay late in his office and show an interest in a patient with *liver* trouble. Mr. T responded feelingly that he wished the analyst would be available to him on the holiday. It was not because he would want to come to an hour then, but he wanted proof of the analyst's commitment to him. To have the analyst work late and see him on a holiday would demonstrate, he felt, the analyst's desire that he be a *liver*, not a blah. He was afraid that when he went home and listened to his mother complaining about her health and about his father, he'd come back a blob again. The analyst reminded him that he often spoke of feeling that his values got all twisted around when he spent time with his family and wondered if the injured man with the twisted head was himself. Mr. T agreed, adding that everything that seemed clear to him about being grown and having independent ideas and values got confused so easily.

The analyst asked about the telephone connection. Mr. T remembered before going to sleep he had had a disturbing telephone conversation with his mother. She had followed her usual course of controlling and pampering and argumentative complaining about herself. His stomach had knots in it and his whole body became tense. He expressed again his reluctance to go to his family. The analyst suggested that as the analysis had progressed and he had been in the office in the dream and felt he was being examined and approved of, he felt he was all right—everything was A-OK. In response to this suggestion Mr. T expressed a degree of defensive wariness. He didn't like to think of himself as needing the analyst so much. There was no gain in trying to get loose of his parents only to get trapped by the analyst. The analyst asked if in his dream he protected himself from getting trapped by the analyst-parent by making the analyst a contemporary like Harry and equally exposed—both naked from the waist up. He agreed saying he liked thinking of the analyst as a friend who shared his thoughts and feelings. He resented how exposed he was and how little he knew about the analyst. With this he returned to a melancholy lament about his trip and fears of coming back a wreck. The analyst asked if he felt hurt at not being told more about the analyst. Yeah, he felt he wanted to know something big, something good about the analyst's accomplishments. He had been thinking again of telling his mother on this trip about being in analysis. But he couldn't get up the nerve. She'd hit the roof. She'd roll all over him. She'd say, "You're crazy. All that money. Doctors are all thieves." And he'd collapse, fold up, and die. The analyst suggested: like the young man in the dream who had been hit by the truck. After a reflective silence, Mr. T stated he'd be back after the holiday. The analyst wondered if the final segment of the dream in which Mr. T and the doctor went together to examine the young man represented his reassuring himself that the analysis would resume and that, with the continuing help of the analyst, he would be able to examine the meaning of his feeling gray and dead-looking. Mr. T. grunted assent and the hour ended.

Mr. T's experiences of a fragmented sense of self were not limited to his response to physical separations from the analyst. To varying degress, he would experience disturbances in self-cohesion whenever he felt loss of the empathic support of the analyst during the ebb and flow of the analytic work. (For many examples of similar transference phenomena, see Kohut 1971.) The most dramatic example of a prolonged fragmentation of his sense of self occurred when the analyst declined a request (demand) that he read a written log of the patient's thoughts and reactions. Mr. T had begun to keep the log after he had developed an increasing awareness of his disconnectedness and its disruptive consequences. To try to help himself pull together his scattered sense of self and make better use of the analysis he resolved to record for himself his daily experiences and "insights." This had a definite synthesizing effect on his work in the analytic hour during the intermittent periods that he kept up this resolve. When he lapsed in the writing, it served as a focus for discussion of his flagging motivation and often of his fragmented sense of self. At one point he determined to ask the analyst to read and review what he had written. The analyst understood Mr. T to have three separate desires: (1) to have the analyst extend his interest and approval beyond the analytic hour; (2) to have the analyst confirm his grandiose fantasy that he had written something that would benefit the world; and (3) to have the analyst do the analysis from the written material and allow Mr. T to escape the demands of the analytic hour. Over several hours, during which Mr. T continued to hope the analyst would agree, Mr. T worked with his wishes and reasons, and the analyst interpreted the meaning of the three separate aspects of Mr. T's desire. Once Mr. T had concluded that the analyst would not agree, in a last desperate proposal he begged the analyst to take the log, do anything he wished with it, and "at least let me believe you care."

Mr. T then went through a period of a completely fragmented sense of self. The behavioral manifestations were not going to work, having intense stomach cramps, and a collapse of his ability to concentrate in and out of the analytic session. The sense of self that Mr. T and the analyst could verbalize over several analytic hours was one of being without substance or form, a glob needing to be held in a huge hand that would give the glob structure and direction. Mr. T's view of himself and the analyst agreed with the analyst's intuitive feel for what was needed—a "holding" environment until Mr. T could restore his sense of self-cohesion. Mr. T's initial moves toward restoration of his sense of self proved very disturbing to the analytic situation. He became filled with righteous indignation and pugnacity, threatening to smash the analyst's head in and seeming only barely able to remain on the couch throughout the hour. This effort at restoring cohesion through narcissistic rage (Kohut 1972, Terman 1975) gradually gave way to a return to a willingness to consider with the analyst the source of his reactions. The analyst reviewed the current source of Mr. T's narcissistic hurt in an empathic way, and Mr. T began to furnish memories that allowed for a reconstruction of early experiences that contributed to this vulnerability of his sense of self to fragmentation.

The *quality* of Mr. T's mother's presence as he had experienced it in early childhood constituted the significant background for his transference reactions. He had clearly sensed himself as his mother's adored golden child, fondled, fed, and vastly superior to other children, all of whom she had regarded as brats. She prided herself that she had not even gone to a movie or left him with a sitter until he was three. Abrupt interruptions in his feeling of inclusion in a shared grandiosity had been frequent and painful. The exclusion at times had been initiated by his forbidden activities: his thumb sucking had been stopped by a mechanical hand holder; his failures in overly early toilet training had led to spankings; his genital fondling to anxious threats that he was doing irreparable harm to himself; and his running out in the street to a severe beating. (It was this exclusion and the fragmented sense of self that followed it that had been reflected in his dream image of being run over by the truck). The abrupt interruptions at other times had occurred when something external to him triggered off his mother's retreat into a state of hypochondriacal anxiety and prolonged sleep (probably a fragmentation of her sense of self).

To summarize, the narcissistic personality disorder patient, such as Mr. T, emerges from childhood with an impaired sense of cohesive self that centers on the line of development of narcissism—the grandiose self and the idealized parental image. He is specifically vulnerable in the regulation of his sense of self-worth. In his treatment, it is this vulnerability that constitutes the dominant transference problem. To meet the challenge of this specific transference, the analyst must understand and be able to empathically sense and respond to the patient's predicament: his multiple alternating and disconnected grandiose and deflated self-images, his fear of spiralling over-stimulation of exhibitionistic, expansive, eroticized tendencies, of humiliation, and of fragmentation of his sense of himself as a cohesive entity. The analyst must recognize that the patient consciously and/or unconsciously requires him to serve as a missing component of his self—a regulator of his sense of pride in himself and in his connection to and acceptance by a valued object. Because of this, the patient often listens to the analyst not so much in terms of the content of what the analyst means to communicate, but in terms of whether the analyst's words and tones and timing contribute to his sense of self-worth and self-cohesiveness. The analyst must accept that he cannot continuously provide an atmosphere of empathic closeness and be alert to evidence of the patient's responses as they affect the patient's sense of self. The analyst must then help the patient recognize his responses of deflation of worth or his self-protective flights into grandiosity or rage. He must help the patient recognize the disconnectedness of his way of experiencing and bring to light current stimuli that the patient has responded to with an actual or feared loss of self-cohesion. Then, often with the assistance of the patient's valuable fresh associations, the analysis can be carried forward by reconstructions of the childhood precursors of similar feelings of empathic failure. A working concept of the development of the sense of self, its cohesiveness, and its pathological fragmentation as it centers on self-worth (the grandiose self and the idealized self-objects) is, I believe, crucial for the analyst's understanding and empathy.

The Borderline Personality Disorder Patient

In the borderline patient, fragmentation of the cohesive sense of self occurs in two of the major component groupings that comprise the normal person's integrated sense of self (Lichtenberg 1975). The borderline patient has a developmental disturbance not only in the line of development of narcissism as does the narcissistic personality disorder patient, but, in addition and more significant, a developmental disturbance in the line of development of the self as an individuated person interacting with an object experienced as separate and discrete. Therefore, the borderline patient has all of the features of fragmentation already noted in the narcissistic personality disorder. However, the unintegrated contrasting self- and object-images, the disconnectedness of experience, the disturbances in the sense of time, the strong tendency to lose sight of shared therapeutic aims, and the long periods during which the patient experiences partial or total fragmentation of a sense of purpose and capacity to direct and integrate his functional capabilities, is the result of a more extensive disturbance in his early sense of self.

Unlike the normal person and the psychoneurotic patient, who at the end of the rapprochement subphase (Mahler, Pine, and Bergman 1975) are able to balance and blend together the divergent organizations of pleasurable (libidinal arousing) trends with the painful (aggression arousing) trends, the borderline patient never fully harmonizes the split groupings. In normal development, in each instance, during the entire separation-individuation struggle, the child requires the adult to supply the blend of gratification and frustration of loving and discipline that assist the child to make transitions from his states of high tension and strong instinctual need to those of low tension and optimal nonconflictual functioning. In instances where the child experiences himself as receiving inadequate, overfrustrating, overinfantilizing, or provocative responses, his primitive aggressive tendencies remain heightened, and the integration of a sense of a self capable of both love and anger (self-constancy) never fully forms or easily fragments under stress. Thus, in the borderline personality disorder, a major source of fragmentation of the sense of self is the pathological persistence of the normal early developmental tendency to organize experiences according to their affective response—

whether pleasurable/good/rewarding or painful/bad/punishing (Segal 1964, Lichtenberg and Slap 1973, Kernberg 1975).

The total experience of the self-image involved, the image of the object involved, and the affective response normally form a schema around which broadening units of experience occur. The self and object and affective units of experience centering on pleasurable/good/rewarding affects in the course of normal separation-individuation become integrated with the self and object and affective units of experience centering on painful/bad/punishing affects. In the borderline patient, splitting of the representations persists as a major defensive response to even mild stress, and the personality traits are organized around this regressive defensive tendency. This central dynamic formulation, so clearly and convincingly proposed by Kernberg (1967, 1968, 1975, 1976), does not in itself definitively differentiate the borderline from the narcissistic personality since splitting of affectively charged self- and object-units takes place in both (see Kohut 1971, Lichtenberg and Slap 1973, Lichtenberg 1975). In my view, the essential difference is that in the borderline patient the conflicts involve struggles both over separation-individuation and over regulation of self-esteem. Therefore, I regard the borderline personality disorder as originating in an infant who can form an adequate primary relationship with what Winnicott (1963) calls the "environment mother," but who has a traumatic experience in his relationship with the "object mother," the specific person with whom he interacts in response to his drives. Thus the borderline patient is unlike the psychotic patient whose experience with the environment mother is disturbed, resulting in organismic panic (Mahler 1968) and a basic vulnerability to severe and often irreversible fragmentation of the sense of self. (For relevant references to the differentiation between psychosis and the narcissistic personality disorders see Kohut 1971; to that between psychosis and the borderline disorders see Kernberg 1975; for disturbances in self-cohesion in psychoses see Searles 1960 and Pao 1977.) Similarly the borderline patient is to be distinguished from the patient with a major psychosomatic illness whose primary pathology lies in the bodily self-grouping of images (see Lichtenberg 1977).

Mrs. C, a forty-two-year-old married woman, was treated with intensive psychotherapy for a borderline personality disturbance. She was in a constant state of irritable distress and was seriously handicapped in her work as a dress designer and in her relations with people. She generally did not regard these difficulties as a consequence of an illness; rather she saw herself as a victim of circumstances. All of her fragmented experiences with people whom she saw as either "good" or "bad" were to her solely situationally evoked. She had attempted therapy in the past without success. The therapist, her family, and all her acquaintances were subject to her shifting attitudes and sweeping judgments. In a fashion that seemed to the therapist to be superficial and theatrical, she would express deep sympathy, love, and appreciation for a person or group and then, if disappointed or annoyed, a totally opposite attitude of belligerent antagonism. She was unaware of the inconsistency and shallowness of her values, and of the inappropriateness of her sweeping all-good, all-bad judgments. When this startling roller-coaster-like fragmenting of her self-experience was pointed out to her, she would defend against its recognition by denial and projection. When she neglected her family or evidenced open hostility toward a person who at other times was admired and loved, she was oblivious to this contradiction. The now-hated person was to her a participant in a totally split set of experiences.

Her persistent depreciation and devaluing of her husband blinded her to her basic dependency on him. She took financial and emotional support from him and required his structuring to limit the chaotic nature of her affairs. All she took from him she treated as her due, no more to be acknowledged and appreciated than the air she breathed.

He was the person most dramatically involved in her use of splitting. During the twenty years of her married life she had displaced onto him the image of an all-bad parent. She generally perceived him as a replica of her depressed mother, who, she believed, had interfered with her efforts to find pleasure and who, she felt, wished to keep her loyal and mutually suffering in a bleak home. On other occasions she experienced him as a sadistic, abandoning father.

The basis for her fantasied bad object was largely her infantile experience with her mother. She had felt that her mother diverted attention from herself to her sickly year and a half younger sister. She also had seen her mother as demanding that she dislike father and suffer loyally with her, sharing her depressed mood. Her fantasied bad object also drew on all-bad images of her father. These derived from his having been unfaithful and brutal to her mother. When Mrs. C was five, he had abandoned the family, plunging them into poverty.

Her fantasied good objects were based on two early sets of experience. First were those with her mother prior to the birth of the younger sister. Second were the good times she had shared with her father, who could create an atmosphere of fiesta for the children.

Outside of her marriage, Mrs. C involved herself with a series of professional colleagues and friends, whom she regarded as faultless. Through a primitive infantile closeness with these people, she fantasied herself able to achieve happiness, an exchange of loving care, and high goals of success. She strove to keep her husband separated from the all-good people for fear he would poison the relationship.

The therapist's primary task during this long period centered on first understanding and then communicating to the patient the nature of her disturbed self-experience. The therapist was confronted with a dizzying outpouring of alternating blissful extollings and angry denunciations. Both by implication and at times by demand, he was treated as though his only role were to agree with her assessments. She insisted he give her at least that comfort rather than add further to her upset by challenging her. The therapist's empathic focus needed to be directed to the particular forms of disturbances of self-cohesion which she was experiencing. He had to help her to recognize that her roller-coaster alternating was itself a painful disruption in the continuity of self-experience, and that her persistent resort to it was related to deeper anxieties. It was necessary that they identify the particular struggle to achieve closeness and accep- tance and the particular fear of ascendant destructive urgency that led her to assert with such defensive intensity that in one or another situation she was being included in an all-good self-object relationship. Through his empathic understanding, she began to appreciate that she was exquisitely sensitive to frequent disruptive inner reactions. These occurred when- ever she felt put aside and abandoned rather than loved (the prototypes being the mother's turning from her to her sister and her father's disappearance) or when she believed she was being possessively controlled rather than given the freedom for triangular experiences (prototypically her mother's dependent clinging to her), or when she believed that she was being treated with humiliating disapproval rather than being appreciated and esteemed (the prototype being a long series of responses by people to her poorly masked infantile demandingness and arrogance). The destructive urges she would feel toward the person whom she perceived as rejecting, restricting or humiliating created an inner disruption that threatened her sense of connectedness to the offending person. The massive use of the defense of splitting of images was employed so that she could maintain some semblance of object relations and be spared feelings of emptiness, anxiousness and low-grade despondency that came with a sense of existing devoid of human contact and sustaining approval. Rage, rebelliousness, envy, and contempt were then directed toward the person pictured as all-bad. She preserved an image of finding and being a partner in an all-good relationship, but her sense of continuity of self-experience was sacrificed.

With the repeated focus of the therapist on the painful nature of this process, a significant lessening of the more diffuse splitting of images occurred. Over a prolonged period, she came to accept that even though there might be some realistic basis for comparing her husband with her parents, she had restricted her perception to only these aspects of his personality; she had depreciated and devalued any awareness of his many good, positive qualities, and obliterated any awareness of her infantile exploitation of him. She began to recognize her derogating distortions of her husband's character, and, paralleling this, her idealizing distortions of certain of her other relationships. This insight led her to a determination that she would work out her life with him.

The splitting of her relationships into good and bad objects as described above was replaced by her seeing her husband as good and bad in alternation. During this period violent attacks during which she would throw things, ask him to leave, and threaten to cut up his clothes, would alternate with periods during which she would strive to arrange an idyllic blissful relationship. In this phase of her treatment, the therapist was subjected to considerable strain. He was concerned about a disruption of the marriage and also, if he failed to deal with the transference pressures, a disruption of the therapy. It was key that he recognize that the focus of the split reactions onto the husband represented progress, however dramatic and anxiety provoking it was. The danger of fragmentation of the sense of self while more overt was also more approachable. The therapist now interpreted her current reactivated separation-individuation conflicts and also offered reconstructions of her past traumas. Mrs. C found it especially useful to see how her anger, mobilized to afford her more of a sense of independence, miscarried into a destructive vilification of her object and ultimately of herself.

In addition, reconstructions that helped her recognize she was reexperiencing her conflict-laden childhood relationships led to floods of painful memories of her experiences with her parents. The defensive need to fragment her experiences abated and her hostility toward her husband now seemed baseless. Painful negative self-images, which had until now been unavailable, were dramatically experienced. They were based on her sense of unworthiness, depression, and guilt associated with vindictive urges toward her family members. Previously, these feelings associated with conflicts over ambivalently perceived objects had been avoided by her defensive splitting. During a lengthy period of working through, she experienced her sense of herself as increasingly cohesive, her overall functioning as increasingly self-directed, and her relationships as more empathic and self-rewarding.

The case material I have selected illustrates the superficial similarity between certain patients with borderline personality disorders and the narcissistic personality disorders. First, the borderline patient's angry interaction with an object perceived as bad may involve "narcissistic rage"

(Kohut 1972, Terman 1975) at a real or imagined humiliation. Second, the borderline patient often finds it difficult to sustain a feeling of quiet affection and respect and thus frequently resorts to idealization to buttress his crumbling feeling of having love for a "good" object. (For a detailed distinction between defensive pseudoidealization and the genuine idealizing transference of the narcissistic personality disorder, see Gedo 1975, p. 500.) The general clinical pictures may resemble one another; the crucial difference lies in the consistent struggle of the borderline patient with his aggressive urges toward any person with whom he reinstitutes his attempt to achieve an affective separation-individuation. Masterson (1976) emphasizes one aspect of the pathologic form taken in the separation-individuation phase. The child experiences pleasure and himself as good as long as he is dependent and compliant. When he is independent and self-assertive he is punished. These two experiences remain split as the broad general organizations that in Masterson's view are pathogenic of borderline patients.

The transference with the borderline patient reveals an underlying or overt prickliness, crankiness, and anger-proneness. With these feelings of generalized irritability omnipresent even when masked by a split into the idealizing transference, the borderline patient is prone to distort the therapist's meaning and intent. He sees entrapment where none exists and abandonment where none is actually threatened. He is frequently distrustful and suspicious and often resorts to primitive projection. The pressure on the therapist to respond to this irritability is intense. If he correctly interprets the patient's inner struggle with his aggression, the patient often feels attacked and harassed—especially as he is so prone to disconnect the background from which the therapist inferred his interpretation. If the therapist avoids interpreting the patient's provocations, depreciations, envy, and negativity, then the treatment tends to become mired down—a repetitious empty ritual. The key for the therapist is to be able to discern (a) how and when he can help the patient recognize and correct his persistent need to form separate emotional self- and object-constellations out of his experience, and (b) how and when he can help the patient recognize the danger of fragmentation of sense of self inherent in his struggle with his aggressive drives. From the patient's point of view his aggressive urges are destructive in their potential and often consciously in their aim rather than self-assertive and aimed toward maintaining the distance from the object needed for separation and individuation. The therapist must recognize that the patient often puts him in the position the patient senses himself to be in (where experiences are disconnected and fragmentary) and observes the therapist cope, often with the deep hope that he himself can.

REFERENCES

Bach, S. (1975). Narcissism, continuity and the uncanny. *International Journal of Psycho-Analysis* 56:77–86.

—— (1976). On the narcissistic state of consciousness. *International Journal of Psycho-Analysis* 58:209–233.

Freud, A. (1968). *Normality and Pathology in Childhood*. New York: International Universities Press.

Gedo, J. (1975). Forms of idealization in the analytic transference. *Journal of the American Psychoanalytic Association*.

Gedo, J., and Goldberg, A. (1973). *Models of the Mind: A Psychoanalytic Theory*. Chicago: University of Chicago Press.

Jacobson, E. (1959). Depersonalization. *Journal of the American Psychoanalytic Association* 7:581–610.

—— (1964). *The Self and the Object World*. New York: International Universities Press.

Kernberg, O. (1967). Borderline personality organization. *Journal of the American Psychoanalytic Association* 15:641–685.

—— (1968). The treatment of patients with borderline personality organization. *International Journal of Psycho-Analysis* 49:600–619.

—— (1975). *Borderline Conditions and Pathological Narcissism*. New York: Jason Aronson.

—— (1976). *Object Relations Theory and Clinical Psychoanalysis*. New York: Jason Aronson.

Kohut, H. (1966). Forms and transformations of narcissism. *Journal of the American Psychoanalytic Association* 14:243–272.

—— (1971). *The Analysis of the Self*. New York: International Universities Press.

—— (1972). Thoughts on narcissism and narcissistic rage. *Psychoanalytic Study of the Child* 27:360–400.

—— (1977). *The Restoration of the Self*. New York: International Universities Press.

Lichtenberg, J. (1975). The development of the sense of the self. *Journal of the American Psychoanalytic Association* 23:453–484.

—— (1977). The testing of reality from the standpoint of the body self. *Journal of the American Psychoanalytic Association* 25:357–385.

Lichtenberg, J., and Slap, J. (1972). On the defense mechanism: a survey and synthesis. *Journal of the American Psychoanalytic Association* 20:776–972.

—— (1973). Notes on the concept of splitting and the defense mechanism of the splitting of representations. *Journal of the American Psychoanalytic Association* 21:772–787.

Lichtenstein, H. (1973). The challenge to psychoanalytic psychotherapy in a world of crisis. *International Journal of Psychoanalytic Psychotherapy* 2:149–174.

Mahler, M. (1968). *On Human Symbiosis and the Vicissitudes of Individuation*. New York: International Universities Press.

Mahler, M., Pine, F., and Bergman, A. (1975). *The Psychological Birth of the Human Infant*. New York: Basic Books.

Masterson, J. (1976). *The Psychopathology of the Borderline Patient*. New York: Brunner-Mazel.

Modell, A. (1976). "The holding environment" and the therapeutic action of psychoanalysis. *Journal of the American Psychoanalytic Association* 24:285–308.

Pao, P. (1979). *Schizophrenia: Psychoanalytic Theory and Treatment*. New York: International Universities Press.

Schur, M. (1969). Affects and cognition. *International Journal of Psycho-Analysis* 50:647–653.

Searles, H. (1960). *The Nonhuman Environment*. Monograph Series on Schizophrenia, No. 5. New York: International Universities Press.

Segal, H. (1964). *Introduction to the Work of Melanie Klein*. New York: Basic Books.

Spiegel, L. (1959). The self, the sense of self, and perception. *Psychoanalytic Study of the Child* 14:81–109.

Tartakoff, H. (1966). The normal personality in our culture and the Nobel Prize complex. In *Psychoanalysis—A General Psychology,* ed. R. M. Loewenstein, et al., pp. 222–252. New York: International Universities Press.

Terman, D. (1975). Aggression and narcissistic rage: a clinical elaboration. *Annual of Psychoanalysis* 3:239–255.

Winnicott, D. (1963). Communicating and not communicating leading to a study of certain opposites. In *The Maturational Processes and the Facilitating Environment,* pp. 179–192. New York: International Universities Press, 1965.

Transferences As Differential Diagnostic Tools in Psychoanalysis

ANNA ORNSTEIN, M.D.

A discussion of "Clinical Application of the Concept of a Cohesive Sense of Self," by Joseph Lichtenberg, M.D.
Clinical phenomena, symptoms and specific "events" such as fragmentation are not reliable differential diagnostic tools in psychoanalysis and psychoanalytic psychotherapy. Rather, it is suggested that this purpose can be better served by the proper diagnosis of the developing cohesive transferences in the course of the psychoanalytic treatment process. The discovery of the selfobject transferences (the various forms of mirror and the idealizing transference) has broadened the scope of analyzable conditions. The recognition of these transferences which arise in relation to the reactivation of infantile narcissistic structures (the grandiose-exhibitionistic self and the idealized parent imago), are helpful in delineating patients with primary self-pathology from the neuroses on the one end and the borderline and psychotic conditions on the other end of the broad spectrum of psychological disorders. It is important to recognize the presence of cohesive transference in order to make a clinically meaningful diagnosis. This is demonstrated with the help of the clinical vignette presented by Lichtenberg. Mr. T is described as suffering from a narcissistic personality disorder—or what we would prefer to call primary self-pathology.

This paper is the latest in a series of publications by Lichtenberg related to narcissism and the self (Lichtenberg 1975, 1978). The present paper is the clinical application of theoretical propositions which the author presented in "The Development of the Sense of Self" (1975). Because of the close thematic relationship between the two papers, I shall first briefly summarize the major thesis of the 1975 publication. There, Lichtenberg introduced the concept and traced the development of "the cohesive sense of self." He integrated the development of what he called "the experiential self" with those developmental events which occur in relation to drive maturation and ego and superego development. He traced the integration of the "experiential" with the "structural" aspects of mental life along three interrelated lines: (a) the development of body image, which is associated with instinctual need satisfaction, (b) the self and object differentiation, which becomes the anlage for object relatedness, and (c) the transformation of infantile grandiosity and idealization as this occurs in the narcissistic sector of the psyche. The "blending" of these three component groups of self-images, Lichtenberg stated, does not imply total extinction of their particular distinguishing qualities. "Rather than extinction, cohesion implies a special kind of blending and balancing. This process permits the balance between the three clusters of self-images to be shifted while the overall sense of the self is so blended together that the individual achieves a feeling of sameness with change" (1975, p. 470). The ability to shift and balance self-images protects the self from experiencing fragmentation.

The paper currently under discussion contains a series of clinical vignettes in which the author demonstrates that the ability to blend and balance the various aspects of the sense of self is characteristic for the "normal" and the psychoneurotic individual in contrast to patients who suffer from narcissistic personality disorders and borderline conditions. This latter group of patients respond with fragmentation of the cohesive sense of self to life stresses which demand of them that one or the other of the self-images predominate.

Before proceeding with my discussion, I shall draw attention to the difference between Lichtenberg's use of the concept of "the cohesive sense of self" and Kohut's concept of "the cohesive self." The word *sense* implies that cohesiveness itself is being experienced, though experiencing or the sensing of cohesiveness is not limited to conscious awareness but includes preconscious and unconscious sensing as well. This total sense of cohesiveness, in turn, is responsible for the *quality* of the sense of self—"its cohesiveness, its continuity over time, and its retaining an essential sense of sameness in the midst of developmental changes" (Lichtenberg 1975). Kohut, on the other hand, maintains that "we cannot . . . penetrate to the self per se; only its introspectively or empathically perceived psychological *manifestations* are open to us" (Kohut 1977, pp. 310–311; italics mine). These psychological manifestations range from a sense of vigor, aliveness, and pleasure in one's activities (the manifestation of a "cohesive self") to a sense of deadness, apathy, hypochondria, and perverse sexual preoccupations or activities (the manifestations of an enfeebled or fragmenting self). "The cohesive self" is an experience-near metapsychological concept for Kohut; for Lichtenberg, "the cohesive *sense* of self" designates the *experiencing* of cohesiveness, continuity and sameness over time.

FRAGMENTATION OF THE COHESIVE SENSE OF SELF AS A DIAGNOSTIC TOOL

In psychoanalysis, the study of pathological conditions facilitates the understanding of "normal" psychological states. Recognizing the points of transition between the relatively healthy and the abnormal, or the lines of demarcation between the two, has been of great diagnostic and therapeutic significance in psychoanalysis. The clinical vignettes in Lichtenberg's paper are offered to demonstrate that fragmentation of the cohesive sense of self could reliably serve as a conceptual line of demarcation between normal adaptational responses and the psychoneuroses on the one hand and narcissistic disorders and borderline conditions on the other. Further, they are used to show that such fragmentations are likely to be triggered in the course of an analysis by failures in the analyst's empathy. Empathy, along with the fragmentation of the cohesive sense of self, thereby attains for Lichtenberg an important differential diagnostic significance.

Fragmentation is described with increasing frequency in the psychoanalytic literature. Clinical observations of the most varied kind and inferences drawn on various levels of abstraction are regarded as manifestations of "fragmentation." Because the concept is of central importance to this paper's main thesis, we shall examine two of the case examples to further clarify the concept, both clinically and theoretically.

A suitable opportunity for such an examination is offered in the clinical vignettes of the hypothetical thirty-year-old female patient and in the case of Mr. T, both of whom are examples of narcissistic personality disorders. Lichtenberg compared an actual thirty-year-old neurotic patient's reaction to one of his interpretations to what would hypothetically occur in a patient with a narcissistic disorder. In both instances, the patients dealt with anger about the analyst's upcoming vacation by "the resurgence of an erotic transference." However, while the neurotic patient was able to accept the analyst's interpretations that the erotic feelings were defensive against anger toward the analyst, the patient with the narcissistic disorder could not accept such an interpretation. Rather, the patient with the narcissistic disorder would, as Lichtenberg says, experience her "erotized transference ... as a restoration of an expansive, sexually attractive self after a period of feeling a sense of low self-esteem." In addition, "*she would regard herself as now free of the danger of fragmentation* and deflation of her sense of worth" (italics mine).

This patient's reaction, given as an example of fragmentation of the cohesive sense of self, was actually experienced by the patient as the opposite of fragmentation: the erotized feelings which the analyst considered to be defensive against her anger restored "an expansive, sexually attractive self." Fragmentation, in this case, was inferred from the patient's inability to connect disparate emotional states, namely her erotic feelings with the underlying angry ones. (A similar "split" is described in the case of Mrs. C, who is diagnosed as suffering from a borderline condition. Here the split was maintained by denial and projection, while in the case of the hypothetical patient the split was maintained by disavowal.)

In the case of Mr. T, fragmentation was described as a rather different phenomenon. In this vignette the patient, following the disruption of a selfobject transference, appeared physically disheveled and sickly. He would "complain of feeling blah, totally devoid of energy. His only wish was to sleep—for hours or days. . . . If he tried to associate, his thoughts would quickly become fragmentary; he would verbalize a disjointed unintelligible mix of incidents, fantasies, and hypnagogic imagery. At these times he would describe a strong hyperawareness of certain body parts—such as the position of his hands or knots in his stomach." "I'm falling apart, I can't think, I can't feel anything about anyone," Lichtenberg quotes the patient.

There are both clinical and conceptual differences in what is described as fragmentation in these two clinical examples. In the first case one can observe that the patient's actual experience was that of an "expanded self" while in the second the patient appeared disheveled and confused; the patient himself felt that he was "falling apart." In the first case, fragmentation was equated with the effect of the defense mechanism of disavowal which did not permit a meaningful connection between two disparate psychic states: fragmentation was here conceptualized on the level of clinical theory. On the other hand, in the second case fragmentation was conceptualized on the level of clinical observation: as a subjective experience. These two clinical examples would indicate that fragmentation of the cohesive sense of self may not be a reliable and useful concept whereby to differentiate the various psychopathological entities.

Fragmentation, when it occurs in the course of an analysis, is usually short-lived and is related to the disruption of one or the other forms of selfobject transferences. In relationship to the existing transferences, fragmentation is an *indirect indication* of the nature of the psychopathology. In cases where the patient is unable to establish a cohesive transference, the diagnosis is likely to be that of a psychosis or a borderline state. The differential diagnosis between the psychoneuroses and narcissistic disorders in the course of a psychoanalysis is best made on the basis of the nature of the evolving transference: object-instinctual in the psychoneuroses and one or another form of selfobject transference in the narcissistic disorders.

Kohut, too, used the stability and cohesiveness of the self as an overriding point of orientation in determining the nature of the psychopathology. For him the cohesive self was an experience-near abstraction, the presence of which could only be inferred (rather than "sensed") from the content of the patient's behavioral and characterological manifestations. In terms of psychopathology, Kohut postulated that at one end of the spectrum of psychopathological disorders the self had *developmentally* attained stable cohesiveness; the objects here were recognized as separate and independent. Psychological illness in this group would take the form of the psychoneuroses since the clinical picture under these circumstances is dominated by the drives and the conflicts related to them. At the other end of the spectrum, the self (and the selfobjects) had never attained cohesiveness; they remained fragmented and archaic. This is the group of the borderline states and the psychoses. It was in the third group, in the middle of the two extremes, that Kohut recognized the group of disorders he called the narcissistic personality and behavior disorders, or what we would now prefer to call the primary disorders of the self. In this group, cohesiveness of self and selfobjects had been developmentally attained but remained "fixated" on an archaic level. This is the group of patients who, as Lichtenberg confirms, are particularly sensitive to failures in the analyst's empathy and who are likely to react to such failures with *temporary fragmentation.*

This developmental view of the cohesive self is similar to our conceptualization of the oedipus complex. Failures in the resolution of the oedipus complex that occur developmentally leave the ego vulnerable to neurotic compromise formations later in life. Psychoneurotic disorders in adults may occur with or without a manifest neurosis in childhood. Similarly, the defects in the developing self may or may not have symptomatic manifestations in childhood. The presence of the original selfobjects (pathological as these may be) can "hide" or camouflage the defect or weakness of the self in the course of its development. "Depending on the quality of the interactions between the self and its selfobjects in childhood, the self will emerge either as a firm and healthy structure or as a more or less seriously damaged one" (Kohut and Wolf 1978). The degree and nature of the damage to the infantile self determines the later manifestations of self-pathology. The cohesive self is a developmental achievement in which inherited and environmental factors had crystallized. In the psychopathological conditions of psychoses and borderline states, self-cohesion has not been attained during early development. In the analyzable narcissistic disorders, the underlying defect or weakness in the self becomes exposed in the course of the analysis by the vicissitudes of the selfobject transferences.

In addition to the fragmentation of the cohesive sense of self, Lichtenberg also suggests that the sensitivity which patients with narcissistic disorders display in response to the analyst's empathic failures could also be utilized to differentiate this group of patients from those who suffer from neurotic disorders. Failures in empathy, in understanding, and in interpreting the patient's transference needs may have an overtly disruptive effect primarily in patients with a narcissistic disorder. However, it is important to emphasize that this does not mean that empathy here is considered as if it were a special ingredient (deliberately employed or withheld) of the analytic atmosphere. Rather, I believe, Lichtenberg would agree that empathy is a mode of cognition that serves as a tool of observation and a guide in interpretations *in all forms* of psychological disorders. It is only through empathic immersion that the analyst can perceive the patient's regressive needs as these become activated in the course of analysis and find expression in the various forms of transference. Empathy cannot be equated with tact and sensitivity, which are also essential in the timing and wording of interpretations.

SELFOBJECT TRANSFERENCES AND
THE FUNCTION OF EMPATHY

The case of Mr. T shall serve us as an example to clarify the relationship between the nature of the transference, empathic interpretations, and fragmentation.

Mr. T is described as a single man in his mid-thirties who entered psychoanalysis with a variety of diffuse complaints: he had no purpose in life, did not enjoy any of his activities, and was generally discontented. This "blah" image of himself alternated with one in which he thought of himself as the smartest engineer at his firm. His "infantile grandiosity" took on "unintegrated forms" such as daredevil stunts, righteous indignation vis-à-vis the analyst, and taking risks with financial speculation. Already, descriptively, one would suspect the diagnosis of a narcissistic personality disorder, and, indeed, in the third year of the analysis there is evidence of the reactivation of an infantile grandiose-exhibitionistic self with all the characteristics of that transference state. At this time in the analysis, the patient became extremely sensitive to the disruption of even a day in the analytic continuity, and "fragmentation of the sense of himself as an integrated, feeling, and functioning human being occurred." During the transition of this merger transference to a mirror transference, a significant event had occurred: the patient demanded that the analyst "read a written log of the patient's thoughts and reactions." The analyst recognized the meaning that the writing of the log had for the patient at this particular time in the analysis. The log represented, Lichtenberg says, an effort by the patient to "help himself pull together his scattered sense of self and make better use of the analysis. . . . This had a definite synthesizing effect on his work in the analytic hour during the intermittent periods that he kept up this resolve." We are puzzled why this understanding of the meaning which the writing of the log had for the patient was not included in the analyst's interpretations. Instead the analyst offered the following set of interpretations in response to the patient's demands: reading the log would fulfill his desire "(1) to have the analyst extend his interest and approval beyond the analytic hour; (2) to have the analyst confirm his grandiose fantasy that he had written something that would benefit the world; and (3) to have the analyst do the analysis from the written material and allow Mr. T to escape the demands of the analytic hour." These interpretations contained only the defensive aspects of the request that the analyst read the log; they were not responsive to the existing transference state. These interpretations increased the patient's despair, and "in a last desperate proposal he begged the analyst to take the log, do anything he wished with it, and 'at least let me believe you care.'" Mr. T then went through "a period of a completely fragmented sense of self." He did not go to work, had severe stomach cramps, and could not concentrate either in the analytic sessions, or outside of them. He experienced himself as someone "without substance or form, a glob needing to be held in a huge hand that would give the glob structure and direction."

Fragmentation here clearly followed the disruption of an emerging mirror transference. The importance that the analyst recognize and interpret his need to be affirmed in his independent activity, the log-writing, was confirmed by the genetic reconstruction that followed. Mr. T was his mother's "golden child, fondled, fed and vastly superior to other children." However, he would be abruptly rejected by her whenever he engaged in "a forbidden activity." The "forbidden activities"—thumb-sucking and masturbation—provided him with comfort and pleasure independent of his mother and were most likely engaged in whenever he was in particular need of being comforted. In this respect, the writing of the log served a similar function. Thumbsucking and masturbation had self-soothing qualities and, like the log-writing, constituted an effort by the patient "to help himself pull together his scattered sense of self."

We are left with the question of whether a comprehensive interpretation which gives legitimacy to the transference request that the analyst affirm and validate the value of his independent efforts at self-soothing and self-healing would have prevented the fragmentation. This is difficult to say. The incident indicated a progressive move in the analysis; a move from a more primitive merger to a mirror transference seems to have occurred. The log contained the patient's own "insights," but he needed the analyst's affirmation of their value in order to experience these as valid and real.

Not that Lichtenberg was not aware of the importance of the nature of the transference in this or in reports of other cases. However, the point has to be made that the occurrence of fragmentation in the psychoanalytic situation cannot be viewed independently of the interpretive process. This process is in turn related to, and has grown out of, the nature of the transference. In the case of Mr. T, Lichtenberg himself draws our attention to the selfobject nature of the transference when he says that "the analyst must recognize that the patient consciously and/or unconsciously requires him to serve as a missing component of his self."

In summary, these sensitively and carefully reported clinical vignettes are invaluable to the psychoanalytic reader. The report of the analysis of one of Mr. T's dreams alone would make this paper a most instructive one. However, the real value of the paper is not restricted to the sensitive reporting of relatively large segments of analytic material. Rather, I see its value in bringing to the reader's attention a frequent clinical observation: that self-esteem problems, narcissistic vulnerability, and other disturbances suggestive of failure in the transformation of archaic narcissism occur along the whole spectrum of clinical categories. In this paper, as well as in the "Development of the Sense of Self," Lichtenberg draws attention to the importance that the "experiential, "—that is, self-related aspects of the psychopathology—has for our total understanding of any given clinical picture. For him, the "blending" of the three component groups of self-images—that is, the body image, self-selfobject differentiation, and the transformation of infantile grandiosity and idealization—is a crucial developmental achievement that is most closely approximated by the "normal" or psychoneurotic individual. This point is illustrated in the case example of Mr. R, the college student. Mr. R experienced rather wide oscillations in his self-esteem. However, in his essentially neurotic personality make-up, his overall sense of self remained well blended so that, in spite of the wide fluctuations in his self-image, he maintained a feeling of sameness with change. Mr. T, who suffered from narcissistic personality disorder, and Mrs. C. who suffered from a borderline condition, both experienced temporary fragmentation because of their inability to maintain a sense of continuity and sameness when one or the other of their self-images had to predominate.

In this paper, Lichtenberg considers the fragmentation of the cohesive sense of self of central importance in differentiating the various clinical entities. However, the concept of fragmentation, as demonstrated in these clinical examples, is not clearly enough conceptualized to serve such a purpose. Rather, I would suggest that in analyzable conditions it is the nature of the transference which better serves the purpose of such a differentiation. The transference, by exposing either the unresolved oedipus complex or a defect in the self, indicates whether a condition belongs, respectively, in the category of the psychoneuroses or in that of the narcissistic disorders. In nonanalyzable clinical conditions, it is the course of the illness and certain specific features of the therapist-patient relationship (within which a cohesive transference cannot be mobilized) that suggest the presence of either a latent psychosis or a borderline condition.

REFERENCES

Kohut, H. (1977). *The Restoration of the Self*. New York: International Universities Press.

Kohut, H. and Wolf, E. (1978). The disorders of the self and their treatment: an outline. *The International Journal of Psycho-Analysis* 59:413–425.

Lichtenberg, J. (1975). The development of the sense of self. *Journal of the American Psychoanalytic Association* 23:453–484.

——— (1978). The testing of reality from the standpoint of the body self. *Journal of the American Psychoanalytic Association* 26:357–385.

Complementarity Between the Styles of the Patient's Material and the Interpretation

DAVID LIBERMAN, M.D.

This paper shows the importance of the characterization of the patterns of interaction between patient and analyst in the psychoanalytic process. These patterns are called "styles" and comprise both the patient's ways of offering his material and the analyst's ways of receiving it, as well as the linguistic characteristics of his interpretations. Different styles in the psychoanalytic dialogue are exposed and correlated with specific ego states, anxieties, and mechanisms of defense. A new stylistic nosography is proposed, correlated with a communicational nosography and the classical psychiatric psychopathological states. A clinical sample of a psychoanalytic session is presented.

It is a well-known fact that the features characterizing the behavior of a patient in the transference situation are the product of his psychosexual evolution during the first years of his life. I should like to state that these features can both be brought together and differentiated as "styles." We may wonder how these features are detected and how important they are for the establishment of a psychoanalytic theory of the patient's evolution based on the observation of the psychoanalytic process. Let us assume that the probable ways of grasping the material, of ascribing meanings to it, and the syntactic characteristics that the analyst chooses for his interpretations also constitute styles. Then the psychoanalytic treatment must be considered a peculiar kind of communicative interaction in which the analyst, by means of the style with which he approaches his patient, is enabled to show qualitative changes in his responses. These changes constitute new stylistic combinations that appear in the course of analysis as a consequence of some growth of the ego in the course of therapy.

AN APPROACH TO THE CONCEPT OF STYLES IN THE PSYCHOANALYTIC DIALOGUE

Saying something in a certain way involves choice and therefore the exclusion of all other possible ways of expressing it. For the analyst who tries to detect the unconscious conflicts in the analytic session, the observation of these options constitutes an avenue toward some knowledge about them. This means that the opening, progress, and outcome of a psychoanalytic therapeutic process will depend on, among other things, the way the patient has chosen to express his conflicts to his therapist. The latter, as has been said, tries to grasp the clues his analysand gives him in the session, and he, too, makes his choices by ascribing meanings to *certain* elements or stimuli coming from his analysand, stressing some verbal, paraverbal and nonverbal aspects of the patient's material and discarding others.[1]

Style comprises the patient's choices in expressing his conflicts and the analyst's choices in detecting the clues to the unconscious by taking the analysand's material in a particular way and verbalizing it in a particular way. Styles create a set of transcendental steps for the success or failure of the establishment of the psychoanalytic process. In the language of communication theorists, the analysand's option when conveying the material, the way the material is received (decoded) and interpreted (encoded), and the way the analysand receives what the therapist has sent, constitute styles and stylistic patterns.

In his "Recommendations to Physicians Practising Psycho-Analysis" Freud (1912) roughly considers this communicational model of the operations that take place in and between both participants of the psychoanalytic dialogue:

> To put it in a formula: he must turn his own unconscious like a receptive organ towards the transmitting unconscious of the patient. He must adjust himself to the patient as a telephone receiver is adjusted to the transmitting microphone. Just as the receiver converts back into sound waves the electric oscillations in the telephone line which were set up by sound waves, so the doctor's unconscious is able, from the derivatives of the unconscious which are communicated to him, to reconstruct that unconscious which has determined the patient's free associations. (pp. 115–116)

1. By paraverbal components we understand all the ingredients of speech, such as tone, pitch, intensity, rhythm, syllabic duration, and omission of parts of words, that are not included in the spoken syntax. The phonetic notation of languages constitutes an incomplete attempt to obviate the impossibility of making an accurate phonological graphic transcription.

Freud's "Leonardo da Vinci" (1910) illustrates both the artist's options as to the ways of conceiving of his work of art according to the structure of his infantile conflict and the observer's options according to the position from which he sees, views and judges that work of art; this depends upon whether the observer is an analyst, a critic, or an outside observer. Freud has noted:

Leonardo's childhood was remarkable in precisely the same way as this picture. He had had two mothers: first, his true mother Caterina, from whom he was torn away when he was between three and five, and then a young and tender stepmother, his father's wife, Donna Albiera. By his combining this fact about his childhood with the one mentioned above (the presence of his mother and grandmother) and by condensing them into a composite unity, the design of "St. Anne with Two Others" took shape for him. The maternal figure which is further away from the boy—the grandmother—corresponds to the earlier and true mother, Caterina, in its appearance and in its special relation to the boy. The artist seems to have used the blissful smile of St. Anne to disavow and to cloak the envy which the unfortunate woman felt when she was forced to give up her son to her better-born rival, as she once had given up his father as well.

A footnote was added in 1919:

(If an attempt is made to separate the figures of Anne and Mary in this picture and to trace the outline of each, it will not be found altogether easy. One is inclined to say that they are fused with each other like badly condensed dream-figures, so that in some places it is hard to say where Anne ends and where Mary begins. But what appears to a critic's eye as a fault, as a defect in composition, is vindicated in the eyes of analysis by reference to its secret meaning. It seems that for the artist the two mothers of his childhood were melted into a single form.) (1910, pp. 113–114)

In "Character and Anal Erotism" Freud (1908) established a correlation between order, parsimony, and obstinacy in obsessive behavior and in the child's reaction to one of his body functions (toilet training). I think that these traits of behavior imply a choice, that is, a style of behavior based on a specific infantile conflict. Freud (1908) said:

It is easy to gather from these people's early childhood history that they took a comparative long time to overcome their infantile incontinentia alvi (faecal incontinence), and that even in later childhood they suffered from isolated failures of this function. As infants, they seem to have belonged to the class who refuse to empty their bowels when they are put on the pot because they derive a subsidiary pleasure from defecating; for they tell us that even in somewhat later years they enjoyed holding back their stool, and they remember—though more readily about their brothers and sisters than about themselves—doing all sorts of unseemly things with the faeces that had been passed. (p. 170)

As regards the way of expressing this infantile conflict as character traits, he adds:

It is therefore plausible to suppose that these character traits of orderliness, parsimony and obstinacy, which are so often prominent in people who were formerly anal erotics, are to be regarded as the first and most constant results of the sublimation of anal erotism. (p. 170)

Possibilities and options. An analysand can convey a state of mind in different ways, according to the characteristics of his intrapsychic organization. This determines his link with his analyst, which is in turn determined by the way the former imagines he is understood by the latter (ascription of roles to the therapist cum receiver-of-the-message).

In a state of sadness in relation to melancholic anxieties, for example, one analysand will be silent, disconnected from the therapist, feeling that time flows outside him. He will eventually say to the analyst: "What we do is futile, superfluous, opaque." Let us now consider another possibility: a patient who is also sad, but who, instead of acting like the previous one, is restless, scratches the cover of the couch, utters some exhalations and then despondently says in a plaintive tone, "I'm tired, I'm good for nothing, and there's no tomorrow for me." There is a third possibility: the patient who is not sad and has never been. We may rather say he has left a trail of victims in the course of his life, many of whom may have ended in suicides and accidents. In this case, the analysand is incapable of feeling (and therefore expressing) the emotional state called "sadness." He will use every possible means to inoculate sadness and pessimism into the therapist in reference to the cosmovision of his psychoanalytic therapeutic practice. And such a patient is often successful in his endeavor.

In the first case the melancholic anxiety is thrown out of the patient's self, and he feels the emptiness left by it; in the second it pervades and engulfs the patient's self. There is a defense against this situation which consists in a splitting of the self, and the melancholic anxieties are located in some bodily function, as happens with patients who suffer different types of organic diseases. In the third case, the patient looks for the analyst's self in order to force into it his own melancholic anxiety.

Following the same sequence, I have found that the stylistic patterns are in the first case characteristic of schizoid patients; in the second, of depressive ambivalent patients; and in the third, of patients who hide their paranoid beliefs through constant acting out in the session.

There are other cases in which melancholic anxieties may arise, although not as strongly as in the previous cases and usually after the loss of an object. This happens at neurotic levels of the personality which I will soon describe. The patient who feels empty as melancholy anxiety is ejected from the self (case 1) and the patient who feels this anxiety as engulfing (case 2) show consolidation around both oral primary and secondary phases. The third case, of the patient who projects his anxiety into the analyst, is shaped up from the anal primary phase. The next three cases I will present, types 4, 5 and 6, derive from the anal secondary phase and the phallic phase (Abraham 1949).

Let us describe the fourth possibility: the melancholic anxieties are controlled by these patients in the session by defensively giving us coherent and very detailed narratives. These are woven together by a sequence of external events organized in chronological order with an infantile mention of the locations of these events. The narration may be so coherent and logical as to impede access to the clue to an emotional state. Then, after three or four narrative sequences, the patient may fall into a state of languor, dejection and he may eventually stop speaking. After making visible efforts, he may manage to utter something like "I feel despicable." And this could be the basic emotional state against which all the previous narrative sequences were verbalized in the session. This case corresponds to patients with obsessive traits.

Another possibility of managing the melancholic anxieties may be found in phobic-counterphobic patients, who are emotionally unstable whenever they are in danger of breaking down their ambitious tasks and of falling into a state of pessimism. The patient needs his analyst simultaneously as an accompanying object to reassure him of his ambitious goals and as a threatening object that may destroy his counterphobic defenses. He is therefore curious: he needs to know our state of mind at the moment. The style of verbal behavior and the way of listening to us is as follows: the patient stops uttering his phrases halfway through, due to the anxiety aroused by the peculiar contact he establishes with us. And when we say something to him, he immediately jumps into us trying to auscultate in our manner of vocalizing whether we are in a frightened or pessimistic state of mind. This is the patient who comes to us with curiosity and anxiety and suddenly puts distance between us.

The last case is that of patients who seek gratification in the session by means of their exhibitionistic behavior. They have hysterical character traits and are constantly threatened by shame (defensively felt as es-

trangement or depersonalization, ridicule or sense of ugliness) when they
are with us. The feeling of shame and the ensuing defenses are derived
mostly from the melancholic anxieties at work inside the patient. The
patient develops a stylistic verbal behavior suitably accompanied by vocal
mimicry and gestures. This is a means of simultaneously gratifying his
exhibitionistic fantasies and overcoming the emotional state I described
above. In many cases, when he feels that these elegant defenses are
threatened, he may also recover by dramatizing his own internal reality.

I have pointed out all these defenses because in the first place they offer
an approach to the patient's clinical material and carry us further away
from the habitual psychiatric terminology while permitting us to conjecture over very precise data that can be differentiated in the way the
patient makes his choice. Let me emphasize that it is an unconscious
option. Thus, when the patient categorizes something in a certain fashion
(in this case, the state of sadness) and does so inadvertently, i.e., unconsciously, we can speak about styles or stylistic patterns that render one
patient clearly distinguishable when he is in a certain emotional state,
expressing himself in just one way and no other. The introduction of the
new nomenclature has an added advantage: patients never have pure
stylistic patterns. We can find in them other interwoven stylistic components and ingredients. In this way, rather than placing our patients in
pigeonholes, we can characterize them by their dialogue within the
treatment. The fixed patterns that take place in a spatiotemporal context
are determined by the duration of the analysis, the place it is carried out,
and the person in charge of it.

There is a correlation between the psychiatric nosography, some communicative patterns of interaction (as stated by Ruesch 1957), and these
new characterizations of different stylistic patterns, which I shall presently introduce.

Table I shows the correspondence between the psychiatric nomencla-
tures, those I used in my book *Communication in Psychoanalytic Therapy* (1966),
following Ruesch, and the new nomenclature I use in *Linguistics, Communicative Interaction and Psychoanalytic Process* (1972).

Let me now stress the advantages of this approach. In our psychoanalytic practice we are often faced with patients who use narrative
techniques. But within these narrative techniques, different possibilities
arise: the narrative may be centered on the comment of self-reproaches
and considerations about the ethics in their own and other people's
behavior. This narrative style contains a lyrical subcomponent that grants
an emotional tone which the patient tries to control by forcing his
objectivity, coherence, and formal logic inside himself. These are the
patients who establish obsessional mechanisms of defense that protect

TABLE I

PSYCHIATRIC NOMENCLATURE	COMMUNICATION, ETC.	LINGUISTICS, ETC.
schizoid patient	non-participant observer	person looking for unknowns without creating suspense
endogenic depression	depressive person	patient with lyrical style
psychopathic personality	action person	patient with epic style
obsessive patient	logical person	patient with narrative style
phobic patient	frightened and fleeting person	patient who looks for unknowns and creates suspense
hysterical person	demonstrative person	patient with dramatic style who creates an esthetic impact

them from falling into melancholic states. Other patients also present a facade of narrative style, but, unlike the previous case, narrative technique here serves to control phobic anxieties. In these patients, the narrative contains some reference to situations involving risk, suspense, courage, or cowardice. This is the case with patients who have obsessional defenses organized for the control of phobias and who eventually restructure counterphobic behaviors. The study of both types of narrative style, each with a different set of subcomponents, enables us to see that behind this similar appearance is a sharp difference. The sets of subcomponents, which are depressive-oral-ambivalent in one case and phobic-phallic-urethral in the other, make for a different prognosis in the psychoanalytic treatment.

These two sets of subcomponents are habitually unconscious for the patient, and the analyst may or may not be aware of these, depending on his options when receiving the material, i.e., his perceptual style. If the therapist can detect and distinguish these, he is in possession of a most valuable tool. By means of the research into segments of dialogue in psychoanalytic processes corresponding to both cases, he will be able to establish prognostic criteria relating to the analysand and his own therapeutic approach.

The logical outcome is a fluent psychoanalytic process. There is a better course of therapy when the therapist can detect the reinforcement of the patient's obsessional defenses. The patient uses these defenses in order to ward off a state of anxiety and to avoid being "wrapped in suspense and unknowns." The therapist's skill will soon render the patient less narrative and more capable of creating suspense and looking for unknowns.

I have brought forth these two possibilities of psychopathological structures because I think that they show off more clearly the importance of understanding the fact that the people we have in analysis have a set of stylistic components and that the subcomponents remaining as accessory ingredients will provide the actual diagnostic and prognostic criterion in analysis. Through this criterion we shall be able to move and work in the therapeutic approach with clear-cut and well-defined patterns. Note also that I am trying to rid psychoanalysis of psychiatry and psychology and to lead it toward the stylistic, that is, to the types of dialogue and communicative interaction that occur between analysand and analyst in the different moments of the analytical process. So far my experience has enabled me to state that it is possible to set up predictive criteria about the situations that might arise. If we study our patients out of the session, the prognosis of the patient will improve since we shall be better prepared to recognize his changing styles.[2]

STYLISTIC COMPLEMENTARITY BETWEEN MATERIAL AND INTERPRETATION

We know that every analysand in the different moments of the sessions goes through a succession of states that he feels as changes occurring simultaneously inside himself, in his relation with his therapist, and in the way he supposes the latter perceives him.

Let us reformulate this in communication terms: in the course of the sessions the patient simultaneously undergoes changes in his intrapersonal states as well as qualitative changes in the link established with the analyst as a person. This in turn corresponds to the succession of roles the analysand ascribes to his analyst in the course of the sessions.

In order to establish criteria of stylistic complementarity we must distinguish between the ingredients of the analyst's and the analysand's styles. The analysand's "styles" correspond to the way he combines the

2. In 1975, I carried out an interdisciplinary investigation about styles of analysands and literary styles with David Maldavsky, with whom I published "Psychoanalysis and Semiotics". This shows how the hypotheses arising from psychoanalytic processes can be extended to the research into other human activities.

verbal, paraverbal, and nonverbal ingredients of his communications.[3] This is not the case with the analyst. The style of the interpretation is restricted to his way of combining the syntactic, morphological, and semantic components of the verbal structure of the phrase that makes up the interpretation.

From the analysand's point of view, the stylistic variations will depend upon the way in which he imagines he is being perceived or considered, or what he imagines is expected from him. Such variations take place as a result of the analyst's interpretations, but if the patient is in a state of useful regression, they will depend upon the meaning the patient ascribes to the analyst as a silent listener.

Interventions about the clues to the unconscious of the analysand constitute a psychoanalytic interpretation if and only if the analyst communicates these clues to the analysand with the highest degree of linguistic adequacy. This also depends on the state of the analysand as a receiver.

Psychoanalytic modifications will depend on the degree of linguistic adequacy between the verbal organization of the interpretation and the patient's condition as a receiver. This is what distinguishes psychoanalytic therapy from any other type of psychotherapy. The greater the degree of adequacy between the structure of the phrase that conveys the interpretation and the patient's state when he receives it, the less the distortion.

Adequacy means stylistic complementarity, and I shall give two examples to convey my point. For a patient who develops a behavior of acting out in the transference, the complementary style of the interpretation will consist of a narrative in which his behavior is described and categorized. When the patient has a schizoid style it will be necessary to interpret with dramatic complementarity. Through our interpretation we wish to introduce "casts" of verbal thought contained in the syntactic and semantic possibilities of the language code that the patient could not manage to build up during his development.

A CLINICAL VIGNETTE

For a better understanding of my exposition, I need to provide seg-

3. Stylistic complementarity derives from patterns of interaction in psychotherapy. We are to understand that complementarity means the differences of roles and characteristics of the messages, as contrasted with a symmetrical interaction, where similitudes predominate over differences. The therapist who argues with an obsessional patient establishes a symmetrical interaction; if he manages to offer an interpretation consisting of an affirmation that modifies the patient's obsessive structure, he has established a complementary relation.

ments of a psychoanalytic dialogue. Even if the starting point is one particular experience, there are sequences of analytic interaction that bring together a series of moments in any analytical process we carry out. This may open a new avenue for categorizing the different senses of the direction of the analytic process.

I shall now describe a generalization which I refer to a set of processes and which constitutes one of many possible occurrences.

After I had interpreted to the analysand that his curiosity as regards analysis was based on mistrust and fear of the unknown, he went through a long period of productive sessions. He recognized he had achieved many things all along his life, but none of them had left him satisfied. Also, he started to bring a more objective image of his parents. This enabled me to infer psychoanalytic hypotheses about the roles he ascribed to me during the sessions. The changes in his style of communicating depended on the role. In the first part of the session I am presenting, I represented a seductive and ambitious mother figure whom he had to control, gratifying her with the narrative of his achievements. When this was over, the patient felt that I lost him, that I incorporated him with hatred. Therefore, the next role he ascribed to me was that of an expelling anus. At the beginning of the session, after I had received him, and he lay down and I got ready to listen to him, he developed what I call "a narrative style." This style consisted of chronological enumerations, coherently verbalized. All of these enumerations had a common subject: the "ambition and optimism" that he tried to impose upon himself and me. While this narrative style persisted, he tolerated no interruptions. If I tried to interrupt, my words were considered a rejection.

After some time, however, this "narrative" style was exhausted and he used another stylistic resource corresponding to the change in the role he ascribed to me. At that moment he considered that my silence, which he had previously felt he needed, had become hostile and spiteful.

Then the "lyrical" style appeared. Verbalization seemed broken. He complained that nothing ever pleased me. He thought I had got tired of him, that I had "sent him to hell," and that I was only thinking of my own things. He complained that his sessions always began nicely, but I spoiled them. He interrupted his utterances and silences with a rattling of his tongue. Then he remained silent and tried to hear whether I moved, because he thought I was angry and might dismiss him, and then I would not have to bear him. He beat the devil's tattoo on the couch. He exhaled with closed lips (pff!).

I was thus confronted with an important choice as regards the moment and styles of interpreting. One of them was the narrative (obsessive) moment, and the other was the lyrical moment (depression, impatience, ambivalence). Both led to cul-de-sacs. The detailed interpretations about his narrative stimulated his obsessive traits due to the symmetry of styles. Interpretations about his resentment, or the resentment projected upon me, strengthened his depressive complaints.

Once I managed to frame an interpretation that brought together all the requirements of adequate complementarity in my verbal style, and this precipitated a different outcome to the sessions. It was as if at last we were putting an end to these sessions that would stop at a certain point in which everything was spoiled, and that we always started over again. In that moment of transference crisis and of feeling ill at ease, I said: "I know I am for you an 'unsatisfiable' person whom you have to end by repudiating. This will always happen when you 'partialize' (render partial) your relation with me and believe that the only thing that matters is to succeed and become proud."

This interpretation tried to show how the patient reacted in the session according to a projection into the analyst of an ambitious, narcissistic, impatient, and rejecting mother to whom he was strongly linked. This form of interpretation, which corresponds to the way a schizoid person might utter an order or a request, brought about the emergence of a new style: "dramatic with esthetic impact."

He suddenly remembered repetitive dreams he had dreamt days before but had not been able to remember during the sessions. He told them with verbal mimicry synchronic with the text of the dreams. Upon narrating them, he identified himself with some of the characters. All of these dreams showed somebody calling him from above. He insisted upon obeying, but he knew that he could not, that he would end up by falling down and having to protect his mouth and head.

This was the first of a series of sessions in which a change appeared: he felt cold. He thought it was due to the fact that he felt out of the session. He was thus showing how the distance in his relation with me had changed as a consequence of my intervention.

He finished his session by resuming his narrative style, repeating the same content as at the beginning of the session but now with an opposite valuation. Now the narrative was one of "pessimism and prudence" instead of the original ambition and optimism. I showed him how, now that I had changed roles with him, he was changing roles with me; but that he changed so much that everything was the opposite, and therefore the same.

The patient smiled and remained pensive. He said: "I know what's wrong. I have mental daltonism, everything is either all black or all white, or all grey. I haven't found the intermediate shades."

This patient had "hysterical," "phobic," "obsessional," and "depressive" registers but never showed any sort of acting out. He was also unable to be detached and to make abstractions. The above interpretation introduced a schizoid stylistic modality with an ingredient of action language, which brought about qualitative changes in the direction of the process.

CONCLUSIONS

The correlations between infantile fixation points, ego-changing structures during the therapy, are detected through the patient's linguistic organization and the way he verbalizes, as well as through the attitude and gestures accompanying verbalization. If the the evolution in analytic therapy is favorable, it leads him to new combined patterns in his way of organizing and verbalizing the phrases, and to some coordination with the elements, gestures, and attitudes accompanying verbalization.

The ideal, most accurate interpretation will be the one bringing together in the phrase such stylistic components as the patient lacks. This complementary interaction leads the patient toward insight in the session that becomes manifest in new patterns of communication by means of phrases uttered by him in reference to his conflicts. These phrases would never have been produced without these complementary interactions.

The theories and method proposed here constitute a contribution to disrupt the impasses in analytic treatment by means of access to new patterns of interaction through greater linguistic precision in the interpretative technique. However, this way of theorizing about the psychoanalytic practice has, I believe, two complications. One of them is the great number of hypotheses this approach entails; the other is the risk of overusing it, trying to maintain a constant ideal complementarity. When an optimal level of work is attained, the analyst effects this stylistic complementarity without premeditation.

REFERENCES

Abraham, K. (1949). A short study of the development of the libido viewed in the light of mental disorders. In *Selected Papers on Psycho-Analysis*. London: Hogarth Press.

Freud, S. (1908). Character and anal erotism. *Standard Edition* 9:167–175.——— (1910). Leonardo da Vinci. *Standard Edition* 11:63–137.

——— (1912). Recommendations to physicians practising psycho-analysis. *Standard Edition* 12:109–120.

Liberman, D. (1966). *La Comunicación en Terapéutica Psicoanalítica*. Buenos Aires: Eudeba.

——— (1972). *Lingüística, Interacción Comunicativa y Proceso Psicoanalítico*. Buenos Aires: Galerna: Nueva Visión.

Liberman, D., and Maldavsky, D. (1975). *Psichoanalisis y Semiotica*. Buenos Aires; Editorial Paidos.

Ruesch, J. (1957). *Disturbed Communication*. New York: W. W. Norton.

The Uncovering of Projective Identification in the Treatment of the Borderline Adolescent

JOSHUA LEVY, PH.D.
RONALD D. BROWN, M.D., F.R.C.P. (C.)

This paper illustrates a clinical finding from intensive family and individual therapy with borderline adolescents: The properly handled uncovering of projective identification leads to the building of parental empathy, and allows for the reopening of emotional growth for the adolescent and his parents. Projective identification is defined and applied in the context of intensive therapy, and its place is established as a link between interpersonal family relations and intrapsychic structure. The process of the uncovering of a specific object-relations conflict which had been defended by projective identification is illustrated by excerpts from the treatment situation.

This paper is an outgrowth of our experience with psychoanalytically oriented treatment of borderline adolescents. An interrelated set of pathological family relations, which has had devastating consequences on the developing child and adolescent, has repeatedly been identified. These relations are subsumed under the complex defensive operation referred to as pathological projective identification. One of our major conclusions is that by gradually uncovering the maladaptive family relations produced by pathological projective identification we help to reopen channels for emotional growth.

We will first present a review of the pertinent literature, followed by

Earlier versions of this paper were presented at the Child and Adolescent Clinic, Allan Memorial Institute of Psychiatry, Montreal, Quebec, Canada, February, 1974 and at the Eighth International Congress of Child Psychiatry and Allied Professions, Philadelphia, July 1974.

our clinical material, which will emphasize the stages we have found to be essential in the effective handling of these cases.

A SELECTED REVIEW OF THE LITERATURE

The term *projective identification* was introduced by Melanie Klein (1946). In this paper she deals with early developmental experience, elaborating the basic splitting process that occurs in relation to the object. She describes early anxieties that result from three sources. These are (1) the operation of the death instinct, (2) "the trauma of birth (separation anxiety)" (p. 296), and (3) frustration of bodily needs. Basic anxieties generated in these spheres relate to the fear of destructive inner impulses that are projected outward and attach themselves to the first external object, or that are bound by libido within the organism.

When, despite these processes, the anxieties of being destroyed remain threatening there occurs an active splitting of the primary object, of the ego's relation to it, and of the ego itself, resulting in a "dispersal of the destructive force within" (p. 297). At the same time the first internal good object, established by introjection of the gratifying breast, "counteracts the processes of splitting and dispersal, makes for cohesiveness and integration, and is instrumental in building up the ego" (p. 297). In this way, splitting, projection, and introjection are seen as the earliest ego mechanisms and as defenses against anxiety. Closely related to these defenses is projective identification. Klein sees this as a means of "expelling dangerous substances (execrements) out of the self and into the mother" with the aim "not only to injure but also to control and to take possession of the object" (p. 300). She adds: "Much of the hatred against parts of the self is now directed towards the mother. This leads to a particular form of identification which establishes the prototype of an aggressive object relation. I suggest for these processes the term projective identification" (p. 300).

Laplanche and Pontalis (1973) note that "the Kleinian usage is consistent with the narrow sense to which psychoanalysis tends to confine the term projection: the ejection into the outside world of something which the subject refuses to acknowledge in himself—the projection of what is bad" (p. 356). What Klein has added to this are the vicissitudes of the internal object relations subsequent to the projection and especially the need to control the possessor of the bad (persecutory) parts.

Malin and Grotstein (1966) have emphasized projective identification as a process that is both a defense and a mode of relating to objects. They argue that "all identification includes projection and all projection includes identification" on the basis that "a projection of itself seems meaningless unless the individual can retain some contact with what is projected" (p. 27).

Jaffe (1968) has presented a review of the usages of projection and projective identification. In his opinion projective identification operates on a continuum: "on the one hand it seeks to effect a split from the object while on the other, it seeks to preserve a tie with the object" (p. 662). He adds: "Dynamically, there is a conflict between the impulse to annihilate the object to which some threatening subjective tendency has been attributed and the urge to protect the object which has been identified with, and cathected as an extension of the self" (p. 674).

In his work on borderline personality organization, Kernberg (1967) has stressed splitting as an essential defensive operation of these patients. He sees projective identification as both a consequence and a support of this defensive splitting. This combination of splitting and projective identification is used particularly against aggressive impulses and images. He states: "projective identification is characterized by the lack of differentiation between self and object in that particular area [the projection of aggression], by continuing to experience the [aggressive] impulse as well as the fear of that impulse while the projection is active, and by the need to control the external object" (p. 669).

Novick and Kelly (1970) differentiate between projection proper and externalization. Projection is seen as a defense against a specific drive derivative directed toward an object. Its interpretation must focus on the need to defend against the anxiety related to drive expression. Externalization, on the other hand, is the ascription to the other of devalued aspects of self-representation. It is aimed at avoiding narcissistic injury. Its interpretation must focus on the need to defend against narcissistic pain. They further distinguish these two mechanisms on the basis of the differential impact on the child of parental externalizations and projections. When externalizations are predominant, the child manifests relatively little anxiety or guilt over drive expression. Rather, he shows severe narcissistic disturbance rooted in the acceptance of the devalued parental self-representations and the inability to integrate these with positive identifications. The child who is the object of projection experiences intense anxiety and guilt in relation to drive expression.

Langs (1976) has given a sound clinical definition (p. 26) of projective identification: "an interactional effort to put one's own inner contents into someone else, in order to manage these inner contents externally and to possibly benefit from the efforts at management undertaken by the other person." He stresses "that it is an interactional effort—an actual attempt to generate some kind of inner state and response in another person." He adds that the concept is different from that of projection, "which is an intrapsychic mechanism . . . in which an individual attributes to someone else aspects of his own inner state and contents without making actual, interactional efforts to put these contents into the other person."

With this emphasis on the interactional aspects of projective identification we can now turn to its conceptualization in the family context. Zinner and Shapiro (1972) have dealt specifically with this topic. They see projective identification as a "conceptual bridge between an individual and interpersonal psychology," and as referring to distorted images that come into play in the interactive life of the family. The parents need to maintain "unconscious assumptions" and "unconscious fantasies" (p. 523). These are translated into family interaction via "delineations—acts and statements which communicate to the adolescent his parents' image of him" (p. 524). When the adolescent alters his self-image to be congruent with these delineations, parental defensive needs are served. The adolescent colludes in this process due to a variety of unconscious motivations.

Slipp (1973) describes a pattern (the "symbiotic survival pattern") particularly apparent in families with a schizophrenic member. Here "a mutually controlling system of interaction leads each individual to feel responsible for the self-esteem and survival of the other" (p. 337). He attempts to provide an object relations theory of family homeostasis in which the child unconsciously senses his parents' needs for him to act out a particular introject in order for them to gain control over past and present (internal) relationships. There is a demand that the other behave, feel, and think according to introjected split good or bad images, instead of viewing the other as a separately motivated individual.

EXCERPTS FROM THE THERAPY

The patient, Anne, was a fifteen-year-old girl admitted to an inpatient psychiatric ward after having fled to a community youth clinic with fears of a homosexual involvement with her mother. Her hospital stay was two weeks, during which time a diagnosis of borderline personality was made on the basis of her primitive defenses, predominance of aggression, susceptibility to regression with lack of external structure, micropsychotic episodes, and the intensity of her abandonment depression (Masterson 1972). She was then referred for intensive outpatient treatment (Anne was treated by R.B. on the ward and by J.L. as an outpatient). She was a tall, somewhat skinny girl with black hair which she used to hide her face. Her mother, a forty-six-year-old skillful bookkeeper working in her husband's company, was intelligent, showed a marked display of affect, and was bewildered by her daughter's symptoms. The father, forty-eight, was a successful businessman who had devoted all his energies in that direction since the patient's infancy. He responded to the immediate crisis with a detached optimism. The patient had a sister who was a twenty-year-old failing university student whose conflicts around her attempts to leave home led to sexual promiscuity.

Here we will present excerpts from the therapy of this borderline adolescent. The first stage illustrates aspects of the pathological family relations; the second stage highlights an intense, painful sadness for the family, a feeling that had been avoided and suppressed during the first stage; the third stage focuses on the uncovering of projective identification and its pathological effect on the developing child over a period of years; the fourth stage reveals the resulting development of more appropriate empathy within the family members.

Stage I: Revealing Split Object Images

Anne started the family therapy sessions with an explosive outburst of murderous rage. The father, sitting between the others, turned to Anne, held her hand, and spoke calmly, softly, and deliberately: "We are all going to speak quietly." Anne withdrew toward her mother, looking at her intently and with hate, screaming: "You treat my father like shit." Her mother brushed it off, saying: "I didn't know you were feeling that way." Anne was crying, and her father again tried to calm her down.

When the storm subsided, the parents slowly and guardedly related some recent historical episodes in their family life. Anne was silent, tense, and withdrawn until her mother mentioned the name of the older sister. With this, the patient suddenly sprang to life again, screaming: "My sister has a split personality; she is an angel when you are home, and very cruel when you are away." Quickly she turned to the therapist, asking: "Do you fish or hunt?" When she was encouraged to explore her question, she launched into a semicoherent tirade about the pervasiveness of cruelty in the world and the joy people experience in killing each other. Siding with the good part of the split that had been revealed in her sister and toward fishing and hunting, the therapist told her that he neither fished nor hunted. She responded more calmly, "I knew that." (This initial intervention took place in a setting of intense, chaotic communications. After attempts at exploration, it was felt necessary to provide a measure of structure by answering her question directly.)

In twice-weekly individual sessions, Anne initially interacted with the therapist by describing terrors of being murdered, by periods of depression and by bouts of rage against her mother. These were followed by nightmares which resulted in her sleeping in her parents' bed, embraced in her mother's arms.

In the family sessions, the mother characterized herself as follows: "I have never felt inadequate in my life. . . . When my husband's business was failing, a year and a half ago, I moved in and saved the business." This self-image of confident competence was in marked contrast to her response to Anne, whom she attacked angrily as a failure, shouting: "What's wrong with you? At school you hate the kids, at home you run after me like a crybaby; you are mad at me. . . . We used to be very close. . . . You were becoming a pianist, then I had to go and work for Daddy and everything collapsed."

Note that the opening question in this quote, asked in anger, is devastating to the child. Compare it to the same question asked with concern and conveying an empathic awareness of the child's pain. Her tone reveals the mother's suppressed rage when Anne refuses to be a pianist. Here mother's splitting of objects has been revealed in her current characterization of the patient as entirely negative; previously she saw the patient as entirely positive as long as she was a budding pianist. This will be elaborated below.

Anne shouted back: "You are as mean as the kids at school. . . . You say it is only in my mind but it's not; you are doing it to me." Here we see her fight against mother's intrusiveness and the latter's attempts to maintain her splitting defense by projecting a weak image onto the patient.

When Anne withdrew sobbing, the father, in a weak manner, asked each one to have a reasonable and logical discussion. Here he was the "outsider" because of the intense, unconscious communication between mother and daughter and his own need to remain distant. Often he did this by simply staying away from the family.

Variations of this destructive impasse in the family interactions took place at home as well. On one occasion the patient withdrew to her room from one of these fights and wrote the therapist a letter describing in detail the various phases of an episode which had just taken place. In referring to her father in the subsequent family session, Anne said: "For some time I felt that my mother had a plan. She tried to tear him apart from me. She told me, 'love me,' but I love him. Her plan did not work. She is very jealous of us." After a short silence Anne went on: "She makes my father feel like shit. She always compares him to her brothers and other men who are more successful in business." While her father, seemingly emotionless, tried to calm her down, her mother rejected Anne's outburst as psychotic material. This had the effect of increasing the patient's wish to live away from home, to move to a farm where she could relate to animals. Animals were her only friends.

In this period the therapist had been attempting to support Anne's struggles to move out of the field of interacting with the mother's intrusiveness. This resulted in Anne's pointing out her mother's splitting defense (her father as unsuccessful versus her brothers as successful) and caused a shift of her mother's devaluating cathexes from the patient to the father. Increased fighting between the parents ensued. The mother was unable to tolerate Anne's adolescent move away from her to the father and tried to bring her back—"love me." The father, for his part, was unable to support her individuation attempts. We hypothesize her withdrawal to animals as reflecting her need to be related to objects that do not project.

In this stage, the therapist has provided needed structure and has encouraged exploration. This led to the revelation of mother's and daughter's split self- and object-images. This in turn led to the beginning of working at their mutual enmeshment and at attempts to extricate themselves from this by running away from each other and from the therapy. With consistent confrontation and interpretation of this coping mechanism, they stayed in treatment despite an increase in the patient's pain and symptoms.

Stage II: Locating the Shifting Projections through the Expression of Emotional Pain and Sadness

The mother started a family session determined to talk only about Anne's staying home from school. Through this topic she revealed alternating modes of insistence and pleading, emphasizing: "Other doctors give answers."

Her question was interpreted as a desperate attempt to control as well as to devalue the therapist, as she had done with her husband and daughter. At the same time she was revealing a hidden negative, incompetent self-image.

The mother then shifted, accusing the father with: "I had to do everything because he was not close to the children." The father responded, for the first time showing overt anger: "You only want me to be subservient to you." Mother: "You are not as empathic as I am. I have an antenna into the children, I live their lives." Father: "You repeat problems over and over. You are so emotional; learn to be not so embroiled; I feel, too!"

Here we see the father rejecting the devaluating accusations, as had Anne and then the therapist. Mother expressed her sense of being within the children. Anne then entered the interchange, reinforcing the father's rejection of the mother's projections. She said: "You say you love him, but you really hate him; you treat him like shit; you compare him to others." The father, becoming more emotional, turned to the therapist, emphasizing: "I worked very hard and I became the director of a company."

Thus, the father asserted his own positive image, after having rejected the negative accusations. After a pause he turned toward his wife and, with the pain and sadness characteristic of this stage, said: "I can never please you. You want me to revolutionalize myself. I can't."

The therapist interpreted the father's attempts to reject being taken hold of from within and controlled by his wife. This allowed him to continue to examine the negative delineations around incompetence, which he did with great sadness: "You hurt me by always saying I was weak in comparison to others. You made me feel guilty because I have not accomplished as much as others." His wife was crying. After a short silence the patient attempted to put the negative image into the therapist, attacking him: "You just sit there. You don't care. My family is falling apart." When the accusatory aspect of this statement was interpreted as guilt related to her feeling of having provoked the increased parental fighting, both parents were able to comfort her saying: "He is trying to help all of us."

In a subsequent session, when Anne left the interview protesting against her parents' pressure to resume school, her mother became tearful and sad. She recalled that at age ten Anne had repeatedly told her of suicidal thoughts. The mother stated that she had ignored those then because they had never crossed her own mind as a child. When Anne returned, they continued with the school issue. Her mother said: "You say you hate the kids, perhaps you hate us." Startled, Anne replied: "No! Why should I hate you?" Her mother replied in a sad yet reaching-out way: "You first hate your parents." She then went on to describe her own wishes as a child to kill her father. The manner of this communication unconsciously gave Anne permission to express her murderous rage without this being treated as proof of her craziness. For the first time, her mother had openly taken responsibility for a negative aspect of herself.

In this stage there was a continuing move toward extrication from habitual enmeshments, facilitated by the therapist's interpretations of devaluating accusations. The resultant increase in the father's self-esteem allowed him to become more effectively involved.

Stage III: The Uncovering of Projective Identifications

In the individual sessions Anne was alluding to a longstanding torturous relationship she had had with her mother around her taking piano lessons. Despite great resistance, the following story was pieced together: When Anne was seven, her mother, convinced that Anne had outstanding musical talents, found a piano teacher who confirmed this belief. The mother then established a very rigid regime of practicing for three hours a day during the week and six hours on weekends. She would sit very close to Anne, making forceful critical comments about how a particular piece of music should be played. This was allowed to continue despite their awareness that the mother's musical knowledge was limited. The teacher, an unmarried woman in her twenties, was equally "devoted" to Anne, screaming and hitting her when she deviated even slightly. When she was nine years old, Anne did win a local prize. This elated the mother and resulted in increased pressure on the patient. Anne stopped taking music lessons eight years later, two weeks before she was admitted to the hospital.

At this stage, Anne's sense of her mother's intrusive forcefulness around practicing the piano and of her mother's elation when Anne won a prize was most striking. When Anne brought this up with her parents, their reaction was first to rebuff her with implicit accusations that only a crazy person would invent such a story. When Anne persisted, the mother slowly and sadly began to recall her intense involvement with Anne and the piano. When the mother's background of piano experiences was explored, there gradually emerged a linking of her behavior toward Anne with dissociated aspects of her own personal history. The mother, the eighth of nine children from a poverty-stricken family, wished to learn to play the piano from an early age. Upon graduation from high school, she worked, saving her money to buy an old piano. She placed this in the crowded family apartment. She then found a piano teacher, a man in his thirties, with whom she had a very special relationship. She fell deeply in love with him and they became inseparable. Within a year, he suddenly died of a heart attack. She never took up the piano again. The mother's personal experience and trauma with the piano came to light spontaneously, shocking them all, and seemed to have a profound emotional impact. In closing that session the mother said to Anne: "I was choking you. I didn't let you breathe."

We wish now to integrate the three major dynamics involved in the projective identification uncovered in this stage.

1. Mother and daughter maintained a special relationship based on the daughter's restoring and reviving the mother's lost idealized object relationship. The mother, as a defense against the depression involved in the loss of her loved piano teacher, had identified with him in becoming her daughter's piano mentor. To complete the defensive revival of this lost relationship, the mother coerced Anne to become her lost idealized adolescent piano performing self. During Anne's latency period, while she carried the "mission" successfully, this defensive operation brought about mutual gratification. Anne was her mother's precious child and her accomplishments as a young pianist provided her mother with deep gratification.

2. To maintain this special relationship, a tight regime had to be built. Deviations resulted in severe conflict, with threats of desertion. The extreme tightness of this regime revealed the operation of that aspect of projective identification in which the other must be forcibly controlled. Further evidence that Anne as pianist represented a projection from her mother lies in the following: (a.) when Anne did badly at the piano, her mother became desperately depressed and there were increased attempts at coercing Anne to be good; (b.) when Anne did well, as when she won the prize, her mother became elated, for she had restored the idealized old love relationship to her own teacher; (c.) when Anne, as part of her adolescent separation-individuation struggles, began to reject her sense of being taken hold of from within by rejecting the "mission" as impossible and stopping her piano playing, the family homeostasis collapsed and there was individual breakdown; (d.) the bolstering of projective relatedness by denial was as described by Kernberg (1967)—for example, the parents' response to Anne's initial attempts to confront them with her subjective experiences of the "piano years."

3. This relationship between mother and daughter could have taken place only with the father's collusion. He had heard of his wife's piano story before the marriage but had "forgotten" it. What emerged in the therapy was that his subtle encouragement of the mother's projective relatedness to Anne was on a "better her than me" basis. This allowed him to maintain a tie with his wife without having to deal with her previous painful loss and response to it.

Stage IV: The Budding of Parental Empathy

Significant therapeutic gains followed the uncovering and the historical reconstruction of the family ties based on pathological projective identification. The sharing and comprehending of the various components of these family relationships resulted in facilitating emotional development in the individual. This was reflected in a decrease in their mutual enmeshments as well as in the dyadic and family relations. The parents became more familiar with the daughter's feelings, thoughts, and wishes, her representations of her parents, and her developmental needs, thus perceiving her more accurately. It is illustrative to compare the difference in mother's handling of the patient's attempts to resist her projections in Stage One and Stage Three: earlier on, the mother's response had the flavor of "you are crazy," while later it was "I see and I am sorry." With this ability to take back into herself what belonged there, the interpersonal aspect of projective identification was no longer active.

Another example came from the parents' handling of the issue of

Anne's schooling. For the first time, they were able to realistically and empathically assess the situation and offer explicit and adequate guidance to Anne without the previous destructive forcefulness and inappropriate emotionality. Anne gradually learned to resist when either parent misperceived her, or when either tried to ally her against the other or subtly ascribed to her responsibility for family unhappiness.

Furthermore, via dramatic episodes relived within the therapeutic setting, the parents realized that Anne was carrying a "split" inside her, and recreating its painful effects in a variety of social situations. For example, she came late to one session and related that while on the bus she had seen a person who looked like a former teacher of hers. She remembered this teacher as cruelly pulling her hair when she had not done her homework. On the bus she became mesmerized watching this person. When she "came to," well beyond her stop, she walked past this lady; instead of carrying out an attack in fantasy, she realized that the lady did not look at all like the teacher but was in fact a ward nurse whom she remembered as being particularly kind to her. With this almost conscious contiguity of the images of a "bad teacher"/"good nurse," the therapist confronted her with manifestations of this splitting mechanism toward the one person of her mother. The mother was able to help heal the split through her more accepting attitude of her daughter and of her own contributions to her difficulties.

CONCLUSION

In conclusion we wish to emphasize several points:

1. Projective identification is a term used frequently (but not often enough) to refer to the complex interface between interpersonal and intrapsychic processes. In this case the interface is seen in the revival of the mother's specific trauma of losing both her loved piano teacher and the possibility of ever becoming a famous pianist. This trauma, grafted onto a relatively deprived background, resulted in periodic depressions. Unconsciously, she perceived her daughter as a potential realizer of her ideal and hence healer of her depressions. Thus the mother had an inordinate self-protective need to create a pianist out of her daughter. She coerced her daughter into accepting this role through the threat of abandonment specifically conveyed by the mother's depressive responses when the patient failed to comply. This would confirm Masterson's emphasis on withdrawing and rewarding object relation units (1976). We have attempted to present detailed clinical data illustrating the patient's initial acceptance of her mother's need to have her become a pianist and her eventual adolescent rejection of this with the reverberations this had

for the patient's and the family's homeostasis. In this way, we use projective identification as a concept parallel to that of delineations (Zinner and Shapiro 1972) but focus on the specificity of the psychological contents that are transmitted from parent to child. We believe that the literature has not adequately stressed the role of the specific trauma in forming the nexus of the projective identification process.

Further, the relation between personal interaction and intrapsychic structuralization requires further investigation. It has recently been approached by Kohut (1971) from the point of view of the psychology of the self. Kohut focuses on the differentiation of the self from an earlier merged self–selfobject matrix via optimal frustrations imposed by the selfobject.

2. Because of the painful object-relational and narcissistic conflicts that surround the use of projective identification in the families of borderline adolescents, its uncovering and working through is a gradual process, the stages of which have been outlined. It is our finding that when the dynamic constellations underlying projective identification are revealed to the family too quickly, before splitting of images has been exposed and before an atmosphere of trust and alliance has been established, the family system operates to close off this area of exploration. For example, in an initial interview with another family, the therapist made clear the adolescent son's having become the embodiment of the meticulous accountant father's split-off irresponsible, messy self. The father had disavowed this before he was five in order to take responsibility for his parents. In this interview all were amazed at the father's revelation of "always" having been the responsible one and the link between this and the identified patient's irresponsibility. However, this whole area remained inaccessible to exploration during the course of a prematurely terminated therapy.

3. Although the stages we have outlined were derived from empirical observation, they follow logically on an understanding of the components of the process of projective identification. At the level of defenses, there is first the splitting, then the self-protective coercive projection of warded-off contents into the other, who must then be controlled. This two-step process was observed in the therapy. First the splitting was dealt with and then the projection, with constant account taken of the underlying rage and depression.

In summary, we have attempted to present detailed clinical material illustrating the complex process of projective identification and its relation to underlying splitting processes, the specifics of the object-relational traumata that are revived via these processes, and the therapeutic effect, manifested in increased empathic responsiveness, of its gradual uncovering and working through.

REFERENCES

Jaffe, D. (1968). The mechanism of projection: its dual role in object relations. *International Journal of Psycho-Analysis* 49:662–677.

Kernberg, O. (1967). Borderline personality organization. *Journal of the American Psychoanalytic Association* 15:641–685.

Klein, M. (1946). Notes on some schizoid mechanisms. *International Journal of Psycho-Analysis* 27:99–110.

Kohut, H. (1971). *The Analysis of the Self*. New York: International Universities Press.

Langs, R. (1976). *The Bipersonal Field*. New York: Jason Aronson.

Laplanche, J., and Pontalis, J. (1973). The *Language of Psychoanalysis*. New York: Norton.

Malin, A., and Grotstein, J. (1966). Projective identification in the therapeutic process. *International Journal of Psycho-Analysis* 47:26–31.

Masterson, J. (1972). *The Treatment of the Borderline Adolescent*. New York: Basic Books.

——— (1976). *The Psychotherapy of the Borderline Adult*. New York: Brunner-Mazel.

Novick, J., and Kelly, K. (1970). Projection and externalization. *Psychoanalytic Study of the Child*, 25:231–156.

Slipp, S. (1973). The symbiotic survival pattern: a relational theory of schizophrenia. *Family Process* 12.

Zinner, J., and Shapiro, R. (1972). Projective identification as a mode of perception and behavior in families of adolescents. *International Journal of Psycho-Analysis* 53:523–529.

Postanalytic Encounters

DANIEL B. BORENSTEIN, M.D.
ROBERT T. FINTZY, M.D.

Outside the psychoanalytic situation, there may be numerous adventitious contacts between analyst and analysand. These interactions can be of major importance in determining the result of an analysis, either by stabilizing and reinforcing or by undoing previous analytic work. This paper focuses upon postanalytic encounters and their influence on the resolution of residual transference and the continuing working through and integrative processes. Important issues include (a) the time after termination, (b) the degree of socialization and (c) the extent of transference and/or real relationship. Clinical examples demonstrate that ex-patients can experience postanalytic encounters as pleasurable and helpful or unpleasurable and unsettling. After termination a more human openness is advocated, rather than aloofness, as catalyst for the continued future growth and development of the ex-patient. Further consideration to the important therapeutic potential of these encounters is urged.

Outside the psychoanalytic situation, there are numerous adventitious contacts between the analyst and the analysand. These contacts can take such forms as waiting room interactions, telephone conversations, letters, or face-to-face confrontations. We believe that these interactions can be of major importance in determining the result of an analysis, either by stabilizing and reinforcing or by undoing previous analytic work. These encounters may undermine or support the therapeutic alliance. They may serve as sources of transference activation or stimulation. The interactions confront the patient with additional information about the analyst and the way he reacts to or deals with these special situations. They frequently provide clues about the personality of the analyst.

We do not believe that these interactions have received sufficient attention in the professional literature or in teaching programs. In this paper, we will focus specifically upon one form of extraanalytic encounter, face-to-face confrontations following the final analytic session. We intend to examine these postanalytic encounters and their influence not only upon the resolution of residual transference but also upon the continuing working through and integrative processes. We believe these encounters are of special importance to the postanalytic period because of the intense transferences that have existed in the relationship, the potential for reactivation of these transferences and the limited opportunity to understand any distortions that may occur. During the first year or two after termination, the patient is quite vulnerable. However, the importance of these encounters extends far beyond one or two years, since the analyst will always be of special significance to the ex-patient.

In "An Overview of the Ending of an Analysis," Rangell (1966) emphasized the importance of the frequently neglected postanalytic period by suggesting that it be designated as a "phase." The useful phase designation highlights the need for the same careful analytic considerations of technique and investigation as are necessary and important during the beginning, middle, and termination phases. Rangell provided us with a macroscopic view of this period. We will attempt to isolate and magnify the phenomena within the postanalytic period as they pertain to our subject. This will include a further consideration of the postanalytic "phase."

REVIEW OF THE LITERATURE

The paucity of written and didactic material on this subject is striking. Freud (1937, p. 222) stated that "not every good relation between an analyst and his subject during and after analysis was to be regarded as transference; there were also friendly relations which were based on reality and which proved to be viable." Greenson (1967, 1971) has drawn our attention to the importance of the "real relationship" within the analytic setting. His position is that the analytic process may be facilitated or hindered according to the nature of the "real relationship." The authors believe that the postanalytic processes would be subject to the same influences, perhaps to a lesser extent.

Anna Freud (1954) indicated that the real relationship is in the foreground early in treatment and gains prominence again during the termination phase. In addition, she stated that "so far as the patient has a healthy part of his personality, his real relationship to the analyst is never wholly submerged" (p. 618). She does not address herself specifically to the postanalytic phase. We do know, though, that Freud himself had cordial and even supportive relationships with his ex-patients. He began socializing with some immediately after termination. In a letter to Fliess, he stated, "E. at last concluded his career as a patient by coming to supper in my house" (Freud 1900, p. 317). When Freud was more aware of transference, he stated, "On the question of therapeutic technique I must express myself plainly . . . thorough analysis of the transference situation is of special importance. What then remains of the transference may, indeed should, have the character of a cordial human relationship" (Freud 1927, p. 113).

Fairbairn (1957, p. 59), referring to extratechnical aspects of the analytic relationship within the treatment setting, had this to say: "the role of the analyst is not merely to fulfill the dual functions of (1) a screen upon which the patient projects his phantasies, and (2) a colorless instrument of interpretative technique, but that his personality and his motives make a significant contribution to the therapeutic process." We believe that the analyst's reactions, governed by both his therapeutic role and his personality, are just as important in the postanalytic period.

The studies in the literature that come closest to the present subject have been in relation to the fate of transference after termination and have focused mainly on the ex-analysand (Pfeffer 1959, 1961, 1963, Firestein 1969, Hurn 1973). In Pfeffer's studies, former analysands were evaluated in an analytic situation by analysts other than their original ones. The striking and unexpected findings from these studies were (a) that the ex-patient related to the follow-up study as though it were analysis and to the follow-up analyst as though he were the treating analyst, including reactivation of the analytic transference, and (b) that the ex-patient manifested a transient intensification of residual symptoms or a transient recurrence of the symptoms for which the analysis was first sought. Pfeffer (1963) suggests that the treating analyst remains a permanent intrapsychic representation. The apparent timelessness of the analyst's significance to the ex-patient is supported by Deutsch's examples (1959) of two patients with successful analyses who had what she considered definite transference residua more than twenty years after termination.

Rangell (1966) has been most helpful with his comments about termination and the postanalytic relationship. While referring to the end of an analysis, he stated: "The 'analytic atmosphere' which was the means to 'further the regressive transference' must now be dissolved to further continuous progression and an optimum or at least unimpeded adaptation to reality. The 'psychoanalytic situation' which has been initiated and maintained now has to be undone. While this dissolution should be accomplished by the end of an analysis, it frequently has to be tested and proven thereafter. Many a patient is left in the 'psychoanalytic situation' post-analytically to his severe detriment" (p. 161). Also, "the desired goal should be a transition to a normal interchange in which the analyst can be seen and reacted to as a normal figure and no longer as an object for continued transference displacement" (p. 162). In referring to isolated posttermination interviews, he described the postanalytic relationship between the patient and the analyst as one of mutual respect and friendly feeling.

Weigert (1952, p. 475) expressed similar ideas when she wrote, "Only when strict observance of objectivity and detachment on the part of the analyst can be loosened will the patient really feel that he is on his own and is accepted as an equal." Rangell (1966, in Firestein 1969, in Hurn 1973) has repeatedly and rightly cautioned that the analyst can make two errors with his former patients: he can persist with his analytic posture during postanalytic social encounters, which can lead to a long, unnecessary period of inhibition and dependence on the part of the ex-patient; or he can make the opposite error by rushing into excessive gratification of the former patient, which can be reacted to as a seduction or threat and lead to bewilderment, anxiety, or acting out. We fully concur that the possibility of these two errors exists and we believe that it is important for analysts to be aware of this when they come in contact with their ex-patients.

In a 1968 panel of the American Psychoanalytic Association on problems of termination, Stock (in Firestein 1969) cited evidence that more complete working through of transference residuals occurs during the posttermination period, the duration of which is indefinable or unpredictable and indefinite. Therefore, she emphasized that it is advisable to keep postanalytic contacts of any nature to a minimum. She did not clarify what she meant by "a minimum" or to what lengths analysts should go in order to avoid these contacts.

Other comments from the 1968 panel revealed a range of ideas about postanalytic contacts. Some analysts develop close friendships with former patients; others plan posttermination consultations; some avoid postanalytic social contacts, while still others avoid postanalytic relationships for at least a year and some avoid all contacts indefinitely. The stated purpose of this avoidance is to refrain from interfering with postanalytic working through, to eschew uncomfortable intrusions of the analysand's unresolved transferences, and to preserve the analytic relationship in order to make further analysis possible if needed. In contrast to this last position, Buxbaum (1950) and Annie Reich (1950) suggested that postanalytic contacts could actually promote the fuller resolution of the neurotic transference, as well as facilitate the final growing up of the patient.

We see then that a diverse range of positions in relation to postanalytic encounters has been expressed. There are two key issues. First, should postanalytic encounters be promoted or should they be avoided as much as possible? If it were clear that these contacts would be helpful, we would encourage them. However, planning specific follow-up contacts during the termination phase or at termination would significantly alter the termination experience. In our view this would tend to interfere with termination and would prolong the final separation. Even after termination, it is difficult for us to conceptualize how a former analyst's actively and unilaterally promoting contacts with his ex-patients would be helpful. We will touch on this issue tangentially as we consider the second key issue—that is, what should analysts do with inadvertent postanalytic encounters? In order to develop some answers to this question, we will focus on three major aspects of the postanalytic situation: (1) time after termination, (2) degree of socialization, and (3) extent of transference and/or real relationship experienced after termination. We are speaking here for the most part of inadvertent contacts and not of encounters that are intentionally promoted. The most important consideration should be the therapeutic potential of these encounters. Even here, psychoanalytic writers have often expressed a range of opinions from zero potential, to negative, to either positive or negative, to positive. Whether or not one believes that postanalytic encounters are helpful, they do occur and analysts should be prepared to respond in the least noxious and, hopefully, the most helpful manner. Analysts are trained well to maximize the therapeutic potential during the active treatment phases. We feel that they should be equally alert to maximize this potential during the postanalytic period, whether the encounter is planned or adventitious.

It seems clear, from the ex-patients' reactions noted in Pfeffer's studies (1959, 1961, 1963) and subsequently duplicated by Norman (in Hurn 1973), that the analyst can largely determine the level of transference reactivation and/or real relationship during a postanalytic encounter. The more the analyst maintains an analytic stance, anonymity, and even stiff formality, the more likely the development of transference reactions; the real relationship would tend to be minimized. Gertrude Ticho's studies (in Balkoura 1974) reinforce this impression. She described follow-up interviews conducted in a structured way which did not yield the regressive and transference phenomena she and others have observed with non-structured interviews. Therefore, if the analyst relates in a cordial manner, transference reactions are less likely to develop and the real relationship will be more prominent. However, extreme overfriendliness could be viewed as seductive or intrusive. Clearly, the authors believe that the nature of the analytic frame (Langs 1976) should be modified during the postanalytic phase.

There is no denying that the analyst has been and continues to be an important figure in the ex-patient's life—partly because transference is never totally resolved, and partly because the analyst has been a significant real person for the analysand. When the analyst remains aloof and remote during adventitious postanalytic encounters, our experience suggests that the ex-patient interprets such behavior not only as a personal rejection but also as a refutation of the validity of his earlier therapeutic relationship with the analyst. The ex-patient may wonder if everything that happened during his analysis was phony, a trick played on him by an unreal and dishonest analyst. The ex-patient may feel confused and question his basic judgment. Our discussions with ex-patients suggest that an analyst's less-than-friendly response may produce a temporary state of ego disruption.

Zetzel (in Firestein 1969, p. 229), in referring to an encounter with a former analysand in a social setting, cited the "hallmark of a successfully terminated analysis: Persistence of positive feeling, absence of a feeling or a need to return, but indication of feeling free to return if need arose." When the analyst fails to show warmth and interest, not only does the former patient lose pleasure in seeing the analyst again but the negative feeling aroused promotes the resurgence of feeling the need to return to analysis, with a simultaneous impression that the door is now closed since the former analyst no longer seems receptive.

So far we have presented a variety of analysts' responses to ex-patients during postanalytic encounters. It is our belief that in order to be of maximum benefit to ex-patients during adventitious postanalytic encounters, analysts must be appropriately friendly and cordial, while steering a path between excesses of aloofness or intimacy. This in no way precludes the possibility of the analyst's being warm but distant in his effort to remain available to the patient for future analytic work.

CLINICAL MATERIAL

The following examples will help illustrate the apparent effects of some postanalytic encounters. The examples are from our personal experiences, plus observed and discussed experiences of colleagues. With one exception, these colleagues, like ourselves, were either analysts and/or psychiatrists. For simplicity, we shall refer to the two members of the interaction as analyst and patient. We do not intend a systematic data gathering of examples at this time. Nor can we prove that a particular encounter was harmful or helpful subsequently as opposed to the apparent contemporary effects. Irrespective of any major long range effects, though, we nonetheless believe it important to draw attention to the possible immediate effects. We readily acknowledge the limitations of our data. We can offer very little in the way of psychoanalytic observations.

The analysis of dreams, fantasies, and free associations under the scrutiny of an analyst would add further cogency to our opinions. Yet we believe that what data we have warrants consideration.

1. A few months after termination, a chance encounter occurred between analyst and patient at a medium-sized social gathering. This was the first postanalytic encounter. The analyst inquired in a friendly way as to how things were going. The conversation was brief and superficial. Later the patient expressed his pleasure over the encounter and told the host that it was helpful to see and talk with his analyst.

2. Two years after termination and after several brief exchanges at public gatherings, an analyst and his patient spoke at a more personal and social level. The conversation turned to a resort area in which the analyst owned a vacation home. The analyst suggested that the two families get together if the patient took a holiday in that area. The patient was very pleased by the friendly offer from his analyst. However, the patient was hesitant and uncomfortable with the idea of attempting this closeness. He recalled a time during the analysis when he was appropriately rebuffed for being intrusive. Now he had the concern that he might be intrusive again if he attempted to see his analyst. Therefore, even though he was pleased with the offer, he doubted that he would accept it.

3. Six and a half years following the end of her analysis, a mental health professional suddenly found herself working administratively side-by-side with her former analyst. His warmth, friendliness, and good humor was final confirmation that his treatment of her during the analysis was not factitious. In her own words, "Now he treats me the same way, and he doesn't have to. He really meant it, and wasn't just doing it because he was the therapist." She stated that the respect she had gained for herself during the analysis was even more heightened.

4. Seven years after termination and after several friendly encounters, an analyst and his patient were staying at the same convention site. The patient was looking forward to introducing her husband and young child to the analyst for the first time. The analyst had expressed the wish to meet them during a previous encounter. When the patient and her family greeted the analyst, the analyst was formal, aloof, and cool. Consequently, the exchange was quite brief. The patient and her family were annoyed by the analyst's inconsistent behavior. Subsequently, the analyst indicated that a less social position was taken to help the patient realize her overidealization. This encounter was placed in sharp relief by an encounter the patient had at the same site with her current analyst. She had been in this analysis for a year. This analyst initiated the greeting and was warm and cordial. The patient and her husband were especially moved and pleased by this analyst's interaction with their child. The child

had been ignored by the first analyst. If there was a need for an analytic stance in these encounters, the need would appear greater for the second analyst.

5. Eight years after termination, with no previous postanalytic encounters, a patient approached his former analyst at a meeting. During their conversation, the patient suggested that he would like to talk with the analyst to let him know what had taken place in the interval and to give the analyst the patient's evaluation of their work together. The analyst repeatedly refused with the statement that things seemed to be going well. The analyst asked questions which revealed that he had forgotten much of the patient's professional interests and current family structure, even though these were major topics of the analysis. The patient felt angry and rejected. He began having obsessional thoughts about the analyst's refusal and forgetting.

6. Twenty years after termination, an analyst encountered his patient at a meeting. The analyst told his troubles to the patient. The encounter led to the patient's remembering his anger toward the analyst, whom he had idealized since the termination.

DISCUSSION AND EPILOGUE

The examples reiterate the importance of these encounters to the patient. It therefore behooves the analyst to be well prepared and to have seriously considered his appropriate participation in encounters, whether these occur soon after termination or long afterward. Frequently, socialization was limited by the patient, but in each case the patient was pleased by the analyst's friendliness. The few examples are not statistically significant, but they do raise issues that deserve further evaluation. We believe that an encounter is never harmful or traumatic when the analyst is cordial; that, since the real relationship should predominate after termination, there is no benefit in the analyst's maintaining an analytic posture, a stance that might very well reactivate transferences and therefore be viewed as inappropriate behavior; that friendliness after analysis does not significantly interfere with future analytic work; that cordiality definitely outweighs the jolt and potential harm of unfriendliness; and that revelation of an analyst's human qualities assists, rather than hinders, the postanalytic processes.

The clinical material presented thus far may be considered superficial and anecdotal since it is a view from the outside and/or from the patient's conscious perceptions. One may well ask what was going on unconsciously. Weren't the patient's reactions and views influenced by residual transference? Similarly, weren't the analyst's reactions and views influenced by residual countertransference? Self-analysis can shed some light on these issues. However, since the capacity for self-analysis is quite variable and is always subject to and limited by resistance, the clearest illumination of the unconscious meanings of postanalytic encounters is provided by further analysis where this is possible. This applies equally for both participants. The ex-patient's returning to analysis with the same analyst could illuminate both the transference and real aspects of the previous encounter to the extent of the analyst's ability and his freedom from countertransference. Subsequent analysis with a different analyst could eliminate any blind spots the first analyst might have in relation to the encounter. Ideally, to study postanalytic encounters in depth, data about the meanings of the encounter would be derived from subsequent, independent analysis of each of the participants. We are unable to provide the ideal but we can fill in more of the picture in regard to example 4 above. We shall refer to the original analyst as Analyst A and to the current one as Analyst B:

Analyst A was consulted by the patient prior to her beginning the subsequent analysis. Analyst A had concurred with the patient's impression that more analysis was indicated and would be helpful. Analyst A, a man, had suggested that the patient see a woman analyst. Analyst A asked that the patient inform him when she resumed analysis. She did, indeed, write to him indicating that after consultation with other respected colleagues she had started analysis with Analyst B, another man. In the past, Analyst A had acknowledged receipt of written communications, but he did not do so this time. A year later, the previously described encounter occurred. Two years subsequently, Analyst A initiated a discussion with the patient about their previous encounter. Analyst A stated that he had been concerned about interfering with the subsequent analysis. He had hoped his being less social would help dissolve the remaining idealized transference. He thought the patient hadn't sufficiently analyzed her anger toward men. He hoped the anger would come out toward him and be analyzed by Analyst B. However, he discovered, through self-analysis of his countertransference, that he was angry at the patient for seeing another male analyst against his recommendation and that he now realized his unconscious anger had influenced his actions. The patient suggested that he could have told her at the time of the encounter of his concern about interfering with the analysis and his intention to be less social as a precautionary measure. He agreed that this would have been the honest thing to do and perhaps he would have done so had he been more in touch with his countertransference. The patient's analysis with Analyst B of the disruptive encounter with Analyst A revealed that the encounter activated transference residua toward Analyst A in which he was viewed as a cold, stiff, ungiving, and selfish individual. This was the predominant transference during the early phases of the first analysis and was linked to the patient's relationship with her father. The reactivated transference was analyzed and was resolved rapidly. However, the patient continued to feel stunned and puzzled, knowing that Analyst A was generally a warm, cordial person and that the way he had acted was thoroughly out of character. These concerns persisted until the discussion between Analyst A and the patient finally cleared the air and led to further meaningful discussion which produced or confirmed additional insights for each of them.

We feel this is an example of the tension that can be created unnecessarily by an analyst during an encounter. It is also a demonstration of the value of patient and analyst working together to resolve the cause of that tension. We question the usefulness of an analyst's acting in different ways postanalytically in an attempt to elicit certain reactions in ex-patients. It seems this is as inappropriate after termination as during the analysis. We wonder if this is a widespread practice.

Rangell (1966, p. 161) suggests that "new external situations challenge the analyst to achieve a continuous adaptation to the new intrapsychic needs of the . . . ex-patient." It seems reasonable that an analyst would wish to relate appropriately to an ex-patient, but it is unclear how the analyst is to accurately perceive the ex-patient's new intrapsychic needs in social or professional settings. A very perceptive and sensitive analyst may be able to gear his behavior and level of interaction to mesh with his earlier knowledge and understanding of the ex-patient. Perhaps this is ideal, but the danger is that not all analysts are that perceptive outside the psychoanalytic situation, or that they may take this as a recommendation to remain forever analytic with ex-patients. We support the position that the analyst use his previous knowledge and understanding of his ex-patient during postanalytic encounters to help the analyst avoid the two potential errors: excessive gratification and continued analytic posture.

A contributing factor to the difficulties experienced in some postanalytic encounters is that sufficient distinction has not been made between the analyst's being cordial, human, and benevolently interested as opposed to his being self-revealing, overly intimate, and excessively social. While the latter behaviors are likely to interfere with the processes of the postanalytic phase, we believe that an absence of the former behaviors will also interfere significantly.

While we are not advocating that these contacts be nurtured, we certainly do not believe that they should be avoided. In our opinion, a cordial, human response would be best whenever a natural occurrence arises. Moreover, it is our opinion that if an analyst's being friendly, courteous, and cordial can ever be harmful, it should be less so with the passage of time. Since there is the apparent danger of activating transferences which may not be adequately analyzed and the possibility of real mistreatment, little can be said in support of aloof behavior. We believe there is no benefit in acting cool toward an ex-patient who has moved to another area or who has had subsequent analysis. To act unfriendly in greeting an ex-patient is to deny that there was and is a meaningful relationship. We cannot conceive of there having been a successful analysis were this the case.

THE POSTANALYTIC PHASE

One of the unanswered questions is for how long after termination is it helpful and important for the analyst to limit his interactions with his ex-patient? To consider this important question of psychoanalytic technique, we must divide the postanalytic period into hypothetical segments. We shall call these the beginning, middle, and end of the postanalytic "phase." We believe the term *postanalytic phase* should refer specifically to that portion of the postanalytic period during which it is appropriate and important that the analyst maintain his therapeutic potential and responsibility. The postanalytic phase begins with termination, which activates a number of acute intrapsychic processes in the patient. Ideally, the transference neurosis will have been resolved prior to termination or shortly thereafter and will not be prominent. Assuming that the analysis came to a successful planned ending without a major modification of analytic technique, we would anticipate an active separation reaction. This would include mourning the loss of the real relationship, identification with the analyst, further working through of the neurotic meanings of separations and, most important, a period of integration leading to autonomy. Residual transferences, not to be confused with the transference neurosis, may be prominent or easily activated during this time. The analyst would clearly want to limit his interactions with the ex-patient during these acute processes in order not to interfere with their resolution. We believe that the length of the acute phase varies from patient to patient but that it usually ends within several months to a year after termination. Modifications of analytic technique during the termination phase would alter the posttermination events.

The middle portion of the postanalytic phase begins with the resolution of the acute posttermination processes. It continues so long as the ex-patient may appropriately return to the ex-analyst for professional help (that is, for consultations or further analysis).

The end of the postanalytic phase would occur if the ex-patient resumed analysis with his previous analyst, if either died, or if both participated in a full and intimate social relationship. The passage of time and the ex-patient's having had subsequent successful analysis with one or more subsequent analysts would lessen the first analyst's need to limit social relations or to maintain his therapeutic potential.

An important question, especially during the middle portion of the postanalytic phase, is how much socializing is possible before significantly damaging an ex-analyst's future usefulness as an analyst for his ex-patient? We believe the socialization would have to extend well beyond courtesy and cordiality. This is clearly an area for future investigation, as is the question of how long an ex-analyst should limit his socializing with his ex-patients. As previously noted, analysts' opinions vary widely as to the optimal duration of limited interaction with their ex-patients, and no formal studies have measured the duration of the acute postanalytic processes. In spite of these considerations, we believe it may be possible to answer the question satisfactorily with some ex-patients, depending upon the nature of their analyses and terminations. If termination comes about naturally at the end of a successful analysis, especially with relatively healthy patients, we believe these patients may at times be in the best position to determine the ideal duration of limited interaction with their ex-analysts. As stated above, after termination patients themselves frequently limit their socializing with their analysts. We wonder if it is the sole responsibility of the analyst to attempt to titrate the degree of socialization with every ex-patient or if this most difficult task might not gladly be relinquished to the healthy and mature ex-patient. It seems quite reasonable for these ex-patients to participate in the decision to preserve their ex-analyst's future therapeutic potential or to terminate that potential through socialization.

We would like to emphasize, then, that this can be a shared decision, and one not solely the responsibility of either the ex-patient or the analyst. Obviously, there are different varieties of neuroses and personality disorders treated by analysts. Certainly this will influence the type of postanalytic phase, and each analyst must be aware of such influences. While there is no prescription for the analyst's postanalytic behavior, it can be safely offered that the analyst who is thoughtfully friendly and guided by his knowledge of the ex-patient would be most helpful. This balance between the ex-patient's evaluation and the analyst's judgment could provide a springboard for a healthy encounter.

UNRECOGNIZED COUNTERTRANSFERENCE RESIDUA

"With due respect for the necessary strictest handling and interpretation of the transference," writes Anna Freud (1954), "I feel still that we should leave room somewhere for the realization that analyst and patient are also two real people, of equal status, in a real personal relationship to each other. I wonder whether our—at times complete—neglect of this side of the matter is not responsible for some of the hostile reactions which we get from our patients and which we are apt to ascribe to 'true transference' only" (pp. 618-619). This perception is especially applicable to the postanalytic encounter.

Clearly there are many possible explanations for the remaining aloofness of the analyst. Among these are: (a) unpreparedness, being taken by surprise; (b) anxiety over encountering the former patient outside the analyst's office; (c) countertransference residua; (d) perpetuation of the formerly unchallenged postanalytic position—that is, the belief in the maintenance of the analytic frame, to the greatest extent possible, even after analysis; and (e) lack of appreciation of the potentially constructive value of social interaction between analyst and former patient.

Countertransference residua are the counterpoint to transference residua. While the former analysand expects to find someone who cares, it might be necessary for some analysts to defend themselves against the hurt of caring feelings for someone they once shared a very special, intimate relationship with but who is no longer available.

Similarly, old hate feelings that the analyst once harbored during the analysis, if not successfully dealt with, could reemerge within the unsuspecting analyst when he is suddenly confronted with the return of a former patient. Needless to say, the countertransference possibilities are myriad and beyond the scope of this paper.

We are most concerned about the stereotype of the analyst who rigidly adheres to an analytic posture with his ex-patients long after termination. In our view this is inappropriate. It deprives the ex-patient and the analyst of feeling the satisfaction of a very special relationship serendipitously if evanescently revived. We hope that this paper will lead to diminished apprehension on the part of the analyst in regard to being himself and to the elimination of an automatic practice of postanalytic aloofness.

Finally, the difference between the analysis with the analyst who rigidly sustains his analytic stance at all times and the one who responds humanly, both during analysis and after, may well correspond to the difference between the patient who has emerged from analysis in a healthier condition versus the one who has added the richest possible experience to his life. This contrast is considerable.

REFERENCES

Balkoura, A. (1974). Panel report: the fate of the transference neurosis after analysis. *Journal of the American Psychoanalytic Association* 22:895-903.

Buxbaum, E. (1950). Technique of terminating analysis. *International Journal of Psycho-Analysis* 31:184–190.

Deutsch, H. (1959). Psychoanalytic therapy in the light of follow-up. *Journal of the American Psychoanalytic Association* 7:445–458.

Fairbairn, W. (1957). Freud, the psychoanalytic method and mental health. *British Journal of Medical Psychology* 30:53–62.

Firestein, S. (1969). Panel report: problems of termination of the analysis of adults. *Journal of the American Psychoanalytic Association* 17:222–237.

Freud, A. (1954). The widening scope of indications for psychoanalysis: discussion. *Journal of the American Psychoanalytic Association* 2:607–620.

Freud, S. (1900). Letter #133. In *The Origins of Psychoanalysis*, ed. M. Bonaparte, A. Freud and E. Kris, pp. 316–317, New York: Basic Books, 1954.

—— (1927). *Psychoanalysis and Faith: The Letters of Sigmund Freud and Oskar Pfister*, ed. H. Meng and E. Freud, pp. 112–113. New York: Basic Books 1963.

—— (1937). Analysis terminable and interminable. *Standard Edition* 23:216–253.

Greenson, R. (1967). *The Technique and Practice of Psychoanalysis*. New York: International Universities Press.

—— (1971). The "real" relationship between the patient and the psychoanalyst. In *The Unconscious Today*, ed. M. Kanzer, pp. 213–232. New York: International Universities Press.

Hurn, H. (1973). Panel report: on the fate of transference after the termination of analysis. *Journal of the American Psychoanalytic Association* 21:182–192.

Langs, R. (1976). *The Bipersonal Field*. New York: Jason Aronson.

Pfeffer, A. (1959). A procedure for evaluating the results of psychoanalysis: A preliminary report. *Journal of the American Psychoanalytic Association* 7:418–444.

—— (1961). Follow-up study of a satisfactory analysis. *Journal of the American Psychoanalytic Association* 9:698–718.

—— (1963). The meaning of the analyst after analysis. *Journal of the American Psychoanalytic Association* 11:229–244.

Rangell, L. (1966). An overview of the ending of an analysis. In *Psychoanalysis in the Americas*, ed. R. Litman, pp. 141–165. New York: International Universities Press.

Reich, A. (1950). On the termination of analysis. *International Journal of Psycho-Analysis* 31:179–183.

Weigert, E. (1952). Contribution to the problem of terminating analyses. *Psychoanalytic Quarterly* 21:465–480.

Some Notes on the Postanalytic Phase

LEO RANGELL, M.D.

A discussion of "Postanalytic Encounters," by Daniel Borenstein, M.D., and Robert Fintzy, M.D. Borenstein and Fintzy's paper deals with a phase of treatment which continues after the analysis and which has been underplayed in the literature. Only one specific postanalytic situation is gone into here, adventitious "encounters" between the former patient and the analyst. The authors emphasize especially an inappropriate continuation of "the analytic attitude" under these conditions and describe the detrimental effects on the patient. I have pointed out previously (1966) that this is only one of two polar errors, the other being a sudden excessive and unexpected intimacy by the analyst with its own train of attendant complications. The reasons underlying both extreme attitudes are discussed. The points made by Borenstein and Fintzy are well taken, although the clinical data and evidence upon which they rest appear limited in scope and depth. The valid lessons and admonitions made by the authors can be expanded and deepened from more cogent and penetrating clinical material. Analytic clinicians have such opportunities to encompass these and other experiences subsequent to the original analysis during postanalytic periods of analysis or psychotherapy.

Drs. Borenstein and Fintzy address themselves in this paper to a subject which has been barely attended to in the psychoanalytic literature. This is mainly because postanalytic experiences in general have not been pinpointed for specific study in relation to the analysis that has taken place and been terminated. Since most writers on the analytic process agree that termination is to a great extent an arbitrary event and that a therapeutic process is set in motion by an analysis which continues for an indefinite time after the analysis is officially over, the neglect of this period and lack of interest in more precise studies of what takes place during it have been conspicuous by their absence. It is for this reason that I suggested in my 1966 paper, as the authors note, that a specific postanalytic phase be designated as still part of the therapeutic process.

The length of this period is indeterminate. While technically it might be considered to go on for life, this is an academic and inaccurate appraisal. Empirically, the duration of a process that can still be called therapeutic varies considerably. In some ex-patients it is a brief and evanescent period, at least consciously and preconsciously. Unconsciously, the entire analysis in many of these cases has been rapidly repressed along with a re-repression of the material that was sought for during the analysis and only partly recovered.

In other examples—not at all rare—a postanalytic therapeutic activity continues for a long and fruitful period afterwards for up to years in duration. Perhaps on an average, a self-conscious self-analysis is operative after termination for a few months or a few years and then recedes into an unconscious process that becomes part of the postanalytic characterologic equipment. Where an analysis has succeeded and structural change taken place, a fortuitous result is an ego-syntonic "analytic" character trait in the analyzed personality of the former analysand.

Drs. Borenstein and Fintzy concentrate especially on one particular type of incident that takes place in postanalytic life, adventitious "encounters" between former analyst and ex-patient. The authors' emphasis is not so much to extract from these what may be of significance to the lingering analytic process still going on between them, but the more direct and immediate effects of such encounters on the affects and state of well-being of the patient. From a number of examples cited and the experiences derived from these, they aim to prescribe the type of attitude to be recommended for the previous analyst under such conditions. (The contributions and variety of constellations emanating from the former patient in these encounters are made less explicit.) The main thrust of the recommendations of these authors is that the former analyst needs to bear in mind the danger of maintaining the "analytic attitude" inappropriately in postanalytic social situations and the propensity of the ex-patient to interpret this as a rejection which can result in unhappiness or regression.

Since this is a discussion paper, I must select from a multitude of thoughts and a spectrum of experiences. On the subject of encounters of the type described, I have written previously of two possible errors in opposite directions. One is maintenance of the analytic attitude at a grossly inappropriate time and place and the untoward consequences of this. But there is equally the other, the opposite type of behavior, a premature and excessive display of intimacy by the analyst, from which other types of anxiety and psychopathology ensue. To the patient hitherto accustomed to quite an opposite stance, this can be as equally unnerving as the opposite type of behavior and can lead to a disequilibrium with a variety of possible outcomes.

Either type of excess can be prompted in the analyst for a variety of reasons, conscious and unconscious. These range from conscious attempts on the part of the analyst to execute his theoretical concept of what is optimum or necessary behavior under these conditions; to unconscious motivations related to countertransference, either lingering from the past and reawakened by the present situation or new types of countertransference specifically stimulated by this new type of encounter; to these attitudes being representative not of the analyst's theoretical persuasions or technical efforts but of his now-released "real" personality. The analyst may himself be inhibited or forward in social situations, the new encounter bringing out attitudes not related to the patient but to himself.

Actually what is called for is not a studied "attitude" of any kind, a careful dosing of conversation either in amount or in type, but a "naturalness" of interchange dictated by the occasion. In fact, and this always comes as a surprise to many on both sides of the couch, such a "natural" attitude should have occurred all along and been mixed with the type of stance also required for the conduct of an analysis. A "natural" human interest in the patient and a scientific investigative attitude fused and blended together comprise "the analytic attitude" in the face and manner of the analyst toward his patient. This "naturalness" on the part of the analyst, in practice usually misunderstood, obscured, or distorted, has been included in writings on technique from Otto Fenichel's monograph on the subject in 1941 to a recent paper by Lipton (1977) that cites its origin in Freud's attitude toward his clinical cases from the beginning (Freud 1909). It is also true, as Lipton says, that this aspect of the analyst's technical approach to his patient is not generally appreciated or applied in psychoanalytic practice and glossed over or underemphasized in writings on technique.

To the extent that a change in attitude is appropriate to the new postanalytic relationship and situation, this should actually have been prepared for during the termination phase, both by action and by discussion and interpretation. Again a "natural" transition from terminal to postanalytic phase is what the analyst should have offered and made possible. The meaning and understanding of the final separation to come, and its eventual experience in mastery and in fact, is a final stage of growth in the progression of the treatment and is often a crucial period of consolidation of previous gains. I would venture the opinion that analysts who err in one direction or the other in these postanalytic encounters behaved similarly during the analyses and did so to the end. When, in the examples described by Drs. Borenstein and Fintzy, excessively rigid, controlled, or seemingly "cold" attitudes were assumed (these, as I said,

may not have been coldness at all but the adoption of the analyst's concept
of the necessary attitude even if this actually stifles rather than enhances
further growth and progress), this same stiff posture was probably
present to the detriment of a natural and productive exchange during the
years of analysis as well. The same would go for the opposite error: the
analyst who is forward in the later encounter was probably intrusive in
the analysis.

My main criticism of the paper concerns what I consider the casualness
and superficiality of the "clinical data" offered. To their credit, the authors
are aware of this limitation of their material; they present their data,
nevertheless, because it is all they have available to make and confirm
their points. The transmittal of a few conscious revelations of their
feelings by ex-analysands, presumably mostly candidates in training, to
peer colleagues investigating this subject is hardly in the category of
"analytic" clinical material. In addition to the fact that this involves only
conscious impressions, its completeness or scope must be questioned even
at that level. The nature of the "material" cited by the authors is little
more than one gets in social exchanges and has almost the same built-in
narrowness and restrictions. From having had personal access from other
sources and vantage points to one or two of the clinical vignettes given by
the authors I am specifically aware of the limitations of the conclusions to
be drawn.

Nevertheless, their intentions have merit, and the earnestness of the
writers in making their points is apparent throughout. Their observations and admonitions are neither incorrect nor valueless. More detailed
and penetrating follow-up studies of postanalytic states (a few such
studies are referred to by the authors) generally confirm their conclusions. While these studies do not center specifically on encounters of
patients with their former analysts, such subsequent experiences are not
rare or uncommon with clinical psychoanalysts after years of practice. My
views and responses to this specific subject come from a variety of such
personal experiences. And to arrive at a deeper understanding of the
dynamics set off by such encounters, I can draw upon postanalytic
therapeutic hours, usually a cluster of such follow-up hours, which in
many instances include analytic work on the effects of such encounters as
revealed in free-associations. This is the only way in which conclusions or
conjectures about the effects of such meetings can be validated with any
sense of analytic value.

During such postanalytic hours of further analytic work, one can see
the same spectrum of sequelae being aroused by such encounters as can
happen during the terminal phase of analysis itself, a spike increase of
transference reactions (not necessarily to the point again of a trans-

ference neurosis), and an actual or barely visible return of symptoms or of the types of anxieties which originally caused the symptoms. Often one also sees evidence of a self-analytic process which to a greater or lesser degree curtailed these reactions and turned them back. At times there was the failure of the latter, which led to the seeking of the present hours of further consultation. Depending on how the analyst behaved during the encounters under study—and this does not mean restriction to the neutral attitude that obtained during the analysis—the reactions can still be constructively recognized for their transference nature. If the analyst induced some negative reaction as the result of his own inappropriate attitude, a successful previous analysis would enable the patient to experience and evaluate this properly as well.

Analysis of such mutual and reciprocal influences can be accomplished during such postanalytic sessions with satisfaction to both participants and a firm cementing of a continuing beneficial postanalytic therapeutic alliance (Zetzel 1956). It is my experience that a relationship that enables the patient to benefit from postanalytic periods of work of short duration represents one of the most durable rewards of a successfully terminated analysis, as pointed out by Freud (1937) and later again by Zetzel (1966). Such a possibility of further therapy, which can go on for years, is compatible, in my opinion, with a more complete ongoing relationship between the patient and the ex-analyst appropriate to the specific conditions after the analysis. While the analyst may always retain a special place in the psychic gestalt of the analysand, it is a test of the efficacy of the analytic work achieved and of the flexibility and reality-testing of both participants to be able to add a dual and expanded reciprocity over and around the original one.

There are also opposite experiences to postanalytic encounters, i.e., postanalytic avoidances. One often comes to be aware that this is the case when chance contacts between ex-patient and analyst produce uneasiness and discomfort in one or the other or both. The causes are myriad and individual, usually indicative of an incompleted or aborted or negatively ended previous analysis. Sometimes this has been unconscious and not brought out before and becomes evident only by the nature of these postanalytic encounters. The reasons run the gamut from real to transference factors, and the prescriptions for reparations vary accordingly. To change these reactions, the simple facing and correcting of misunderstandings, reanalysis or further partial analysis with the same or another analyst are all possible remedies. Such remedial procedures, however, are not always possible.

Drs. Borenstein and Fintzy point to an important area of continuing "clinical" experiences that can go on for years and that are worth being aware of and being ready for.

REFERENCES

Fenichel, O. (1941). *Problems of Psychoanalytic Technique.* Albany, N.Y.: Psychoanalytic Quarterly.

Freud, S. (1909). Notes upon a case of obsessional neurosis. *Standard Edition* 10:153–319.

——— (1937). Analysis terminable and interminable. *Standard Edition* 23:216–253.

Lipton, S. (1977). The advantages of Freud's technique as shown in his analysis of the Rat Man. *International Journal of Psycho-Analysis* 58:255–273.

Pfeffer, A. (1959). A procedure for evaluating the results of psychoanalysis: a preliminary report. *Journal of the American Psychoanalytic Association* 7:418–444.

——— (1961). Follow-up study of a satisfactory analysis. *Journal of the American Psychoanalytic Association* 9:698–718.

——— (1963). The meaning of the analyst after analysis. *Journal of the American Psychoanalytic Association* 11:229–244.

Rangell, L. (1966). An overview of the ending of an analysis. In *Psychoanalysis in the Americas*, ed. R. Litman, pp. 141–165. New York: International Universities Press.

Zetzel, E. (1956). Current concepts of transference. *International Journal of Psycho-Analysis* 37:369–376.

——— (1966). The analytic situation. In *Psychoanalysis in the Americas*, ed. R. Litman, pp. 86–106. New York: International Universities Press.

The Use of Psychoanalytic Concepts in Crisis Intervention

ROBERT A. GLICK, M.D.
ARTHUR T. MEYERSON, M.D.

Crises have a dynamic structure. Repressed neurotic conflicts and defects in ego organization determine vulnerability to specific stresses. Selection of focus in crisis intervention follows from the recognition of those rigid defensive patterns and adaptive incapacities which have either partially failed or been overwhelmed by the current stress. Aiming at the old problem in the new situation allows crisis work to go beyond symptom relief to improved conflict resolution and coping abilities. Therapeutic activity, rather than passivity, is the hallmark of crisis intervention and involves suggestion, abreaction, manipulation, clarification, and dynamic interpretation. Individuals in crisis are characteristically in a partially regressed state of transference readiness and availability, particularly as this involves intensified dependency wishes. Management of the transference requires recognition of negative, as well as positive, responses and the limitation of further regression that might lead to continual adaptive failure. A variety of specific countertransference responses are commonly evoked in crisis work. These must be recognized for effective treatment to proceed.

The need to develop effective brief forms of treatment has been stressed by many psychoanalytic writers. Efforts to apply psychoanalytic understanding to brief therapy has produced an important and growing body of literature (see Aldrich 1968, Alexander 1965, Balint et al. 1972, Barten 1971, Bellak and Small 1965, Frank 1959, Furst 1938, Gillman 1965, Glick 1976, Malan 1963, 1976, Mann 1973, Rado 1965, Sarvis, Dewees, and Johnson 1959, Semrad 1954, Semrad, Binstock and White 1966, Sifneos 1960, 1972, Small 1971, Sterba 1951, Stone 1951, Strupp 1969, and Wolberg 1965).

These authors have largely centered their efforts on the application of psychodynamic principles to brief therapy rather than to crisis intervention or resolution. Patients suitable for brief therapy, like those suitable for more longterm work are mainly elective, motivated by the ego-alien, painful quality of their symptoms, character traits, or situations. They generally elect to apply to a routine clinic setting or to a private therapist for relief of their symptoms. The choice of brief or time-limited, rather than prolonged therapy, may be the result of the patient's desire for quick relief, financial considerations, the therapist's bias, or a belief that this patient's major presenting difficulties arise from a singular conflict that can be resolved within a time-limited framework.

The efforts of community mental health programs and general hospital emergency and walk-in-clinics to bring effective treatment to large numbers of people in acute or crisis situations have highlighted the need for crisis-oriented therapies, and brought workers with diverse training into the crisis setting (Caplan 1961, Rosenthal 1965). These programs have stimulated questions about the applicability of traditional psychotherapeutic approaches (including brief, focal psychotherapy) to different social, racial, and economic groups, and to the crisis situation.

This paper focuses on the application of psychoanalytic principles to work with patients presenting with those acute, overwhelming states generally termed crisis or emergency psychiatric situations. The authors' experience as psychoanalysts who direct general hospital psychiatric emergency services has led to a developing conviction of the value of applying and modifying psychoanalytic concepts in doing such work. This paper is an attempt to propound a psychoanalytic view of crises and to offer examples of crisis situations in which a dynamic approach has proven efficacious in the treatment of acutely disturbed patients.

CRISIS DEFINITION

There are inevitable life crises in which age, loss, external events, and change demand efforts to adapt and master. Most individuals live through such experiences without coming to our attention. Those who do represent some partial failure of coping or insufficiency of mastery.

Emotional crises requiring professional intervention therefore can not be fully understood by a mechanistic model in which an external event overwhelms a passive individual. All individuals have a vulnerability to crisis (or are crisis prone) based on the adequacy of the resolution of previous neurotic conflicts and the extent of ego defects. A crisis has a dynamic structure in which a precipitating stress calls upon the individual's repertoire of personality traits, characterological defenses, adaptive capacities, and unconscious conflicts (Harris, Kalish, and Freeman 1963). As Fenichel (1945, p. 467) avers, "Conflicts arise when new experiences occur that are connected with what had previously been repressed."

Mann (1973, p. 32) states, "A crisis is an exacerbation of a lifelong conflict situation that may find what seems to be different avenues of discharge at different times." Crisis theory is an application of Waelder's "principle of multiple function" (1936) by which the ego is viewed as constantly attempting to deal with the conflictual demands of instinct, superego, ego ideal, and reality. Reality can be an unforseen accident, as studied by Lindemann (1944) at the time of the Coconut Grove fire, or an unpredictable unfolding of an endogenous mental disorder, and as such stir up repressed conflicts and tax self-observing and coping capacities.

By viewing the presentation of an individual in crisis as an opportunity to observe a cross section of important character patterns that contribute and lead to the crisis situation, crisis interventions can offer possibilities for increased mastery over previously repressed conflicts. Improved adaptive capacity can result when defensive patterns shift from rigid and immature to more flexible and mature. This transcends the goal of symptom relief.

Case 1

A thirty-two-year-old housewife and mother of three was seen after a superficial but dramatic suicide gesture. Her husband had said that he was unhappy in the marriage and considering divorce. No psychiatric intervention had been sought after a similar episode eighteen months before.

Her initial presentation to the psychiatric resident was of a hopeless, helpless victim of anticipated abandonment. She felt overwhelmed and unable to recognize viable alternatives to suicide. Her mother was a quiet, passive woman dominated by her controlling and cold husband. The patient's husband, who was much like her father, had represented an escape from the home, and a chance to be loved and valued by a man.

Both initially and in the second session, the patient was unaware of any anger at her husband whom she simply saw as necessary for her survival. It was clear, however, that she had been repeatedly passively provocative to him when he was indifferent to her needs, to the point at times of nearly getting him to hit her.

Supervisory discussion of this case at this point revealed that the resident saw this woman as the victim of a cold rejecting man and as helpless to do anything about her situation. The resident candidly acknowledged that he, himself, felt angry at the husband for "being such a bastard." This was the opportunity to point out that he was experiencing the anger that the patient could not allow herself to experience directly and that prompted her defensive helplessness and passivity.

Armed with this understanding, the resident explored with the patient her problems in recognizing and expressing anger at the husband. He began to appreciate the repetitive nature of the pattern both with her husband and in the past with her father, on whom she felt profoundly dependent as well. The crisis decompressed as crisis treatment continued.

After several sessions, this woman felt less helpless and more assertive with her husband. The marriage, while far from satisfactory, was no longer crisis ridden, and they agreed to enter marital therapy.

Emergency rooms, crisis centers and police stations are often the setting for the assessment of such patients presenting as victims of psychological or physical punishment. A mechanistic or the external view of crisis that accepts the apparent victimization of the patient, can lead to ineffective treatment. Patients like the woman above may create the crisis as a defense triggered by unacceptable hostile impulses.

An adequate definition of the crisis clearly demands more than an appreciation of the present reality. Within the here-and-now structure of the crisis are the vulnerabilities to stress dictated by past neurotic conflicts, by limitations and defects in ego function, and by chronic psychopathological mechanisms. The selection of focus in crisis intervention evolves rapidly from the therapist's assessment of the present stress. The treatment then is directed to that which has failed in the adaptive capacity of the patient or that which has become reinvolved.

TECHNICAL AND THERAPEUTIC ACTIVITIES

Therapist activity is crucial to effective crisis intervention. This activist role can be contrasted with a caricature of the passive psychoanalyst who says little, asks few questions, and never gives direction or advice about the present reality of the patient's life. It seems valuable to clarify those elements essential to the activity of the therapist in crisis work. In Bibring's article (1954) on psychoanalysis and the dynamic psychotherapies he enumerates the technical principles of treatment and their curative effect. Bibring outlines the technical procedures used by the therapist as: (1) suggestion, (2) abreaction, (3) manipulation, (4) clarification, and (5) interpretation. We shall discuss them in relation to crisis treatment rather than psychoanalytic treatment.

Suggestion is the attempt to induce beliefs in the patient, to have him adopt ideas or attitudes different from his present ones. The helplessness, paralysis and fear experienced by a crisis patient can be modified by specific inquiry into his thoughts, feelings, and behavior.

In the housewife's treatment, the therapist translated for her the suicide gesture and passivity into her inability to openly express her anger with her husband; he repeatedly suggested that she was not as helpless as she felt and that talking about her feelings about her husband and not acting on them in a provocative manner would help resolve her difficulties. Here the patient was being told that her mechanistic view of herself as a passive victim was insufficient and maladaptive, that she was actively attempting to deal with inner emotional conflict which, while beyond her awareness, was nevertheless affecting her behavior and her husband. With such crisis-prone, passive, dependent individuals, the therapist is also suggesting that anxiety will be more tolerable, and helplessness will diminish as the underlying problems become clearer.

With patients who suffer with poor reality testing, psychotic symptoms, the therapist suggests the reassuring difference between the patient's chaotic experience and reality as understood by the therapist.

Case 2

A nineteen-year-old college student was seen after several nights of sleeplessness, agitation mounting to near panic, and feelings that other students were talking about him, looking at him strangely, and thinking "he was queer." He had recently been rebuffed by a girl and was also in danger of failing his exams. He described to the psychiatrist that his life had a "nightmarish" quality, that he felt sick and weak, and that certain changes were occurring in his body. He had vague thoughts of throwing himself in front of a subway. In the first session, the psychiatrist told him that he was in a state of severe emotional turmoil which was producing disorders of perception, and that this aggravated his concerns about his sense of adequacy as a man and as a student.

The patient felt less agitated, cried, and revealed that he felt he was losing his mind and that he wanted help. Treatment was arranged.

Suggestion, however, can be mistaken for premature advice. A full understanding of the crisis is needed before effective direction can be given.

Case 3

A young woman was seen in consultation after an acute anxiety attack which followed her acceptance of her boyfriend's proposal. After calming down and discussing her situation, she was advised to reconsider the marriage. She left perplexed and did not return for further consultation. A recurrence of the anxiety attack led to consultation with a second therapist who learned that considerable guilt over a prior affair had evoked her anxiety. This issue was then explored in subsequent crisis therapy.

Abreaction, emotional discharge producing a relief of acute tension, was one of the earliest of curative processes noted by Freud (1895) in his work with hysterics. It was his view at the time that the emergence of "strangulated affect" into consciousness in association with unacceptable ideas would be the basis for the resolution of hysterical reactions. While much has been modified in the understanding of hysterical disorders, abreaction is still seen as a treatment of choice in certain traumatic reactions. It is particularly relevant in community mental health work in urban centers. Postrape and postmugging victims may benefit from an abreactive approach which facilitates early working through of the experience to decrease posttraumatic residual impairment.

Probably the most common example of abreaction seen in crisis and emergency psychiatric work is with acute grief reactions. Here an individual has suffered a loss (not necessarily of another person) and needs the opportunity to experience the intense pain and/or rage. This can be seen where grieving has been delayed or deflected in some fashion.

Case 4

A fifty-seven-year-old woman has lost her husband three months prior to consultation. She had been "quite strong" after his death, and able to cope with the loss. Consultation was prompted by headaches, uneasiness, vague chest pains, and an anxious sense of "losing my mind." After the initial description of her complaints and of her idealized husband, she was asked what it was like to be alone. She immediately burst into tears, and painfully expressed how guilty she felt because she was so angry at her husband for leaving her. The therapist's question gave her permission and opportunity to express what had been an unacceptable feeling, which had led to her symptoms.

In crisis work, Bibring (1954, p. 750) feels that "emotional expression of painful tendencies when met with sympathy results in a gratifying feeling of being accepted and understood." He goes on to say this implies "the gratification of certain neurotic needs." This latter question will be dealt with in the discussion of transference. Abreaction offers an early experience of symptom relief in crisis work. The therapist actively encourages and facilitates this through empathic exploration of the painful traumatic issues in the present crisis.

Manipulation is a more complex notion. It connotes, for many, coercion, and is therefore insufficiently appreciated as an essential part of therapist activity in crisis work. Quite simplistically, manipulation means getting the patient to act in a way different from his own expected behavior. Frequently, for example, crisis patients experience tremendous pressure to act to relieve stress or to resolve the crisis. Some decision seems imperative: to leave or to stay, to tell or not to tell. Since he is temporarily overwhelmed by conflict, the patient's capacity for assessing choices is compromised. In such a situation the manipulative technique necessary before any further exploration is possible involves relieving the patient of the burden of any action. He must be told that no decision need or can be made at this time. The patient must see that he can not expect decision of himself while in crisis. The task of the crisis treatment will be to understand the nature of his conflict and thereby resolve it. This technical intervention aims at neutralizing obstacles both to understanding and improved adjustment.

Other modes of manipulation may involve instructing the patient as to why he may be avoiding issues or why it may be valuable for him to act in a different way—for example, the acutely phobic patient whose anxiety prevents him from entering feared situations. The therapist must direct the patient to attempt to face the anxiety producing situation. In Bibring's terms we are not dealing with manipulating the environment to lessen stress, as would be seen in a more mechanistic, extrapsychic view of crisis, but rather helping the patient to have a different experience.

The patient in case 1 was encouraged to see that her suicidal behavior was an experience of an unrecognized emotional conflict—this conflict centering around rage at insufficient caring and helplessness as a mode of defense. The therapist attempted to have her experience her anger at her husband directly, and not to indulge in her crisis-generating provocation.

The patient who says that he can't because they will be too angry or they will never speak to him again can be manipulated (for example with advice to act in an adaptive fashion) so that he is confronted with his prior infantile self-representation. What is being considered is a form of experiential learning.

Strupp (1969) has discussed the role of learning in psychotherapy. Occurring in relationship to the therapist, experiential learning (as opposed to cognitive learning) comes from the mastery experiences in treatment. Such mastery experiences both of such painful affect states as anxiety and of external stresses as loss or disappointment, can be viewed as reinforcing adaptive adult behavior and diminishing the limitations and destructive quality of infantile maladaptive behavior.

We believe that mastery experiences resulting from therapeutic manipulation can be, in and of themselves, sufficient for crisis resolution and ego growth, especially for patients with more immature, inadequate character structure who are not psychologically minded or self-reflective. However, with patients more capable of, and motivated for, insight, subsequent interpretation of the manipulative intervention is necessary to modify any magical view of the therapist.

Case 5

A man was seen in crisis consultation because he was very upset over his wife's request for a divorce. He did not want to lose her and would not get a lawyer. He had decided instead to let her lawyer handle both sides of the matter. After his initial agitation subsided, he was told by the therapist that he must get a lawyer to protect his own interests. He followed the advice; but it emerged in subsequent sessions, in conjuction with a reported dream, that he unconsciously equated a lawyer with a sadistic attacker. He preferred to be the victim to avoid the guilt of his own sadistic impulses. Further understanding of this distortion and the meaning of the therapist's advice were pursued in subsequent treatment sessions.

Clarification, Bibring's fourth therapeutic operation, requires that the therapist organize and reflect back to the patient a clearer, less distorted picture of the confusing array of thoughts, feelings, and behavior that the patient experiences in crisis. Since the self-observing capacities of the ego are compromised during the crisis, the therapist offers himself as an adjunct to those ego functions in the patient and as an object for identification.

Clarifications are accomplished through questions that highlight the difference between the patient's experience and an objective view and through statements to the patient that demonstrate the distortions. Dynamically, it is conscious, and some preconscious, material that is clarified. In the example of the delayed grief response (case 4), the therapist pointed out to the patient that her symptoms, her need to be strong, and the growing awareness of her loneliness were interrelated as a potentially understandable problem in mourning for her deceased husband. With the college student (case 2), his nightmare was translated into an emotional decompensation precipitated by failures that produced profound alterations in self-esteem and emotional regulation. Clarifications draw on the therapeutic effects of suggestion, abreaction, and manipulation to create for the patient a sense of being understood and accepted. Rapport, thus established, fosters further work in crisis resolution and aids the patient in his efforts to adopt the therapist's views of the crisis.

Interpretations, by contrast, are interventions which attempt to bring into conscious awareness the unconscious structure of the crisis in terms of impulses and motives, fears and inhibitions, defenses and compromise formations. The goal is to demonstrate to the patient the underlying conflict which led to his present distress. Interpretations are generally of two types: dynamic and genetic: dynamic, based on current unconscious fantasies and conflicts; genetic, drawing on infantile and childhood historical material which attempts to link current maladaptation with unresolved earlier conflicts. In psychoanalytic treatment, genetic interpretations and genetic reconstructions, transference patterns and childhood memories are the bulwark of the technique, slowly leading to insight into, and modification of, character structure. In crisis treatment interpretations are almost always of a dynamic type, in part because of the scarcity of childhood material available during crisis intervention, and in part because of the involvement of the patient in current problems. As Alexander (1965, p. 93) states, "The understanding of the past should always be subordinated to the problems of the present." Stone (1951) emphasizes this in his discussion of the principles of brief treatment when he urges that the focus of interpretaton be kept on immediate reality and that the therapist avoid challenging useful adaptive capacities or heightening peripheral conflicts.

Offering the patient a concise, clear, dynamic interpretation of his present crisis is almost always helpful. Our experience has lead us to believe that such an intervention, formulated in language meaningful to the patient and involving his current reality, increases rapport, provides reassurance, and allows the patient to begin to think about his problems in new, less chaotic, more understandable terms.

Technically, dynamic interpretations in order to be therapeutically effective require a great deal of the therapist: an empathic response to the patient, a clear understanding of the structure of conflict underlying the crisis, tact, and skillful timing. A common error in this work is to assume that through interpretation of unconscious processes the patient will integrate the material, give up his symptoms, and resolve the crisis. A successful interpretation, in crisis work as in psychoanalysis, furthers the work, not ends it.

Case 6

A young woman librarian discovered that she was pregnant. She felt overwhelmed by anxiety and indecision about an abortion and came for crisis consultation. After presenting all of her rational, liberated views about abortion, she remained quite upset. She described how, in the relationship with her boyfriend, she was "victimized" by his anger and insensitivity yet could not get angry with him nor leave him. She told of a recent dream in which she saw a family in the park, and the father was carrying a little girl.

After gathering more information about the circumstances of the pregnancy, the history of the relationship, and background material about the young woman, the therapist interpreted to the patient that she unconsciously wished to be treated like her boyfriend's little girl, that her "accidental" pregnancy involved her wish to have a child and to be a child, and further that her indecision about an abortion (which indeed seemed like a realistic decision) reflected her own fear of destructiveness and guilt.

The patient returned having thought a great deal about the therapist's interpretation and recognized some other elements in her life which seemed to corroborate it. After further discussion she decided to have the abortion and felt acutely relieved. She then went on to discuss her need to understand more about this pattern in her life.

The more psychologically minded and motivated the patient, the more interpretation of unconscious process leads to favorable outcome. In this we are in agreement with Malan (1967). With more concretely organized and less insightful patients, treatment relies more heavily on manipulative and directive approaches.

THE ROLE OF TRANSFERENCE

What is it that gives these therapeutic operations their power? The transference availability and readiness of the patient in a crisis situation is the vital component that makes the therapist's activity therapeutically "curative" (Bibring 1954). Recognizing and understanding the structure and power of transference responses are therefore essential in guiding the therapist's activity. .

The concept of transference is a crucial contribution from psychoanalytic clinical theory to all dynamic therapies and quite specifically to the understanding and effectiveness of crisis intervention. As defined in the *Glossary of Psychoanalytic Terms and Concepts* (Moore and Fine 1968), "Transference is the displacement of patterns of feelings and behavior originally experienced with significant figures of one's childhood to individuals in one's current relationships. This unconscious process thus brings about a repetition not consciously perceived of attitudes, fantasies and emotions of love, hate and anger, etc., under many different circumstances." Transference, then, is a universal characteristic of all interpersonal relationships, not strictly limited to psychoanalysis or psychotherapy.

In psychoanalysis, transference phenomena are facilitated and intensified for the purpose of generating a transference neurosis. Here the patient's pathological behavior becomes focused and organized around his relationship with the analyst, thereby "replacing his ordinary neurosis by a transference neurosis of which he can be cured by the therapeutic work" (Freud 1914, p. 154). The cure of the "artificial illness" comes through interpretation and working through. Freud's assessment of the therapeutic importance of transference and the recognition of its universality apply to crisis intervention. "In the hands of the physician it (the transference) becomes the most powerful therapeutic instrument and it plays a part scarcely overestimated in the dynamics of the process of cure" (Freud 1919, p. 247).

An individual in crisis has regressed in his coping capacities and ego adaptation to an earlier more childlike mode in which he feels overwhelmed and helpless. He has positive wishes for help from the therapist which involve intense infantile dependent strivings and the correlated idealization of powerful parental figures. This transference readiness is apparent in the vast majority of crisis patients.

Case 7

A twenty-three-year-old female, medical student presented with complaints of intense and overwhelming anxiety. She had suffered from such anxiety attacks with palpitations, cold sweats, and nausea for six years, and these were usually associated with her menstrual flow. This attack was different in that she had experienced an overwhelming desire to "punish" herself and to "relieve the anxiety" by "digging a sharp pencil into my face," which she had done. The precipitating event appeared to be her impending marriage to a medical student who had recently begun his ward work and was therefore far less available to her than he had been for the six or seven years of their courtship.

An immediate and striking aspect of this young woman's presenting picture was the seductive and dramatic nature with which she told her story and related to the crisis worker. She was flirtatious, crossing and recrossing her legs, patting her hair, smiling seductively and reacting to the worker's questions and comments with a childlike admiration and receptivity. She described herself as "frightened of men," obsessional, and skeptical and her style of dress was seductive. The therapist thought that her hysterical mode of relating to him might not be typical for her. This proved to be the case. Not only was she different than she had been in the past, her seductive behavior appeared only with the worker, not with others in her life. The pressure of the impending marriage and the loss of contact with the fiancé appeared to have so stimulated the patient's latent fantasies of being a "femme fatale, really promiscuous," that anxiety and guilt, usually well controlled, now overwhelmed her. The seductive, sexualized transference allowed for an early and clear understanding of the nature of the conflict.

Alexander (1965, p. 97) cautions that "the key to successful psychotherapy, however, is not to allow regression in the transference to be an aim in itself." Stone (1951), Mann (1973), and others stress the need to recognize the regressive pull in the transference and to avoid stimulating or facilitating this pull. This can be accomplished by keeping the focus of treatment on the highly specific, present dynamic crisis, and by not questioning, undermining, or tampering with other areas of adaptive functioning. Effective crisis intervention demands adherence to a *rule of parsimony*, doing just enough and maybe just a little less than the patient may desire. As Stone (1951) advises, the therapist should avoid evoking superfluous conflicts. Skillful neglect of potential transference issues is required as one assesses the patient's emotional responses in the treatment setting. The therapist should mobilize identification with his adaptive capacities for problem solving and crisis resolution.

Thus, the young woman's seductive, hysterical transference behavior was not dealt with in terms of its relationship to the therapist. What was done was to focus on this seductive, hysterical behavior as long suppressed, connected with a central conflict, and now mobilized by her life situation. This allowed for insight, relief of symptoms, and a lasting alteration of ongoing behavior so that the patient found sex more enjoyable, and could tolerate nonsexual closeness with men other than her fiance, something that had made her considerably anxious since adolescence.

Often in crisis work, alleviation of stress is sought through demands on the therapist for direct environmental manipulation. The patient may see himself as increasingly weak and helpless, and the therapist as more and more idealized and therefore responsible for dealing with reality. When crisis treatment requires attention to such specific environmental realities as marital, financial, educational, and vocational stresses, the therapist must avoid the encouragement of a magical omnipotent transference representation. This would only aggravate the already compromised self-representation of the patient as ineffective to deal with reality.

All interventions by the therapist into the patient's life must be kept to a minimum. Only when the therapist is convinced that the patient is incapable of acting on his own should he manipulate the patient's environment. In such situations, particularly with patients who have infantile character organizations, magical views of the therapist may be unavoidable. Generally, however, regression is further minimized by interpreting the magical omnipotent transference representation in terms of the reciprocal infantile, inadequate and dependent distorted self-representation of the patient. Such an interpretation is different from the anticipated wish for relief in all crisis patients, which would not be interpreted.

It should be clearly noted that there is a distinct difference between the nature of technique in classical psychoanalysis and in psychoanalytic crisis work. In psychoanalysis, the couch, free association, the analyst's anonymity, and relative silence all foster a regression in the transference and the emergence of a transference neurosis. Patients generally retain sufficient perspective and control over drive derivatives and affects, such as clinging dependency, to analyze them rather than demand gratification. Even those patients who do make such demands are, by the nature of the selection process for analytic treatment, in possession of sufficient ego skills and coping mechanisms to deal with the frustration of their demands. Crisis patients, in contrast, may as a consequence of their intense and immediate transference feelings and distortions demand any and all kinds of gratification without any technical provocation on the part of the therapist. Thus, the normally reticent, controlled young graduate student (case 7) made rather intense demands for rescue, for external controls over her self-punitive needs and nonverbally for loving, sexual contact.

Here, rather than allowing the regression, as might be the case in analysis, or gratifying at least some needs, as is the case with some crisis patients, the therapist interpreted her demands as a reexperiencing of her wish for a strong, indulgent, and loving father to take over, rescue her, and calm her fears of men. She had described her father as cold, unavailable, and physically abusive. This interpretation led to a quick diminution in demands and anxiety, reestablishment of autonomy, but no regression of sexuality. The therapist might have asked a classmate to provide the patient with more external control by staying with her for a few days, but this was deemed unnecessary.

THE ROLE OF COUNTERTRANSFERENCE

As used in the psychoanalytic literature, the term *countertransference* "refers to the attitudes and feelings, only partly conscious, of the analyst toward the patient. These may be reflect the analyst's own unconscious conflicts. . . . The analyst has displaced onto the patient attitudes and feelings derived from earlier situations in his own life; the process is analogous to transference" (Moore and Fine 1968, p. 29). Countertransference, like transference, is a component of all therapeutic situations. In crisis treatment, the patient's characteristic helplessness and neediness and the atmosphere of urgency and complexity are especially evocative of particular unconscious conflicts in the therapist.

When recognized and accepted, countertransference responses can be useful guides to the patient's dynamic conflicts and to effective modes of intervention. When present (as they must be) but unacknowledged, these responses can seriously interfere with treatment. Therefore the discussion of countertransference responses is an essential part of education and supervision in crisis work.

In our experience the major form of countertransference responses seen in therapists learning to do crisis intervention follows directly from the overwhelmed state of the patient and his demand for help. Unconscious identification with the helpless, childlike patient prompts a variety of defensive responses, often involving fantasies of, or wishes for, omnipotent control.

Conflicts evoked in crisis work which involve passivity and helplessness produce serious limitations to the tolerance for uncertainty in the crisis setting. Most commonly, the inexperienced or unaware therapist experiences a sense of great pressure to resolve the crisis quickly, frequently with premature decisions or dispositions. He does not give himself, the patient, or the patient's social network sufficient time to explore and to understand the crisis, and then to assess resources that can be mobilized. The painful unconscious identification with the frightened child-like patient fosters an urgent and illusory identification with the wished for powerful parent who assumes complete control of and responsibility for the patient—a grandiose rescue fantasy.

Case 8

This situation is typified by a therapist, early in his experience in crisis work, confronted with an anxious, screaming, histrionic young woman. While at work, she had developed symptoms of acute anxiety with physiological manifestations and was brought to the emergency room by a co-worker. She pleaded with the therapist "to do something," feeling as if she might die or go crazy. Feeling very confused and overwhelmed by this patient, he initially planned high doses of sedation and hospitalization. When he and his supervisor discussed the situation, he was advised to take more time, to treat the hyperventilation syndrome associated with the anxiety attack, and then discuss with the patient what led up to her anxiety. Her husband was also called and came to the emergency room.

After the attack was aborted, it was learned that her marriage was in considerable difficulty, her husband was having an affair, and that her attack had occurred when a man at work flirted with her. Now it was possible to construct a more complete picture of the present crisis and to organize a plan for dealing with the problems in the marriage.

Here premature assumption of control, prompted by the therapist's discomfort, could have led to inappropriate and regressive treatment. In some uncertain or anxious therapists, harsh, critical, and rejecting attitudes are evoked by the helplessness and demandingness of the patient in crisis. These therapists identify defensively with punitive superego, prompting anger, contempt, and ridicule of the infantile patient. Commonly, this becomes manifest in "not taking over for the patient," in remaining emotionally distant and unempathic with the patient's emotional pain, in "gallows humor" about "the case," and in insistence on the plan regardless of the patient's objections.

Case 9

A middle-aged chronically psychiatrically ill man presented at the emergency room with mounting agitation, vague ideas of reference, and feelings of desperation. He had recently lost his job as a clerk, had no family to assist him, and was becoming both panicked and depressed. The therapist correctly assumed that his present decompensation resulted from his job loss and his vague referentiality from projected rage. However, the patient's pathetic helplessness and neediness prompted the therapist to give him a prescription for tranquilizers, tell him to go to the unemployment office, and return to the clinic in one week.

Two days later, the patient returned at night fearful of being attacked, unable to sleep, and considering suicide. This time, he was given tranquilizing medicine and observed overnight, taken by a social worker to the unemployment office, and given daily follow-up appointments.

In this example, the therapist responded to the patient's wish for rescue from his helplessness initially by providing less than necessary intervention. In other circumstances, therapists tend to respond with the situation by hospitalizing such a patient. In many acute situations with depressed patients, the therapist may develop one or two typical behavioral responses—namely, excessive distance, often hostile in nature, or excessive supportive warmth. The dangers inherent in either response are considerable. The cold, hostile physician will exacerbate already operative feelings of isolation and separation in the patient and no therapeutic alliance will develop. The overly supportive therapist will stimulate superego dominated responses of feelings of worthlessness and self-directed rage in the patient. Both responses in the therapist often represent an identification with the depressed, needful patient. This identification may trigger a defense of distance and coldness in those who act out a defensive identification with a cold, rejecting parent. There are also those who may act out, in their excessive warmth, a rescue fantasy or family romance, wherein they represent the rescuing or indulgent parent they would wish for themselves. This defends against the hostility toward the demanding patient that they once experienced toward their own ungiving parents.

Some crisis patients may express their demand for rescue through such nonverbal behavior as suicidal gestures, conversion symptoms, or threatening behavior. They may directly demand special attention and consideration in the form of drugs, hospitalization or some special verbal or behavioral response in the treating person. Here, the therapist's own rescue fantasies may lead to acting out and further escalation of the patient's behavior. Quite often the response to feeling manipulated by the patient prompts a countermanipulation of consciously rationalized punitive behavior designed ostensibly to extinguish the patient's manipulative behavior. The therapist assumes a barring-the-door posture toward the patient or withholds medication because he unconsciously identifies with the parent who first says no to all requests and then listens. Such responses reflect therapist conflicts over his own demandingness.

There is a growing interest among psychiatrists, and more recently among psychoanalysts, in the effects of racial, religious, cultural, and age differences between patients and therapists (Goldberg, Myers, and Zeifman 1974, Meyerson, Moss, Belville and Levenson 1973, Schachter and Butts 1968). In the emergency or crisis situation, these differences can play a dramatic role in effecting the treatment and disposition of patients (Meyerson, Moss, Belville and Levenson 1973). Guilt over racial prejudices and consequent overidentification with the socially victimized patient may blur recognition of passive or paranoid trends.

Occasionally, the therapist who has had some particular crisis in his or her own life may confront a patient in a similar crisis. Recalling and understanding this experience may help the therapist deal empathically and convey hope for a similar mastery of crisis in the patient. However, where the therapist has failed to master traumatic elements in his own crisis, he may find himself reexperiencing his original panic and helplessness and will feel threatened by the patient. This is particularly important in situations where the therapist may have suffered the loss of a close relative, a major illness, a separation or divorce. Such experiences can evoke conflicts over dependency, abandonment, rage, and sexual guilt.

The adequacy of the therapist's resolution of such conflicts will dictate the degree of empathy and insightfulness he can bring to understanding the patient's similar crisis. Where rigid defenses, such as denial, reaction formation, or self-directed rage, predominate, the therapist will be severely compromised in his work with the same type of crises. The therapist's tendency may be either to overprotect the patient as they wish to be protected, or to reject their demands for help in insulating themselves from their own painful feelings.

CONCLUSION

Adequate crisis intervention requires the application of certain psychoanalytic concepts. Crises in general reflect the emergence of unconscious conflict evoked by a current stress. Attempts at mastery of the conflict fail and further interfere with coping capacity. Assessment of the structure of the crisis produces a focus for intervention. Therapeutic activity by the therapist involves suggestion, abreaction, manipulation, clarification and interpretation. Transference manifestations in crisis work must be recognized and regression avoided. Countertransference responses may arise as the therapist attempts to defend against unconscious identification with the helpless patient; wishes for omnipotent control, rescue fantasies, and punitive rejection of the patient are unconscious motives that can intrude into successful crisis intervention.

REFERENCES

Aldrich, C. K. (1968). Brief psychotherapy. *American Journal of Psychiatry* 125:5–37.

Alexander, F. (1965). Psychoanalytic contributions to short term psychotherapy. In *Short Term Psychotherapy*, ed. L. R. Wolberg, pp. 84–126. New York: Grune and Stratton.

Balint, M., Ornstein, P., and Balint, E. (1972). *Focal Psychotherapy*. London: Tavistock.

Barten, H. (1971). *Brief Therapies*, New York: Behavioral Publications.

Bellak, L., and Small, S. (1965). *Emergency Psychotherapy and Brief Psychotherapy*. New York: Grune and Stratton.

Bibring, E. (1954). Psychoanalysis and the dynamic psychotherapies. *Journal of the American Psychoanalytic Association* 2:745–768.

Caplan, G. (1961). *An Approach to Community Mental Health*. New York: Grune and Stratton.

Fenichel, O. (1945). Brief psychotherapy. *Collected Papers*, vol. 7, pp 12–13. New York: W. W. Norton.

Frank, J. D. (1959). The dynamics of the psychotherapeutic relationship. *Psychiatry* 22:17–39.

Freud, S. (1893–1895). Studies on hysteria. *Standard Edition* 2.

——— (1914). Papers on technique. Remembering, repeating, and working-through. *Standard Edition* 12:144–156.

——— (1919). The "uncanny," III: relation of imagination to reality. *Standard Edition* 17:245–252.

Furst, R. (1938). Problems of short term psychotherapy. *American Journal of Orthopsychiatry* 8:260–264.

Gillman, R. (1965). Brief psychotherapy—a psychoanalytic view. *American Journal of Psychiatry* 122:601–611.

Glick, R. A. (1976). Anxiety and related states. In *Psychiatric Emergencies*, ed. R. A. Glick et al., pp. 121–134. New York: Grune and Stratton.

Goldberg, E. L., Myers, W. A., and Zeifman, I. (1974). Some observations on three interracial analyses. *International Journal of Psycho-Analysis* 55:495–500.

Harris, N., Kalish, B., and Freeman, E. (1963). Precipitating stress: an approach to brief therapy. *American Journal of Psychotherapy* 17:471–

Lindemann, E. (1944). Symptomatology and management of acute grief. *American Journal of Psychiatry* 10:141–148.

Malan, D. H. (1963). *A Study of Brief Psychotherapy*. London: Tavistock.(Springfield, Ill.: Charles Thomas).

——— (1976). *The Frontier of Brief Psychotherapy*. New York: Plemum.

Mann, J. (1973). *Time Limited Psychotherapy*. Cambridge: Harvard University Press.

Meyerson, A., and Glick, R. (1976). Suicide. In *Psychiatric Emergencies*, ed. R. A. Glick et al., pp. 89–107. New York: Grune and Stratton.

Meyerson, A., Moss, J. Z., Belville, R. S., and Levenson, B. (1973). The elderly patient in a general hospital crisis clinic (abstract). *Gerontologist* 13:65.

Moore, B., and Fine, B. (1968). *A Glossary of Psychoanalytic Terms and Concepts*. New York: American Psychoanalytic Association.

Oremland, J. (1972). Transference cure and flight into health. *International Journal of Psycho-analytic Psychotherapy.* 1 (1):61–75.

Rado, S. (1965). Relationship of short term psychotherapy to developmental stages of maturation and stages of treatment behavior. In *Short Term Psychotherapy*, ed. W. R. Wolberg, pp. 67–84. New York: Grune and Stratton.

Rosenthal, H. (1965). Emergency psychotherapy: a crucial need. *Psychoanalytic Review* 52:446–459.

Sarvis, M. A., Dewees, S., and Johnson, R. F. (1959). A concept of ego-oriented psychotherapy. *Psychiatry* 22:277–287.

Schachter, J. S., and Butts, H. F. (1968). Transference and countertransference in interracial analysis. *Journal of the American Psychoanalytic Association* 16:792–808.

Semrad, E. (1954). The treatment process. *American Journal of Psychiatry* 3:426–427.

Semrad, E., Binstock, W., and White, B. (1966). Brief psychotherapy. *American Journal of Psychotherapy* 20:576–596.

Shafer, R. (1973). Termination of brief psychoanalytic psychotherapy. *International Journal of Psychoanalytic Psychotherapy* 2:135–148.

Sifneos, P. (1960). Concept of emotional crisis. *Mental Hygiene* 44:169–179.

——— (1972). *Short Term Psychotherapy and Emotion Crisis*. Cambridge: Harvard University Press.

Small, L. (1971). *The Briefer Psychotherapies*. New York: Brunner-Mazel.

Sterba, R. (1951). A case of brief psychotherapy by S. Freud. *Psychoanalytic Review* 38:75–80.

Stone, L. (1951). Psychoanalysis and brief psychotherapy. *Psychoanalytic Quarterly* 20:215–236.

Strupp, H. (1969). Toward the specification of teaching and learning in psychotherapy. *Archives of General Psychiatry* 21:203–213.

Swartz, J. (1969). Time limited brief psychotherapy. In *Seminars in Psychiatry*. New York: Grune and Stratton.

Waelder, R. (1936). Principle of multiple function. *Psychoanalytic Quarterly* 5:45–62.

Wolberg, L. R., ed. (1965). *Short Term Psychotherapy*. New York: Grune and Stratton.

Crisis Intervention and Psychoanalysis: Compatible or Antagonistic?

JOHN A. TALBOTT, M.D.

A discussion of "The Use of Psychoanalytic Concepts in Crisis Intervention," by Robert Glick, M.D., and Arthur T. Myerson, M.D. Crisis intervention and psychoanalysis are frequently considered antagonistic or antithetical. Reasons for this seeming incompatibility of the two therapeutic modes are discussed along with the ways in which psychoanalytic concepts and techniques are used in crisis intervention. It is concluded that, while different, the two modalities are not antagonistic but extremely compatible.

Crisis intervention and psychoanalysis are often spoken of as if they are incompatible and perhaps even antithetical modes of treatment. Glick and Meyerson have performed a valuable service by presenting us with some of the ways in which psychoanalytic concepts may be applied to crisis intervention. However, their greater contribution is in opening up a dialogue concerning the compatibility or incompatibility of psychoanalytic and crisis intervention philosophies, concepts and techniques. This discussion has profound implications for the provision of mental health services, the training of mental health professionals, and current research efforts in psychotherapy.

In order to further this examination, I will present some of the historical developments concerning crisis intervention and psychoanalysis and then some specific aspects of crisis intervention that appear antianalytic. This will be followed by a presentation of those analytic concepts and techniques that can be utilized appropriately in crisis intervention along with clinical examples demonstrating some of the interfaces between crisis intervention and psychoanalysis. I will also discuss the ways in which psychoanalytic concepts are central to the provision of crisis intervention. A major focus will be Glick and Meyerson's contribution, evaluated within a framework of the myths of psychoanalysis and crisis intervention.

HISTORY AND BACKGROUND

Following the colonization of America until the time of the introduction of Freud's ideas, the history of psychological treatment in the United States was essentially that of governmental, institutional, custodial care. Except for the concepts embodied in nineteenth-century moral treatment, there was little psychological conceptualization of mental illness which could be applied to treatment. Instead experts concentrated on the phenomenological or organic aspects of emotional distress.

The introduction of Freud's ideas into the mainstream of American psychiatry occurred simultaneously with several other relevant developments—the mental hygiene movement, the establishment of child guidance clinics, and the diversification of psychiatric facilities from state hospitals to psychopathic hospital and then to general hospitals. Psychoanalysis, both as a body of knowledge and a mode of therapy, altered the landscape of American psychiatry by introducing a psychological method of understanding and treating emotional disorders.

One can date the beginnings of crisis intervention in this country to World War I, following Thomas Salmon's study (1917) of the difference between the treatment of psychiatric casualties by British and French military physicians. The British evacuated their troops back to English hospitals, where, even following recovery and the end of the war, they constituted a sizable population of psychiatrically impaired individuals. The French, on the other hand, kept their troops close to the battlelines and had a strikingly lower incidence of postwar impairment (Hausman and Rioch 1967). From this study came the three essential tenets of battlefield and, subsequently, emergency psychiatry: immediacy, proximity, and expectancy. Immediacy referred to the importance of evaluating and treating psychiatric casualties as soon as possible following the onset of acute symptoms, and had its civilian impact in the insistence that waiting lists be abolished and emergency psychiatric services be established in general hospitals. Proximity referred to the necessity of treating psychiatric casualties as close to the battlelines and to their fellow soldiers as possible. This carried over to postwar psychiatric practice in the belief that psychiatric services should be located locally and proximate to afflicted persons' neighborhoods and that psychiatric patients should be treated close to if not within their homes, families, and familiar social settings. Expectancy referred to the expectation of and overt articulation of the expectation of the patient's prompt recovery from the psychiatric condition and has been utilized predominantly in the treatment of those conditions known to be time-limited, that is, acute stress reactions, situational reactions, and affective illnesses responsive to psychopharmacological intervention.

To these three cardinal principles of combat psychiatry, a fourth—community—was added following World War II (Talbott 1969). This referred to the importance of the social setting and environment in both the causation of and alleviation of psychiatric conditions. The civilian applications of this principle have been profound, ranging from the introduction of social therapies, therapeutic milieus, and family treatment to the embodiment of the concepts of community psychiatry into a structure of community mental health centers.

Crucial to the development of the theory and practice of crisis intervention were the contributions of Lindemann, (1944) and Caplan (1964), both of whom emphasized the disequilibrium engendered in the individual by the crisis situation and the necessity to get the affected person back to his prior level of adaptation. Both were trained in psychoanalysis, and Caplan deals extensively with the importance of developmental stages in personality development.

In the ensuing years, crisis intervention achieved increasing importance as a treatment method, but theoretical contributions to the area were less impressive. As two recent reviews (Linn and Talbott 1977, Smith 1977) have demonstrated, most developments have concerned primarily technical matters, for example, life-stress units, stages of crisis reactions, and tasks of crisis therapy rather than conceptual issues.

WHAT SEEMS ANTIANALYTIC ABOUT CRISIS INTERVENTION

Several aspects of crisis intervention, already mentioned or inherent to its practice, seem quite at variance with psychoanalytic theory and practice. I have separated out several of these elements and will discuss each of them briefly.

The expectation that the patient will recover promptly is a feature of crisis intervention that derives from the experience of combat psychiatrists in treating psychiatric casualties. To this day, Army psychiatrists are instructed to tell victims of combat reactions that they will be removed from the source of stress (e.g., the battle) for a short time, given rest, hot food, a shower, and perhaps medication, and then returned to their original assignment. This stands in marked contrast to the lack of guarantees and instructions given most analysands, who not only are not expected to recover rapidly but are not even told they will. It is curious that to the average psychiatrist the rule not to promise or expect recovery overrides the rule to the contrary—even though the latter is documented as useful and effective whereas the former is based on pure assumption rather than scientific evidence. Psychoanalytic and psychiatric purists might well be correct in their assumption that for some patients expectancy is not a good principle to apply. At present, however, we simply do not know. This example illustrates one of the issues concerning the seeming incompatibility of crisis intervention and psychoanalysis. For regardless of whether this principle would be useful in psychoanalysis, it is regarded as evidence of the differences between the two treatment methods.

The importance of the social situation, whether familial, vocational, living, or environmental, is integral to crisis intervention, both in the evaluation process and in treatment. Crisis intervenors must focus on the immediate precipitant or stress that has brought the patient to treatment. Since these stressors are so often found in the immediate environment of the patient, home visits, family interviews, and contacts with the patient's social network are often crucial, both to identification of the precipitant and to resolution of the crisis. The psychoanalyst, by contrast, is in most instances not confronted with an immediate problem but is concerned with the genetic, familial, and developmental issues in the patient's background that have occasioned his current personality structure and characterological problems. And, while the psychoanalyst will surely inquire into the patient's work, marriage, family, home, and neighborhood, he will not necessarily evaluate them firsthand or utilize them as therapeutic agents.

The object of returning the patient to his/her premorbid state is probably the most important goal of crisis intervention but is almost irrelevant to psychoanalytic work. The focus of crisis intervention is on prompt and complete return to the level of functioning experienced by the patient before the onset of the crisis and not on personality reorganization. Thus, defenses, unless part and parcel of the crisis state, are not exposed or analyzed, but rather are considered part of the person's personality givens. The analyst, by contrast, regards the fluctuations in the patient's environmental situation in terms of their symbolic meaning or relevance to past history and developmental issues. Thus for the analyst the return to premorbid functioning is not the ballgame—what is important is the patient's ability to unravel the threads of his conflicts and to tie them together again in a more productive and adaptive manner.

The irrelevance of past or genetic material is a feature of crisis intervention not shared by psychoanalysis. To some crisis intervenors past history is irrelevant, and the sole focus is on the here and now. This is clearly in marked contradistinction to the attitude of psychoanalysts, for whom the present has interest and relevance only in relation to the past. Obviously this feature, more than the three I have mentioned already, is subject to considerably more flexible interpretation than I have accorded it. Many persons involved in crisis intervention do not disregard past history, especially as it relates to prior problem solving, but they do prefer to spend time on current problem solving efforts. Likewise, many analysts are not callous in their inattention to present crises *qua* crises, but see their resolution as importantly related to past problem solving.

Unconscious material is unimportant or irrelevant to most crisis intervention, while it is central and crucial to psychoanalysis. Here again, while clearly there are intermediate positions, we find the two modalities poles apart. The crisis intervenor focuses on the reality and on accessible ego functions rather than on predominantly intrapsychic (id and superego), unconscious, or primary process material. The goal, resolution of the crisis, precludes rather than negates attention to these factors.

Symptoms and functioning are crucial, rather than personality organization and presence of conflict. To the crisis intervenor, it is the level of functioning and the presence or absence of symptoms that are most important. It is almost immaterial how conflicted or neurotic the individual is if he/she is symptom-free, or unbothered by symptoms, and restored to previous levels of functioning. To the analyst, however, many symptoms are ego syntonic, and a resolution of a problem that merely substitutes one bad adaptation for another, regardless of the comfort it might afford the patient, is still, if neurotic, worthy of analysis.

Resolution should be possible in a few weeks. While this is an altogether reasonable goal for crisis intervention, with complete or almost complete restoration of functioning, it certainly seems short-sighted to the psychoanalyst, for whom treatment is better measured in years than in weeks.

An active role by the therapist is necessary in crisis intervention, whereas one may be more passive in analytic situations. Obviously, this aspect also is not so absolute as I have stated it, but this characterization is nonetheless widely accepted. The crisis intervenor is interested in performing the evaluation, arriving at the diagnosis, and solving the overt problems as quickly as possible. Therefore the therapist takes an active role, questions quickly, and interrupts and cuts short—techniques considered either unimportant or counterproductive in psychoanalysis.

The therapist's use of himself or herself may constitute an important ingredient in crisis intervention. In crisis intervention, the psychiatrist may well telephone community care-givers, make home visits, provide tangible evidence of help (e.g., medication), or reassure the patient regarding his experience by citing patients with similar situations who recovered or by reference to personal experience. Any of these would constitute serious breaches of psychoanalytic technique.

Immediate intervention is necessary in crisis intervention to prevent maladaptive or regressive solutions, whereas psychoanalytic treatment conveys no such sense of urgency. In fact, it depends on thorough and thoughtful exploration of the underlying dynamics and conflicts.

IN REALITY THE INTERVENOR USES PSYCHOANALYTIC CONCEPTS AND TECHNIQUES

As I began to make clear in the preceeding section, while many aspects of crisis intervention seem incompatible with psychoanalytic practice, there is more to the picture than the presentation of polar positions would suggest. In this section I propose to demonstrate that many psychoanalytic concepts and techniques are actually employed in crisis intervention work.

Transference, one of the cornerstones of psychoanalysis, far from being an annoyance or interference in crisis intervention, is in fact terribly useful in its performance. Transferential reactions are indicative not only of some of the determinants of the current problems underlying the crisis but are also frequently useful in arriving at an accurate appraisal of appropriate solutions to the crisis.

A thirty-two-year-old married mother of five children, all under six years old, presented to the emergency room because of crippling anxiety which prevented her from caring for her home and children. This appeared shortly after her mother, who had helped her greatly around the home, moved to Florida. She soon began to berate the psychiatric resident for not helping her, and it became clear that she had considerable unexpressed anger toward her father and husband for saddling her with additional responsibility without commensurate help.

Interpretation, another cornerstone of psychoanalysis, is commonly used in crisis intervention. It does not often involve interpretation of the transference but more frequently involves interpretation of existing problems, reactions or adaptive maneuvers in the light of previous patterns. For example, in the case cited above, the resident, following a family interview that verified the situation, interpreted to the patient her anger at him as being part of her resentment of all males for placing excessive responsibility on her without adequate resources to fulfill that responsibility.

Psychodynamics, crucial to psychoanalytic understanding of the patient and his/her subsequent treatment, may also be extremely helpful to the questions in crises of why now, why so critical, and why is the precipitant so powerful? A psychodynamic understanding often also provides the intervenor precise information about how and where to intervene to interrupt the crisis cycle. In the above case, the woman's wish to be cared for and her fear of abandonment if she were not an uncomplaining "good girl" emerged from the history. This provided the resident the critical information that allowed him to challenge these assumptions and to bring them into the open in the family interviews. In addition, the resident's knowledge of the patient's tendency not to articulate her needs for help enabled him to offer homemaking services, etc., as a partial solution to the crisis.

Symbolism, especially as it relates to the precipitant, the importance of the crisis situation, or the roles of potential care-givers, can provide insight into the crisis as well as possible therapeutic maneuvers. Granted, its role is more limited and circumscribed than in psychoanalytic work, but frequently it is extremely useful. Again, referring to the above case, the resident learned that many of the woman's fears of being trapped and suffocated related to her sense that her mother offered her an escape if she were ill, wanted to go shopping for herself, or wanted to attend a monthly meeting with a group of high school chums. She saw the mother's departure as an end to any small degree of freedom and thus as entrapment and suffocation.

The *past history* is of importance to the crisis intervenor despite some experts' statements to the contrary. Frequently the past history provides the clues to the patient's current dilemma, both its inception and resolution.

A twenty-three-year-old law student presented to his internist with the acute onset of palpitations, sleeplessness, anorexia, and suicidal preoccupation following his parents' declaration of their opposition to his marriage to a woman he had been living with for over a year. They refused to discuss the matter with him and he felt hopelessly trapped. The internist referred him to a psychiatrist, who ascertained that both the mother and the father were survivors of World War II concentration camps, had lost their entire families to Nazi extermination, and conducted all activities as a family unit while the patient was growing up.

Personality change, while not a primary or even stated goal of crisis intervention, frequently occurs, since in crises the lever for change is available. While not conceived of in terms of total personality reorganization, small characterological changes may begin and lead to more comprehensive changes. In the case of the law student, the interviews with the student's fiancee and family revealed not only the dependency conflict regarding his primary family but many of his unrealistic expectations regarding his fiancée. In individual sessions, discussion of these issues produced some initial shift in his methods of relating to both family and prospective spouse almost immediately.

A wider choice of adaptive maneuvers in response to problematic situations is a frequent goal of analytic work and may result from crisis intervention as well. While in psychoanalysis this usually occurs in response to analysis and working through; in crisis intervention it may be the result of identification with the crisis intervenor, realization of alternate solutions presented by the psychiatrist, or discussions of possible options within the social network. In the case of the law student, part of the resolution of the crisis occurred when the family saw the son's probable marriage as expanding and ensuring continuance of their almost annihilated family. They then became less concerned that he spend all vacations and non-scholarly time with them. The primary patient, in turn, saw that acquiescence was not the only response to requests for family unity.

The use of *unconscious material* is also frequently helpful in crisis intervention, as of course it is in psychoanalysis. Frequently during a crisis situation, slips, dreams, and fantasies have a vividness and clarity, for both intervenor and patient, that make their utilization especially potent. With the case of the law student, during the initial interview he was describing how his parents resented his girlfriend's influence on him, how she dictated his choice of clothes and leisure activities and how she "led him around by his noose." Unconsciously, he equated his marriage and departure from his family as the death of a member and saw immediately how powerful this dynamic was.

The *crisis as entrée* into more long-term treatment is another feature of crisis intervention. While many would insist that almost anyone who has a crisis situation that resolves in a few weeks with crisis intervention is a candidate for further treatment, there are clearly some patients whose only ticket of admission to treatment can be a full-blown crisis and for whom resolution of the crisis without further treatment is inadvisable.

A twenty-eight-year-old unmarried investment broker was brought to the emergency room in a confused state, having been found wandering along the Brooklyn Bridge, leaning over the side, seemingly lost in thoughts and crying. An interview revealed that he was intensely distraught over a recent romantic breakup. Upon prodding, his estranged girlfriend agreed to come to the emergency room, where a reunion was effected. The next day the patient gave a clear, coherent story but expressed some vague reluctance to leave without a further appointment. It soon developed that he had profound fears of homosexuality and an inability to sustain an intimate relationship with a woman or to disengage from an intensely interdependent relationship with his widowed mother.

This immediate breakup, while precipitating a crisis, was only the tip of the iceberg; its resolution served not so much to restore the *status quo ante* as to place him in proximity to longer term therapy.

An understanding of developmental phases is often crucial to the work of crisis intervention, especially when the crisis involves an interpersonal or family situation. Often crises occur at times of developmental importance (e.g., patients' children achieving various stages, parents aging), and the psychoanalytically trained psychiatrist is best able to understand such situations. In the case of the Wall Street broker cited above, the history revealed that the man's father had died on the verge of great financial success as a broker when the son was six, and the patient's oedipal and phallic developmental stages were profoundly influenced by this occurrence.

The *importance of accidents and traumatic events* is another aspect of psychoanalytic thinking that assists the crisis intervenor. The fact that many "accidents" are the result of motivated behavior, that events which occur outside of one's control may severely threaten a person preoccupied with control, and that losses (real or symbolic; immediate, delayed, or anniversary) have special meaning to individuals, are all features that analysts are sensitive to and that help in the process of evaluating and intervening in crises related to accidental events.

An eighteen-year-old Army draftee presented in the emergency room of the post hospital shaking and stuttering following the explosion of a grenade in his locker. It developed that the "accident" was the result of his bringing a "dud" back from the grenade range and then tossing it around the barracks with his friends. A piece of shrapnel narrowly missed his genitals, and a friend with whom he was warmly competitive was badly hurt. Crisis intervention involved abreaction and taking a complete history, with adequate attention to his boyish phallic competitiveness and doubts about his sexuality.

The *interplay of social and intrapsychic* factors is yet another feature of crisis intervention to which the psychoanalyst may be especially sensitive. Through his medical and psychoanalytic training and experience, the analyst is able to sort out the relevance of somatic, social, and intrapsychic determinants and resultants in the crisis. In the above example, the interplay between the soldier's competitive strivings as a young man, his own impulses and sexual conflicts, as well as the social pressure to be a man, to take chances, and to show no feelings, all were weighed and understood. Likewise his shaking and stuttering, both somatic deterrents to action and aggression, were comprehensible to the analyst.

MYTHS OF PSYCHOANALYSIS AND CRISIS INTERVENTION

Glick and Meyerson's contribution has raised many issues concerning psychoanalysis and crisis intervention, most of which could be considered part of the mythology of psychiatry. An example of this sort of mythology is that of the importance of genetic material and the patient's past history to the analyst and irrelevance to the crisis intervenor. As these authors have demonstrated so ably, this is a tautology which exists mainly in people's thinking and which certainly is not borne out in practice. They have touched on several other such myths as well.

The first is *the myth of activity or passivity* on the part of the therapist. Analysts work as actively and think as intensively as others in the field, and crisis intervenors certainly do not act thoughtlessly or because action is an end in itself. Rather, in questioning, clarifying, or interpreting both act as much as is needed and is enabling to therapy.

The second myth is that of *analytic versus supportive interventions.* In the pantheon of acceptable therapeutic maneuvers, interpretation is held most high and suggestion and advice giving most base. In point of fact, as the authors have illustrated, there are varieties among all interventions, and in addition, when one looks closely at a specific intervention, it is unusual for it to consist purely of one type of maneuver. Surely there are different types of interventions, but they are part of a spectrum rather than discrete entities, and it neither ennobles nor shames one to use a variety of maneuvers in crisis intervention.

The third myth involves that of the *purity and unity of transference.* As the authors point out, there are differences between transference (universally present), transference readiness (in crisis patients), and the full-blown transference neurosis (to which many aspire but few are called). In crisis intervention, one uses what one has rather than waiting around for the rainbow, and this means that the patient's transference readiness and transference reactions to the therapist are powerful forces in and of themselves, without a complete transference neurosis.

The fourth myth is that of *environmental manipulation.* The authors support the popular view that such maneuvers should be used only if the patient cannot act on his or her own, or to avoid furthering regression, dependency, or magical thinking. The problem is that inexperienced therapists waver between being totally sucked into acting for the patient and letting the patient flounder about helplessly. I encourage errors on the side of overinvolvement, thinking that one may always analyze such overenthusiasm but may not so easily recover the patient's loss of functioning. There is also frequently a question of where one can get the biggest bang for his buck.

A twenty-six-year-old unmarried black female bank officer presented with sleeplessness, dizziness, and headaches that prevented her from working. All of these started immediately after she was promoted and transferred to work under a sexually provocative and attractive older man: "old enough to be my father." History taking revealed the apparent oedipal origins of the crisis, but intervention was aimed at a rapid transfer to another area in the bank rather than analysis of the underlying conflict. This decision was based on the patient's relative lack of psychological-mindedness, the unavailability of treatment close to her home, and her limited financial resources.

Another myth is that of the glory of *free association*. As has been reaffirmed so often, free association marks the end rather than the beginning of analysis, and the idea that free association is a special commodity owned only by patients in psychoanalysis—a commodity that persons in crisis shall never see—is sheer nonsense. Patients associate, we use those associations as clues in treatment, and all the snobbery in the world can't change it.

A sixth myth involves that of *the extreme danger of countertransference acting out*. As the authors illustrate, because we are loathe to take too much control out of patients' hands we fall prey to underactivity. This is based on our own feelings toward the patient. As Glick and Meyerson explain, patients in crisis arouse intense feelings, both realistic humane ones and transferential ones. Sorting them out is crucial, but one must not become so preoccupied with self-analysis that inaction results.

A forty-year-old married architect presented with extreme agitation and hysterical outbursts of crying following the discovery that her husband was having an affair with his coworker. She pleaded for a tranquilizer to calm her and allow her to sleep. The resident resisted, fearing that if he complied his peers and his supervisor would criticize him for having been manipulated and for having acted out a rescue fantasy. The patient returned with suicidal ideation the following evening and was again denied medication. The third night, hallucinating tiny green men and voices telling her to jump out of her window, she obtained admission to the hospital.

The seventh myth is that the therapist's *identification with the crisis patient is counterproductive*. The assumption here is that the therapist, identifying with the person in need, will react either by indulging in his or her rescue fantasy or by withholding and denying. In my experience, a more common fate is that the therapist is more empathetic and understanding with a patient in crisis than with many other psychiatric problems—for the simple reason that while all of us have lost loved ones, been in terrible straits, and survived auto accidents, few of us have hallucinated, been suicidal, or suffered from ulcerative colitis. Thus, our familiarity with the feelings engendered by crises lends strength to our knowledge that crises are resolvable, that persons not only recover but grow from them, and that there are solutions and ways out of seemingly insoluble problems.

The last myth is that *hospitalization represents a failure of crisis intervention.* Hospitalization may be neither a failure of crisis intervention nor an overresponse; it may in many instances represent the best form of crisis intervention.

A sixteen-year-old high school student was brought to the emergency room by his mother after slashing at his wrists with an exacto craft knife. Examination of the patient and his mother revealed that he was falling short of his successful businessman father's expectations in school and sports, felt trapped and desperate, and expressed a wish to leave the home. Following the interview, and after everyone's agreement that a full family session would be scheduled the next day, as he was leaving the emergency room the patient got into a shoving match with the parking lot policeman. Mother and son returned to the emergency room immediately. The son agreed to hospitalization and subsequent enrollment in a New England boarding school, where at last word he was doing well.

CONCLUSIONS

Crisis intervention and psychoanalysis have frequently been considered incompatible and even antagonistic therapeutic modalities. Certainly, if psychoanalysis is defined only as a five times a week, insight-oriented, intrapsychically focused psychological therapy aimed at personality reorganization through such techniques as free association, dream analysis, and transference interpretation, it would seem antithetical to crisis intervention as defined as a short-term, symptom-oriented, and environmentally focused therapy intended only to restore the individual to his or her previous adaptive level through a combination of individual, family, and environmental interventions.

However, as I have attempted to demonstrate, while these extreme polar definitions may be useful to theoreticians, they do not apply to clinical situations, where clinical activity occupies a more central part of the spectrum. Thus, while it may be important to separate crisis intervention and psychoanalysis for teaching and research purposes, in terms of therapeutic services they occupy parts of a spectrum.

In addition, while the definition of what constitutes psychoanalysis has been the object of considerable discussion over the past half-century, recent practice has begun to shift and expand the definition of analysis and analyzability (Cooper 1978). Part of this change may be the result of changing patient populations, but a portion is also certainly due to changes in patterns of mental health services—including the development of crisis intervention itself.

Finally, to discuss why psychoanalysis and crisis intervention seem antithetical, it is necessary to attack several straw men. But it should be made clear that they *are* straw men and not indisputable facts. Analysts do leave their offices, prescribe medication, see families, and respect symptom alleviation.

In summary, I have attempted to demonstrate that while there are seemingly several points where psychoanalysis and crisis intervention seem antagonistic and antithetical, in practice psychoanalytic theory and practice offer the crisis intervenor a great deal and detract from his efforts not at all. It is important for all of us concerned with the teaching and practice of psychotherapy to acknowledge the mutually constructive contributions of such separate therapeutic practices as psychoanalysis and crisis intervention if we are to continue to strive for the most efficient and effective psychotherapeutic armamentarium.

REFERENCES

Caplan, G. (1964). *Principles of Preventive Psychiatry.* New York: Basic Books.

Cooper, A. (1978). The relation of diagnosis to psychoanalytic treatment. Unpublished manuscript.

Hausman, W., and Rioch, D. (1967). Military psychiatry: a prototype of social and preventive psychiatry in the United States. *Archives of General Psychiatry* 16:727–739.

Lindemann, E. (1944). Symptomatology and management of acute grief. *American Journal of Psychiatry* 101:141–148.

Linn, L., and Talbott, J. (1977). Eclecticism: the new flexibility in psychotherapy. In *The Eclectic Approach in Crisis Intervention.* New York: Roche.

Salmon, T. (1917). War neuroses ("shell shock"). *Military Surgery* 41:674–693.

Smith, L. (1977). Crisis intervention: theory and practice. *Community Mental Health Review* 2:1–13.

Talbott, J. (1969). Community psychiatry in the army: history, practice and applications to civilian psychiatry. *Journal of the American Medical Association* 210:1233–1237.

A Verbal Group Technique for Ego-Disturbed Children: Action to Words

MARK J. BLOTCKY, M.D.
MARC SHEINBEIN, Ph.D.
KENNETH M. WIGGINS, M.D.
JUDITH H. FORGOTSON, M.D.

The evolution of latency groups began over three decades ago with the inception of the activity group. Through modification and a greater emphasis on verbalization this developed into the play therapy model. At that time it was generally felt that verbal techniques were too threatening for latency age youngsters and that ego-defective children could not make use of a group approach. More recently successful work has been reported with both verbally oriented groups and groups with severely disturbed children. After tracing these developments, this paper describes a verbal, nondirective, insight-oriented group technique for ego-defective children. This technique is derived from the dynamics of latency, the techniques of individual play therapy, and the model of more conventional group psychotherapy. Clinical vignettes are reported to clarify the technique and demonstrate its efficacy. Though this approach is both demanding for the therapist and socially provocative in general, we think the results reported here require serious consideration and further evaluation.

REVIEW OF GROUP TREATMENT FOR LATENCY CHILDREN

Only recently has the stage of latency been better understood. This lack of clarity has been evident in all aspects of clinical practice—signs of

The authors wish to express their gratitude to Ms. Marsha Rubin, group cotherapist, and Dr. F. Diane Fagelman, group therapy supervisor.

pathology, mode of treatment, technique, and prognosis. The latency age child's capacity for peer relationships was first put to formal therapeutic use by Slavson (1943) with the organization of activity groups. His model minimized verbalization and stressed the expression of drives, conflicts, and defenses through play. A benign regression was allowed within a permissive, accepting atmosphere, thus allowing earlier conflicts to be relived and resolved within the context of that stable environment. Verbal interpretations were generally not made, and gains were made instead through behavioral interactions with peers and therapists. The group consisted of eight same-sexed children and met in a large, well-equipped playroom in which a meal was served.

Various authors have felt that verbal free-associative techniques were too threatening for latency age children (Bornstein 1951) and that more severely disturbed children could not make use of a group experience but instead needed the "deeper transference work" available in individual therapy. It was not until Foulkes and Anthony (1957) described their technique for dividing group sessions into an activity and discussion phase that the translation of play into verbalization was emphasized. They stressed the necessity of bringing behavior under the control of secondary process.

Ginott (1961) made a benchmark contribution in describing his play therapy group. He defined his goal as similar to individual therapy: namely, effecting basic structural change. To this end, Ginott used direct interpretation. His play therapy group offered two media for symbolic expression—play and verbalization. The child could then use the medium that best met his own needs. Although Ginott used interpretation, he felt that identification was the crucial therapeutic process. The group setting discouraged withdrawal and supported a more positive relationship with the therapist by making him less frightening. It further provided a place for building peer relationships, sublimating impulses, and learning new adaptive social skills. The focus of treatment was always the individual child. Group goals were not set, nor group cohesion expected.

Scheidlinger (1960, 1965a,b) has described a modified experiential play group approach for deprived, severely disturbed latency age children. These children exhibited poor ego boundaries, disturbed reality testing, inadequate impulse control, confused identity formation, and significant oral conflicts. He felt that attempts to promote introspection, free association, and verbalization would be too threatening to their latency ego organization and instead recommended that the therapist be more directive, verbal, and ready to use physical restraint. He emphasized three guidelines for work with such children: (1) restitutive gratification, both real and symbolic, (2) guided regression, and (3) socialization with internalization of controls. His premise was that some restitution for past deprivation allowed a regression through which past conflicts could be relived and reworked. The resultant attachment to the therapist and the group allowed the therapist to make demands for internal controls.

Lifton and Smolen (1966) worked with autistic and schizophrenic children, ages 4–12, in what they termed "relationship group psychotherapy." Although group discussion was encouraged, this technique was characterized by a degree of control over both play and fantasies. The therapist was not neutral, and the children were not encouraged to use the group as they chose. Free play was felt to promote confusion, withdrawal, and panic. Play materials were provided to stimulate interaction and encourage contact with reality. Mirrors and mannequins enhanced the development of an integrated body image. This group met three or four times weekly for two-hour sessions. On the premise that ego defects are in part the result of disturbances in relationships (rather than only vice versa), the approach emphasized the individual child's relationship with the therapist.

Schiffer (1969) described play therapy for children six to nine years old as providing experiential rather than ideational insight. His experiential approach was based on the premise that problems can be resolved through a sustained rehabilitative experience with an adult who functions as an optimal parental surrogate. Therapeutic gains derive from the process of reworking past traumas within the family analogue—the play group. It was a substitutive experience, opposing and neutralizing the destructive influences of the past. The therapist remained peripheral yet accessible, intervening only when the frustration tolerance of the child or the group was threatened or to protect against injury. By providing such a permissive atmosphere, the therapist allowed a regression through which the child could relive the past. Schiffer excluded narcissistic characters, sociopaths, psychotics, and children with severe rivalry problems.

Gratton and Rizzo (1969) working with young, near-mute, autistic, and psychotic children provided three actively involved therapists. Their nondirective approach provided no play materials. The group was mixed and met three to five times weekly. They reported the slow appearance of group process. Within three months the play became more organized, and after six months real group cohesion was achieved. Though working with psychotic children three and four years old, Speers and Lansing (1965) provided much to our theoretical and technical formulations. In an impressive report they demonstrated a permissive, nondirective technique by which preschool ego-defective children could be treated in an outpatient group.

In the last decade reports of verbal latency groups in various settings have been added to the literature. Berkovitz et al. (1966) described play groups in a child placement agency which encouraged verbal exploration. Barcai and Robinson (1969) reported a successful verbal group of lower socioeconomic class children, ten to twelve years old, in a school setting. The therapists did not provide play materials and stated that these children had a surprising ability to verbalize feelings and to understand the present as being partly a projection of past experiences. In an excellent paper, Epstein and Altman (1972) described the ineffectiveness of their play group and its subsequent conversion to a verbal group. Their conceptual base was that in children given the opportunity to express feelings through activity, the resultant catharsis would lead to a break-through of repressed affects and impulses with subsequent changes in behavior and a new level of integration. The authors felt that from this point structure and expectations would support each child in observing his behavior and would allow him to move toward internal control. Unacceptable behavior was then defined as any that detracted from this purpose. The therapists confronted a child with his infantile behavior, demanded he stay seated, and then encouraged a discussion of behavioral alternatives.

In a residential setting, Bardill (1972) used behavior-contracting to create an atmosphere in which conventional group therapy techniques could be employed with older latency age children. This group empha-sized verbal expression and interpersonal transactions within a very structured system. Points were given for various interactions, and these points were then used to purchase more concrete rewards. Sands and Golub (1974) described an outpatient group technique using little or no play materials. They divided their sessions into a short activity period followed by a verbal discussion of the play. This evolved into a time-limited technique in which talking, not activity, was the medium. The therapist identified himself with the wish of the child to grow up. In contrast to some reports, group process was available for therapeutic intervention. Semonsky and Zicht (1974) outlined a weekly outpatient technique for boys ten to thirteen with serious behavior problems. Although play materials were provided, "talk sessions" were an important aspect of therapy. They described behavior similar to, though less intense than, what we are to report here. Food served at the end of each session was thought to be important in coalescing the group.

Sugar (1974) described an outpatient model for interpretive group psychotherapy in which the therapists remained friendly and informal but did not attempt to gratify instinctual longings. He outlined three phases of treatment which roughly correspond to our own findings. Transference reactions, although not as clear as an individual therapy, were intense, and emphasis was placed upon recognizing and interpreting them. Sessions were held weekly in a playroom with the usual toys. These toys aided in communications, served as props for the enactment of various scenes, and allowed for a substitutive expression of drives.

This focused review of the literature traces the evolution of latency psychotherapy groups. It contains evidence that the latency age child can verbalize in a group without play materials and, further, that the severely disturbed child can be effectively treated within a group. Although diverse opinions are reported, there seems to be a growing impression that transference reactions and group process can be put to therapeutic use. Many excellent reports were omitted in order to highlight those developments most significant to the work presented here.

IDENTIFICATION AND SETTING

The setting for this project is a psychiatric inpatient unit (Wolff 1972) in a general pediatrics hospital. The unit is composed of fourteen children age five to thirteen. They are divided into four living groups with each child spending essentially his entire day with his particular group. Children are assigned to groups according to their age and general level of functioning. No sex discrimination is made except for sleeping arrangements. Each of these groups is involved in group therapy led by cotherapists who are not directly involved with daily milieu. Nosologically, these children are given various diagnoses: childhood schizophrenia, severe character disorder, severe developmental deviation, specific behavioral disorder, borderline, and occasionally early infantile autism or severe neurosis. The major area of disorder is separation-individuation with early disturbances in narcissism and object relations. These children exhibit poor impulse control, an inability to tolerate tension, omnipotent fantasies and fears, disturbed reality testing, and magical thinking. A few have a formal thought disorder. A comprehensive diagnostic evaluation including a careful examination of intrapsychic, intellectual, familial, social, educational, neurologic, and physiologic parameters is completed on each child. Many children have EEG abnormalities; a few have clinical seizures. Testing often reveals specific perceptual deficits if not subnormal intelligence. Overall, these children have significant ego defects and function very poorly in many spheres.

The children in the group involved in this study were primarily late latency age boys who presented with marked disturbances in behavior. Their inability to attend to tasks, to maintain impulse control, and to tolerate frustration were daily problems. Prior to admission they were involved in inappropriate aggressive and sexual behavior. Several previous attempts at group therapy with them had failed. Some of the therapists had formed "clubs" involved in task-oriented play. These were leader-directed and were not seen as especially constructive on evaluation by the therapists and their supervisors. Instead these clubs were more similar to, than different from, the rest of the child's day. Other therapists provided a nondirective, permissive atmosphere but soon found themselves overwhelmed with anxiety when confronted with these youngsters' behavior. Increasingly inclined toward limit-setting, they gradually saw the group revert back into a clublike experience. To the extent that these therapists' limit-setting was in response to their own anxiety rather than the children's needs, they had become more directive, less accepting, and less permissive.

The therapeutic milieu provides a structure of consistent limit-setting and is designed to include many informal behavior modification techniques. Within that context verbalization is encouraged and accepted. Individual psychotherapy on the unit is usually a form of relationship therapy rather than a more nondirective, insight-oriented one. This inpatient setting was itself a crucial variable in the whole project with relevance to both the children and the therapist.

PSYCHODYNAMICS OF LATENCY

As others (Kestenberg 1969, Lewis 1974, Maenchen 1970) have outlined, psychoanalytic technique varies with the child's developmental stage. The onset of latency is marked by an intensification of defenses (Bornstein 1951) which in turn presents increased resistance to analysis. However, significant ego advancement in the area of self-observation enhances the therapeutic alliance and the child's capacity for insight. The ego structure of latency (Sarnoff 1971, 1976) allows adaptive fantasies which can reduce anxiety and aid in conflict resolution. Latency is marked by a regression to anal-sadistic drives that are defended against by sublimation, reaction-formation, fantasy, regression, and repression. Though the ego organization of latency is characterized by rigid defenses, fantasies reveal the hidden struggles against aggressive and incestuous drives. These defenses allow the child to redirect his energy toward cooperative play. As activities with primary objects decrease, relationships with peers and authority figures gain in importance. These newfound peer relationships are supportive but may threaten the latency ego's fragile structure and the child's sense of identity.

Latency can be divided into two phases. The early phase (ages six to eight) is characterized by the child's self-preoccupation. Fantasy is the primary means of adjusting to emotional stress, and objects are less available for gratification. The later phase (eight to twelve years) is marked by an increasing availability of objects through which gratification may be obtained. There is some softening of the superego, and the youngster is able to accept his oedipality with less disguise.

Cognition and reality testing make significant advances such that the preadolescent generally can no longer use fantasy for drive discharge. Instead, fantasy becomes a means of vicarious problem solving. Sarnoff (1976) describes four cognitive skills which develop around the age of eight and produce the shift to late latency: concrete operational thinking, abstract conceptual memory organization, the shift in fantasy contents from thoughts about fantasy objects to thoughts about reality objects, and the reorganization of introjected parental images that make up the contents of the superego. However, this nascent latency organization is greatly threatened by affects, fantasies, introspection, and verbalization and is liable to rapid regression under stress. So latency is clearly not a quiescent period, for the ego strengthening that consolidates previous gains is essential in the preparation for adolescence (Josselyn 1948, Blos 1962, Engel 1962).

Group therapy is not a superficial attempt at individual therapy with several children simultaneously. It is a special treatment modality with certain advantages and disadvantages for each individual child. However, some generalizations can be made. Peer support makes the therapist less frightening to the child and enhances the development of a treatment alliance. The group offers a real opportunity for identification as well as for the development of adaptive social skills within new extrafamilial relationships. As the child sees aspects of himself in his peers, he feels more understood and less alone. His interactions provide contemporary material which is then available for observation and therapeutic intervention. At other times, so much material may be presented that it becomes difficult to process and organize. It is often at these times that a group becomes destructive for an individual child.

Verbalization offers much therapeutic leverage in the treatment of ego-disturbed children. While play is often viewed by child therapists as equivalent to free association in the adult, it cannot truly be "free." Behavior demands limits not involved with verbal productions. Thus, regardless of exactly where these limits are drawn, the child can push the therapist and demonstrate that his play is not "free" (A. Freud 1965). Developmentally, the acquisition of speech is closely related to separation-individuation, reality testing, and secondary process thinking (Spitz 1957, 1965, Hertzler 1965, Ekstein 1966, McDevitt and Settlage 1971). Verbalization supports the child's sense of self-control, autonomy, and freedom. It expresses, promotes, and implements his separation from mother through a series of maturational steps. The infant's need for immediate instinctual relief by tension discharge yields to expression through speech and eventually to thought itself. With ego-disturbed children this developmental sequence is centrally related to their core pathology. Progression along this continuum enhances internal structure and impulse control.

The maturation of memory organization and its relationship to the nature of free association have been recently described by Sarnoff (1977). He describes a shift in late latency from unfocused fantasy play to verbalization as a means of communicating with the therapist. The capacity to recall latent abstract content through verbalization appears during late latency. Yet under stress this cognitive pattern evidences regression as well. Three discrete forms of memory organization have been described in the latency age child: affectomotor memory organization, verbal conceptual memory organization, and abstract conceptual memory organization. The affectomotor system is acquired first, consists of purposeful patterns of motor activity, and is least impaired by regression. It therefore is invaluable in play therapy, making otherwise unavailable material alive and accessible. The affective component of this memory system consists of recalling patterns in the rather more vague form of affects and perceptions. This system is certainly related to Piaget's sensorimotor stage of cognitive development and Spitz's description (1965) of coenesthetic organization. Conceptual memory involves the ability to recall learned patterns in the form of verbal signifiers. Verbal conceptual memory refers to the recall of experience through verbal schemata for naming. Abstract conceptual memory refers to recalling experiences through verbalized abstract concepts. This latter system appears between six and eight years of age and allows the child to retain the meaning of events in abstract memory with or without words. Thus one would expect the late latency child to have the capacity to verbalize present and past experience at a significant level of abstraction but also to suffer regression of this cognitive organization under stress.

Our treatment goals were similar to any insight-oriented work with children. The child is first helped to observe his behavior, both adaptive and maladaptive. This behavior is then connected to his feelings and underlying conflicts. As the child regresses, he gains understanding of these conflicts and relives with some restitution the previously unresolved parent-child relationship. As this new integration takes place, the child's inner pain is lessened, and new modes of interaction become viable.

RATIONALE FOR GROUP TECHNIQUES

The initial technical formulation drew greatly from the literature describing individual psychotherapy with the severely disturbed child

(Axline 1969, Ekstein 1966, Haworth 1964, Maenchen 1970, Pearson 1968, Szurek and Berlin 1973). Since past failures with this group seemed related to countertransference difficulties and the subsequent mismanagement of limits, a careful concrete formulation of guidelines was made. This outline would quickly confront countertransference problems as they occurred. A cotherapist was used as a check on these difficulties as well as for increased support and energy (Kassoff 1958). The technique was designed to establish certain protective limits without being pejorative. The child may not harm himself, others, or materials and must remain in the room. It was essential that interventions neither constrict nor contaminate the child's material. Thus the therapist did not stop or discourage play. Instead he sought discussion to clarify it and fantasies to expand it. Verbalization was openly encouraged and supported through his expectation. As a model he chose verbal rather than behavioral expression whenever possible and yet was always ready to use physical restraint to prevent a child from harming himself or others.

The group met twice weekly for forty-five minutes in the unit's living room. This 20' x 10' tile-walled room was furnished with chairs, steel-framed rockers, a sofa, many cabinets, several large windows, a television, a piano, a small library, and two small tables. Toys, crafts, games, and food were not provided. This room was at the end of a hall along which were the children's bedrooms. The door was locked with respect to entrance but not exit.

This approach establishes an accepting, permissive, but safe atmosphere. As others have described, the regression which occurs in such an atmosphere allows restitutive gratification and supports the uncovering and reworking of conflicts. It is only through this reliving of unresolved early (pregenital) parent-child relationships that such disturbed children can achieve internal organization and control. Attempts at socialization without such reworking are futile for the therapist and empty for the child. This brief explication of the approach conveys its general tone and style. Further elaboration continues throughout this report but especially within the clinical vignettes.

RESISTANCE PHASE

The original group was made up of four boys—Barry, Mac, Gary, and Ralph—all aged nine to eleven. While Barry, Mac, and Ralph left the group at the time of their discharge, Ellen, Bart, Kathy, and James were added at the time of their admission. Thus the group remained stable with 3–5 members.

Barry, a ten-year-old schizophrenic boy, had for years been tolerated and infantilized by his somewhat passive but quite concerned parents. Barry often flew into tantrums with his mother. On one occasion he threatened to kill her and had often destroyed furniture. His affect was flat, and his thinking disorganized.

Mac, a ten-year-old borderline boy with a duodenal ulcer, had been exploited and aggrandized by his parents, whose marriage was constantly on the verge of collapse. Mac had little ability to bind anxiety or tolerate frustration. His omnipotence, denial, and magical thinking were of near psychotic proportion, and he was repeatedly involved in antisocial behavior.

Gary, a nine-year-old boy, had petit mal epilepsy and borderline intelligence. His parents had separated several years prior to his hospitalization, leaving his mother feeling frightened and helpless. In defense she clung to Gary as if he were her own mother. Gary became increasingly destructive, demanding, and impulsive. He is best described as having a tension-discharge disorder with some neurotic components.

Ralph, an effeminate eleven-year-old borderline boy, had been abandoned by his parents except for an occasional letter. His early years were characterized by unstable, unpredictable, and at time sadomasochistic relationships. His "as if" quality was most evident in his flamboyance. He was often described as a "con man" who stimulated peers to act out vicariously for him. Prior to hospitalization he had become combative and physically destructive. In the hospital, he functioned as the leader of the group.

Ellen, a ten-year-old girl who had a terribly infantile yet powerful relationship with her parents, was admitted for aggressive, incorrigible, and violent behavior. She had many features of a tension-discharge disorder yet was easily managed on the unit.

Bart, a nine-year-old boy, was admitted for extremely impulsive, destructive behavior. Bart's maternal grandmother had died when he was three years old. His mother subsequently became seriously depressed, worsening a marriage already strained by a self-involved politician father. Bart is best described as having a tension-discharge disorder but with certain clear neurotic depressive components.

Kathy, a ten-year-old hysterical girl, was coy, flirtatious, helpless, and passive. She was admitted after a long negative pediatric and neurologic evaluation for multiple somatic complaints. Her many conversion symptoms abated immediately after admission. The extent of her regression prior to her admission indicated serious separation-individuation difficulties. Her parents had been chronically preoccupied with her health but even more specifically with her bodily functions.

James, a ten-year-old borderline boy, was admitted for hostile, severely combative, and self-destructive behavior. Though he presented very primitive, poorly integrated material, his thinking remained organized. His parents had always been emotionally unavailable and preoccupied with their own conflicts. Parenting had therefore been unreliable and consisted primarily of criticism, limit-setting, and retaliation.

In the first session the therapists described the goals and format of the group. The children were told that this was a place to talk about feelings, thoughts, and behavior so that they might better understand themselves. The guidelines previously described were briefly explained. The boys became anxious, ran around the room hitting each other, banged the rocking chairs against the walls, and used obscene language. Finding themselves in a less structured environment, they faced their own inner affects, impulses, and conflicts with only their own weak egos as defense. During this early phase of resistance there were many "fights" and aggressive displays. Sexual and exhibitionistic behavior occurred but far less frequently than aggressive and anxiety-ridden behavior. On one occasion one of the boys urinated into a wastebasket. The nondirective nature of the model was anxiety provoking and at times even disorganizing for them. The therapists were immediately confronted with determining at exactly what point the accepting and permissive attitude became destructive rather than facilitating. When should limits be set? Should children be allowed to shove or hit each other in therapy? Is there really anything destructive about urinating or exhibiting oneself within this group? The therapists were surprised at the intensity of their feelings about the group's behavior, and intense countertransference reactions became an immediate concern.

In the beginning hours it was tacitly accepted that behavior would be the major symbolic mode of expression. Clarifications and interpretations were made but usually without any clear response, verbal or behavioral. There was little cohesion, each member expressing his own internal anxiety without reference to interpersonal relationships. Despite its social inappropriateness and the therapists' anxiety, allowing this behavior promoted a controlled regression in which the child's conflicts could be observed. Anxious, hostile, sadistic, erotic, messy, demanding behavior were all accepted. Nothing was required of the child other than that he follow the basic guidelines. Such permissiveness was based on the therapists' understanding and acceptance of the children's needs. A facade would be perceived immediately by the group and result in increased defensiveness with either disorganized or inhibited play. The atmosphere created was one of acceptance. The behavior was neither condoned nor encouraged, but carefully observed. If limits had been set due to therapist anxiety, the regression would have been prevented and the conflicts remained layered under defenses. As the child's material was clarified within the regression, his behavior was viewed as a communication of his attempts at conflict resolution (Lifton and Smolen 1966). Especially when presented in play, conflicts were interpreted from the side of the ego, usually connecting the behavior to an affect rather than an impulse.

Early in treatment, confrontations emphasized the ambiguity of play. The therapist often asked a child to clarify his behavior verbally. This supported verbalization and helped the child gain secondary process control. Disorganized excited behavior unavailable to ego integration was interpreted as defense. Although uncommon, this confrontation was often important in slowing the regression and assuring the integrity of the child's ego. Regressions were almost always associated with cognitive pattern changes as well. For the most part communication did remain behavioral during this initial phase. A typical hour was filled with hitting, shoving, fighting for chairs, spitting, and other provocative behavior.

*Hour #6 (October 11).*Mac began counting how many times he would hit Gary after group because Gary had aggravated him earlier. Throughout the hour, Mac harassed Gary physically and verbally, finally shoving him out of his chair and threatening to grab his penis. Ralph watched passively. The therapist repeatedly encouraged Mac and Gary to verbalize their feelings. Mac finally acknowledged being anxious, stating that he knew he could not "get away with this anyplace but in here," and ultimately, "I don't want anyone to talk about anything during group today!" Gary sat on the therapist's lap and drooled on him, thus communicating his helplessness, fear, and anger at the therapist for not protecting him. When it became clear that Gary was unable to verbalize these feelings, the therapist did so for him. Gary called Ralph a name, and Ralph looked hurt but only mumbled something under his breath. Toward the end of the session, the therapist suggested that Gary had been mad at Mac and directed his anger at Ralph. He further suggested that Mac's behavior was his way of dealing with uncomfortable feelings. One of the therapists reminded the group that he was to be gone for two weeks. Mac replied, "Good, then we'll raise hell!" Ralph then asked several reality-oriented questions about the therapist's absence, including where he was going and why. The therapist answered the questions and the session ended.

Frequently the aggressive provocative behavior required physical restraint. Often when a therapist restrained a child, the other children would taunt and tease them both. At times this resulted in violent struggles. Exploration of the obvious vicarious elements in the taunting frequently converted the communication into words.

*Hour #9 (November 6).*In the previous hour Ellen had been in a physical power struggle with one of the therapists. Throughout the session she had spit, kicked, hit, pinched, and bit. At the beginning of the ninth hour, Mac was very aggressive and disruptive, preventing anyone from talking. The therapists attempted to explore his behavior. "You are running around the room pushing, shoving, and hitting people. It makes me wonder if you are upset?" Mac said that he was extremely angry about a canceled visit with his parents. Unable to control himself, Mac was restrained by one of the therapists before he could hurt a peer. The other therapist tried to verbally clarify connections between Mac's behavior and his feelings of sadness, pain, and anger. While exploring this, Mac became tearful and said, "I just want to be left alone." He was soon released and went off into the corner to tearfully look out the window. His peers became involved in aggressive behavior, and one of the therapists suggested that their behavior represented some feelings about Mac's crying. One of the group responded, "Well, what can we do about it anyway?" It was suggested that they might try to let Mac know they understood what he was feeling.

The relationship between behavior and feelings was clarified for the children through observation of their own interactions. In turn these observations enhanced group cohesion as they emphasized interpersonal relationships. This and the following hour exemplify their lack of internal control, the therapist's management dilemma, and the children's search for new more adaptive modes of behavior. Both the impulsive behavior and the permissive management caused such strong affective reactions in the milieu staff that their attitude was ambivalent at best during this period. Their reactions will be discussed more fully later, in the section "Therapist-Staff Alliance," but include some of the same countertransference difficulties encountered in the therapists.

Hour #11 (November 13). The three boys anxiously ran around the room while Ellen watched. They talked about how strong and phallic they were and compared themselves to the male therapist. "I'm the biggest. I'm the strongest. I'll bet mine's bigger than yours!" The therapist clarified their concerns about how "big, strong, and manly" they were, and the boys became less agitated. However, when their fears were connected with the admission of a girl into group, two of the boys exhibited themselves and the other went around the corner to unzip his pants. One of them, laughing anxiously, then urinated into a wastebasket. The therapist clarified their fears of bodily harm. He then suggested that their exhibitionism was related to Ellen's presence and that their nakedness reassured them that their bodies and penises were okay. At the end of the session the therapist suggested that the wastebasket be cleaned up. They looked at one another for a moment, and then two of the boys volunteered. Ultimately, the one who had urinated took responsibility for cleaning up his mess. Their behavior communicated their attempts to defend against the castrated helplessness stimulated by the presence of a girl. For these boys, being masculine served as defense against core pregenital struggles.

Our initial formulation emphasized the need for latency age children, ego-disturbed ones in particular, to communicate through behavior. It was our subjective impression that such material would not have been available with a less permissive therapeutic technique.

The first three months of treatment continued with provocative, socially inappropriate behavior. In a session shortly after the one above, two of the boys removed all of their clothes and excitedly ran around the room. At the end of that session they settled into their chairs and verbalized their guilt. Although they were never asked to put their clothes on, the therapist openly stated that this behavior was socially inappropriate and must again represent some very powerful fears of helplessness and bodily damage.

During this resistance period it seemed clear that these children were able to verbalize only after their behavior had been accepted. As treatment progressed, we developed an additional criterion for allowable behavior: the play must maintain an interface with the child's observing ego. In other words, play that was expressive of panic or that was otherwise unavailable for discussion would be shut down. Exhibitionistic play was allowed when, rather than merely increasing their guilt, anxiety, and confusion, it offered the opportunity for greater integration. Though the children were usually unable to explore the underlying affects or conflicts which drove the exhibitionism, they would regain control before the session's end and dress themselves. Most important, they were able to discuss the behavior itself. The content centered around issues of power, helplessness, and fear. Other group members offered support by remarking on the social inappropriateness of the behavior and at times by expressing their disgust. Often after therapy the group would spontaneously discuss such behavior with the child-care workers. During these discussions the group explored various aspects of their behavior, including how upset it made them, how they should only do it during therapy, how afraid they were before doing it, how doing it made them more afraid, and how nice it was not to be punished. This ability to discuss the behavior was taken as validation that the material was in fact available to their observing egos, to secondary process control, and for further ego integration. The play was not so frightening as to be dissociated or repressed; the therapists' stance was tentatively confirmed as facilitating.

This management of limits was decisive in cementing a therapeutic alliance during the early phase of treatment. Certainly it is now clear that countertransference dilemmas were ubiquitous. Even after pondering the situation over a period of several years, we are no closer to a black or white answer, only more comfortable with our uncertainty. To our minds, most of the puzzle yet to be unraveled involves the management of sexual behavior. On some occasions it was clear that limits were set improperly due to countertransference difficulties.

In one session Mac asked to use the restroom. Knowing Mac was aware of the limit, the therapist did not respond. Mac again asked to leave the room but met no response. His peers encouraged him to leave, and suddenly he darted out the door. Instead of physically controlling Mac, the therapist allowed him to return and then asked how he felt about being allowed to leave. Mac looked anxious but denied any feeling. The therapist apologized to him for not stopping him and asked if he understood the apology. Mac said he did. The therapist's error was first in not responding verbally to Mac's implied conflict about control: "You're wondering if you need help from me to control yourself?" Secondly, the therapist, angry at Mac, was unable to set the limit and thereby make it clear that Mac's presence was important. Further, the therapist's anger had caused him to respond to Mac as if they were in a struggle for control rather than trying to clarify Mac's attempt to set up such a struggle. In a later and similar incident with another child, both he and Mac described feelings of sadness about the therapist's allowing them to leave the room.

In another session, one of the boys was inadvertently allowed to physically hurt another. The therapist explored the group's feelings and thoughts about the interaction. They were unable to look at the therapist's role in this until he had apologized for not controlling them. They then expressed anger toward the therapist and discussed their wish to have been stopped in this and in their earlier exhibitionism. They feared their lack of control and knew that it made them feel bad afterwards. The therapist reassured them of his confidence that they could control themselves aggressively and sexually, and supportively recalled how they had always spontaneously dressed themselves.

This latter session raised questions in our minds again about our permissive stance. Here the group clearly stated their anger about being allowed to act out, their fears of losing control, and their subsequent guilt after acting out. However, it is not so simple that one can take such statements as a direct guide to therapeutic technique. One would not consider "preventing" an adult hysteric from falling in love, even though he knows full well she may feel guilty. Though a very complex problem, it is easily formulated in a question: To what extent can a therapist treat a child's play as verbal communication and when must he respond to it as behavior in a social sense?

As the group evolved, a strong coalition developed among the children with a defiant, rebellious attitude toward the therapists. The group repeatedly used physical attacks to provoke a power struggle. United, they found they could attack the therapists and occasionally escape into the hall. This struggle dominated session after session, leaving the entire group physically exhausted. Therapy became a ritualized battle with all the frustration, gratification, fear, and guilt inherent in the physical interactions. During this period there was an obvious reduction of anxiety, disorganization, and isolation. However, the combative behavior was repetitive, stereotyped, and intrapsychically defensive. Once it became apparent that verbal intervention would be ineffective, the therapists were confronted with all the complex factors involved in limit setting.

The use of limits has been discussed at length in the literature (Schiffer 1952, Ginott 1961, Axline 1969). While limits served various functions in this group, some easier to formalize and apply than others, they primarily assured the safety of all participants, both physically and emotionally. Just as diligently as the therapist prevents a chair from being thrown, he must guard against overwhelming anxiety and destructive, abusive interactions. The therapist may also use limits to redirect impulses into symbolic and sublimated channels. The child finds his impulses less frightening as he gains mastery over them and finds himself becoming more socially acceptable. In the process he gains new adaptive skills. Limits may be used to confront the child with reality by deflating his omnipotence, magical thinking, and narcissism. However, this is a delicate task with children who defend against feelings of annihilation and helplessness with fragile omnipotent, narcissistic defenses. Confrontation may be felt as an attack, the result of their own harsh superego projections. At times limits may be set for an impulse-ridden child to protect him from his superego. This seems especially indicated when playing out his conflicts would only frighten him and increase his guilt without facilitating better integration. Other children may need limits to support examination of why they act on their impulses when they repeatedly feel guilty afterward. On rare occasions limits may be used to help the therapist maintain an accepting, empathic, and respectful attitude. Limits keep behavior from exceeding the therapist's tolerance and are successful to the extent that the therapist lacks neurotic conflicts in the areas the children are trying to rework. Such limits apply only to behavior and never to verbalization. Limits may be set at times for reasons related to particular dynamic interactions within the group. Such limits may be viewed as "artificial" or as attempts to "manipulate" affect and promote verbalization.

After many attempts to explore Ralph's behavior verbally, it was suggested that he sit alone so that he might better be able to talk about his feelings. Ralph and the group responded negatively to the mere suggestion, and the limit was never set. On another occasion, the group had continually and actively ignored a peer who during recent sessions had tried to talk about her problems. The others argued loudly, wrestled, or laughed so as to disrupt her verbal efforts. Verbal confrontations were futile and on one occasion the therapist tried to set a limit by telling the group to shut up so that the girl might be heard. The group could not respond until the therapist set the limit without the anxiety-provoking anger inherent in the words "shut up." The limit placed in sharp relief both the girl's sense of helplessness and the boys' disregard for her.

Of course at times limits must be set for such external reasons as time, vacation, or illness. Ginott (1961), for example, has felt that limits may occasionally be set for reasons of law, ethics, or social acceptability. One must be certain that such limits do not originate in the therapist's own superego. In this group, limits were designed not to allay therapist, staff, or parental anxiety, but only in response to the children's needs as best they could be discerned.

With this perspective on limits, an understanding of the dynamics at play in the rebellion was critical. These attacks represented a particular kind of resistance. The group was challenging the therapists' sense of competence, their expectation of verbalization, and their ability to tolerate intense emotions and impulses. Therapy could not proceed or defenses be modified until these attributes in the therapists were assured. Just as in adult work, the therapist's consistent unwavering pursuit of understanding must be tested (Greenson 1967). The partial identification with this aspect of the therapist (his analyzing ego) creates one strand of the working alliance. Of secondary importance in the resistance was the group's scapegoating the therapists to enhance their peer relationships. However, verbal attempts to explore these and other dynamics were without response. Some form of limit-setting would be necessary to confront the resistance.

In an ongoing dialogue, the unit staff emphasized the children's investment in group therapy and the therapists. The children's overt furor was in fact a defense against very intense affectionate, dependent, and regressive longings. With such an attachment their presence in group could now be made contingent on their behavior (Scheidlinger 1965). Internal controls could be demanded on the same basis as in the normal development of the toddler.

Technically, then, the hall was made part of the therapeutic setting. If a child could not control his behavior in the living room, he was to be in the hall. The therapist would first suggest that the child control his behavior. If there were no response, and the behavior continued, the therapist would verbalize his intentions to restrain him, to ask him to leave, or to force him to leave. Remarkably, a therapist might now have to push a child out the door and into the hall.

After an explanation, the children ran from the room to spend the rest of the session in regressive play and language in the hall. The therapists stayed in the living room and talked. In the second session, one child remained with the therapists, and within a few sessions all the children remained in the room. It is important to note that being out of control and leaving the room was permitted and at times even demanded by the therapists; but it was clear they preferred that the child control himself and remain in the room.

The ritualized attempts to leave the room were a behavioral resistance. A verbal interpretation of this transference-resistance would have included the rebellion as defense against positive affect, dependency, regression, and fears of both separation and fusion. The therapists' behavioral response was in effect such an interpretation, demonstrating awareness of the children's unconscious positive transference longings. Such transference-resistance analysis establishes another crucial strand of the working alliance (Greenson 1967). Space does not allow further elaboration on the vicissitudes of establishing such an alliance with ego-disturbed children. However, as illustrated in the following clinical material, one was certainly negotiated within this group.

THERAPIST-STAFF ALLIANCE

Any therapeutic work with children requires involvement with a third party: parent, guardian, caseworker, or inpatient staff. Because the child cannot be totally responsible for himself, the therapist must form an alliance with this third party as well as with the child. When therapy deals openly with very intense feelings and archaic conflicts, this alliance becomes increasingly more difficult (Blotcky et al. 1975).

The inpatient staff was apprehensive and skeptical about the competence of therapists who were not involved in immediate day-to-day milieu management. They held the therapists' responses to the children's conversation and behavior suspect, and felt that inappropriate behavior was being sanctioned rather than merely accepted. Staff perceived this project as destructive to the overall treatment program. Furthermore, it threatened their sense of therapeutic competence by stirring them to question their own formulations.

Resistance was evident in both subtle and overt forms. Sometimes children were unavailable for therapy. At other times resistance was heard in the tone of the child-care worker's voice as he related a child's description of that day's session. Such affect was likely perceived by the children as deprecatory of the therapist, of the treatment sessions, or, most unfortunately, of their own internal life.

Some of this resistance was related to countertransference difficulties within therapists and staff. Such reactions are a serious and pervasive problem in treating such primitive children as are in this group. Their archaic conflicts induced intense anxiety, affects, and reactions in everyone.

Two of the many examples of this capacity to induce countertransference reactions seem especially cogent. On one occasion the unit director glanced through the window in the living room door. Seeing several children exhibiting themselves, he impulsively opened the door to comment that "children who can't keep their clothes on just might not be ready for family visits." Such an intrusion was unprecedented, unplanned, and more in response to affect than to reason.

At another time the group was regularly presented by one of the therapists in an open supervisory session. Those who participated often found themselves stimulated to heated discussions in response to their own anxiety. Thus, even secondhand, the material was quite potent.

Countertransference in the therapists could be the topic of an entire paper, but it seems relevant to describe its most troublesome aspects here. The direct demands made upon play therapists by children appear to expedite the development of countertransference reactions. There seems to be a positive correlation between the intensity of these demands and the necessity for narcissistic endowment of the patients in order to maintain consistent empathy (Rubenstein and Levitt 1957). Two primary reactions proved most difficult and have been touched upon in the clinical material presented. The first is the rage, so unacceptable to us as helping professionals. The anger was related to the therapists' narcissistic need to "fix" the kids, to control what seemed uncontrollable, but, probably more important, to defend against intense feelings of fear and impotence. The second area of major difficulty was in understanding the children's sexuality and our own response to it. It seemed tedious at best and shameful at worst to examine our own excitement, fears, and confusion. Probably no area is more confusing to man than sexuality, and we became more acutely aware of our own personal beliefs, attitudes, and conflicts when confronted with such stark behavioral material as described in these latency age children. Our countertransference problems in these and other areas were tackled through the mutual support of cotherapists and with the help of a supervisor not involved with the unit in any way. Finding a safe setting in which to explore these issues seemed an absolute necessity.

Repeated attempts were made to help staff become aware of their resistance. Both formal and informal meetings resulted in intellectual discussions without closure. It took nearly three months for staff to openly express their anger and confusion. The therapists shared their conviction in their theoretical base but also some similar concerns and anxiety about the material and how to manage it. This initiated a dialogue which rapidly produced a lasting staff alliance.

Parallel to these discussions, a research project was designed to measure variables with regard to the therapy sessions and the children's pre- and posttherapy functioning. One purpose of this endeavor was to objectively assess the impact of these sessions on the children and thus resolve some of the questions of both staff and therapists. Possibly more important, the project was a way to unite therapists and staff as peers with a common goal. The research design supported the treatment alliance, as it was a concrete representation of the therapists' respect for the staff and their willingness to collaboratively examine their treatment model. The significance of the factors creating this therapist-staff alliance are difficult to separate and sort out, but certainly as that relationship became less conflicted the working alliance with the children solidified and stabilized.

To summarize the resistance phase: group development had progressed through a tumultuous resistance phase. In the permissive setting the children's anxiety about their impulses was demonstrated in their provocative testing behavior. A resistant coalition, which scapegoated the therapists and defended the children, developed into an overt rebellion. Through understanding that resistance and the dynamics of latency, the therapists were able to make a behavioral interpretation. On the crest of the therapeutic alliance, they could see a new treatment phase on the horizon.

TREATMENT PHASE

As difficult as the initial phase was, the middle phase was equally rewarding. Behavior and interactions that were confusing became more predictable and comprehensible, and often even interpretable. Material about unit and home life became apparent and was easily connected to the children's immediate behavior and feelings. Patterns of interaction with parents, staff, peers, and therapists were clarified and pointed out. On occasion transference interpretations were made. The children had internalized to some extent the therapists' expectations and understanding of therapy. Now there were times when the children could use their observing egos, gain some distance from the material, and learn something about themselves.

Two major destructive group processes became evident. The first was scapegoating, whereby group members displaced feelings onto one of their peers in order to avoid uncomfortable feelings themselves. The scapegoat would then allow and even encourage such interaction based on his own dynamic needs. During the resistance phase the group had scapegoated the therapists in displacing their sibling rivalry and thus enhanced their peer relationships. However, many less dramatic forms of scapegoating continued during the treatment phase.

A similarly destructive process was the suppression of verbalization as occurred in Hour #6. A child's identification with a verbalizing peer often reawakened his own anxiety about similar conflicts. Suppression occurred as a defense against the pain and fear elicited primarily by discussion of family problems or loss of a parent. It took the form of boisterous play, laughter, or physical fights. The therapist was ineffective unless he could identify and interpret the resistance motivation. Blatant disregard for a child's painful feelings was often negatively responded to by the therapist if confrontation and interpretation had failed. Although limits were not set, the therapist might eventually remind a child that he could leave if he were too uncomfortable. In this way the group could support his peers' discussion. A child was never forced into the hall because of disruptive verbalization; however, on two occasions a child left because of his own anxiety.

A technique found extremely useful for controlling destructive behavior was limiting a child to a particular chair. This technique allowed James, a very disturbed boy, to borrow enough structure and ego to control his behavior and remain in the room. James always preferred using the chair to exclusion into the hall. Frightened of his impulsivity, he was quite willing to accept the chair as a limit. This technique has obvious advantages and almost entirely supplanted exclusion into the hall, which could become very destructive with certain children. Similar techniques for supporting a child's ego have been reported elsewhere (Sugar 1974).

We were amazed, as were Barcai and Robinson (1969), who reported earlier, at the sensitive areas that could be verbally explored within a latency group. These youngsters could be empathic, supportive, and understanding.

*Hour #54 (May 7).*Ralph spoke of his effeminate characteristics and of his often being mistaken for a girl. With the group's support he explained how he once exposed himself to convince some peers of his masculinity. The group was empathic, understanding, and helpful. They then suggested that his mode of dress might be confusing. The therapist used this opportunity to recall past exhibitionism in the group and wondered if it had been to communicate feelings similar to Ralph's.

Increasingly, the children were able to respond to a peer's pain with support, understanding, and attempts to help rather than with fear and suppression of verbalization. The clarity of play during this phase is well illustrated when just prior to the termination of one cotherapist the children played out their concerns about being taken care of as well as their identification with the feeding aspect of the therapists.

Hour #44 (April 1)."Tea party" was a fantasy/game in which the children served the therapists a meal. The therapists actively interacted with the children in the play. Sometimes the orders were silly; sometimes they were socially appropriate meals. Frequently there were anal messing aspects to the way they served the food. Often they made pizzas with "crazy" things on top of them. The session was a way to deal with their separation fears around the loss of the therapist. Attempts to connect their play with the anticipated loss were unsuccessful in stimulating discussion. This resistance was reflective of their core problems around separation.

Although the therapists did not actively interpret, clarify, or confront, they were behaviorally involved in the play in an accepting way. As in individual therapy, such play allows children to observe and rework their pregenital conflicts. With time, the alliance became strong enough and the group secure enough that the members began to observe and discuss group process.

*Hour #60 (June 4).*As in several previous hours, the boys anxiously tried to sit near Ms. R. Frequently they looked at the male therapist (Dr. B) as they negotiated their seating arrangements. On Dr. B's initiative, the members compared and contrasted their feelings about Ms. R and himself. They discussed their sexual feelings and openly acknowledged their discomfort with them. The content included competition, power, and jealousy. Attempts to help Kathy, the only girl, verbalize her feelings were unsuccessful. She blushed and giggled but was unable to talk. Exploration of the oedipal material continued during the next few hours with some transference understanding gained by at least one member.

Hour #62 (June 11). After some negotiation, Gary sat on Ms. R's lap. There was some cuddling, and then he moved to sit between her and Kathy. He began flirting with them both. When he felt rejected by Kathy, he began tugging and poking her. He turned to Ms. R and began talking with her. As he became sexually aroused, the flirting became more aggressive and provocative, and Ms. R rejected it. Dr. B suggested that Gary's sexual feelings made him uncomfortable with Kathy and then with Ms. R and that he had begun fighting to relieve the anxiety. Gary acknowledged this with a smile but became increasingly provocative. It was again suggested that Gary's behavior reflected his anxiety and guilt about his sexual feelings and that his fighting was to hide this from himself. Gary then walked over to Dr. B and put his head on his lap. Dr. B suggested that this confirmed the interpretation and that Gary wanted Dr. B's acceptance despite the frightening sexual feelings. Throughout, Bart and Ralph had vicariously encouraged Gary's flirting while Kathy had sat passively inhibited.

Hour #63 (June 13). Bart sat on Ms. R's lap, while Kathy looked longingly at them, giggled, and rubbed Ms. R's arm. Dr. B initiated a discussion by asking Kathy about her giggling. She was unable to explore it and only blushed. Dr. B then recalled for her the previous hour and Gary's feelings for Ms. R. Kathy then acknowledged her affectionate feelings for Dr. B and some feelings of embarrassment associated with the warmth. At that point Gary became both verbally and physically provocative with Ms. R. This was again interpreted as defending against sexual feelings that made him anxious. Gary continued, and Dr. B pursued it by reflecting that this might be related to his competitive feelings. Gary became increasingly agitated and provocative. Dr. B noted that Gary seemed so anxious that he might need to choose between controlling his behavior or leaving the room. Gary apologized and pleaded but then returned to the teasing behavior with Ms. R. She repeatedly grabbed his hands while verbalizing limits. Eventually he was able to calm down. As the hour ended, he became sad and tearful.

Immediately upon leaving the session, he became disruptive, aggressive, and unmanageable. He was fearful that his separated parents would divorce and he would lose his father. This had been a carefully defended topic which the therapists had attempted to explore many times in earlier sessions. Gary now said that he felt as if Ms. R were his mother and Dr. B his father. He feared anger and rejection from them both. In later hours he was able to discuss this directly within the group. Ultimately he began meeting with his mother to discuss his fears, anger, sadness, and guilt.

Although one may question allowing Gary to play out such modified sexual fantasies and conflicts given the disruptive behavior immediately after the session described, the results seemed clear. Gary had displayed through behavior what he had been unable to verbalize. His anxiety was due not to the absence of controls during therapy but to his general ego-weakness in the face of powerful instinctual pressures, an intense and unresolved oedipal conflict, and fears of abandonment (some realistic).

Hour #65 (June 20). This was Ralph's last session in group, and the children had planned a surprise party with soft drinks and ice cream. Ralph was surprised and everyone responded with laughter. Some jokes were made about the "crazy" flavors of ice cream they had put in the sodas. The therapists initiated a discussion of how group would be after Ralph was gone and supported him in discussing his own feelings. The group then spoke of their mixed feelings about his leaving. Gary said, "I just want you to know that I *am* worried about my parents getting a divorce and losing my daddy," as if to offer him this meaningful piece of personal information before his discharge. One therapist asked Ralph how he felt he would do and then discussed with him his own appraisal of Ralph's growth during the hospitalization. The therapist suggested to him that he might have some difficulty with his needs to manipulate and that he try to be aware of this aspect of himself. Ralph acknowledged this, and as the session ended the therapists hugged Ralph and wished him well.

Hour #66 (June 27). This was the first session after Ralph's discharge. Bart climbed all over a rocking chair, banging it back and forth against the wall. He said that he was mad. When the therapists asked him to elaborate, he answered in nonsensical phrases. Kathy sat listening silently. Gary had brought his radio and turned his chair away from the group to isolate himself. Ms. R empathically tried to help Bart get in touch with his anger without any success. Gary then asked him if he were mad about the incident the night before. Bart quickly settled into a discussion with Gary about that difficulty. Soon this became an exploration of what the group was like without Ralph. Bart was unhappy since Ralph had left. Gary felt left out because Bart had a better relationship with Kathy than he. The group was quite verbal and explored their fears about which of them would be excluded now that there were only three of them.

These vignettes illustrate how these latency age children were able to genuinely observe themselves and the group process, and then examine the changes within that process. They also demonstrate how communicating an understanding of a child's behavior can change that behavior within a group just as in individual therapy. An example is Gary's intervention with Bart, which shifted his behavior and allowed him to verbalize his concerns. At times, as in the illustration, this may be done even more readily by a peer than by a therapist.

The role of a mixed group in latency is controversial. It was obvious that within this predominantly male group the addition of a female did increase the overall anxiety level. In response the boys exposed themselves, defending against fears of castration, abandonment, disintegration, or fusion. Whatever the dynamics, their anxiety was clearly heightened. However, the mixed group was never felt to be unmanageable and occasionally even facilitated material clarifying some of the youngsters' concerns.

DISCUSSION

The evolution of this group is similar to that reported by others (Schiedlinger 1960, Lifton and Smolen 1966, Schiffer 1969, Gratton and Rizzo 1969, Sugar 1974). The early resistance phase corresponds to Schiffer's preparatory phase, in which the therapeutic atmosphere allowed the expression of thoughts and feelings but also led to increasing anxiety and guilt. The therapist's acceptance tended to alleviate these feelings but only after the children first tested the stability of the unfamiliar ground. Uncomfortable with their new experience they attempted to re-create previous conflicted relationships within the present situation. During this phase the guided gratification and regression as described by Schiedlinger (1960, 1965a) were essential in allowing conflictual material to become available. In our experience the group became more cohesive as the transference intensified. Using the analogy with a family, siblings find support in each other as their control struggle with parents intensifies. So also, as the group members entered a control struggle with the therapist, their mutual identifications became apparent. The therapists nurtured the observing ego of the group by clarifying behaviors as interactional. These clarifications supported their understanding of interpersonal relationships and their awareness of group process. Peer relationships were fostered through mutual empathy and identifications, as in Hour #54. The children were confronted with their infantile, unproductive patterns of behavior and the group was invited to verbalize their views. Whenever possible, confrontation was an observation and not a limit. Discussion was always encouraged but never demanded. Play was not disparaged or neglected, but instead accepted and clarified. Its restriction usually led to increased anxiety and defensiveness, with a subsequent deterioration of verbalization and cognitive patterns.

The therapist's role was active and involved but not intrusive. He observed behavior as communication and verbally reflected it back for the group—whenever possible without intervention. He aligned himself with the children's ego by not responding to his own or their anxiety in ways that would shut off further exploration or integration. Socially unacceptable play was allowed in an attempt to undermine projective defenses and to socialize severely punitive and ineffective superegos. The therapist encouraged the children to use the group as they chose, to express fantasies in word or play—in essence, to free associate. When their anxiety became disorganizing, the therapist confronted that process and if necessary set appropriate limits. At the same time, the therapist conveyed his confidence that the children's feelings would destroy neither them nor him and that he could be trusted to set protective limits.

The resistance phase has been described in some detail. Most prominent were anxiety, disorganization, isolation, and play rather than verbalization. At three months, noticeable changes were evident in the group's resistant posture. Once the group had coalesced with the establishment of a working alliance, the addition of a child stimulated regression and resistance but the persistent isolation and disorganization never recurred.

The treatment phase first declared itself in the rebellious buds of group cohesion. The changes were striking to observe as over the course of merely a few weeks the treatment alliance crystallized. The children began to identify with and trust the therapist's analytic position. With a tested and reliable alliance and an expanding observing ego they were able to do more than merely discharge tension or gratify impulses. They were now able to use verbalization. Behavior became a secondary mode of communication. As they grew to understand the connection between behavior and internal motivation, they developed the first signs of increased internal control. Fighting and exhibitionism became unusual occurrences except during times of particular stress. Isolation and withdrawal disappeared as their pain was repeatedly shared with their peers. At times, panic and disorganization did reappear. Such excited behavior represented both tension-discharge and defense of especially sensitive areas. However, by appropriate interpretation and reaffirmation of his observing stance, the therapist was now able to support the children in observing and understanding themselves. The therapist's anticipation of such anxious behavior readies him to observe and analyze it.

CONCLUSION

In our experience these severely disturbed latency age children were able to deal verbally with many conflictual areas. They used the support of the group ego in establishing meaningful verbal contact with peers and therapists. It is our impression that these children could not have been treated with a completely verbal technique, for only through the acceptance of their "terrible" behavior were they able to verbalize. We have demonstrated this ability but not through the exclusion of play. One cannot expect ego-disturbed latency children to sit still and talk. In accord with Sugar (1974), it seemed clear to us that this group would never have moved past the initial resistance phase had the therapists fallen into a more directive role, even if this were the exclusion of play.

Schiffer (1969) felt that the young latency age child could not gain true ideational insight but only experiential insight. Our group of older latency age children did use transference relationships to increase their understanding of previous and present relationships. Although they achieved some ideational insight, it was our impression that conflict resolution was less related to this than to the corrective emotional experience.

Several factors were significant in the successful outcome of this project. Unlike most therapy groups, these children lived together. On the unit they developed intense relationships and a certain rapport which must have had great influence on the nature of the whole treatment process. The alliance with the inpatient staff was of immeasurable support to both the therapists and the children. The ongoing dialogue provided timely reports of the children's day-to-day life and their behavior. The frequency of sessions, twice weekly, seemed important in strengthening the working alliance and in supporting the intense regression. And certainly the inpatient unit itself offered considerable outside structure for these ego-impaired children.

What have we learned, and what other techniques might be employed? First, this technique seemed to successfully achieve the stated goals: the acquisition of insight, the diminution of pain, and an integration to higher levels of adaptation. In our experience, the absence of toys, the exclusion of food, and the presence of a mixed group were certainly manageable. The use of a cotherapist was essential in meeting both the children's and the therapists' needs. Much energy was spent with the cotherapist in mutual support and was crucial in counteracting a persistent tendency toward using more directive techniques.

However, certain variations in technique might have been more effective and certainly warrant further exploration. The use of food might be helpful in managing the anxiety of the initial phase. In this project food was excluded to avoid the limits involved around its management. It also might be advisable to provide a few carefully selected toys to support sublimation, displacement, and the communication of fantasies. In this regard, puppets, costumes, masks, and a punching dummy might be introduced. In our experience, the children often brought toys into the group, and unless dangerous these were always allowed. Although their symbolic meanings were rarely open for exploration by the group, they served as significant data for the therapist.

Patient selection for a verbally oriented, nondirective latency group is an important issue. Overtly psychotic, autistic, and organically impaired children are inappropriate for such groups. Mute children must probably be excluded because of the emphasis on verbalization. However, the technique seems especially applicable to latency youngsters diagnosed as having severe character pathology, a severe developmental deviation, a behavior disorder, a severe neurosis, or a tension discharge disorder, or who are considered borderline or atypical. The technique certainly seems appropriate for the mild to moderately neurotic child, though other techniques may be better suited. The one psychotic child in this group did poorly and was noticeably disruptive to group process.

The literature is still sparse in detailed accounts of groups with ego-disturbed children. It is interesting to speculate whether the technique examined in this paper could be effective on an outpatient basis. There have been reports on latency groups with moderately ill outpatients, but none with such seriously impaired youngsters. It is our impression, however, that with certain modifications the technique might be applicable on an outpatient basis to many ego-disturbed children. Some of the critical parameters would be the third-party alliance, the home situation, and the school setting.

REFERENCES

Axline, V. (1969). *Play Therapy*. New York: Ballantine Books.

Barcai, A., and Robinson, E. (1969). Conventional group therapy with pre-adolescent children. *International Journal of Group Psychotherapy* 19:334–345.

Bardill, D. (1972). Behavior contracting and group therapy with pre-adolescent males in a residential setting. *International Journal of Group Psychotherapy* 22:333–342.

Berkovitz, I., Chikahisa, P., Lee, M., and Murasaki, P. (1966). Psychosexual development of latency-age children and adolescents in group therapy in a residential setting. *International Journal of Group Psychotherapy* 16:344–356.

Blos, P. (1962). *On Adolescence: A Psychoanalytic Interpretation*. New York: Free Press.

Blotcky, M., Wiggins K., Sheinbein, M., and Forgotson, F. (1978). The development of a therapist-staff alliance on an inpatient unit. *Acta Paedopsychiatrica* 43:233–241.

Bornstein, B. (1951). On latency. *Psychoanalytic Study of the Child* 6:279–285.

Buxbaum, E. (1945). Transference and group formation in children and adolescents. *Psychoanalytic Study of the Child* 1:351–365.

Coolidge, J. and Grunebaum, M. (1964). Individual and group therapy of a latency-age child. *International Journal of Group Psychotherapy* 14:84–96.

Ekstein, R. (1966). *Children of Time and Space, of Action and Impulse*. New York: Appleton-Century-Crofts.

Engel, G. (1962). *Psychological Development in Health and Disease*. Philadelphia: W. B. Saunders.

Epstein, N., and Altman, S. (1972). Experiences in converting an activity group into verbal group therapy with latency-age boys. *International Journal of Group Psychotherapy* 22:93–100.

Foulkes, S., and Anthony, E. (1957). *Group Psychotherapy: The Psychoanalytic Approach*. Baltimore: Penguin Books.

Freud, A. (1965). *Normality and Pathology in Childhood: Assessments of Development*. New York: International Universities Press.

Ginott, H. (1961). *Group Psychotherapy with Children: The Theory and Practice of Play-Therapy*. New York: McGraw-Hill.

Gratton, L., and Rizzo, A. (1969). Group psychotherapy with young psychotic children. *International Journal of Group Psychotherapy* 19:63–71.

Greenson, R. (1967). *The Technique and Practice of Psychoanalysis*. New York: International Universities Press.

Haworth, M. (1964). *Child Psychotherapy*. New York: Basic Books.

Hertzler, J. (1965). A *Sociology of Language*. New York: Random Books.

Josselyn, I. (1948). *Psychosocial Development of Children*. New York: Family Service Association of America.

Karson, S. (1965). Group psychotherapy with latency-age boys. *International Journal of Group Psychotherapy* 15:81–89.

Kassoff, A. (1958). Advantages of multiple therapists in a group of severely acting-out adolescent boys. *International Journal of Group Psychotherapy* 8:70–75.

Kestenberg, J. (1969). Problems of technique of child analysis in relation to the various developmental stages: prelatency. *Psychoanalytic Study of the Child* 24:358–383.

Lewis, M. (1974). Interpretation in child analysis: developmental considerations. *Journal of the American Academy of Child Psychiatry* 13:32–53.

Lieberman, F. (1964). Transition from latency to prepuberty in girls: an activity group becomes an interview group. *International Journal of Group Psychotherapy* 14:455–464.

Lifton, N., and Smolen, E. (1966). Group psychotherapy with schizophrenic children. *International Journal of Group Psychotherapy* 16:23–41.

MacLennan, B., and Rosen, B. (1963). Female therapists in activity group therapy with boys in latency. *International Journal of Group Psychotherapy* 13:34–42.

Maenchen, A. (1970). On the technique of child analysis in relation to stages of development. *Psychoanalytic Study of the Child* 25:175–208.

McDevitt, J., and Settlage, C. (1971). *Separation-Individuation*. New York: International Universities Press.

Pearson, G., ed. (1968). *A Handbook of Child Psychoanalysis*. New York: Basic Books.

Rose, S. (1973). *Treating Children in Groups*. San Francisco: Jossey-Bass.

Rubenstein, B., and Levitt, M. (1957). Some observations regarding the role of fathers in child psychotherapy. *Bulletin of the Menninger Clinic* 21:16–27.

Sands, R. and Golub, S. (1974). Breaking the bonds of tradition: A reassessment of group treatment of latency-age children. *American Journal of Psychiatry* 13:662–665.

Sarnoff, C. (1971). Ego structure in latency. *Psychoanalytic Quarterly*. 40:387–414.

——— (1976). *Latency*. New York: Jason Aronson.

——— (1977). Developmental considerations in the psychotherapy of latency-age children. Unpublished manuscript.

Scheidlinger, S. (1960). Experiential group treatment of severely deprived latency-age children. *American Journal of Orthopsychiatry* 30:356–368.

——— (1965a). Three group approaches with socially deprived latency-age children. *International Journal of Group Psychotherapy* 15:434–445.

——— (1965b). The concept of latency—implications for group treatment. Presented at the Forty-Second Annual Meeting of the American Orthopsychiatric Association, New York.

Scheidlinger, S., and Rauche, E. (1972). Psychoanalytic group psychotherapy with children and adolescents. In *Handbook of Child Psychoanalysis*, ed. B. Wolman, pp. 364–375. New York: Van Nostrand Reinhold.

Schiffer, M. (1952). Permissiveness versus sanction in activity group therapy. *International Journal of Group Psychotherapy* 2:255–261.

———— (1969). *The Therapeutic Play Group*. New York: Grune and Stratton.

Semonsky, C., and Zicht, G. (1974). Activity group parameters. *Journal of the American Academy of Child Psychiatry* 13:166–179.

Slavson, S. (1943). *An Introduction to Group Therapy*. New York: International Universities Press.

Speers, R., and Lansing, C. (1965). *Group Therapy in Childhood Psychosis*. Chapel Hill: University of North Carolina Press.

Spitz, R. (1957). *Yes and No: On the Genesis of Human Communication*. New York: International Universities Press.

———— (1965). *The First Year of Life*. New York: International Universities Press.

Sugar, M. (1974). Interpretive group psychotherapy with latency children. *Journal of the American Academy of Child Psychiatry* 13:648–666.

Szurek, S., and Berlin, I., eds. (1973). *Clinical Studies in Childhood Psychosis*. New York: Brunner-Mazel.

Van Scoy, H. (1971). An activity group approach to seriously disturbed latency boys. *Child Welfare* 50:413–419.

Wolff, W., Herrin, B., Scarborough, D., Wiggins, K., and Wiman, F. (1972). Integration of an instructional program with a psychotherapeutic milieu: developmental redirection for seriously disturbed children. *Acta Paedopsychiatrica* 39:83–92.

What Did The Therapists Say?
What Did The Therapists Do?

JOHN E. MEEKS, M.D.

JOHN E. MEEKS, M.D.

A discussion of "A Verbal Group Technique for Ego-Disturbed Children: Action to Words," by Marc J. Blotcky, M.D., Marc Sheinbein, Ph.D., Kenneth M. Wiggins, M.D., and Judith H. Forgotson, M.D. The treatment experience described in this paper raises questions about the function of overt behavior in psychotherapy. Some ideas are described regarding its function, purpose, and correct management.

Anyone who has worked in an inpatient setting recognizes the tremendous anxiety that the nursing staff feels almost constantly. This tension is greatly increased by any departure from therapeutic routine, especially one that threatens to undermine behavioral controls. It is not at all surprising that the unit director would pop into a group therapy session to tell a naked child that youngsters who can't keep their clothes on are not likely to get weekend passes. The amazing thing is that he did not tell the therapist, "and therapists who permit such things aren't welcome to return to our unit." It is a tribute both to the flexibility of the unit staff involved with the youngsters described in this paper and to the therapeutic conviction of the authors that a cooperative relationship could be established that would permit this experiment in group therapy.

This desire to control behavior and the conviction that such controls are prerequisite to psychotherapy is by no means limited to those who work in inpatient settings. By and large, most dynamic psychotherapists favor thought over action and verbalization over any other form of expression. In fact, workers in inpatient treatment centers may be more aware of the value of physical activity in the emotional life of children and adolescents than are many outpatient therapists. Most inpatient programs provide generous amounts of physical activity. Much of this is highly structured and recreational, designed at least partially to drain off energy and provide "constructive outlets" for the enormous drive toward activity that characterizes most young people. However, many programs include dance therapy and other ancillary techniques which are seen as more directly therapeutic. The notion that physical activity is cathartic and that it will lead to quieter and more easily managed youngsters is, of course, erroneous. Everyone who works in an inpatient center recognizes that the actual effect of such activities is to make the youngsters "high." Fritz Redl (1966) pointed out on many occasions the need for scheduling the child patient's day so that quiet activities would follow active ones in order to allow the youngsters a chance to calm down and tighten their controls.

Experienced inpatient staff members realize that when the reins are loosened it is often difficult to tighten them once again. In many inpatient settings it is the patient's primary therapist who is suspected of regularly loosening the reins. Often the staff, who are entrusted with the hour-to-hour management of youngsters, view the therapist as too permissive and as someone who is insufficiently interested in checking acting out behavior. When group therapy is a normal part of the treatment program, the nursing staff often exercises tremendous pressure on the therapist to focus on acting out and its control. They believe that the therapist's prestige and special relationship with the youngster can be used as leverage to prevent unwanted behavior. If the therapist is unwilling to use his treatment time in this way and if the youngster continues to be disruptive in the treatment program, questions often arise as to whether the patient should be dropped from the program—particularly, the staff says openly or secretly, since Dr. So-and-so insists on "coddling" him.

These attitudes are not difficult to understand. The task of remaining continuously engaged with a needy, emotionally disturbed child without relief over an eight-hour period is almost inhumanly demanding. Most people who undertake this task are idealistic and strongly committed to helping young people. Unfortunately, treatment progress is often slow and the staff are often not viewed as helpers by the children. Often, the staff experience continuing conflict and are placed in the role of embattled policemen. So long as a youngster's behavior remains antisocial and disruptive, it is very difficult for staff members to recognize that he is growing emotionally. It is small wonder that the turnover rate of nursing staff in treatment programs of adolescents and children tends to be high. This is accounted for by the well-known phenomenon of "burn out," a process of gradual disillusionment and growing fatigue.

The task of tolerating unacceptable behavior is made much more difficult by the fact that the staff has to deal with fairly large numbers of youngsters, particularly in some treatment programs where staffing is minimal. In these situations the staff feel like firemen, dashing about extinguishing new flames in constant dread of the moment when a group conflagration might engulf the entire unit. It should be noted that this fear is quite real and that dangerous riots have erupted in many inpatient settings.

In view of these factors it is not surprising that verbal behavior is much preferred to action in most treatment centers, especially those where youngsters are treated in a group setting. This paper is of special interest because it deals more sympathetically with the role of action—overt behavior—within the therapeutic alliance in group psychotherapy.

As noted earlier, the proper management of action within therapy has always troubled psychiatry, and it is an open secret that the profession has had more success with patients who do not characteristically demonstrate their conflicts by acting on them. The authors I am discussing describe a group therapy experience in which action appears to have been turned to positive therapeutic ends. However, they also tend to value verbalization above action and postulate a communication continuum extending from action to verbalization.

In a general developmental sense, it is difficult to disagree with this widely accepted viewpoint. Psychic organization does proceed from a nonverbal "body ego" through stages of concrete representation to abstract capacity that relies heavily on verbal skills. However, this schema may be primarily a Western bias, an overevaluation of thought and language that views verbal communication as the acme of human psychic development. If matters were this simple, wouldn't the compulsive who thinks and talks too much and acts only sporadically and awkwardly, if at all, be our ideal? In fact, we realize that, perhaps second only to "acter-outers," the compulsive is the most difficult patient to engage in a therapeutic alliance and to influence in a positive way.

The oversimplification involved in regarding the capacity to verbalize feelings as the high point in emotional development can be recognized both in looking at those things we value artistically and in reflecting on everyday life. In the area of art, the subtleties of dance demonstrate the potential richness of action communication. The dancer can "say" many things that cannot be stated in words. Graphic art—which one might characterize as "frozen action"—can communicate nuances that rapidly fade and that sound nonsensical when spoken or written.

In our everyday personal lives we all recognize the importance of action. The joys of sports and physical exercise in general, music and dancing, and the daily ritual of habitual actions, gestures, and the handling of familiar objects are so important to our sense of the meaningfulness of life that they tend to be taken for granted. The enormous importance of these nonverbal expressions in our emotional life is usually revealed only when our routines are disrupted by illness or other dislocations from routine.

This richness of nonverbal behavior is, of course, recognized by psychiatrists in general and by child and adolescent psychiatrists in particular. All of us realize that youngsters often tell us more with their behavior, posture, or physical attitude than they tell us in words. In fact, we frequently recognize the contradiction between what the patient is saying and what his body tells us he actually means. Still it may be that our fascination with language leads us to the covert assumption that nonverbal communication is somehow less important or "real" than words. At times it seems that we acknowledge nonverbal communication soley in order to be able to translate it into verbal terms. We seem to study action communication so that we can explain verbally what the actions "mean."

I believe that moving hastily to such translations can be harmful. For example, in her tenth psychotherapy hour, a seventeen-year-old girl recalled her first therapy session in the process of talking about her fears of the treatment process. "That first day I came in and your office seemed so large. I could see your desk, covered with papers and the pictures on the wall. Mainly though, there were *so many* chairs and I was sure you would make a big deal out of which one I chose to sit in, so I stood in the middle of the room and asked you where I should sit. You said, 'wherever you like' and I picked the most uncomfortable hard-backed chair in the room, kinda behind your plant. I figured you'd jump on that, but you didn't."

"What did I do?"

She laughed. "You just leaned back in your chair as though to say, 'I'm not going to chase you. Come out whenever you like.'"

"Was that helpful?"

"Oh, yes. If you'd come after me, I'd have never come back."

She then began to speak of her ambivalently loved mother, whose death two years prior to treatment precipitated her depression. For the first time she spoke of her mother's "uncanny" ability to know about her affairs, and her fear and resentment in her lack of privacy.

Action is important and the process described in this paper whereby a collection of severely impaired latency youngsters were able to progress from a state of intense primitive sibling rivalry to the ability to share feelings and mutual support through an intermediate stage of collusion against the therapist illustrates not only the importance of understanding and accepting action behavior but also the potential positive effect of "acting out." The difference between this group therapy experience and many others is simply that the hostility toward the therapist was expressed in more behavioral terms. The stage of mutual and collusive hostility toward group therapists is frequently observed in less primitive groups. This period of treatment can be extremely trying with adults and, particularly if unrecognized, often may actually cause the premature termination of many adolescent psychotherapy groups. However, in this group the process is overt, unmistakable, and extremely threatening to the life of the group. It is interesting that the therapists resolve this problem with a behavioral interpretation that would delight the proponents of paradoxical intention. The therapists tell the youngsters that if they continue to run out of the room they will have to leave! The approach works and shortly all of the youngsters are remaining in the therapy room. The authors explain this success on the basis that their action "demonstrated their awareness of the children's unconscious transference longings." One could also argue that the therapists simply came up with a way of remaining "one up" by *requiring* behavior which they had previously tried unsuccessfully to *prevent*, thus regaining control of the group.

These two different explanations for the technique's success imply two different views of how people respond to "help." The opinion that the interpretive impact of the maneuver explains its effectiveness is based on the idea that people "want" to use help and need assistance in understanding unconscious feelings that may defeat their effort to utilize the proffered assistance. On the other hand, those who insist on the manipulative view of the interaction tend to view patients as more inherently resistive to change. Both views have a certain popularity because they both strike a responsive chord in most clinical practitioners. Perhaps this is because the therapeutic alliance is, in fact, slowly negotiated through a variety of ego states. At times the patient's cooperative and growth-oriented relationship with the therapist leads to a real openness to interpretive work. At other points in therapy the patient seems to continue in treatment only because of a desperate wish to utilize the therapist as a source of pathological gratification—a stance that threatens to totally subvert therapy.

It would be interesting to pursue the hypothesis that at resistance points the therapist must abandon his verbal approach and utilize action—or perhaps, more precisely, counteraction—in order to advance the therapeutic process. Of course, with adults engaged in intensive psychotherapy or psychoanalysis, the therapist's action may be quite subtle. For example, the therapist may revert to silence or conversely increase the amount of talking he does. However, it would be interesting to study carefully the action interchanges preceding and following each session when the therapist and patient are less fettered by prohibitions against physical activity.

Therapists who have been filmed or videotaped during a therapy session are often surprised and sometimes dismayed to observe their postural and behavioral responses to the patient. These actions are frequently important communications to the patient. Their impact can usually be observed in the associations and behaviors that follow their occurrence.

It is also interesting to note the average therapist's response to suggestions that action behaviors should be changed. Many people feel awkward and dishonest if they deliberately and consciously use action techniques to influence the patient. This is a remarkable contrast to the comfort with which therapists carefully choose their verbal responses in an effort to advance the therapeutic process. Action interventions are often viewed as manipulations, unfair and even coercive, while using the "right" words is viewed as skillful and admirable.

Perhaps the problem is in the immediacy and affective intensity of action. As therapists, we are possibly more likely to be motivated by countertransference in our actions than in our words. The possibilities of losing control and behaving in a nontherapeutic way are greater when we interact with the patient at the nonverbal level. One possible result of this is the "frozen" therapist so frequently caricatured in hostile comic fictional presentations of the psychiatrist at work. Of course, this absence of action communication is itself a strong statement regarding our relationship with the patient.

In any case, examples of the therapist's direct activity in the group psychotherapy of children and adolescents are commonly described in the literature. In these situations one sometimes has to stand, to shout, to hold a child, or to even walk out of the room in order to reshape the confluence of forces that seem to be flowing in a negative, resistance-oriented manner. Perhaps the same results could be obtained by verbal interventions, but, if so, it seems strange that so many experienced group psychotherapists would choose to utilize action techniques. Certainly the therapists with this group did not feel that words alone could resolve the group resistance of running out of the therapy room.

I once had a talkative friend who was chided for her verbosity. She replied, "I have to keep talking, otherwise I won't know what I'm thinking." It seems that action, at times, played the same role for the youngsters in this therapy group. The authors observe that often the children could discuss their feelings only after they had acted them out. In these instances, behavior seemed to operate as a precursor, even an organizer, of thought and verbalization. The actions required an external reaction from the therapist before the youngsters could tolerate internal reflection regarding the feelings that gave rise to these behaviors. The authors also note the powerful effect that these actions had on their own responses to their young patients. Although they mention primarily the troubling, anxious reactions stirred by sexual and aggressive behavior of this kind, it is quite possible that more positive responses were also mobilized. To oversimplify this point, it is difficult for a therapist to stay distant and emotionally remote from a youngster who is urinating in a wastecan! It is a communication very difficult to ignore. Action creates involvement. Involvement, however, creates anxiety, and the therapist may be tempted to suppress disturbing behaviors rather than to understand and utilize them therapeutically. The paper under discussion demonstrates that if anxiety in the therapist is managed so that action is not prematurely suppressed, this forced involvement can lead to that emotional engagement which catalyzes growth—the therapeutic alliance.

It may be that the explanation for the greater comfort with action that is often observed in group psychotherapy as compared to individual treatment is related to the usual presence of a cotherapist in the treatment room. The danger of continuing destructive actions is diminished by the presence of a second therapist who can provide limits and feedback. It may be that the safety factor offered by the second therapist permits a greater relaxation and "letting go" than would be wise when working alone. One can be more confident that one's actions as well as one's verbal interventions are truly directed toward cementing the therapeutic alliance.

Perhaps considering patient action and therapist's counteraction as possible routes toward establishing a working alliance can also help in clarifying the role of limit-setting in the therapeutic relationship. The authors evolved the guideline of interrupting behaviors that seemed entirely defensive or that appeared to be the product of rather complete ego disorganization. In the author's words, "play that was expressive of panic or that was otherwise unavailable for discussion would be shut down." This could be restated, "behavior that actually threatened the therapeutic alliance was resisted." This would include the frightened and disorganized play of the individual child, disruptive efforts to interfere with verbalizations of others in the group, and behaviors aimed at eliciting direct inappropriate impulse gratification from the therapist. Limiting the latter behavior is important. The authors concern themselves with this point but are distracted by their recognition that any therapist's notion of "inappropriateness" can be shaped more by neurotic anxiety (especially in the sexual area) than by the real requirements of the therapeutic alliance. However, even when such neurotic inhibitions are eliminated, the need to frustrate remains as a realistic requisite to the development of a therapeutic relationship.

The question of what and when to frustrate remains overwhelmingly difficult to answer, particularly in the intense and rapidly unfolding process of group psychotherapy with children. The complexities of each youngster in regard to level of object relations, cognitive development, life experiences, psychopathology, and diagnosis make each incident almost unique. Our efforts to respond helpfully must always be approximations informed only partially by diagnostic planning and guided to a large extent by that complex gestalt of the other that we call empathy.

One guideline might be mentioned, largely for retrospective evaluation of the stands therapists have taken regarding specific behaviors. "Did the position I (we) took lead to more organized behavior, verbal or otherwise?" The evaluation would have to be extended to the group as well as the individual child. It should be recognized that "more organized" does not mean more compliant or socially acceptable. The group rebellion described by the authors was neither of these but certainly marked a positive turning point toward coherence and cohesion in the group. When it had served its purpose, the therapists correctly turned to a new "behavioral interpretation" that moved the group even further toward a cohesion that could also include the adult therapists. This new organization represented a still higher level of group function. As the authors suggest, the patients may complain when limits are not set without changing the therapist's conviction that permissiveness was appropriate. After all, patients often wish that therapists would do more for them, even when they can do it themselves.

However, there are other questions that go beyond the question of permissiveness. Surely there are times when the therapeutic response would be to join in the youngster's action. At those times permissiveness is not enough and limits are certainly not in order. At a verbal level therapists have no difficulty with this concept. Child therapists frequently enter into a youngster's fantasy and are willing to play roles in various dramas that the child might wish to stage. In Gardner's mutual storytelling technique (1971) the therapist even actively alters the youngster's verbal behavior in order to offer new alternatives, concepts and solutions.

Why are we not equally free in our actions? We have already considered some possibilities. Could it also be that we are less secure in our therapeutic identities when we go into action? In a very real sense no one has taught us in a formal way to play with children, to live with them, or to act with them. We are amateurs in that arena. We become quickly suspicious of our own or our colleagues' countertransference in action situations and we have few guidelines that would lead us to be sure that we are behaving appropriately and helpfully. Perhaps we need greater contact with our friends the dance therapists and with others who understand how to join in action without either using it for our own purposes or distorting the patient's important communications. Certainly we need continuing supervision informed by actual observation of our actions and not limited to a report of what we *said*. Gradually our capacity for self-observation would surely improve.

I would like to clarify that I feel we must be very cautious in this area until we learn more about the appropriate use of counteraction in response to patient's action in the therapeutic situation. By no means am I advocating a wild and undisciplined joining in or absence of limits. I am merely suggesting that there are important modes of communication that we utilize unknowingly and in an uninstructed manner. It is an area that should not be ignored and that the paper under discussion puts on the agenda.

Recalling our attention to this point, I wish to again thank the authors for sharing honestly their struggles with these unhappy and active children and their efforts to develop concepts to explain the ways in which they did relate to this therapy group in a helpful way. Their ultimate success is a stimulus and an example for all of us.

REFERENCES

Gardner, R. (1971). *Therapeutic Communication with Children. The Mutual Storytelling Technique.* New York: Jason Aronson.

Redl, F. (1966). *When We Deal with Children: Selected Writings.* New York: Free Press.

Moral Narcissism

ANDRÉ GREEN

Narcissism, to which so many theoretical works have been devoted during these last few years in France, has been the object of very few clinical studies. An earlier work (1963) on the phallic-narcissistic position led me to define more accurately a state observed in the clinic and first described by Reich. I should now like to give a more solid contour to another clinical impression, to verify its validity in individual experience and, if possible, to attribute a structure to it. We shall now take up the matter of moral narcissism.

> Virtue is not merely like the combatant whose sole concern in the fight is to keep his sword polished; but it has even started the fight simply to preserve its weapons. And not merely is it unable to use its own weapons, but it must also preserve intact those of its enemy, and protect them against its own attack, seeing they are all noble parts of the good, on behalf of which it entered the field of battle.
> —Hegel, *The Phenomenology of Mind*

> Because you have no inkling of these ills;
> The happiest life consists in ignorance. . . .
> —Sophocles, *Ajax*

OEDIPUS AND AJAX

The legendary heroes of antiquity provide the psychoanalyst an inexhaustible source of material of which he does not hesitate to avail himself

Translated by Nancy Osthues. This paper appeared originally in French in *Revue Française de Psychanalyse*, vol. 33, pp. 341–371, 1969.

fully. Usually he calls upon these lofty figures in order to embellish a thesis. I will work from an opposition that allows each of us to refer from a memory, to a common example that might then recall one or another of our patients. Dodds, in his book *The Greeks and the Irrational* (1951), opposes the civilizations of shame to the civilizations of guilt. It is not irrelevant to recall here that according to Dodds the idea of guilt is connected to an interiorization, we would say an internalization, of the notion of fault or sin: it is the result of divine transgression. Shame, however, is the lot of fatality, a mark of the wrath of the gods, of an Ate, a merciless punishment barely related to an objective fault, unless it be that of immoderation. Shame falls upon its victims inexorably: without doubt one must impute it less to a god than to a demon—infernal power. Dodds ties the civilization of shame to a sociotribal mode in which the father is omnipotent and knows no authority above his own, whereas the civilization of guilt, moving toward a relative monotheism, implies a law above the father's. In each of the two cases even the reparation of the fault is different. The passage from shame to guilt is a road leading from the idea of impurity and pollution to consciousness of a moral wrong. In short, shame is a fact where human responsibility barely plays a part: it is a lot of the gods, striking the man liable to pride or *hubris*, whereas guilt is the consequence of a fault; it carries the sense of a transgression. The first corresponds to the talion ethic, the second to the ethics of a more understanding justice.

Without generalizing to any great extent, it seems that one might oppose these two problematical questions, shame and guilt, by comparing the cases of Ajax and Oedipus. Ajax, you may remember, was next to Achilles the bravest of the Greeks. When Achilles died, Ajax hoped to be given his weapons, but instead they were offered to Ulysses. The details of how this came about vary, depending on which version of the myth you refer to. According to the earliest, the choice was made by the Trojans, who, defeated by the Greeks, named the enemy they most feared. They named Ulysses who, though perhaps not the bravest, was nonetheless the most dangerous because the most cunning. According to later versions—and Sophocles sided with this tradition—it was the Greeks themselves who chose Ulysses.

Ajax thought this choice unjust and insulting. He decided to take violent revenge: execute the Atridae—Agamemnon and Menelaus—take prisoner the Argives, and capture Ulysses that he might whip him to death. However, Athena, offended by Ajax for having refused her aid during the battle with the Trojans, drove him insane. Instead of carrying out his exploit by fighting with those he wanted to punish, he destroyed the Greeks' flocks in a bloody slaughter while in a state of madness. The

perpetrator of this hecatomb recovered his sanity only once the wrong
has been done. Sane again, he understood his madness. Twice mad, with
grief and with shame because he was unable to triumph either by right or
by force, his pride wounded, he killed himself by falling upon—some say
and it is probable—by impaling himself upon Hector's sword, which he
had received as a trophy.

Reading Sophocles, one realizes that shame is the key word of his
tragedy. "The loud voiced rumor, mother of my shame," says the chorus
upon learning of the massacre. Madness itself is an excuse for nothing—it
is the worst shame of all—since it is a sign of the reprobation of a god.
Here madness carries dishonor, because it is responsible for a murderous
act devoid of glory. It ridicules a hero who aspires to the highest degree of
bravery by forcing him to savagely destroy harmless animals. It burdens
him with "grevious conceits of his infatuate glee." As soon as sanity
returns, it is evident that death is the only possible solution. Ajax, having
lost his honor, can no longer live in the light of day. No tie can resist the
temptation of nothingness. Parents, wife, children, all of whom will be
practically reduced to slavery by his death, do not suffice to hold him back.
He aspires to hell, praying for the night of death: "O darkness, now my
light." He leaves his remains behind him like an impurity and lets those
who held him in contempt decide what course to take: exposure to the
vultures or reparative burial. The ethic of moderation is stated by the
messenger: "'For lives presumptuous and unprofitable fail beneath sore
misfortunes wrought by heaven,' the seer declared, 'whenever seed of
man ceases to think as fits humanity!'"

It seems to me fitting to compare the example of Ajax with that of
Oedipus. Oedipus's crime was no less great. His excuse was disregard,
deception on the part of the gods. The punishment which he inflicted
upon himself obliged him to accept the loss of his eyes, which desired to
see too much; to banish himself, with the help of his daughter Antigone;
to live among men with his impurity and consume it. Before his death, he
even allowed himself to become a subject of litigation and contestation
between his sons (whom he later cursed), his brother-in-law, and Theseus
(under whose protection he had placed himself). In the woods of Colonus,
on the outskirts of Athens, Oedipus waited for a sign from the gods. After
the revelation of his faults, his life was entirely devoid of pleasure, but it
was the life given by the gods and the gods took it back when they saw fit.
Above all, Oedipus then clung to his objects. They were his very life as
they helped him remain alive. He could not abandon them, even at the cost
of becoming a sinister stake in the games of his children. Oedipus hated
some of his children (his sons, naturally) but paternally loved his daughters, even though they were the fruit of incest.

You can see that we have opposed two problematical questions corresponding to two types of object choice and object cathexis: in the case of Oedipus, objectal object cathexis, generated through the transgression of guilt; in the case of Ajax, narcissistic object cathexis, generated through the disappointment of shame.

CLINICAL ASPECTS OF NARCISSISM: MORAL NARCISSISM

The apologue of Ajax, which served as an introduction, leads us directly to a question: Does it not seem evident that this form of narcissism is in some way related to masochism? Is not self-punishment in the foreground here? Before we settle the question and decide whether masochism is, after all, what best qualifies the theme of Ajax—who does not seek punishment but rather inflicts it upon himself in order to save his honor, another key word of narcissism—let us stop here for a moment and take a look at the relationship between masochism and narcissism.

While discussing tension-unpleasure and relaxation-pleasure in "The Economic Problem of Masochism" (1924), Freud was led to dissect masochism, as an expression of the death instinct, into three substructures: erotogenic masochism, feminine masochism, and moral masochism. I would like to propose a similar dismemberment based not upon the effects of the death instinct—a theory to which I adhere completely—but rather upon those of narcissism. It appears to me from clinical observation that one can distinguish several varieties or substructures of narcissism:

Bodily narcissism concerns either the perception (affect) of the body or display of the body. It is the body as object of the Other's gaze insofar as the one is extrinsic to the other, just as narcissism or the feeling of the body (the body as experienced from within) is a narcissism of the scrutiny of the Other insofar as the one is intrinsic to the other. Consciousness of the body and perception of the body are its elementary bases (Green 1967).

Intellectual narcissism becomes evident when intelligence takes over self-control with superabundant self-confidence despite contradiction by the facts. There is stubborn and untiring repetition that "that doesn't keep it from being so." This form, which I will discuss no further, recalls the illusion of domination by intellectualization. This is a secondary form of omnipotence of thought, an omnipotence of thought brought about by secondary processes.

Moral narcissism will be described in a later section.

In *The Ego and the Id*, Freud (1923) attributed to each instance a specific material. What the instinct is to the id, the perception is to the ego, and the ideal to the superego. This ideal is the result of instinctual renunciation; it opens the indefinitely rejected horizon of illusion. It therefore appears that moral narcissism—insofar as the relationship between morality and superego is clearly established—must be included in a close relationship of ego/superego or, more precisely, since it is a matter of the function of the ideal, of the ego ideal/superego. What follows will show that the id is in no way an outsider to the situation. If we suppose that the id is dominated by the antagonism between *life instincts* and *death instincts*, that the ego undergoes a perpetual exchange of cathexes between the *ego* and the *object*, and that the superego is torn between the *renunciation of satisfaction* and the *mirages of illusion*, we suppose that the ego, in its state of double dependence on the id and the superego, serves not two masters but rather four, since each of the latter is split in two. This is what usually happens to everybody; no one is free of moral narcissism. Therefore, the pleasure in our relationships is due to the general economy of these relationships, provided that the life instinct prevails over the death instinct and that the consolations of illusion prevail over pride in instinctual renunciation. But this is not always the case. The pathological structure of narcissism we should like to describe is characterized by an economy that heavily burdens the ego by the double consequence of the victory of the death instinct and of instinctual renunciation, which confers upon the Nirvana principle (the lowering of tensions to a zero level) a relative preeminence over the pleasure principle. This follows from what has just been posited—the predominance of pride over the satisfactions of illusion. Hence an overcathexis of the ego to the detriment of the object.

Does not the dominating effect of the death instinct and of instinctual renunciation take us back to the severity of the masochistic superego? Approximately yes. Precisely no.

MASOCHISTIC FANTASIES AND NARCISSISTIC FANTASIES

"The true masochist," writes Freud (1924), "always turns his cheek whenever he has a chance of receiving a blow." This is not the case with the moral narcissist. Paraphrasing Freud, we would say, "The true moral narcissist always volunteers himself whenever he sees a chance of renouncing a satisfaction." Let us, in effect, compare masochistic fantasies, so revealing, with narcissistic fantasies. Concerning masochism, it is a matter of being beaten, humiliated, befouled, reduced to passivity (but a passivity that demands the presence of the Other). Lacan (1966) feels, in regard to the masochist's requirement of the Other, that it arouses anxiety in the latter to a point where the sadist can no longer sustain his desire for fear of destroying the object of his pleasure.

None of this holds for the narcissist. For him it is a matter of being pure and therefore alone, and of renouncing the world—its pleasures as well as its displeasures—since we know that one can always get some pleasure out of displeasure. Subversion of the subject by the inversion of pleasure is within the grasp of many. What is more difficult and more tempting is to be beyond pleasure-seeking displeasure without seeking pain by vowing endurance. This is done through poverty, destitution, solitude, even hermitage—all states that bring one closer to God. Is God hungry or thirsty, is God dependent upon the love, the hatred of men? Some of the latter may believe so but they do not know who the true God is: the Unnameable. This profound asceticism, described by Anna Freud (1936) as a defense mechanism common to adolescence in the normal development of the individual, and to which Pierre Male (1956) has often returned in his studies on the adolescent, can take pathological forms. Suffering will not be sought, but neither will it be avoided, no matter how much energy is employed by the subject to do so. Freud (1924) has said of the masochist that in fact he desires to be treated like an infant. The moral narcissist's plan is just the opposite. Like the child he is, he desires to resemble the parents who, for one part of him, have no problem dominating their instincts. In other words, he wants to be a grown-up. The consequences will be different in the two cases. Through his masochism, the masochist masks an unpunished fault, the result of a transgression in the face of which he feels guilty. The moral narcissist has committed no fault other than that of remaining tied to his infantile megalomania and is always in debt to his ego-ideal. The consequence of this is that he does not feel guilty but rather *is ashamed of being nothing more than what he is or of pretending to be more than what he is.* Perhaps one can say that masochism operates on the level of a relationship concerning possession of what is improperly obtained—"Ill-gotten gains seldom prosper"—whereas narcissism is situated on the level of a relationship concerning being: "One is as one is." In the case of moral masochism the subject is punished not so much for the fault but for his masochism, Freud reminds us. Libidinal coexcitement uses the road of unpleasure as one of the most secret passages leading to a pleasure of which the subject is unaware. This is seen in the Rat Man, who told Freud about the torture which aroused his horror and reprobation yet felt a pleasure of which he was unaware. In moral narcissism, whose aims fail (as do those of masochism), punishment or shame is brought about by the insatiable redoubling of pride. Honor is never in a position of safety. All is lost because nothing can clean the impurity of soiled honor unless it be new renunciations which will impoverish the relationships with the object, leaving all the glory for narcissism.

The dominant trait of the opposition is revealed here: through the negation of pleasure and the search for unpleasure, the masochist maintains a rich tie to the object which the narcissist tries to abandon. Use of the adjective *rich* may be criticized because we are accustomed to giving the word normative qualities. Otherwise we might say a *substantial* relationship with the objects, insofar as, in their turn, the latter nourish the fantasied objects which, finally, the subject will feed upon.

To resolve this conflict the narcissist will attempt increasingly to impoverish his object relationships in order to reduce the ego to its vital object minimum, thus emerging triumphant. This attempt is constantly frustrated by the instincts, which require that the satisfaction pass through an object. The only solution is a narcissistic cathexis of the subject, and we know that when the object withdraws itself, is lost, or disappoints, the result is depression (Pasche 1969).

This remark leads us to understand the particularities of these patients' cures. Whereas masochistic patients present problems, anticipated by Freud, of a negative therapeutic reaction that perpetually underlines the need for self-punishment, moral narcissists, faithful and irreproachable patients, lead us, through a progressive rarefaction of their cathexes, to a dependent behavior where the need for love and, more precisely, the esteem of the analyst is the oxygen without which the patient can no longer breathe. More precisely, it is a question of a need for a special kind of love, as it is aiming for the recognition of the sacrifice of pleasure.

But, as Freud (1924) wrote, "even the subject's destruction of himself cannot take place without libidinal satisfaction." What satisfaction does the moral narcissist find in his impoverishment? The feeling of being better because of renunciation, is the foundation of human pride. This recalls the relationship between this clinical form of narcissism and the primary narcissism of the child and its tie to autoerotism.

If it was Freud who said that masochism resexualizes morality, we would like to add: *narcissism turns morality into an autoerotic pleasure in which the pleasure itself will be suppressed.*

PARTIAL ASPECTS AND DERIVATIVES
OF MORAL NARCISSISM

The opposition between masochistic and narcissistic fantasies has allowed us to come to the heart of the principal aspect of this structure. We shall now briefly consider some of its partial or derived aspects before outlining its metapsychology.

We have already mentioned *asceticism*, when it lasts beyond adolescence and becomes a life style. This asceticism is quite different from that which subtends a religious conviction or a rule, again in the religious sense of the term. It is, in fact, unconscious. It uses as a pretext limitations of a material nature in order to force the ego to consent to a progressive shrinking of its cathexes so as to tighten the ties between desire and need, bringing the order of the former to the level of the order of the latter. One drinks, one eats only for survival, not for pleasure. One eliminates dependence in regard to the object and to desire (insofar as it is different) through meager autoerotism, devoid of fantasies, whose aim is relief through hygienic evacuation. Or else one operates a massive displacement onto work and immediately puts into action a pseudosublimation which is more of a reaction formation than a destiny of instinct through inhibition, aim displacement, and secondary desexualization. This pseudosublimation will have a delusional character because of its megalomanic undertones amalgamated with an overall idealization which implies denial of its instinctual roots.

These last remarks lead us to consider a second aspect of moral narcissism. We discover it behind the features of a syndrome rarely mentioned but nonetheless very frequent: *affective immaturity*. Affective immaturity, which we have learned to recognize little by little, is not a benign form of conflict solution; far from it. On the one hand, the term *immaturity* is well deserved because this is indeed a case of retardation whose consequences are as serious for the affective cathexes of the subject as intellectual retardation is for the cognitive investments. On the other hand, affective immaturity is based upon a substratum of denial of desire and its instinctual base. This denial justifies the fact that early authors such as Codet and Laforgue (1925) classified it as *schizonia*, a psychotic form. One is often astonished by the quasi-paranoid form of behavior. Affective immaturity is the appanage of young girls but is found also in young men—with, however, a more serious prognosis. We know its banal aspects: sentimentality, not sensitivity; a horror of human appetites, oral or sexual, a failure in sublimation which would imply their acceptance; the fear of sex, especially of the penis, which conceals a desire (present in both sexes) of an absolute and incommensurable nature; and the attachment to daydreams that are childish, affected, and willingly messianic. One recognizes these people in everyday life because they often put themselves in the position of a scapegoat; this does not bother them, so sure are they of their superiority over common people.

Perhaps these cursory elements are not sufficient to enable us to distinguish between hysteria and affective immaturity. The essential difference seems to me to reside in the exorbitant amount of tribute paid to the ego-ideal in affective retardation. Here we must recall Melanie Klein's remarks on idealization (1952). She saw idealization as one of the most primitive and most fundamental of defense mechanisms; idealization centered on the object or the self. It is this distinction of an economic order that enables us to establish more clearly the separation between hysteria and affective retardation, as though the latter were the product of a highly exaggerated narcissism in the face of a growing decathexis of the object.

One might fall into the trap of seeing behind all of this behavior nothing more than a defensive position against instinctual cathexis. What characterizes these choices is, above all, immense pride—behind the misleading forms of intense humility—having nothing in common with the ordinary possibilities of narcissism. While there is, it is true, a defensive meaning to this sheltering of the instinct and its objects from vicissitudes, one may imagine that this arrangement would protect the subject. This cannot be denied, and one sometimes has the impression that the patient feels intense anxiety because cathexis appears to carry with it the considerable risk of disorganization of the ego. Just as the stimulus barrier protects the ego by refusing external stimuli which exceed a certain amount and which, because of their intensity, would put the fragile organization of the ego in danger, so in this case the refusal of the instinct is aiming for a similar protection. It is more exact to say that these patients feel extremely fragile and have the idea that admission of the instinct into their consciousness would imply for them the danger of perverse or psychotic behavior. One patient told me that if she did not watch herself constantly, if she let herself become passive, it would not be long before she would become a bum. Now, everybody is a bit of a bum—on Sunday, during a vacation—and more or less accepts this; the moral narcissist cannot. This is why it seems necessary to insist upon the narcissistic cathexis of pride.

Messianism is accompanied in women by an identification with the Virgin Mary, who "conceived without sin," a phrase whose consequences have been so serious for female sexuality; it is a much more dangerous notion than "to sin without conceiving," to which women also aspire. In men, the equivalent is identification with the Paschal Lamb. This is not simply a matter of being crucified or of having one's throat cut; it implies being innocent as a lamb when the holocaust arrives. However, we know that the innocent have often been accused by history of crimes they allowed in order to remain pure.

This idealized behavior, always destined to failure because of the conflict with reality, carries with itself, as we have already stated, shame rather than guilt, dependence rather than independence. The idealization includes certain particularities within the analytic cure:

1. The *analytic object* is difficult of access, for the material is buried beneath the narcissistic cloak of what Winnicott would here call a *false self*.

2. The *narcissistic wound* is felt to be an infraction, an inevitable condition of the coming to light of the objectal material. Here mystification is directed not only toward desire but also toward the subject's narcissism, toward the guardian of his narcissistic unity, an essential condition of the desire for life.

3. The cure is anchored in *actively passive resistance* in order to satisfy the subject's desire for dependence, a dependence having the power to make him stay with the analyst eternally and to bind the analyst to his chair, like a butterfly caught in the net of the analytic situation.

4. The desire for *unconditional love* is the sole desire of these subjects. This desire takes the form of a desire for esteem, of a narcissistic valorization whose express condition is the burial or putting aside of drive conflict and of access to pleasure tied to the use of the erotogenic zones.

5. *Projection* is a corollary of this desire and is put into play with the tactical aim of provoking the analyst's reassuring denial. "Assure me that you do not see in me a fallen angel, depraved, banished, who has lost the right to be held in esteem."

THE METAPSYCHOLOGY OF MORAL NARCISSISM

What we have just outlined in descriptive terms must now receive its metapsychological credentials. (I use the term *metapsychology* in its general meaning.) Thus we must examine the relation of moral narcissism to (a) the varieties of countercathexes; to (b) other aspects of narcissism; to (c) the development of the libido—erotogenic zones and object relations; (d) id, ego, and superego; and (e) bisexuality and the death instinct.

The Varieties of Countercathexis

The concept of the defense mechanism has been considerably extended since Freud. However, the multiplicity of defensive forms (the catalogue of which is to be found in the work of Anna Freud [1936]) does not enable us to account for the structural particularities of the major forms of the nosography which one tries vainly to ignore. Our only hope lies in a reflection concerning countercathexis—repression seen as a defense, *not the first* but nonetheless the most important in the individual's psychic future. (I am thinking here of the distinction in Latin between *prima* and *summa*.) In effect, Freud described a series of forms which we must now recapitulate and whose function is to regulate—to encircle—all of the other defenses.

1. *Rejection* or *Verwerfung*, which some, along with Lacan (1966), translate as *forclusion* (English *foreclosure*). One can argue about the word but not about the thing itself, which implies radical refusal of the instinct or the instinct presentation and which, directly or in disguise, expels the instincts, which nonetheless return through reality, by way of projection.

2. *Denial* or *disavowal*, depending on the translation, or *Verleugnung*, repression of perception.

3. *Repression* itself or *Verdrängung*, which is specifically directed toward the affect and the instinct representative (Freud 1927). .

4. Finally, *negation*, *Verneinung*, which is directed toward the faculty of judgment. This is an admission into the conscience in a negative form. "It is not" is equal to "It is."

In its clearest and most characteristic aspects, moral narcissism seems to correspond to an intermediate situation somewhere between rejection and disavowal—between *Verwerfung* and *Verleugnung*. Here we shall point out the seriousness of its structure, which brings it close to psychosis.

Several arguments support this opinion. First, the idea that it is a question of a form of "narcissistic" neurosis, something which clinical studies have accustomed us to consider with uneasiness. Next there is the dynamic itself of the conflicts, which implies a refusal of instincts associated with a refusal of reality. There is a refusal to see the world as it is, that is, as a battlefield upon which human appetites indulge in an endless combat. Finally, there is the considerable megalomania of moral narcissism, which implies a refusal of object cathexis by the ego. Nonetheless, it is not a matter of a repression of reality as in psychosis but more so of a denial, a disavowal of the order of the world and of the personal participation of the subject's desire. In this regard, if we recall that Freud describes disavowal in connection with the fetish tied to the sight of castration, we can see that the moral narcissist engages in a function of similar filling up by stopping with an omnipotent divine image the holes through which the absence of protection reveals itself, while offering himself in an effort to obstruct this unbearable deficiency. "If God does not exist, then anything is permitted," says the hero of Dostoevski's *The Devils*. "If God does not exist then it is permitted for me to replace him and to be the example which will cause belief in God. I will therefore be God by proxy." One understands that the failure of this undertaking brings about depression (in accord with the mode of all-or-nothing) without mediation.

Other Aspects of Narcissism

The three aspects of narcissism we have particularized—moral, intellectual, and bodily narcissism—present themselves as variants of the cathexis which, for defensive reasons or for reasons of identification, are preferred according to the individual conflict configuration. But, just as the narcissistic relationship is inseparable from the object relationship, the diverse aspects of narcissism are interdependent.

In particular, moral narcissism has a very close relationship with intellectual narcissism. We recall that we understand intellectual narcissism to be that form of self-sufficiency and solitary valorization which makes up for the lack of human desires with intellectual mastery or intellectual seduction. It is not rare for moral narcissism to ally itself with intellectual narcissism and to find in this kind of displacement an addition to pseudosublimation. A hypertrophy of desexualized cathexes, which ordinarily occasions the displacement of partial pregenital instincts (scoptophilia-exhibitionism and sadomasochism), supports moral narcissism. We know of the affinity certain religious orders have for intellectual erudition. The aim of this intellectual research of a moral or philosophic character is to find through philosophy, or God, *reasons* for an ethic which opposes an instinctual life, which views it as something that must at any price be not just repressed or surpassed, but *extinguished*. The shame felt for having an instinctual life like every other human being gives the impression of hypocrisy concerning the unavowed aim of the work. This shame is displaced into intellectual activity which becomes highly guilt-ridden. A term is lacking here: one would have to say that it becomes *shame-ridden*, as though the vigilant superego were to become an extra-lucid persecutor who remembers and reads behind the intellectual justification the desire for absolution for the remnants of instinctual life which continue to torment the ego. Also punished is the fantasy of grandeur included in this kind of search which aims, rationally and intellectually, to increase the moral superiority of the subject.

In other cases intellectual activity, a synonym for the paternal phallus, undergoes an evolution so that childhood efforts made in school become objects of blocking during adolescence.

Here one ought to go more deeply into an analysis of sublimation and of regression from action to thought. As this would enlarge our field beyond the limits we have set, a brief discussion must suffice:

Intellectual activity, accompanied by fantasy or not, is highly eroticized and guilt-ridden, but is above all *felt to be shameful*. It is accompanied by cephalalgia, insomnia, difficulty in concentration or in reading, and inability to put knowledge to use. It is considered shameful because the subject, while engaging in this activity, relates it to sexuality: "I read works of a high human or moral value, but I do so in order to fool those around me and to pass myself off as what I am not—since my mind is not pure and since I have sexual desires." It is not rare in this case to find that the mother has accused the child of pretention or of unhealthy curiosity.

Intellectual activity can also represent an escape hatch for *aggressive instincts*. To read is to incorporate power of a destructive nature; to read is to feed upon the corpses of the parents, whom one kills through reading, through the possession of knowledge.

In the case of moral narcissism, intellectual activity and the exercise of thought are supported by a *reconstruction of the world*—the establishment of a morality, a truly paranoid activity which constantly remakes and re-models reality according to a pattern in which everything instinctual will be omitted or resolved without conflict.

To sum up, the percept-consciousness system, insofar as it is nar-cissistically cathected, is in a state of "surveillance," tightly controlled and thwarted by the superego, just as in the delusion of observation; it has, however, a different type of economic equilibrium.

But it is above all with bodily narcissism, as one might suspect, that moral narcissism has the closest relationship. The body as an appearance and source of pleasure, of seduction and conquest of others, is banished. In the case of the moral narcissist, hell is not other people—narcissism has eliminated them—but rather, the body. The body is the Other, resur-rected in spite of attempts to wipe out its traces. The body is a limitation, a servitude, a termination. This is why the uneasiness experienced is primordially a *bodily uneasiness* which expresses itself in the fact that these subjects are so ill-at-ease with themselves. For them the session of analysis which allows the body to speak (intestinal sounds, vasomotor reactions, sweating, sensations of cold or heat) is a torment because, though they can silence or control their fantasies, they are helpless as to their bodies. The body is their absolute master—their shame. (This intolerance of bodily reactions suggests a reprisal against the body and its drives related to an early relationship with the mother—she herself being reluctant to admit her own libidinal trends, which are reactivated through the baby's reactions.) This is why, on the analyst's couch, these subjects are petrified, immobile. They lie down in a stereotyped manner, allowing themselves neither change of position nor any kind of movement. It is understandable that visceral motor activity bursts out in the face of this driving silence of the relational life. This is, of course, nothing but the displacement of the sexual body, of that which does not dare name itself. During a session of analysis, a fit of vasomotor reaction will cause the subject to blush, and the emotion will bring on the tears which are the expression of the humiliation of desire. So, contrary to the pleas of the body, its appearance will become repulsive, harsh, discouraging—even to an analyst undemanding of the criteria of attraction.

We are pointing out those aspects which appear to be defensive, but here again we must not neglect the hidden and prideful pleasure to be found behind this humility. "I am neither man nor woman, I am neuter," one such patient said to me. It is, however, important to note that this uneasiness, painful though it may be, is a sign of life. When after the analysand has succeeded in controlling the anxiety in all its forms, including the visceral—and this is not so impossible as one might think— the moment of silence arrives and the he experiences an impression of frightful blankness. The lead helmet of psychic suffering has been replaced by the lid of the coffin, and what is now experienced is a feeling of inexistence, of non-being, of an interior emptiness far more intolerable than what the subject was to be protected from. Before, at least, something was happening, whereas control of the body prefigures a definitive sleep, a premonition of death.

Psychic Development: Erotogenic Zones and the Relation to the Object

This dependence upon the body that we find in the narcissist, and particularly in the moral narcissist, is rooted in the relationship with the mother. We know that love is the key to human development. In the latter part of his work, Freud never ceased comparing the imprescriptible demands of the instinct with the no less imprescriptible demands of civilization requiring renunciation of the instinct. All development is marked by this antinomy. In *Moses and Monotheism* (1939) Freud gives us the following:

> When the ego has brought the super-ego the sacrifice of an instinctual renunciation, it expects to be rewarded by receiving more love from it. The consciousness of deserving love is felt by it as pride. At the time when the authority had not yet been internalized as a super-ego, there could be the same relation between the threat of loss of love and the claims of instinct; there was a feeling of security and satisfaction when one had achieved an instinctual renunciation out of love for one's parents. But this happy feeling could only assume the particular narcissistic character of pride after the authority had itself become a portion of the ego. (p. 117)

This passage shows that it is necessary to look at the notion of development from at least two angles: on one hand, the development of the object-libidio from orality to the phallic and then genital phases; on the other, the narcissistic libido from absolute dependence to genital interdependence. Now, the security which must be gained can only be acquired— so as not to suffer the loss of a parent's love—through instinctual renunciation, which permits the acquisition of self-esteem. The supremacy of the pleasure principle, as well as evolution, is possible only if from the start the mother guarantees the satisfaction of needs, so that the field of desire can open as the order of the significant. This is so also in the sphere of narcissism, which can establish itself only insofar as the security of the ego is assured by the mother. However, this security and the order of need can suffer from a precocious conflictualization brought on by the mother. Then one witnesses the crushing of desire and its being dealt with as need. Also, the narcissistic wound, because of the *impossiblity of experiencing omnipotence* and therefore of surmounting it, brings with itself excessive dependence upon the maternal object that assures security. The mother becomes the pillar of an omnipotence attributed to her, accompanied by an idealization whose psychosis-inducing character is well known, particularly since it must be accompanied by the crushing of libidinal desire. This omnipotence is even more easily created because it corresponds to the mother's desire to bear a child without the contribution of the father's penis. In short, it is as though the child, because of his conception with the help of this penis, were a debased, damaged product.

D. W. Winnicott has worked on this problem of dependence. He has shown how the splitting of the remaining part of the psyche from what has been refused leads to the construction and adoption of what he calls a "false self" (Winnicott 1975).

The fact that this problematical narcissism is contemporaneous with an orality in which dependence upon the breast is very real, increases this reinforcement of dependence even more. During the anal phase—when, as we know, cultural constraints are important—the demands of renunciation become imperatives and reaction formations predominate; at best one will end up with an obsessive and rigid character, at worst with a camouflaged psychopathic paranoid form bearing fantasies of incorporation of a dangerous and restrictive object animated by an antilibidinal omnipotence. All of these pregenital relics will heavily mark the phallic phase and will confer upon the boy's castration anxiety a fundamentally devalorizing character, and upon the girl's penis envy an avidity of which she will be ashamed and from which she will hide as best she can.

Id, Ego, Superego

Let us examine narcissism in relation to the id. Here we can speak only of primary narcissism. In a recent work I demonstrated the necessity of distinguishing between that which pertains to the id, which is usually described by the term *elation* or *narcissistic expansion*, and that which is the exclusive domain of primary narcissism, which I characterize as the lowering of tensions to zero level. We have just seen that the level of moral narcissism is to use morality as a crutch in order to free itself from the vicissitudes involved in the tie to the object and therefore, by this roundabout method, to obtain liberation from the servitudes attached to the object relation, in order to give the id and the ego the means to be loved by a demanding superego and a tyrannical ego-ideal. However, their effort at mystification fails: first of all because the superego is not so easily fooled; second because the demands of the id continue to be voiced in spite of the ascetic maneuvers of the ego.

If what I have said is so—that is, if moral narcissism turns morality into an autoerotic pleasure—then one understands better how the ego can be interested in these operations, using all the means at the disposition of secondary narcissism, robbing the cathexes destined to objects. Here is the travesty which permits it to say to the id, according to Freud's phrase, "Look, I am so like the object, you can as well love me." One might add, "And at least I am pure, pure of any suspicion, pure of any impurity."

However, it is definitely between the superego and the ego-ideal that the relationship is the closest. We have often insisted upon what Freud described in 1923 (and to which he never ceased to return since that date) as the order of the phenomena proper to the superego: the function of the ideal, which is to the superego what the instinct is to the id and what perception is to the ego. Briefly recapitulating: if, at the start, everything is id, everything is instinct and, more precisely, antagonism of the instincts (Eros and destructive instincts), the differentiation as to the external world leads to the existence of a corticalization of the ego that differentiates perception and, correlatively, the instinct presentation. The division into ego and superego, plus the fact that the latter plunges its roots into the id, brings along with repression the need to represent the world as one desires it and also as it is—that is, in such a way that a system of connotations permits control of it. Secondarily or in compensation this leads to the setting up of the function of the ideal desire's revenge upon reality. This function—a function of illusion—makes possible the spheres of fantasy, art, religion.

For the moral narcissist, the ideal, which is capable of evolution while renouncing none of its original demands, retains its original force. Finding its first application in the aggrandizement of the parents, that is, in the idealization of their image, the ego ideal preserves all the characteristics of the relationship with the parents, the mother in particular. In the case of these subjects, the love of their ego-ideal is as indispensable as the love they expect from their mothers, as indispensible as the nourishment given by the mother whose love was the first illusion. "I am nourished, therefore I am loved," says the moral narcissist. "Anyone who is not ready to nourish me cannot really love me." During therapy, the moral narciss-ist will demand and try to obtain the same unconditional nourishment, or love, by means of privation and reduction of cathexes (the very opposite of the aims pursued by the therapy). This is an attempt to assure the domination over and the servitude by the Other. Here again we find the tie of love and security of which we spoke. To be sheltered—sheltered from a world which favors excitation—by the analyst's narcissistic love as guarantee of survival, of security, of love: that is the desire of the moral narcissist.

And the superego? We now discover one of moral narcissism's most fitting traits. In fact, the moral narcissist lives in a state of constant tension between the ego-ideal and the superego. The idealizing function of the ego-ideal is seen for what it is: its function of decoy, of diverted occult satisfaction, of troubled innocence. The superego reveals the trap of this travesty and refuses to be taken in. In turn the ego-ideal tries, through its sacrifices and holocausts, to ridicule the superego, which then pierces the "sin of pride" of megalomania and severely punishes the ego for its masquerade.

The ego-ideal of the moral narcissist builds itself upon the vestiges of the ideal ego: that is, upon a force of omnipotent idealizing satisfaction which is ignorant of the limitations of castration and which therefore has less to do with the oedipus complex of the oedipal phase than with the preceding phases.

Here we would like to bring to your attention a remark concerning the religious superego. Every superego carries in itself a germ of religion because it is created through an identification not with the parents but rather with the parents' superego: that is, an identification with the dead father, the ancestor. However, not every superego merits the qualifying term *religious*. A specific feature of any religion is that it takes the superego as foundation and forms it into a system—the dogma—a necessary mediator of paternal prohibition. It is certainly this feature that Freud was referring to when he called religion the obsessional neurosis of humanity. Conversely, since there is reciprocity, he also maintained that obsessional neurosis is the tragicomic travesty of a private religion. Moral narcissists have numerous similarities to obsessives, especially in regard to the intense desexualization they try to instill in their relationships with the object and also in the profound aggression which they camouflage. We have already mentioned the relation to paranoia. Grouping these observations, one can say that the more the ties to the object are maintained, the more the relationship will be obsessional. The more these ties are detached, the more the relationship will be paranoid. Any failure, in the first case as well as the second, any deception inflicted upon the ego-ideal by the object, brings on depression.

Let us say more concerning the relationship between shame and guilt, and about Dodd's speculation that Greek mythology finds its echo in individual pathological structures. Shame, as we have said, is of a narcissistic order, whereas guilt is of an objectal order. This is not all. One may also think that these feelings, the bases of the first reaction formations long before the oedipus complex, are constitutive of the precursors of the superego. This occurs before the interiorization of the superego, heir to the oedipus complex. Therefore, linking shame to the pregenital phases of development explains not only its narcissistic prevalence but also its cruel and intransigent character that allows no possiblity of reparation.

Certainly this is a matter of schematic opposition. Both shame and guilt always coexist. However, in the analysis a distinction must be made. Guilt in relation to masturbation is tied to the fear of castration; shame has an irrational, primary and absolute character. Shame is not a question of the fear of castration but rather of the prohibition of any contact with the castrated person, insofar as he is the proof, the mark of an indelible impurity that can be acquired on contact. It must be stated that only a defusion of narcissism and the object-tie enables shame to have such a great importance. As any defusion favors the liberation of the death instinct, suicide because of shame can be better understood.

Let us go back to the ego. A point concerning sublimation was left suspended and deserves our further attention. I have mentioned pseudosublimation, a sublimation others might call a defensive sublimation. To my way of thinking, this conception is not apt; it puts a true sublimation, an expression of what is most noble in man, in opposition to a defensive sublimation, nothing more than a failed sublimation. Undeniably, there do exist sublimations which are the offspring of certain pathological forms. These can be viewed as emergency exits from conflict, without necessarily being reaction formations. And insofar as any sublimation is governed by the threat of castration, this leads to the need to end the oedipus complex, at the risk of running even more serious risks for the libidinal economy. Thus sublimation has the destiny of an instinct. It is therefore a defense, one favored by the existence of instincts whose aims are inhibited.

What there is to say about moral narcissism in this respect is instructive. One can observe not only these escape sublimations, for which the subject will later pay dearly, but also a process of inhibition, indeed a halting of the sublimation by secondary guilt (we must not forget that shame is always first) in the partial impulses, scoptophilia in particular. When the subject tends toward pseudosublimation, this mechanism is only on rare occasions a pleasure: of a lesser value than sexual pleasure, and at a higher price, but a pleasure nonetheless. The essential part of this observation of the ego is the completion of the constitution of what

Winnicott calls a *false* self. This takes over the idealizing and depriving behavior at the cost of what is called authenticity, the difference being that the process *is totally unconscious.*

In the face of this *false self* it is important not to disregard its economic function. I have already mentioned that which in the midst of moral narcissism acts as a defensive process, as well as that which acts as a substitute satisfaction (pride). But one must not neglect the essential economic consideration that makes moral narcissism and the *false self* that *subtends it* the backbone of these subjects' egos. It is therefore dangerous to attack it, at the risk of seeing the entire structure crumble. Life, with its potential of disappointments, very often does just this and then comes depression or, succeeding this, suicide.

Bisexuality and the Death Instinct

The last aim of narcissism is the obliteration of the trace of the Other in one's desire, therefore the abolition of the primary difference, the difference between One and the Other. But what is the meaning of the abolition of this primary difference in regard to the return to the maternal breast? The aim of moral narcissism in this abolition of tension to zero level is either death or immortality, which is the same thing. This explains why, confronted by these patients, we have the feeling that their life is a protracted suicide, even when they appear to have given up the idea of a violent death. However, this suicidal form reveals the fact that object inanition, consumption are sacrifices for the love of a terrible god: self-idealization. With the suppression of the primary difference, one simultaneously brings about the abolition of all the other differences and, it goes without saying, of the *sexual difference.* It is basically the same thing to say that desire must be reduced to zero level and to say that one must do without the object which is the *object of lack*—the object becoming a sign that one is limited, unachieved, and incomplete. Freud, in *Beyond the Pleasure Principle* (1920), refers to the Platonic myth of the androgyne, a figure evoking the fantasy of a primitive completion prior to sexual differentiation. For the moral narcissist the inconveniences of sexual differentiation must be supressed by self-sufficiency. Narcissistic wholeness is not a sign of health but rather a mirage of death.

Moral narcissism is a narcissism which is positive and negative at the same time. It is positive in its concentration of energy upon a fragile and threatened ego; negative because it is a valorization, not of satisfaction, not of frustration (this would be so in the case of masochism), but of *privation.* Autoprivation becomes the best bulwark against castration.

Here appears the need for a differential analysis, according to the nature of the deficiency, that is to say, according to sex. One cannot repeat this often enough: the fear of castration concerns both sexes. Penis envy concerns both sexes but with different particularities from the start. The man fears castration of what he has, the woman of what she could have. The woman desires a penis insofar as it is her destiny, through coition or procreation for example. The man desires a penis insofar as his, like the female clitoris, is never sufficiently valorizing. We must remember the indestructability of these desires.

Moral narcissism enlightens us in this respect. In the case of a man, it leads, through the behavior of deprivation, to the following defense: "I cannot be castrated because I have nothing left, I am stripped of everything and have put all my belongings at the disposition of whoever wants to take them." In the case of a woman the reasoning would be: "I have nothing but I want nothing more than the nothing I have." This monastic vocation in man or woman is an attempt to deny the lack or, on the contrary, to love it. "I lack nothing. I have therefore nothing to lose and even if I did lack something I would love this lack as though it were myself." Castration continues to lead this chase, because this deficiency will be displaced in the direction of the moral perfection to which the moral narcissist aspires and which will constantly leave him far from his self-imposed demands. There, shame will expose its face, which will have to be covered with a shroud.

One does not wipe out the trace of the Other, not even in the desire of the One, because the Other will have taken on the face of the One and will repeat to it unceasingly: "You must love only me. No one but me deserves to be loved." But who is hiding behind the mask? The double, the image in the mirror? The doubles come to live in the frame of the *negative hallucination of the mother.*

We cannot return to this concept, which I have recently elaborated (1967). Here we will extend this hypothesis by demonstrating that if negative hallucination is the base upon which moral narcissism stands in its relationship with primary narcissism, then the father is involved. The negation of the absence of maternal environment joins with the father as primordial absence, as an absence of the principle of kinship, whose ulterior ties with the law will be perceived. In the case of moral narcissism it cannot be denied that this detour is aiming only for the possession of a phallus—a paternal phallus—as a principle of universal domination. The negation of this desire in the form of a celebration of renunciation does not in the least change its ultimate aim. Also, it is not by chance that in both sexes it is a matter of a negation of castration. God is asexual but God is the father. For the moral narcissist his phallus is disincarnate, void of his substance, an abstract and hollow mold.

Before finishing with the relation between moral narcissism and the death instinct, we must return to the subject of idealization. It is greatly to the merit of Melanie Klein (1952) to have given idealization the place it deserves. For her, idealization is the result of the primordial splitting between the good and the bad object and, correspondingly, between the good and the bad ego. This dichotomy overlaps the one that exists between the idealized object (or ego) and the persecuting object (or ego) in the paranoid-schizoid phase. Consequently, the excessive idealization of the object or of the ego appears as the result of the splitting. Through this, there is an attempt to maintain in exclusion (in the ego as in the object) all persecutory parts. This point is confirmed in clinical work. The idealization of the ego is always the corollary of an extremely threatening feeling, for the object as well as for the ego. This joins our observations on the importance of destructive aggression in moral narcissists. Idealization joins forces with omnipotence in order to abolish, neutralize, or destroy the destructive instincts that threaten the object and, through retaliation, the ego.

Here one can perceive more clearly the relations with masochism which pose many questions in the interpretation of moral narcissism. I consider masochism to represent the failure of the neutralization of the destructive instincts oriented toward the ego: hence the failure of moral narcissism and of its work of idealization. Moral narcissism must therefore be understood to be, at the same time, the success of the defense and, consequently, success in the search for megalomaniacal pleasure beyond masochism, the megalomania being due to the liberation from conflict tensions. It must be clear that moral narcissism is not the only way out in the face of a masochism that might attain the ego; rather, it is only one of several methods used to keep this threat in the background.

Should we conclude that moral narcissism is a protection from masochism? I do not think so, for the reason that it is the dichotomy between idealization and persecution that is primary. The splitting shows the two positions at the same time. It is necessary to emphasize the fact that idealization is no less mutilating than persecution, in that it removes the subject from the circuit of object relations. In order to be understood more clearly, I would say that persecution underlies paranoid delusion, whereas idealization underlies schizophrenia in its most hebephrenic forms. In its milder forms, this problem is obviously less evident. Melanie Klein would say that in these cases the depressive stage has been reached. This explains why the breakdown of the moral narcissist takes on the face of depression and not that of delusion or schizophrenia. In all of these cases, one can see that it is the intensity of the destructive instincts, uncontrolled by the splitting, and the accentuation of idealization that are responsible for the regression. Thus, the two positions, idealization and persecution, go hand in hand. Beyond this there is a chaotic state which does not recognize the primary symbolizing division, that of good and bad.

TECHNICAL IMPLICATIONS IN THE TREATMENT OF MORAL NARCISSISTS

The cure of moral narcissists poses delicate problems. I have already pointed out some of the more serious obstacles to the treatment's evolution. They involve difficulty of access to material tied to the object relation beyond the reconstitution of narcissistic dependence upon the mother (and therefore upon the analyst). In my experience it appears that the key to these cures involves, as always, a desire for the analyst, and a provocation of the analyst's countertransference. For eventually the analyst, knowing that he must continue such a relationship, finally feels that he is his patient's prisoner. He becomes the other pole of dependence, as in those cases when one does not quite know what distinguishes the jailer from the man he is guarding. The analyst is then tempted to modify this analytic situation in order to make it advance. Since the least guilt-inducing variant is kindness, the analyst offers his love, without realizing that he is pouring the first jet into the Danaides' barrel. But the fact is that the desire for this love is always insatiable and that one must also expect to see the reserves of love used up: they are limited and therefore exhaustible. It seems to me that in that case the analyst commits a technical error because he is responding to a desire of the patient, a move we know to be always perilous. Since it is a matter of moral narcissism, the analyst then becomes a substitute moralist, indeed a priest. The result is that the analysis loses its specific feature, the spring of its efficacy. It is exactly as if one were to choose to respond to a delusional symptomatology by placing oneself on the level of its manifest expression. To do so is to create an impasse.

The second possibility is that of the transference interpretation. As long as it remains expressed objectively through the words of the analyst, there is only a slight echo in this material covered by the narcissistic carapace. One might as well try to awaken the sexual desire of someone dressed in armor. Resignation remains. It is certainly the least dangerous of all these attitudes. Let it be, let it happen. Since the privations required by therapy have no effect other than that of reinforcing the moral narcissism, the analyst then risks engaging himself in an interminable analysis, the patient's need for dependence thus being largely satisfied.

So it seems that no solution appears. There is, however, one that I would not dare mention here without apprehension, if in certain cases it had not allowed me to make perceptible advances. It is a matter of (and the undertaking is perilous) analyzing narcissism. Analyzing narcissism is a project which, in more than one way, could appear impossible. However, after a sufficient passage of time when the transference is after all established and the repetition behavior has been analyzed, the analyst can resolve to pronounce the key words: shame, pride, honor, dishonor, micromania, and megalomania. And he can thereby free the subject of a part of his burden, since the worst frustration a patient can feel during an analysis is not to be understood. As tough as the interpretation may be, as cruel as it can be to hear the truth, it is less cruel than the iron yoke in which the patient feels imprisoned. Often the analyst cannot bring himself to use this method, because he has the feeling he is traumatizing his patient. He therefore puts up a good front while within he is ill at ease. If we believe in the unconscious we ought to suppose that these attitudes, camouflaged by the civility of analytical relations, are perceptible to the patient, through the most subtle indications..

The analyst must be an artisan of the separation from the patient, with the condition, however, that the patient does not feel that this separation is a way of getting rid of him. Moreover, let us add that often those who treat these patients, when face to face with the realization of their subjects' inaccessibility, get rid of them in most affable ways, at least superficially. In short, we defend here nothing other than a technique of truth, certainly not an orthopedic technique.

This interpretive attitude can at times permit access to the idealization-persecution problem, and can thereby uncover what is lurking in the persecution implicit beneath the facade of idealization. Protection from persecution (on the part of the object and suffered by the ego; on the part of the ego and suffered by the object) is, at the same time, an escape from persecution in a camouflaged form. Through this, the object-tie to the mother can be reconstituted. Then the ego's reproaches concerning the object and the object's reproaches concerning the ego will be evident. Recourse to narcissistic sufficiency can be accounted for only by the deficiency of the object, whether this deficiency is real or the result of inability to satisfy the unquenchable needs of the child.

HEROIC FIGURES OF MORAL NARCISSISM

Everything I have elaborated here, except for my apologue of Oedipus and Ajax, is drawn from observation of patients. Their implied narcissistic regression makes them caricatures of the normal portraits that anyone may discover among those around him. While not quite caricatures, certain heroic figures—other than Ajax, who is an extreme case—may be contemplated.

Think of Brutus, for example, as portrayed in Shakespeare's *Julius Caesar*. Brutus assassinated Caesar not because of desire or ambition but because of patriotism, because he was a republican and saw in his adoptive father a threat to the virtue of Rome. When one assassinates for virtue, afterwards one is never virtuous enough to justify the assassination: therefore this refusal to tie oneself by oath to the other conspirators, as each has to answer only to his own conscience.

> . . . No, not an oath . . .
> And what other oath
> Than honesty to honesty engaged
> That this shall be or we will fall for it?
> (Act II, sc.1)

Above all, honor! Brutus has already warned us: "I love the name of honor more than I fear death" (Act I, sc. ii).

And so, in consequence of this principle, this act of insanity by this least of political debutants (Cassius is aware of this and warns Brutus that he doesn't know what he's doing, an act permitting the most feared of his rivals, Marc Antony, to make the funeral oration). And so also, before the battle he must fight, the violent reproaches to the courageous Cassius, his ally, whom he accuses of being what we would call today a war profiteer. And so, finally, his suicide, offered as supplementary evidence of his incorruptible virtue. His heroic cause, however, is not necessarily that of the Republic, of the state, or of power.

Love also has its heroes of moral narcissism. The most beautiful of them all is the analyst's patron saint, Don Quixote, particularly cherished by Freud. Recall the episode in which Quixote goes to the Sierra Morena and wants to live there as a hermit. He strips himself of his few possessions and begins to tear his clothing, to batter his body, and to leap around madly, all of which astonishes Sancho Panza. When the latter demands an explanation, the illusioned hildalgo explains to this common man that he is only conforming to the rules of the code of love as stipulated in the novels of chivalry. Quixote is looking for the feat capable of perpetuating his name in the name of love, a love which must not only be pure, with no sign of carnal desire, but which must also totally dispossess him of his fortune. He must come to this destitution of himself and of his individuality, by imitation of Amadis or Roland, to the point of madness—or at least an imitation of it. "But I have now to rend my garments, scatter my arms about, and dash my head against these rocks; with other things of the like sort which will strike you with admiration." This he says to Sancho Panza, who tries in vain to reason with him. "Mad I am and mad I must be," adds Quixote whose madness here is a sign of virtue. And of Quixote's description of Dulcinea as the "ever honored lady," Sancho sees only that "she will pitch the bar with the lustiest swain in the parish; straight and vigorous, and I warrant can make her part good with any knight-errant that shall have her for his lady. Oh, what a pair of lungs and a voice she has . . . and the very best of her is, that she is not at all coy, but as bold as a court-lady. . . ." Certainly this is not the way Quixote sees Dulcinea. One can say that here it cannot be a matter of narcissism but rather of objectal love; it is for the love object that Quixote inflicts upon himself privations and cruelty. But no, it is only a matter of the narcissistic projection of an idealized image and it is not the least of the strokes of genius of Cervantes that he ends his book with Quixote's repudiation: "'No more of that, I beseech you,' replied Don Quixote, 'all the use I shall make of these follies at present is to heighten my repentance.'"

Doubtless Quixote and Sancho Panza exist only on paper. But they live in us if not in themselves. In the same way, is not Falstaff the absolutely and completely amoral narcissist, whose monologue on honor merits both our reprobation for its coarseness and our admiration for its truth? We are caught between an indispensable illusion and a no less indispensable truth.

All of these figures have been described by a philosopher. Have you not recognized, again and again in these pages, Hegel and his beautiful soul? Concerned about the order of the world, wanting to change it but anxious for his virtue, he would like to knead the dough with which man is made, while at the same time keeping his hands clean. But beware of doing as Hegel, who, having immortalized this beautiful soul with his pen, could only conclude *The Phenomenology of Mind* with a triumph that could well have been that of the beautiful soul.

That beautiful soul of moral conscience, do we not feel how close it can come to the delusion of presumption, to this law of the heart whose reference is paranoia? In any case, its narcissistic character has not escaped Hegel: "Contemplation of itself is its *objective* existence, and this objective element is the utterance of its knowledge and will as a *universal*." There is even its tie to the most primary narcissism: "We see then here, self-consciousness withdrawn into the inmost retreats of its being, with all externality, as such, gone and vanished from it—returned into the intuition of the ego as altogether identical with the ego, and intuition where this ego is all that is essential, and all that exists." The consequence of this is "absolute untruth, which collapses within itself."

Would we appear to be engaging in the denunciation of virtue and the defense of vice? To do so would be to give in to a fashion which today sees Sade as our savior. We will content ourselves with the recalling of this truth, pointed out by Freud, who indissolubly tied sexuality and morality, the diversion of one automatically bringing about the diversion of the other. Georges Bataille (1957), to whom tribute must be paid, has profoundly understood this consubstantiality of erotism and the sacred. "I must earn your love," a patient said. To which I answered: "Yes, but what kind of love are you talking about?" She was obliged to recognize, in spite of her vain and hopeless efforts, that Eros, that black angel, for her had turned white.

CONCLUSION

Several points have been left in suspense. First of all, it is necessary to point out that the structure of moral narcissism here is rigidly final. It characterizes certain patients by the predominance of its features. No one is totally free of moral narcissism. One can also call attention to this structural particularity as a phase in the analysis of certain patients. Also, concerning some of the cases I have described, though they may well have the outlines of this structure, they are not definitively tied to it. They can evolve—experience has taught us this—and can attain other positions. It is with satisfaction that we can observe favorable evolutions in cases where they were no longer hoped for.

Let us also take another look at the ties between moral narcissism and moral masochism. It is useful to distinguish them. Is not one a camouflage for the other? Rather than consider their relationship in terms of the covering of one by the other, I think that, if their relationship is dialectical, it is nonetheless a matter of a different series. If, however, one must admit their oneness, I would say that the true masochism is moral narcissism, insofar as there exists in the latter an attempt to reduce the tensions to zero level—the final aim of masochism insofar as its destiny is tied to the death instinct and the Nirvana principle. To repeat: the connection with suffering implies the relationship with the object—narcissism reduces the subject to itself, toward the zero which is the subject.

Desexualization is directed toward the libidinal and aggressive instincts, toward the object and toward the ego. The open range given to the death instinct is aiming for the annihilation of the subject considered as the last fantasy. Here death and immortality converge.

Truthfully, extreme solutions are never encountered; all that one establishes in the clinic, and particularly in the selectivity of the *psychoanalytic* clinic, are orientations toward curves, moving to their asymmetric limits. In this regard, the relations between shame and guilt are much more complex than we have said. However, the destructive character of shame is major: *guilt can be shared, shame can not be.* Nonetheless, ties form between shame and guilt: one can be ashamed of one's guilt, one can feel guilty about one's shame. But the analyst clearly distinguishes the splitting planes when, faced by his patient, he feels the extent to which guilt can be tied to its unconscious sources and how it can be partially surpassed when analyzed. Shame by contrast takes on an irreparable character. The transformation of pleasure into unpleasure is a solution for guilt; for shame, the only thing possible is the path of negative narcissism. A neutralization of affects is at work, a deadly enterprise where a labor of Sisyphus is carried out. I love no one. I love only myself. I love myself. I do not love. I do not. I. O. The progression is the same for hate: I hate no one. I hate only myself. I hate myself. I do not hate. I do not. I. O. This progression of propositions illustrates the evolution toward the affirmation of the megalomaniacal "I" in the last stage before its disappearance.

REFERENCES

Bataille, G. (1957). *Erotism*, trans. M. Dalwood. London: Calder, 1965.

Codet, H., and Laforgue, R. (1925). Les arriérations affectives: la schizonia (essai pathogénique sur les états de dissociation névrotiques et psychotiques). *L'Evolution Psychiatrique* 1:102-126.

Dodds, E. (1951). *The Greeks and the Irrational*. Berkeley: University of California Press.

Freud, A. (1936). *The Ego and the Mechanisms of Defense*. New York: International Universities Press, 1946.

Freud, S. (1920). Beyond the pleasure principle. *Standard Edition* 18:7-64.

———(1923). The ego and the id. *Standard Edition* 19:1-66.

———(1924). The economic problem of masochism. *Standard Edition* 19:159-170.

———(1927). Fetishism. *Standard Edition* 21:152-157.

———(1939). Moses and monotheism. *Standard Edition* 23:7-137.

Green, A. (1963). Une variante de la position phallique-narcissique. *Revue Française de Psychanalyse* 27:117-184.

———(1967). Les fondements différenciateurs des images parentales: l'hallucination négative de la mere et l'identification primordiale au père. *Revue Française de Psychanalyse* 31:896-906.

Klein, M. (1952). Notes on some schizoid mechanisms. In *Developments in Psychoanalysis*, ed. M. Klein, P. Heimann, S. Isaacs, and J. Riviere. London: Hogarth Press.

Lacan, J. (1966). *Ecrits*. Paris: LeSeuil.

Mâle, P. (1956). Etude psychanalytique de l'adolescence. In *La Psychanalyse D'Aujoud'hui*, ed. S. Nacht. Paris: P. U. F.

Pasche, F. (1969). De la depression. In *A Partir de Freud*. Paris: Payot.

Winnicott, D. W. (1975). *Through Paediatics to Psycho-Analysis*. New York: Basic Books.

Infancy, Aloneness, and Madness

M. MASUD R. KHAN

fleurir ne suffit pas aux roses
au fond de son miroir
il faut que l'amoureuse
les regarde la voir
—Jean Lescure

The human infant is the only living organism that emerges out of the womb into its new environment, both traumatically and physically immature. Hence the necessity of extensive and extended infant-care by the maternal coverage, and/or her substitutes.

Of course Freud was the first to establish this equation. Yet it took some twenty years for this to be taken seriously as a *fact*, and not merely as a concept: thanks to three persons—Anna Freud, Melanie Klein and Winnicott.

In this article I shall not be concerned with the myriad vicissitudes of infant-mother relating that lead to psychopathology later. But talk of the infant-in-care *alone* with himself in the quiet states of well-being. Because a very large part of infancy and early childhood is spent in that state and little has been written about it by analysts, except for Winnicott.

What is the nature and function of this aloneness in infancy? Primarily it provides both the *space* and the *time* for the innate biologic capacities to actualize into a personalized psychic state. Gradually *the* infant becomes *an* infant: a person in his own right and in his own privacy of being.

Secondly, a lot that was maturationally incapable of being rendered into psychic experience at that early stage goes into *oblivion*. I believe Freud meant this by his concept of primary repression. But what goes into *oblivion* is not lost. It will turn up later in private mad states of being. And here I am deliberately using the word *mad*, as distinct from the concept of psychotic. Because each adult is mad in a very private way and also alone.

How we experience and actualize this madness and aloneness in adult life is the next question. In three ways: through art and literature; through sharing unexcited mutuality with the *other*; and in the mystic states of being, like the Persian sufis or the Zen priests.

The real predicament for the analytic clinician arises when the analysand brings his *mad* state and need to be alone to his session. The latter is often mistaken for resistance and the analysand hides his true need and screens it with compliant guilt and acceptance.

But that is not the worst that we do as clinicians. The worst starts when we try to make sense of the *non*-sense of the analysand's spoken madness in terms of our conceptual vocabulary, through which we are addicted to listening to the analysand's normal or pathological material and interpreting it. We mis-guidedly, and from concern, try to make sense of this *non*-sense by either reconstructing *the facts* of infancy (Winnicott) or its *fantasies* (Klein). Neither helps and the creative potential of the madness lapses back into oblivion and the analysand is no longer either mad or alone, but merely lonely and lost!

Addiction and Paranoid Process: Psychoanalytic Perspectives

W. W. MEISSNER, S.J., M.D.

Multiple aspects of the problem of drug abuse and addiction are formulated in terms of the dynamics of the paranoid process, specifically emphasizing the complex interactions of introjection, projection, and the paranoid construction. The effect of projection is to modify the experience of the drug substance so qualities and capacities, often powerful and magical, are attributed to it, allowing it to serve as an external agency contributing to the maintenance of internal introjective configurations and correspondingly to the preservation of an inner sense of self-cohesion. The projective dynamics deal primarily with the vicissitudes of aggression and narcissism, and are given a sense of organization and meaningful integration by the cognitive elaboration of the paranoid construction. They also serve to locate the drug-taking behavior in a larger matrix of familial, social, and other environmental influences, which tend to give support to the projective system. The interaction of these projective psychological dynamics with the pharmacological action of drug substances completes the drug equation and helps to shed further light on the selection of specific drug substances as having addictive potential.

The psychoanalytic contribution to the study of addictions, specifically alcoholism and the variety of drug addictions, has a meager history. The reasons are multiple but must surely include the variety of selective factors that tend to segregate addictive patients and the practitioners of psychoanalysis: it is a fact that analysts see very few alcoholics or drug addicts. A related question, as yet unresolved, is whether the addictive population is afflicted with a degree of psychopathology that by and large excludes effective psychoanalytic intervention. But whatever the reasons, the basis for a more comprehensive and systematically elaborated theory, one embracing the multiple dimensions of addictive phenomena, has been lacking.

Despite these limitations, the analytic interest in addictive phenomena is long-standing and has contributed perhaps the most significant body of theory about addiction, specifically as a psychological condition. The history of these developments, so cogently synthesized by Yorke (1970), leaves one with a sense of disparate and fragmented approaches. These reflect the scattered emphases of their respective authors but do not yield a more comprehensive view responsive to the more contemporary experience of drug usage and drug dependence.

More recent attempts to articulate a comprehensive view of addiction have been more satisfactory. Wurmser (1974), for example, emphasizes the role of dispositional factors in relation to the activation of a "narcissistic crisis" expressing an underlying narcissistic conflict. Krystal and Raskin (1970) attribute the pathogenesis of drug states to the intolerance of the ego for painful affects, particularly anxiety and depression, to the pathological vicissitudes of object- and self-representations, and finally to the corresponding or consequent modification of consciousness introduced by reason of the drug effects.

While such presentations have significantly advanced our understanding of the psychopathology of drug states, they remain somewhat fragmented and limited in perspective. The intent of the present paper is to try to provide a more comprehensive frame of reference within which a more adequate statement of the complex interaction of variables may be possible. Such an undertaking must remain tentative, but I would hope might have some heuristic and even pragmatic value.

However, a more comprehensive understanding of drug phenomena must also face certain specific issues. A primary question is that of diagnosis. Earlier analytic studies tended to emphasize the more primitive aspects of addictive behavior and linked addictive states more closely with the psychoses or psychosis-like conditions. Even the contemporary literature has a strong tendency to describe addictive phenomena in terms of psychotic processes, or to relate it to a psychotic potential in the patient, or frequently to establish a strong link between addictive and borderline conditions. Such formulations were most likely a by-product of the selective factors we have already mentioned as well as of the generally limited psychiatric experience with addictive patients.

In more recent years, with the increased availability of drugs and the epidemic phenomenon of drug use and abuse, psychiatrists have gained a much greater appreciation for the variety of personality organizations within which drug dependence can take hold. There is increased awareness that the outcome of drug dependence in any given individual may reflect the influence of external determinants in addition to intrapsychic dispositions. Consequently, the diagnostic issue remains open and controverted.

In addition, the role of cause and effect in producing drug dependence is a difficult problem to sort out. This is particularly true of the psychological aspects of the problem, since the mere fact of addiction does not logically entail correlative psychological impediments or vulnerabilities as predispositions or causal determinants. The extent to which personality variables may be altered, modified, determined, or influenced by toxic pharmacological effects remains as yet unknown.

As our experience with drug states expands and our awareness of the variety of conditions within which drug dependence can arise is extended, the theoretical weight of complex determinants has undergone a significant shift. The original psychoanalytic perspective on addiction was derived from Freud's formulations and emphasized the role of libidinal factors. Masturbation, in fact, was considered the primary addiction. Only in recent years, however, have the varieties of drug experience become more apparent. The insufficiency of intrapsychic determinants in comprehending such phenomena has became increasingly apparent. More recent considerations have laid increasing emphasis on the role of the environmental setting and contextual determinants as playing a significant role in the emergence of drug dependence (Zinberg 1975). Thus the implicit demand for any comprehensive theory of drug dependence requires, if not that such contextual determinants be assigned a specific role, at least that the formulation of the key variables of the theory remain open to the determining influence of such contextual and socially embedded phenomena.

An additional problem in the understanding of drug states is presented by increasing sophistication in the understanding of specific pharmacological effects. Early theoretical approaches to the problem tended to consider drug dependence as a monolithic or univocal phenomenon. Thus, as Yorke (1970) has noted:

> the majority of writers do not distinguish between addiction of different kinds of drugs, tending to treat them as identical and including alcoholism too as part of the same pathology—which may or may not be the case. (p. 143)

Broadening experience with a variety of types of addiction has made it increasingly probable that specific qualities of the pharmacology of addictive drugs may have to be included in the drug dependency equation. The earlier view, for example that of Glover (1932), tended to emphasize the addictive potentiality of the patient's personality while minimizing the addictive potential of specific pharmacological entities.

The addictive phenomenon was regarded as a by-product of intrapsychic determinants, independent of external determinants or of the specific pharmacological properties of the drug. Current knowledge of the pharmacology of various drugs requires that we include the specific pharmacological effects as part of the drug dependency equation.

THE PARANOID PROCESS

In the present reflection we will try to focus the complex interaction of intrapsychic determinants, environmental and contextual variables, and specific pharmacological effects in terms of an overriding framework provided by the paranoid process (Meissner 1978b). The intention is to define the complex aspects of the problem of addiction in terms of specifiable parameters of the paranoid process in the hope of providing a more integrative context for the understanding of drug phenomena and of evolving a more secure basis for meaningful psychotherapeutic intervention and modification of drug dependent states.

The central elements of the paranoid process include: (a) the core introjects around which the subject's inner world is structured (these introjects represent the critical internalizations of significant object relations in the individual's developmental history and provide the basis for the organization and integration of the self-system); (b) projections which derive from the core introjects and contribute to the progressive modification and differentiation of object-representations and their correlative object relations; and finally (c) the paranoid construction by which the meaningful and sustaining patterns of environmental reference are cognitively organized to provide a congruent context for the support of specific projections. The integration of projections with the paranoid construction constitutes the subject's projective system (Meissner 1978b).

At the heart of the etiological complex that gives rise to drug dependence and addiction lies the organization of the subject's introjects. The introjects are the core elements of the paranoid process. They provide the structural matrix around which the individual organizes his sense of self. This matrix also provides the basis and source for projective elaborations. They are constituted by critical internalizations derived from object relations with significant figures in the child's developmental history. They form the core structuralizing organization around which the child progressively integrates and differentiates a sense of self. To the extent that the developmentally based introjective process is successful in setting up, organizing, and maintaining a consistent, stable, and coherent sense of self, a matrix for the facilitation of significant structuralizations is possible. This allows the introjective matrix to be progressively transformed into structural agencies, most particularly the macrostructural components of intrapsychic structure, ego and superego. Given the normal developmental progression, there is an inherent tendency of the introjective configuration to be modified in the direction of relatively autonomous, stable, and cohesive intrapsychic formations.

However, developmental vicissitudes complicate and impede this progression and result in the fixation of the introjective organization at relatively primitive and regressive levels. At these primitive levels of organization, the introjects are stamped with the mark of their origins—specifically, with the quality of the primitive and conflictual object relations out of which they derive. Consequently, as internalized configurations they are relatively susceptible to regressive pulls and are continually caught up in the pressures and counterpressures of drive and defense. These internalized configurations are also impregnated with relatively primitive components of narcissism and unresolved aggression, and reflect a pathological organization of the sense of self that may be more or less conscious, possessing an inherent instability, lacking cohesiveness, and easily regressing to levels of fragmentation and dedifferentiation. Thus these configurations are highly susceptible to largely defensively motivated externalization through projection.

An important point to be made about the introjective organization is that it is not limited to or characteristic of any single diagnostic category or developmental level. Rather, the introjective organization is a general phenomenon of human psychology that can be identified at all levels of personality organization from the most primitive and psychotic to the most healthy and adaptively functioning neurotic. It should be noted, however, that the more primitive the organization of such introjects, the more they derive from and can reflect vicissitudes of early object relationships and related developmental difficulties. They are then more susceptible to regressive pulls, so that the self-organization to which they are so intimately related remains relatively fragile and subject to regressive fragmentation and dissolution. Consequently, the more fragile the inner organization and cohesiveness of the introjective alignment and its correlative self-organization, the more intensely and urgently the self-organization requires adjunctive stabilization from external sources.

These external sources may take a variety of forms. They may include various types of group affiliation and membership, religious dedication, political fanaticism, and clinging to various self-sustaining individual relationships (as is often the case in a highly dependent and narcissistically motivated therapeutic relationship). Alternatively, they may take the form of perversion or fetishism, or perhaps the addictive form of dependence on specific drug substances. In all of these expressions of the underlying need for an extrinsic sustaining support for the inner fragility of the self, it is not simply the dependence on the extrinsic source that is in question but rather the organization of the extrinsic supply and its coordination and integration with the inner needs and propensities of the self-organization through the process of projection. In all of these cases the extrinsic source is modified and transformed so that it becomes a meaningful object or object-substitute that is now actually linked—no longer only potentially—with the needs and deficits of the self-system.

The quality of object relations in the drug population tends to be characterized by relative constriction and an infantile and predominantly narcissistic character particularly noteworthy in sexual relationships, whether heterosexual or homosexual (Hartmann 1969). In addition to the predominance of oral narcissistic determinants, there seems to be an intense need to replace a lost object. Not only does the beginning of drug taking often follow upon a significant experience of loss but the patient may also return to the use of drugs in the context of the loss of an object. The drug is somehow meant to replace the absent object, usually one of the parents or, in the context of treatment, the therapist (Hartmann 1969). The attempt to stabilize a relationship with a lost parental object serves as the unconscious underlying motivation of the addiction.

The addict seeks to make the drug an available object that is predictable, dependable, always under control of the subject, and consequently never lost (Pinderhughes 1971). For such individuals the threat of a loss of the object constitutes a severe separation anxiety equivalent to annihilation (Krystal and Raskin 1970). Early developmental experiences with the primary object seem to have been too frustrating or too seductively gratifying, with the result that ambivalence toward the object is correspondingly intensified. Consequently, these individuals have a chronically unsatisfied and constant need for external supplies. They yearn for fusion with an object that allows them a cessation of all inner tensions. The drug serves as the substitute object through which fusion can be realized and the state of tensionless gratification achieved.

Under the impulse of the primitive ambivalence there is an intense craving for reunion and fusion with the lost object, yet at the same time an impelling need for separation. The primitive drama is rehearsed over and over again but does not reach a solution. In the use of the drug there is a repeated fusion with the lost object that can be controlled and repeatedly introjected. Thus the lost object assumes proportions far more suitable to the addictive need than are less available and controllable human love objects (Krystal and Raskin 1970).

In order to understand the dynamics of this interaction with the drug-object, it seems necessary to postulate that the drug functions after the manner of a transitional object. The transitional mode of experience is familiar to us through the work of Winnicott (1953). We can note at this juncture that the composition of the transitional object takes place through the interplay of introjective and projective processes whereby the real external object becomes the vehicle of projective elements derived from the subject's own introjective frame of reference (Meissner 1978b). In the drug experience, then, the external drug substance is projectively modified by the drug-taking individual in such a fashion that the omnipotent, gratifying, narcissistically reconstituting qualities of the drug are in effect projectively derived from the subject's own inner frame of reference. It is this process that Krystal and Raskin (1970) refer to as "transsubstantiation." The transitional quality of the drug experience has been noted by Hartmann (1969), and its close relation to fetishism noted by Berman (1972), who elaborated upon the formulations of Greenacre (1969) concerning the connection between transitional phenomena and fetishism. The similarity to fetishism has also been noted by Wurmser (1974).

In terms of the explanatory schema provided by the paranoid process, these relatively primitive, narcissistically embedded, and intensely ambivalent introjects derive from early experiences in the relationships to significant objects. In the case of the highly orally contaminated and primitively ambivalent internalizations in question here, these experiences would seem to derive primarily from the relationship with the mother, although significant paternal influences cannot be excluded. The resulting introjective configuration provides the pathogenic core around which the individual's sense of self and its correlative attributes are organized.

The original introjective experience is permeated by the need to preserve some sense of availability and internal relatedness to a relatively unavailable, unresponsive, or excessively ambivalent love object. The same need persists and is reexpressed and rehearsed in the drug experience, except that in the drug experience the drug substance becomes a substitute object by reason of its integration as a transitional object through projective transformation. This transitional transformation or "transsubstantiation" of the drug substance gives it its magical power and illusory potentiality for easing inner tensions and bringing surcease and gratification to the addict's inner torment (Frosch 1970).

THE TYPOLOGY OF ADDICTION

The problem of shifting emphases and meanings is reflected in attempts to define the term *drug addiction*. The former tendency to emphasize the addictive aspects of the drug-dependent personality or the addictive potentiality of the drug itself has given way to more nuanced formulations which seem less decisive about these issues and at the same time open to the complex range of possible influences. Thus the World Health Organization in 1957 adopted the following revised definition:

> Drug addiction is a state of periodic or chronic intoxication detrimental to the individual and to society, produced by the repeated consumption of a drug (natural or synthetic). Its characteristics include: (1) an overpowering desire or need (compulsion) to continue taking the drug and to obtain it by any means; (2) a tendency to increase the dose; (3) a psychic (psychological) and sometimes a physical dependence on the effects of the drug. (Krystal and Raskin 1970, p. 10)

This delimits a broad and far-reaching field of study within which four important dimensions can be delineated.

Degree of drug usage. This parameter defines a continuum of drug usage stretching from the casual, occasional, or experimental use of drugs to compulsive drug abuse. The experimental user may take the drug out of curiosity or as a result of social pressures of various kinds, but he feels no inner or compelling need for the drug effect. Such experimenters compose by far the largest group of drug users, and their drug usage does not properly fall under the rubric of addiction. Consequently, such experimental drug users can be much more readily understood on the basis of extrinsic causes and environmental determinants than in terms of any intrapsychic components. It is the compulsive addict whose drug usage is symptomatic of deeper underlying psychological problems.

Degree of actual drug effects. This relates to the necessity of distinguishing the extent to which psychological manifestations are a function of the drug effects. Thus, addiction to various types of drugs (Yorke 1970) must be considered. The earlier view of addictive states as more or less univocal tended to ignore any differentiation between the pharmacological effects of different drugs. Thus Meerloo (1952), for example, was able to describe a relatively unvarying addictive process that started with a wish for an "artificial ecstasy" and ended in craving for a single specific drug. This last was the stage of true addiction. He felt that the observable differences in the process could be reduced to a set of common unconscious determinants that characterize all addicts, namely a craving for ecstatic experience, an unconscious drive to self-destruction, and finally an unconscious and unresolved need for oral dependency. The question of a common set of psychological characteristics remains unresolved, but it seems clear that the view that the addictive substance is irrelevant to the addictive process (Glover 1932) is no longer tenable.

Degree of psychopathology. Experimental findings seem to support the notion that relatively severe psychopathology is found in association with heavy drug usage and sociopathy (Westermeyer and Walzer 1975). Thus, psychiatric disorder and heavy drug use often coexist even though the causal relationship between them remains unspecified. Even with a drug of such low addictive potential as marijuana, heavy users have usually been found to manifest disturbed interpersonal relationships and are often unemployed or underemployed (Mirin et al. 1971), and social functioning is often impaired (Hochman and Brill 1972).

In his early paper on addiction, Rado (1933) emphasized the basic depressive character with its associated early narcissistic vulnerability, intolerance for frustration and pain with a constant need to exchange such discomfort for an emotional "high," a lack of affectionate and meaningful object relations overcome by a pseudo-closeness with other drug takers during the drug experience, and finally the use of an artificial technique to maintain self-esteem. In her study of drug-taking adolescents, Dora Hartmann (1969) observed that these characteristics applied not only to those who had become confirmed addicts and for whom drug taking had become a way of life, but also to a certain intermediate group. She describes an experimenting group in which early object relations and ego development were not severely disturbed. In this group were those who used drugs more or less out of defiance of parental authority or curiosity, and who were able to stop the drug use when this type of acting out was no longer necessary. However, the intermediate group she describes utilized drugs as a means of maintaining self-esteem. This "artificial technique," in Rado's terms, allowed them to avoid tolerating the frustrations of facing reality and to avoid the active work required to establish more mature object relations—an essential task of adolescent development. This intermediate group maintain a pseudo-closeness to other drug users without much emotional commitment, and sexual gratification remains at a masturbatory level.

Zinberg (1975) sharply challenges the view that severe personality maladjustment or psychological vulnerability of whatever kind can serve as an adequate basis for understanding addictive phenomena. While it is true that such individuals readily develop drug dependencies, he contends that this represents only a small fraction of the drug-using population, and more particularly of the addict population itself. He regards this view as a result of a retrospective falsification that looks at drug users and addicts after they have developed a preoccupation with the drug experience. Then the assumption arises that the personality attributes manifested after drug dependence has been established are similar to those prevailing previous to its establishment. Without denying that internal factors may be involved in various aspects of drug usage, Zinberg (1975) insists that "there are no psychological profiles or consistent patterns of internal conflicts or phase-specific developmental sequences that can be put forward as the determining factor in this history of drug use and addiction" (p. 569).

The question of plasticity. This question has been admirably discussed by Edwards (1974). Plasticity of any psychoactive substance is concerned with the degree to which the behavior produced by the substance is potentially susceptible to modification. While the notion of drug dependence generally implies loss of behavioral plasticity, it remains a significant fact that drug-dependent behavior always continues to exhibit some degree of plasticity.

As far as the use of drugs is concerned, plasticity includes not only the direct influence of the drug on the organism and the plasticity of the intoxicated behavior itself, but also the degree of plasticity of the drug-seeking behavior of the individual: specifically, the frequency and quantity of drug use, the settings and occasions, and the degree to which he gives the drug-taking behavior priority over other activities. Both aspects of drug-related behavior are influenced and modified by environmental factors.

As Edwards points out, the failure to consider this dimension of drug dependence may have led to an excessive emphasis on the absoluteness of clinical typologies in drug studies. Thus, to the degree that alcohol-dependent behavior is plastic, it can be molded in a variety of forms in different cultures and in different personalities. He comments:

> Alcohol dependence in one country, or as it affects one type of personality, can be very unlike the alcohol dependence seen in another culture, or as it exhibits itself in a person of a different temperament. The open invitation is then to assume that there are fundamentally different pathologies. If, however, the matter is analyzed within terms of the concept of plasticity, we may instead deduce that there is one essential dependent pathology with behavioral forms which cluster into "types" under the impact of pathoplastic factors. Instead of truly distinct types of alcohol dependence, there may be one dependence with a variety of faces. (p. 186)

Edwards cites a body of evidence provided by MacAndrew and Edgerton (1969) regarding contrasting societies in which intoxication may be accompanied by wild acting out in one social context, while the same drug intoxication in another society involves no violation of social controls. Edwards concludes that much which has been conventionally assumed to be an inevitable "disinhibiting" pharmacological effect of alcohol stands now in need of reappraisal in the light of cultural evidence. (p. 182)

Consequently, the notion of plasticity allows us to regard drug behavior as a result of a core dependence state that may be more or less plastic in its inferences; the degree of psychopathology and the role of environmental and contextual determinants may be to some degree correlative. Thus cultural or environmental factors may modify not only addictive symptoms and behaviors; they may modify also the extent to which pathogenic determinants play a significant role in the addictive phenomena. Conversely, the degree of intensity of psychopathology or of compulsivity may reciprocally influence the extent to which cultural or contextual factors can exercise a plastic influence. We will return to this issue in our subsequent discussion.

THE CAUSES OF ADDICTION

The causes of addictive states must be complex and multiply determined. Following Freud's lead (1895), Wurmser (1974) has suggested a hierarchical ordering of causes or reasons for drug addiction or dependence. He distinguishes four types of cause: precondition, specific cause, concurrent cause, and precipitating cause.

Preconditions are those factors without which the effect could not come about but which are incapable of their own accord of producing the effect, regardless of the extent or degree of intensity to which they are operative. Wurmser suggests a predispositional constellation for addiction, with the need for defense against affects and the compelling wish for regressive gratification as the most specific of these dispositional factors.

The *specific cause* is always present wherever the effect is found and is sufficient to produce the effect if it is present in the required degree or intensity, provided the preconditions are also satisfied. For Wurmser, the specific cause of addiction is a narcissistic crisis representing a more or less acute exacerbation of an underlying narcissistic conflict.

Concurrent causes are not present in every instance, nor are they able, regardless of intensity, to produce the effect by their own power. Nonetheless, they operate in conjunction with preconditions and specific causes to bring about the etiological configuration. Here Wurmser places the emphasis on cultural conflicts, particularly value conflicts relating to the limitations of human existence, the dissolution of external superego representatives, and the increasing abolition of the influence of authority and tradition. Under these conditions the drug becomes the symbolic expression of liberation from authority, the symbol of protest and rebellion. Here, too, belong the extrinsic determinants of social, economic, and political factors that play upon and foster the use of drugs. Poverty, inadequate housing, social degradation, violence, the undermining of family structure, and the complex of factors that sustain and nourish the drug traffic: all would seem to fall under the rubric of concurrent cause.

Last but not least in this hierarchy of causes is the *precipitating cause*. It is that which appears last in the equation and immediately precedes the emergence of the effect. The precipitating cause thus completes the etiological equation and brings about the effect. The precipitating cause in Wurmser's schema is the advent of the drug as a result of easy availability and social compliance with peer influence. He comments:

> The *advent* of the drug suddenly allows a previous desperate search to crystallize around the one object and activity that relieves the unbearable tension. In sum: there is no compulsive drug use without this trigger factor; but there is still an overriding emotional compulsiveness directed toward other activities and objects. It can be assumed that only the latter two sets of factors (concurrent and precipitating ones) are identical for experimenters and compulsive users alike. (p. 828)

Moreover, as Hartmann (1969) has noted, none of the psychological preconditions can be taken as pathognomonic for drug users or drug addicts. Any of these factors can be found in neurotic patients with or without drug taking or drug abuse. The factors are not specific to drug taking and can also be found in neuroses, depression, delinquencies, and even psychoses. The explanatory power of the drug equation must therefore rest on the combination of the necessary, specific causes with sufficient preconditions, and this complex of causes must carry the brunt of intrapsychic explanation in the understanding of drug addiction.

Thus there is a critical interface in any consideration of the causes of addictive conditions: that between the role of intrapsychic factors and the extrinsic, environmentally derived and determined causes related to the social and/or cultural setting within which the drug behavior occurs. As Zinberg (1975) has observed, there is a growing acceptance of the idea that understanding the effects of illicit drugs and the motivation for their use requires that personality variables and the drug, as well as the setting, be taken into account. The specific behavior, the taking of illicit drugs, cannot be removed from its social matrix.

Another area in which the effects of social setting can be described is that of placebo effects, but suggestive mechanisms do not adequately explain even these. Rather, as Edwards (1974) suggests, the pathoplastic effect of the social setting on drug-related behavior is as complex as the cultural elements themselves and as multiply determined. The cultural control of drinking among Jews, for example, is not determined by attitudes toward alcohol alone but takes place within a general matrix of Jewish cultural attitudes, values, and aspects of self-esteem and self-image.

Certainly, among the environmental or contextual factors that play a significant role in determining drug behavior, the influence of the addict's family must be given primary consideration. Most descriptions of the families of addicts emphasize the patient's close relationship to the mother and the relative distance between the addicted son and his father. The mother tends to be overprotective, controlling, and indulgent, and unconsciously strives to keep the addicted child in an infantilized position (Schwartzman 1975, Calogeras and Camp 1975). The addict and his family participate in the shared belief that he is unable to resist drugs when exposed to them. This feeling of powerlessness against the effects of the drug is reinforced by family members. If the addict becomes abstinent, other members of the family communicate to him their conviction that this is only temporary. This implicit belief system is powerfully reinforced by the mother's overprotectiveness, which frequently undercuts any attempt by the father to insist on more mature, responsible behavior. The addict is seen as inadequate by all members of the family.

Within the family setting, the addictive behavior is a result not only of intrapsychic determinants operating within the patient but also of complex forces and influences generated within the family system. These operate to reinforce the preconditions of addictive behavior and to subconsciously force the patient back into a position in which he is required to maintain his addiction. Thus, the addictive behavior of the addict is in some manner and expression of a deeper family pathology and serves important functions in the homeostatic balancing of destructive psychic forces within the family. The contextual processes which operate as concurrent causes of addictive behavior must take into account not only the more broadly focused social and cultural influences, as we have suggested, but also the more specific and immediately operating forces that arise out of the subculture and dynamics of the family group.

ADDICTIVE PSYCHOPATHOLOGY

In addressing ourselves to the specific aspect of the psychopathology of addiction, a primary issue is that of diagnosis. The question revolves around the problem of the level of psychopathology that tends to be associated with addictive phenomena. Within psychoanalysis there is general agreement that drug dependence is a syndrome, a form of chronic relapsing symptomatology that generally, if not invariably, reflects some form of underlying mental or emotional disturbance. This emotional disorder is reflected in the addict's craving for and dependence on the drug substance (Krystal and Raskin 1970).

Drug dependence may in fact be seen in a variety of clinical entities. Drug states are often compared to psychoses or psychosis-like conditions. However, while the psychotic attempts to alter his relationship with reality, the addict is more interested in modifying his own consciousness, often in the interest of avoiding dysphoric affects (Krystal and Raskin 1970). Thus the tendency has existed to link the addictive states with the psychoses, seeing them, for example, as a form of larval psychosis (Bychowski 1953) or seeing the drug as holding off an acute psychosis that may sometimes overwhelm the ego when the drug is withdrawn (Szasz 1958).

The link with psychotic phenomena has been increased by the analogies drawn to the psychotic states of mania and paranoia. Freud (1930) had originally called attention to the manic analogue by describing mania as a condition of intoxication without the use of an intoxicant. Similarly, Fenichel (1945) emphasized the role of addictive drugs in elevating self-esteem, a position reinforced by Lewin's identification (1950) of the states of elation in manic illnesses and drug states. Rado (1957) described the cycles of depression and narcotic elation and the craving for such elation that are involved in narcotic bondage.

Similar appeals to the manic-depressive analogue were made by other authors as well (Glover 1932, Rosenfeld 1960, Guarner 1966). In Rosenfeld's view, the addiction served to bolster a manic defense in the face of underlying depressive or paranoid anxieties. A similar connection was established with paranoid manifestations, particularly linking alcoholism with homosexuality and paranoia—a dynamic configuration advanced by Freud (1911) in his analysis of Schreber.

An important conceptual breakthrough in this area was contributed by Glover (1928, 1932), who suggested that both alcoholism and drug addiction are transitional states that lie between the neuroses and the psychoses. The addict is in many ways much sicker than the neurotic, yet can only with rare exceptions be described as psychotic. Thus in Glover's view drug addiction reflects an underlying fixation of a transitional oedipal system that lies between more primitive oedipal nuclei reflected in paranoid anxieties and the oedipal configuration responsible for later obsessional reactions. The addiction thus serves to control sadistic impulses less violent than those found in paranoia but yet more severe than those found in the obsessions. Drug addiction can serve as a protective barrier against a psychotic reaction resulting from severe regressive states. The parallels between Glover's analysis of these transitional states and later formulations regarding the psychotic character (Frosch 1970) and the borderline personality (Kernberg 1967) are noteworthy.

Despite these formulations, it must be remembered that psychopathology is only a precondition for drug dependence and must be combined with other specific and precipitating causes to bring about the addictive state. Nonetheless, severe chronic drug dependence is found more frequently in severe character disorders and among individuals with borderline or psychotic personality organization than in those who would not be so diagnosed. Keeping in mind the distinction between experimental or recreational drug use and drug dependence, the degree of pathology is generally minimal in the former, while among chronic drug users and drug dependent individuals there is a significant degree of ego pathology (De Angelis 1975). The link between serious pathology and drug addiction must be taken seriously, as is suggested by the finding that some 44 percent of adolescent heroin addicts studied were found to be either schizophrenic or borderline (Gerard and Kornetsky 1954). Yet, at the same time, the number of addicts who become psychotic or who can be found in mental hospitals remains remarkably small (Vaillant 1966a,b).

To these cautions, however, we can add Wurmser's telling comment (1974) that the core difficulty in the treatment of addicted patients is not withdrawal from drugs but rather coming to terms with the deeper emotional need to use a drug, any drug, and often other equally harmful external means to seek relief from their inner torment. However, the diagnostic question is by no means closed, and the characterization of addicts in such ominous diagnostic terms may not tell the whole story. Such low-level character disorders may reflect the model group of compulsive drug-dependent subjects within a wider cultural context provided by Western industrialized societies. The argument as to the influence of social or contextual factors in the etiology of drug dependence remains undecided.

While the issues of diagnosis and etiology remain more or less open questions, there has been no dearth or variety of descriptions of aspects of addictive psychopathology. One of the primary emphases in the literature falls on the invariable tendency of the drug-dependent individual to seek relief or to avoid intolerable psychic pain. The addict's psychic impairments and vulnerability leave him in a position of helplessness to deal with dysphoric affects so that he turns to the drug as an adjunct to help him deal with inner pain and tension. Wurmser (1974) regards compulsive drug use as an attempt at self-treatment so that the drug or drug usage becomes equivalently an artificial or surrogate defense against overwhelming affects. As Wieder and Kaplan (1969) observe:

The dominant conscious motive for drug use is not the seeking of "kicks," but the wish to produce pharmacologically a reduction in distress that the individual cannot achieve by his own psychic efforts. (p. 403)

Drug-dependent individuals frequently demonstrate little capacity for awareness of affects and a conspicuous absence of conscious anxiety or depression, even though anxiety or depressive equivalents may be frequently present (Krystal and Raskin 1970). The addict is thus intolerant of painful affects. A remarkably consistent aspect is the presence of a rather severe latent depression that may be defended against by a variety of defensive maneuvers, including massive denial, and hypomanic or obsessive-compulsive mechanisms. This underlying depression has been frequently noted and has become a central facet of the understanding of addictive states (Rado 1933, 1957, Hartmann 1969). If this attempt at self-treatment through the use of drugs is interrupted, the patient's ego may decompensate into forms of violent, even homicidal rage, or severe suicidal depression (Wurmser 1974). This tendency to suicidal depression is particularly marked among hard-core addicts (Frederick, Resnik, and Wittlin 1973).

This constellation of depressive, narcissistic, and aggressive elements is strongly related to suicidal dynamics (Meissner 1977) and reflects aspects of the introjective organization. Relief from such internally distressing and dysphoric affects is sought by projective resolutions. This mechanism is familiar enough in cases of frank clinical paranoia in which the projection relieves the pressure on the introjective system and masks the underlying depression—the classic paradigm in cases of superego projection. In addiction, the projective resolution may be elaborated into a paranoid construction in which the addict may evolve a set of beliefs, attitudes, and values toward the world around him that portrays him as victimized and disadvantaged. The drug takes its place within this schema as projectively transformed, magically providing ease of inner distress, relieving the depressive pressure, and generally filling in for the functions of lost or yearned-for objects (usually infantile and parental).

Some evidence suggests a connection between alcoholism and depression. It has been observed that suicide attempts in alcoholics most commonly occur during periods of guilt and remorse following prolonged drinking episodes. Moreover, experimental intoxication (Tamerin and Mendelson 1969) suggests that an initial phase of euphoria is followed by an intensification of depression and anxiety. Again the etiological sequence is obscure. Hence, whatever the function of the initial depression, the intoxication with alcohol may serve to intensify it to suicidal proportions (Mayfield and Montgomery 1972). In this connection we can recall

Menninger's notion (1938) that some forms of addiction are equivalent to chronic suicide.

Drug usage may also serve as a defense against various forms of aggression. Based on his experience with narcotic addicts on methadone maintenance, Khantzian (1974) was led to hypothesize "that a significant portion of these individuals become addicted to opiates because they discover that the drug acts specifically to reverse regressive states by attenuating, and making more bearable, dysphoric feeling involving aggression, rage, and related depression" (p. 65). Dealing with such unpleasant and painful affects is facilitated by a form of "shunt" (Krystal and Raskin 1970) that devolves around defenses against the awareness of affects and the alteration of consciousness facilitated by the taking of the drug. This modification of states of consciousness through interaction with the pharmacological effect of the drug has the primary function of modifying the experience of affects (Wurmser 1974, Galenter 1976) and the introjective configuration they reflect.

One of the most powerful aspects of drug-dependent behavior and the one that stamps it most peculiarly as addictive is its quality of compulsiveness. Removal of the drug of choice not only provokes severe depression, anxiety, or various forms of acting out; the drug user will also resort to pharmacologically unrelated drugs or combinations of drugs quite independently of physical withdrawal. The intensity of this compulsion and the correlative need to seek relief is a measure of the psychopathology (Glover 1932, Wurmser 1974).

One of the central themes in the understanding of addictive pathologies is the triad of regression, orality, and narcissism. This regressive triad has had a prominent role in psychoanalytic views of addiction from very early on. Freud (1905) himself noted the important role of orality in addictive states and even suggested that in some cases there may be a constitutional disposition linking addiction with forms of oral perversion. Components of oral fixation or oral regression were emphasized by Glover (1928) in the analysis of alcoholism, drug addiction, and manic-depressive insanity. Similar emphases on the role of oral erotism, oral fixation, passive narcissistic aims, oral regression, and unresolved needs for oral dependency have been persistent motifs in the literature (Rado 1933, 1957, Fenichel 1945, Meerloo 1952, Marmor 1953, Hartmann 1969). The addictive need to restore narcissistic equilibrium through symbolic union with the maternal breast as well as the operation of Lewin's oral triad (1946)— the wish to eat, to be eaten, and to sleep—have been emphasized (Savitt 1954, 1963, Krystal and Raskin 1970). At least some aspects of the projective transformation of the drug substance in addiction corresponds to this symbolic reunion—both in terms of its oral and narcissistic dimensions and in terms of its reattachment to the lost (part-) object.

The role of archaic, omnipotent narcissism in the pathology of addiction and the function of the drug substance in temporarily restoring narcissistic balance have been frequently noted (Rado 1933, Hartmann 1969). Such narcissistic impairments set the stage for a vulnerability to depression that is more or less chronic (Krystal and Raskin 1970). In the same vein, Fenichel (1945) commented on the addictive fixation to passive narcissistic aims.

The increased titre of pathogenic narcissism tends to undermine the quality of, and the capacity for, object relations. The importance of maintaining an omnipotent narcissistic equilibrium, through either reinforcement of the grandiose self or idealization of an archaic self-object, has been noted by Wurmser (1974). Any restrictions, limitations, or imbalance within this narcissistic configuration produce an upsurge of primitive affects. The most prominent and most destructive is narcissistic rage, which may reach murderous or suicidal proportions. The affect of shame is connected with the failure of the self to maintain its grandiose ideal. There is also a tendency to feel a sense of hurt, rejection and abandonment that results from falling short of the goal of total union and acceptance from the idealized object.

The role of the drug substance, particularly narcotics, lies not only in diminishing or eliminating these troublesome affects related to narcissistic vicissitudes, but also in its redressing of the narcissistic balance. Calogeras and Camp (1975) have described narcissistic rage and its self-destructive and socially destructive consequences as an element in the drug experience. It is the specific narcissistic trauma combined with an underlying and more chronic narcissistic vulnerability that Wurmser (1974) describes in terms of the narcissistic crisis. He writes:

> This narcissistic crisis is thus the point at which the conflicts and defects converge with a particular external situation and with the availability with the seeming means of solution: the drug. By definition a "narcissistic crisis" would have to entail a particularly intense disappointment in others, in oneself, or both—so intense because of the exaggerated hopes, and so malignant because of its history's reaching back to very early times. Precipitating external events of such a crisis can most typically be found in family crises, coinciding with the maturational crisis of adolescence. (p. 840)

A number of the essential aspects of the addictive process are described in Berman's account (1972) of amphetamine addiction in a young female hysteric. Her deep-seated feelings of feminine inadequacy, deficiency, and worthlessness, as well as revulsion and shame focused on her own genitals, reflected the depressive core of her introjects. This provided the basis for her pathogenic feelings about herself. These were constantly being enacted and struggled against in a variety of self-demeaning and masochistic ways, including sexual promiscuity. The patient had begun taking amphetamines for dysmenorrhea at age thirteen and continued to take them as diet pills thereafter, though in increasing doses. The effects were dramatic:

> The amphetamines played a crucial role in her everyday life. She depended on them to provide the strength and energy for her flurry of activities and projects at work, to give her the vitality that won her the reputation of "human dynamo." In her social life it was the pill that made her vivacious, sparkling, and sexually active. It served to defend her against the intolerable feeling of weakness and femininity. She often took an extra pill before dates to prevent herself from feeling tired, uninteresting, and like "a lousy lay." She had to adjust her dosage carefully to avoid feeling too sexually overpowering, particularly around the time of her period when, she had heard, a woman's male hormones were increased. (Berman 1972, p. 329)

Gradual reduction of the dosage brought fears that she would become weak, lifeless, dull, lethargic, sexually uninteresting, and unlovable. Her view of herself was dominated by concerns over genital inadequacy—a "deranged, globby, mushy, hairy mess." She continued to carry half an amphetamine pill in her purse, just in case she might need a burst of energy. When asked about this, she replied that it was a "clutch"—a slip for "crutch." She associated "clutch" to the gearshift of a car, something she could clutch onto. This description was accompanied by clenching an imaginary gear shift directly over her pubic area. The fragment of pill had been transformed into a phallic substitute that served to compensate for her feelings of damaged and defective femininity. The pills were originally taken to relieve menstrual cramps (weak, sick femininity) and later for obesity (flabby, unattractive femininity). The pills provided a masculine sense of stamina, strength, mental acuity, and sexual prowess. The pill became a phallic substitute representing the father's penis and her inadequate introjection of his phallic capacities.

At a deeper level, the pill came to represent the availability of oral supplies, like the candy she kept at her bedside, which helped defend against primitive fears of oral abandonment. The fear of being left with nothing was both oral and phallic. Her mother had encouraged her use of diet pills, reviving earlier oral conflicts over diets and feelings of deprivation. The diet pill, therefore, came to symbolize the feeding and depriving mother. Berman (1972) comments:

It was this unique quality of the drug, this lending of itself to objective and subjective symbolization, that facilitated its incorporation into the symptom complex. Within this solitary pill carried inside her little purse, was symbolically condensed the oral and phallic elements of her neurosis. It served as a mortar which knit these elements together, and through its profound symbolic-pharmacologic effects it reinforced and solidified the neurosis. Nowhere was this more evident than in her struggle to relinquish the pill. As Glover points out, the addict can easily reduce the drug to the last, most diluted drop; after that it is difficult, for this drop contains the symbolism. (pp. 336–337)

A similar set of dynamics was displayed in one of my own analytic cases, a young man who had also developed an amphetamine addiction. The organization of this patient's introjects was dominated by his view of himself as small, weak, vulnerable, and castrated, unable to measure up to adult standards or to perform the tasks that adults perform. This patient's introjective organization was determined by early castration motifs reinforced by a congenital heart defect that became a focus of obsessive concern for his anxious and possessive mother. His condition was finally operated on, in somewhat traumatic fashion, at age five. Instead of feeling cured and well, the patient felt himself to be permanently weak and defective—even though he was strongly built and was able to engage in rather strenuous sports, particularly wrestling. But after his operation, he recalled not being able to reassure himself that the large scar across his chest would not fall open one day, leaving him vulnerable and helpless. He spent anxious hours examining the scar, probing it, testing it, but unable to convince himself that he was whole and well.

In addition, the operation and the wound became the object of his mother's anxious preoccupation. He was the youngest of three boys by about seven years. He became her baby, and she worried about and protected him—only reinforcing his feelings of defect and inadequacy. This state of affairs was further complicated by his older brothers: the oldest was a ladies' man to whom my patient looked up in admiration. In fact, the two played at being father and son, a sort of substitute relationship in which the brother was viewed as a sexually proficient stand-in for the patient's own father, whom the patient saw as weak and controlled by the mother. The second brother was the family student and set a high standard of academic achievement. My patient felt he could never match his older brothers, and that he was doomed to failure, both sexual and academic. When he approached a sexual encounter or an academic challenge—whether an examination or writing a paper—the patient felt that he could not hope to perform without the help of his pills. The pills became the talisman of masculine strength, capacity, and proficiency. Without this talisman he could not hold an erection, but would come in his pants like a helpless infant soiling himself. Without it he could not perform effectively in studying for exams or writing papers.

As the analysis of these elements of his drug use proceeded, it became clear that the drug was the repository for the more masculine, aggressive, and competitive aspects of himself, which he had kept repressed. For him to be strong, masculine, and aggressive meant to lose his mother's concerned investment in her sick baby. He would also run the risk of competing with his much older, stronger, and more powerful brothers. They, in turn, were displacements from the patient's more infantile view of and introjection of the father, which was denied and repressed, covered by the patient's need to devalue the real father. These elements of the patient's personality were distilled and projected into the drug so that it became a magical substance that gave the patient the strength and capacity he had need to deny in himself. The same dynamic is observable in Berman's patient (1972) in whom repressed and denied phallic and aggressive strivings are projected onto the drug substance, endowing it with symbolic significance and power. The drug, thus transformed, serves to redress the narcissistic vulnerabilities and deficits in both patients. In both, genital defects come to reflect and represent deeper and more pervasive defects in the patient's sense of self related to the organization of core introjects.

To continue the discussion of addictive psychopathology: under the impetus of ego psychology, drug dependence and addiction have been viewed as a form of ego pathology, in which the use of the drug substance induces a specific state of ego regression (Wieder and Kaplan 1969). The continuing dependence on the drug leads to increasing impoverishment of the ego's resources and a diminished capacity for mastery of anxiety and depression. The ego's adaptive capacity, freedom of action, and autonomy are continually undermined (Rado 1933, Hartmann 1969). Thus the preexistent ego pathology is compounded by the regressive drug-dependent condition. Dependence on the drug allows the individual to cope with and reduce inner tension and stress in a manner his own psychic mechanisms are incapable of. The childhood ego is a form of incomplete psychic structure that requires a relatively constant object to maintain psychic equilibrium. Dependence on such an object or its substitute is characteristic of psychotic or borderline personalities. In states of drug dependence the drug itself becomes that object substitute (Jacobson 1961). Such ego deficits are very likely more to the point in more primitively organized personalities in which the introjective organization is so pathogenic that ego development and functioning is affected. The same distinction can be drawn between lower levels of borderline pathology (pseudoschizophrenics, psychotic characters) and higher order forms of borderline pathology in which ego defects are much less apparent (Meissner 1978a). In lower-order forms of pathology, in which ego defects are prominent, the drug may also serve a prosthetic function (Wieder and Kaplan 1969).

In contexts in which pathogenic introjects dominate the intrapsychic organization, as is frequently seen in forms of psychotic and lower-order borderline psychopathology, there is little room for unimpeded growth of autonomous ego functions. The development of an autonomous ego depends upon critical and relatively nonconflictual ego identifications in the course of developmental experience. Internalizations organized on the introjective level, however, remain highly susceptible to drive-derivative influences and are thus readily subject to regressive pulls. It is difficult to determine any explanatory priority—that is, whether faulty internalizations give rise to defective ego structures or vice versa—but in any case these impediments seem to go hand in hand. The shift in emphasis to the organization of introjects shifts the frame of reference from that of an ego psychology to a theory based more on object relations.

Similar structural deficits have been noted in the organization of the superego and its functioning. Glover (1928) regarded alchoholism as a disastrous attempt to cure the abnormalities of a primitive conscience. Similar self-destructive aspects could also be found in drug addictions (Glover 1932). To this should be added the predominance of relatively archaic forms of shame and guilt, which may be closely linked with primitive and global fears of humiliation and revenge. The archaic superego is thus capable of a considerable degree of vindictiveness and corruptibility (Wurmser 1974). There is in drug addicts a general deterioration of superego functioning; they therefore cannot be expected to follow the usual rules or codes of social behavior. The deceitfulness and exploitation of those around them is accompanied by little acceptance of responsibility and a great deal of blaming of others for their difficulties, most particularly the authorities, who interfere with the availability and use of drugs (Zinberg 1975). This suspension of superego functions affects not only the prohibitive and punitive aspects of the superego but the functions of the ego ideal as well. There is an overriding lack of life-guiding values and ideals or personal myths (Wurmser 1974). The blocking of superego functions, along with the awareness of intersystemic tensions, may be one of the primary reliefs sought through the use of drugs (Krystal and Raskin 1970).

The regressive and narcissistic aspects of such primitive superego functioning call our attention back to the essentially introjective quality of superego organization and its relationship to developmental parameters. Sandler (1960) observed that the prolongation of superego dependence reflected the earlier infantile dependence of the child on his parents as the source of narcissistic gain. If such narcissistic reimbursement can be achieved elsewhere, the dependence on the superego can be abandoned. Thus drug addiction can take the form of replacing dependence with addiction to an external substance. In other words, if the intrapsychic organization of the addicted individual were structured around a more clearly differentiated and effectively structuralized superego, there would be no need to resort to addiction.

THE PROJECTIVE SYSTEM

In discussing the operation of the projective system in addictive states, we come closest to the operative aspects of the paranoid process in addictive psychopathology. In a clinical sense, the presence of paranoid traits in addicted personalities has been frequently noted and documented. There is generally a tendency to blame others, particularly authority figures, for the addict's misfortunes. There is a general attitude of suspiciousness and guardedness, and constant complaints of being victimized, cheated, disadvantaged, and exploited. There is a constant tendency to blame and the repeated complaint that the powerful figures, including doctors, nurses, probation officers, and counselors, are not sufficiently considerate or helpful to the poor disadvantaged addict.

Along with this series of complaints, however, there is an overwhelming sense of self-loathing and devaluation. As Zinberg (1975) has noted, the flavor and content of the productions of these patients are decidedly paranoid, yet they cannot be described as paranoid in specifically psychotic terms. It is this quality of the addictive paranoia that led Glover (1932) to describe the addictions in terms of "transitional states" rather than psychoses. Behind the argumentative, troublesome, and contentious facade erected by these patients there lurk phobic anxieties that reflect the inner compulsion to put and keep themselves in a weak, vulnerable, and helpless position.

In this connection, Khantzian (1974) has noted the tendency for significant behavioral and psychological shifts to accompany stabilization of such patients on methadone. The patients become much quieter, less labile, and show significantly less hostile projection and paranoid reactions. However, as such patients were withdrawn from methadone support, they experience a reemergence of patterns of aggressive-impulsive outbursts, projections, paranoia, and, frequently enough, patterns of psychotic thinking and behavior. These observations suggest that the drug serves to modulate or modify a more general paranoid trait.

A similar connection between drug use and paranoid manifestations has been observed by Seitz (1974) in a hippie population. In these drug users there was an initial disavowal of emotion, a disavowal facilitated by drug use—consistent with the role of drug usage in affect defense. But Seitz also documented, with the continued use of drugs, an insidious shift from a masochistically bound aggression that expressed itself in the form of an increasing reliance on paranoid-projective mechanisms. In these cases, the resort to specifically paranoid-projective mechanisms seems motivated by the need to defend against an underlying depressive core. Other paranoid attitudes, particularly toward authority figures, have been defined as well in drug users among army personnel garrisoned in Europe (Calogeras and Camp 1975). Tendencies toward blaming, irresponsibility, suspiciousness, guardedness, distrustfulness, and general projective demeanor was noted by Glover (1928). He also noted (1932) that in other forms of addiction addicted personalities may reveal a superficial obsessional or hysterical layer, but that the core of the pathology rested on an underlying paranoid layer that must be resolved in order for cure to be achieved.

The core problem in addictive states is an underlying depressive organization, with the attendant dysphoric affects of anxiety and depression, frequently accompanied by feelings of shame and doubt based on an inner narcissistic vulnerability. The avoidance of the core depression may take the form of a manic defense or may follow a pattern of paranoid reaction. Glover (1932) has described these patterns of resolution of underlying depression but also emphasizes that the paranoid resolution differs from that seen in clinical paranoia. In clinical paranoia the patient is threatened by external enemies, whereas in addiction the patient uses the drug to destroy an internal enemy.[1]

The theme of relief from dysphoric affects is a recurrent leitmotif in studies of drug-taking behavior and addictive states. Hartmann (1969) describes frank clinical depression in eight of ten orally fixated adolescents prior to drug use. She describes two adolescents who were severely depressed: a nineteen-year-old girl on alcohol primarily, but also

---

1. From the point of view of the tripartite theory, the superego has long been recognized as an internal persecutor. From the perspective of the paranoid process, the victim-introject is always accompanied by a correlative introjective configuration, the aggressor-introject, that may remain internalized in depressive conditions or may be externalized in more paranoid states. Thus the aggressor-introject may be seen as providing the core of pathological superego organization, particularly in depression. The victim-introject is the necessary, if often implicit, component in such states. The use of the drug is accompanied by superego modifications, not as a pharmacological effect but as a result of projective concomitants. While superego severity may be reduced, other idealizing functions are blocked as well. Both magically powerful and sadistically destructive aspects may be projected onto the drug, reflecting the underlying introjective ambivalence.

amphetamines and marijuana, and a fifteen-year-old boy who drank heavily, then later switched to marijuana. The girl used alcohol to moderate her depression but at other times found the depression intolerable and resorted to amphetamines and marijuana, frequently overdosing. Hartmann comments:

> The drug replaced the absent object, the mothering father, the analyst; it helped her forget and lifted her depression and anxiety. As a secondary gain, it also drew the need-satisfying objects to her. Her frustration tolerance was so low that she sometimes took drugs a few minutes before her appointment with her analyst because she could not tolerate waiting that long to relieve her tension. (p. 393)

The young boy found relief from his severe depression in marijuana, but it was accompanied by social withdrawal to a small group of drug-taking friends. The drug came to replace his passive longings for mother, alcohol, and analyst, and finally became more important than treatment. Similar effects have been reported with a variety of addictive substances (Wieder and Kaplan 1969).

From the point of view of the paranoid process, we are dealing with the shifting emphases between the organization of introjects in the intrapsychic realm and the correlative projections as they affect the individual's relationship with reality. The core depression relates to the introjective configuration in which there is embedded the feeling of inner weakness, inadequacy, vulnerability, and evil. These aspects of the victim-introject are invariably accompanied by elements of sadistic evil destructiveness which derive from an "identification with the aggressor." At the same time the organization of the introjects is patterned along narcissistic lines as well, so that elements of inferiority, narcissistic vulnerability, and shamefulness coexist with components of superiority, specialness, entitlement, and grandiosity.

When the victimized and inferior components of the introjective organization are in the ascendant, the depressive aspects of the patient's pathology predominate. Other incompatible components (aggressive, superior) of the introjective configuration are correspondingly either repressed or externalized. It is through this projective externalization that the drug substance becomes modified, in terms of the transitional object model, into an external object endowed with the loving and hating characteristics of one or both of the patient's parents (Glover 1932). Thus the patient's drug usage and psychic interaction with the drug become a sort of pseudoparanoid system.

If I may return to the example of my own analytic patient, his introjective organization was dominated by his sense of victimization and vul nerability, along with the inferior dimensions of his pathological narcissism. The taking of a few amphetamine pills turned him into a phallic narcissist, gave him a sense of power and competence, and helped him overcome his narcissistic vulnerability. My conclusion was that these aggressive and narcissistically superior dimensions were part of his existing personality structure and were externalized and attributed to the drug even as they were repressed and denied in himself. The projection allowed him to express what was too risky, threatening and conflicted in his own make-up. In this patient, the use of amphetamines allowed him to come closer to the effective use of his own inherent potential even though the result had a moderately phallic and narcissistic quality. In more extreme cases, where the pathology is more primitive and the aggressive and narcissistic polarities more extreme, the drug usage may have a more pathological outcome.

Similar dynamics are identifiable in the cases of heroin addiction reported by Radford et al. (1972). Susan's impoverished sense of self and self-esteem, her feelings of inadequacy, inferiority, and vulnerability, all reflected the internal configuration of her introjects that underly the depressive and suicidal core of her personality. Her object relations reflected an insatiable, never-ending object hunger and a relentless search for an idealized need-satisfying object. The drugs became the projective vehicle that responded to and filled these needs; they made her feel strong, courageous, and less empty, weak, and helpless. Similarly, Richard's homosexual fears, his sense of passive inadequacy and vulnerability, his sense of identification with the physically damaged, weak, and castrated woman, and his feelings of paranoid vulnerability and victimization reflected the core introjective organization. Here again, with the drugs his sense of well-being, capacity, and self-esteem was increased. He no longer felt weak, inadequate, and vulnerable, but was filled with a sense of masculine adequacy and self-confidence.

It should be noted, however, that the projective device is immediately and phenomenologically intended to relieve the inner tension and pressure related to the depressive system organized around the aggressively toned and narcissistically vulnerable introject. This formulation is thereby rendered highly specific; it appeals to more than the mere notion of affect defense in the explanation of addiction. The projective device, moreover, may support a manic defense or a more specifically paranoid resolution. If the projective component transforms the drug substance into the craved, nurturing, idealized, narcissistically satisfying object, the outcome is more likely to express itself in terms of satiation and euphoric intoxication. This follows the essential pattern of manic defense. Insofar as the projective component reflects the underlying ambivalence toward the primary objects and displaces the inner sense of evil and sadistic destructiveness, the resolution may become more specifically paranoid. The drugs may assume either noxious or benign characteristics. Insofar as the drug interaction is derived from early and usually highly ambivalent object relationships, the drugs take on a highly ambivalent tone. They can therefore readily take on sadistic and destructive properties, as Glover (1932) so clearly indicated.

This dimension of the projective mechanisms accounts for the counterphobic attitude to drugs that has been described by Szasz (1958). He describes a series of cases in which the patient took the drugs not in order to secure the drug effects but rather to expose himself repetitively to the dangerous and destructive effects of the drugs so that he could resist succumbing to them. The predominant motif in these patients' experiences was the fear of inner weakness and vulnerability that prompted them to attempt to master these anxieties by a variety of counterphobic maneuvers. Szasz (1958) comments:

> The object of addiction is consciously "liked" and craved. At the same time, in part consciously but in larger part without such awareness, this object is feared since it represents (by displacement) a "phobic object" whose power and fearful qualities derive from other sources. The essence of the "addiction," at least in these cases, appeared to lie in the ego's deliberate exposure to the dreaded situation—albeit in a symbolically displaced and disguised manner—in the hope of thus achieving mastery over it. (pp. 315–316)

The sadistic and destructive properties of the drug substance were in part attributed to it by the projective devices we have been describing (Meissner 1978b, Glover 1932). Thus the issue of mastery is addressed not simply to the drug substance as such or to its pharmacological effects but rather to that which the drug comes to represent by reason of its transitional transformation.

PHARMACOLOGICAL INTERACTION

The interaction between intrapsychic determinants and specific pharmacological effects was given little serious consideration in analytic thinking about addiction and has only recently become a matter of concern. The general tenor of analytic thinking about drug effects was set by Rado's early observation that "not the toxic agent, but the impulse to use it makes an addict of a given individual" (1933, p. 2). This emphasis reflected the general focus on intrapsychic determinants and the insistence that the compulsive and addictive aspects of drug-dependent behavior are a reflection of inner psychopathology. Thus Glover (1932) emphasized the tendency to compulsive addiction even to inert substances and his conclusion was that in fact any substance could function as a drug given the proper psychic conditions. He described these as "psychic addictions." Similarly, Wurmser (1974) has commented on the tendency for compulsive drug users to substitute other symptoms when the drug effect of choice is suspended, or frequently the replacement of the unavailable drug by a completely unrelated drug substance. He concludes that the compulsive drug use must be regarded as one symptom along with others expressing an underlying pathological disturbance. Consequently it is not the withdrawal from drugs that presents the most difficult problem with such patients, but rather the coping with the patient's emotional need to use a drug, in fact to use any drug or any other equally harmful external means to find relief from inner tension.

In general, this analytically sanctioned approach tends to minimize the specific effects produced by the pharmacological actions of the drug itself. However, in terms of the operation of the paranoid process, it seems more reasonable to suggest, following the transitional object model, that the projective element deriving from the inner introjective frame of reference combines with specific qualities inherent in the drug substance to produce the peculiarly illusory and magical effect attributed to the drug. This symbolic interaction has been articulated by Wieder and Kaplan (1969). The drug's influence is mediated through its psychodynamic meaning and pharmacological properties. The symbolic significance attaches not only to the drug itself, which may represent an object or part-object, but also to the act of using it and to its physiological concomitants.

This pharmacogenic effect represents diffuse, direct, and indirect physiological modifications expressed psychically as modifications of the personality structure. Whatever the individual psychopathology, a given drug in sufficient dosage will produce a specific state of intoxication. However, the personality structure determines the individual's reaction to this pharmacogenic effect. Wieder and Kaplan (1969) comment:

> When an individual finds an agent that chemically facilitates his preexisting preferential mode of conflict solution, it becomes his drug of choice. (p. 429)

The same characteristic of pharmacogenic effects has been described by Edwards (1974) in terms of the modification of drug effects by pathoplastic environmental and personality factors.

Such effects are not random events or the products of chance selection. Rather, they are specifically determined and have specific outcomes

Besides the operation of intrapsychic dispositions, other peripheral factors play a significant role in the production of specific pharmacogenic effects, as, for example, the dosage, the route of administration, the immediate environmental setting within which the drug is being taken, and even the broader setting of cultural and social attitudes, prohibitions, and actions that set the frame of reference within which the drug behavior takes place.

The chronic need for certain pharmacogenic effects may derive from developmental and structural defects in the individual personality. Developmental defects stemming from identifiable levels of psychological development may play a role in the determination of the symbolic equation involved in drug taking. It should be noted, however, that this aspect of the equation does not dictate that the craving should be directed to a single drug substance or that it should not tolerate significant degrees of plasticity or modifiability. It is a frequent enough experience that drug users will experiment with a variety of drugs and then focus on one particular substance to satisfy their craving. However, this may also result in the use of combinations of drug substances to achieve similar effects. Thus, shifts from one preferred addictive drug to another, or from one combination to another, may reflect shifts in the underlying psychodynamic configuration that would make different pharmacogenic effects necessary. As Wieder and Kaplan (1969) point out, such a shift may have considerable significance for therapeutic interventions.

Certain properties of the pharmacological action of different drug classes can contribute to the complex psychopharmacological interaction we are describing, insofar as pharmacological effects may answer to different kinds of psychic needs and/or provide a more or less available matrix for projective modification.

The psychotomimetic or hallucinogenic drugs produce striking alterations in perception, mood, time sense, and sense of self. There is a loss of the normal sense of boundaries of the self and the discrimination from the object world with subjective experiences of fusion and merger with lost or yearned-for objects. The psychedelic drugs likewise counter the state of emptiness, boredom, and meaninglessness so often found in addiction-prone personalities. The drug induces an illusion that the self is mystically expansive and grandiose, and that the patient's environment becomes impregnated with cosmic significances.

The narcotics, including opium and its derivatives as well as some of the synthetics, produce a state of quiet lethargy and diminished engagement with external reality (Wieder and Kaplan 1969). Addicts frequently report the subjective sense of a calming and stabilizing action of the drug (Khantzian 1974). There is an effect of anesthesia and analgesia, in which affective pain is blocked and consciousness reduced (Krystal and Raskin 1970). Frosch (1970) and Wieder and Kaplan (1969) emphasize a state of blissful satiation that can lead to the hypercathecting of fantasies of omnipotence, magical wish fulfillment, and self-sufficiency.

In addition, Wurmser (1974) has noted the capacity of both the sedative-hypnotic drugs, such as barbiturates, and the narcotics to calm intense feelings of rage, pain, and loneliness as well as the anxieties related to these affects.

The stimulant or energizing drugs, including the amphetamines, meth-adrine, and cocaine, seem to increase awareness of drive feelings and impulse strength, diminish the awareness of fatigue, and lead to a feeling of assertiveness, self-esteem, and increased frustration tolerance. They induce a restless form of activity that seems to serve the denial of passivity (Wieder and Kaplan 1969). They also seem to provide a sense of aggressive mastery, control, invincibility, and even grandeur. This effect serves to bolster defenses against underlying depression or more general feelings of unworthiness and weakness (Wurmser 1974). The sense of active mastery has likewise been observed by Frosch (1970).

The energizing and activating quality of the amphetamines and related drugs serves to counter and to bolster the defense against the passivity and vulnerability of depression. In this sense the individual using such drugs may prefer to tolerate the excitement, anxiety, agitation, or hypo-mania rather than to be afflicted by depression, passivity, or boredom. The hyperalertness and activity associated with the drug has been com-pared to a manic defense against depression (Krystal and Raskin 1970). Nonetheless, it should be remembered that the abuse of these drugs can produce a paranoid-like state that has been analogized to paranoid schizo-phrenia. In terms of our understanding of the mechanism of the paranoid process, we can suggest that the activating and energizing properties of these drugs serve to shift the balance in the intrapsychic economy from the predominance of introjective components to a defensive mobilization of projective functions. The predominance of aggressively toned and narcissistically embedded introjects underlies the pathology of depres-sion. The shift to a more active alignment would allow for the mobiliza-tion of projective defenses and a consequent mitigation of the depressive posture and its associated affects. These features of the effects of amphetamines and their interplay with the depressive alignment of the introjects has been graphically described in Berman's case (1972) of amphetamine addiction.

Both alcohol and marijuana seem to have similar effects in low doses, both seeming to diminish defenses against drive and impulse discharge (Wieder and Kaplan 1969). In light to moderate doses, both alcohol and the barbiturates seem to release inhibitions, probably as a result of a release of higher central nervous system regulatory centers. Both alcohol and the sedative drugs serve to relieve internal distressful states associated with anxiety and conflicts (Khantzian 1975). With both alcohol and marijuana use, perceptual acuity is accentuated; the subject becomes hyperactive and overtalkative; he is frequently impressed with his profound thoughts and depth of feeling; he experiences changes in time sense and body image; and he may act out sexual and hostile impulses.

The proposition being advanced here is that, in keeping with the operations of the paranoid process, different drug substances have specifiable pharmacological effects that are susceptible of a certain degree of plasticity or of modification by a variety of influences coming either from the external frame of reference within which the drug is administered or from the internal psychic dispositions of the individual user. My hypothesis is that the qualities and circumstances of the drug provide a vehicle for the specific projective elements that are generated in and derive from the subject's intrapsychic frame of reference. The projective process does not commandeer the drug substance and bring it into the service of intrapsychic needs in any absolute or apodictic sense. The drug substance, in combination with the attendant circumstances of its administration and application, must provide a suitable substrate that allows the drug to be conjoined with the individual's projective elaboration. In each case of addiction there is a specificity of drug preference that is based on the ultimate fit between the subjective needs and the pharmacologic properties of the drug and the extent to which they can be successfully amalgamated to meet the inner needs of the drug-taking individual.

THE PARANOID PROCESS AND THE DRUG EQUATION

It remains, finally, to relate the various parameters of the drug problem we have been discussing to the perspective provided by the paranoid process (Meissner 1971, 1972, 1978b). The paranoid process may provide a frame of reference within which disparate aspects of the complex variables that interact and contribute to the phenomenon of drug dependence may find their appropriate location and expression. The derivation from the introjects makes it possible for the projective content to express and fulfill precisely those complementary elements the self requires to maintain its internal stability. In the addictive process the drug substance is subjectively modified by projective components and thereby acquires transitional illusory properties that often have a magical or mystical quality. Through this transitional transformation (or "transsubstantiation"), the drug substance comes to substitute for or replace a significant

self-sustaining object relationship that the self has lost in some psychically significant manner. From this point of view, the compulsiveness of
the drug taking and drug behavior is dependent not simply on the
physiologically habituating or addicting potentialities of the drug itself
but derives from the inner necessity of the drug intake for the maintenance of the stability and coherence of the self. In most addict subjects,
the intensity of the threat and the severe anxiety associated with it
operate at a level of severe or primitive separation anxiety or, even more
ominously, at a level of annihilation anxiety.

The elaboration of the transitional object–drug substance in this manner is not simply a matter of the transformation of an external substance
by a projective distortion. The inherent pharmacological properties of the
substances themselves contribute to this process to some degree. The
drug taker experiments with a variety of drugs or combinations of drugs
until he finds that proper mix that sufficiently modifies his inner state of
affective disorganization or turmoil (Wieder and Kaplan 1969). The
question then is more or less that of the particular effect or combination
of effects the drugs provide that answer to the inner subjective need of
the drug-taking individual in such a way that they can usefully become
the vehicle for, and perhaps the stimulus of, the essential self-sustaining
projections. These transitional and projective integrations may have any
of a variety of dynamic significances depending on the quality of the
projection, the portion of the introjective matrix from which it derives,
and, ultimately, the pathogenic object relationship that it revives and
replaces.

A point in this discussion so far left to one side is the influence of
extrinsic modifying components in the process we have been describing.
A critical component of the paranoid process is what we have come to
refer to as the "paranoid construction" (Meissner 1978b). The paranoid
construction, varying in degree of relationship to a variety of extrinsic
social, cultural, or even political factors, occurs in drug dependence.
Projective transformation of the drug substance cannot simply stand
alone, but the phenomenon and the experience of the taking of the drug
must be embedded in a broader sustaining matrix within which the
implicit significance of the drug experience can be maintained. It is this
aspect of the drug experience and the operation of the paranoid process
that gives rise to the frequently observed phenomenon of the drug
subculture and the often paranoid opposition that is directed against the
surrounding society, particularly authority figures. Thus the drug taker
may in fact develop a fairly elaborate paranoid system with the implicit
purpose of sustaining the drug culture along with its inherent values and
convictions, which give the taking of the drug and the individual addict's

relationship to the drug substance a specific sustaining context and meaningfulness. The paranoid construction serves as a sustaining frame of reference within which the projections are continually validated and sustained; as an ultimate motivating focus for the entire process, the inner coherence and stability of the pathogenic introjective organization can be maintained.

Extrinsic forces within the social matrix can contribute to and interact with this process in different ways and in varying degree. Thus, prohibitive laws or strict legal reinforcement or condemnatory social attitudes can serve as a sustaining matrix within which the paranoid quality of this construction and its inherent projective elements can find meaningful integration and convincing support. Whatever adaptive qualities this resolution may have, it unavoidably involves a pathological dependence on the drug. In the most primitively organized personalities functioning on a psychotic or borderline level, the drug addiction may serve as a form of particularized or delimited paranoia that may allow relatively autonomous functioning in other areas of the individual's experience. Such individuals, however, remain at risk in view of the well-known tendency for such paranoid systems to generalize.

These elements, I suggest, are at play in every instance of drug addiction. One does not need to demonstrate severe psychopathology in order to understand the phenomenon of drug addiction. It is entirely conceivable within this frame of reference that an individual may turn to the use of drugs in an addictive fashion in order to answer specific internal psychic needs having to do with the temporary sustaining of the sense of self and its inherent narcissistic organization and equilibrium. It is also readily understandable, given a shift in circumstances and surrounding influences, that some individual might find dependence on the drug no longer functional. It is likewise easier to understand within this perspective the effectiveness of religious conversion or meditative techniques in replacing dependence on drugs (Carrington and Ephron 1975). These experiences or alternate contexts provide a variant expression of the paranoid process that may in a significant number of cases satisfy the inner needs of the subject and serve to sustain a sense of meaningful belonging, participation, and self-cohesiveness.

Finally, with reference to Wurmser's etiological schema (1974), we can say that the introjective organization is the necessary precondition without which the effect of drug dependence would never come about but which can never of itself produce that effect. The specific cause, which is never missing and which might itself in sufficient intensity bring about the effect, is the narcissistic crisis or, more specifically, the threat to the organization, stability, or cohesion of the self that demands the resolution the paranoid process provides. The concurrent causes, which do not produce the effect but exert their influence along with the preconditions and the specific cause, are the external factors relating to social and cultural conditions and their effects. Finally, the precipitating cause is the availability of the drug itself. The final outcome or specific effect of the etiological equation is the organization of the specific paranoid system, which involves the drug substance as transitional object, the purpose and objective of the entire system being the organization, maintenance, or sustenance of the individual's self-system.

THERAPEUTIC IMPLICATIONS

While the emphasis in this paper has not been therapeutic, some tentative suggestions for the psychotherapy of addictive states can be drawn from the present formulations. My intention has been to propose that the explanatory schema of the paranoid process provides a sufficiently flexible frame of reference for the understanding of a number of aspects of addiction. Recognizing the often confusing heterogeneity of drug-related conditions, I hoped to provide here an account of the core psychological elements that enter into a wide variety of addictive forms. That account is limited in that it does not arise from a strictly inductive basis, except insofar as I have been able to utilize my own small experience with addiction in my own patients and the few deeper accounts in the literature. The hypotheses generated here are for the most part extrapolations from the paranoid process. What follows, then, is more a set of heuristic hypotheses than empirically validated conclusions.

The therapeutic implications of the paranoid process have not yet been formulated in detail. But some preliminary and schematic indications of its impact on psychotherapy are available (Meissner 1976). The perspective of the paranoid process emphasizes the projective transformation of the addictive substance. This process results from the complex interaction of pharmacological properties of the drug, its physiological effects, and its availability for becoming the repository for symbolic significances. These give the drug unconscious psychological and psychodynamic meaning. These derivative and transforming significances are brought about by projections that represent externalizations of aspects of the subject's own internal introjective configuration.

The therapeutic line of approach this suggests runs from a careful exploration of these projective aspects to a clarification and illumination of the underlying introjective organization. The therapeutic work, therefore, entails a clear delineation of the projective dimension and its unequivocal connection with the patient's introjects. In cases of addiction, this would require a careful exploration in detail and an understanding of the meaning of the drug, a systematic uncovering of its projective elements, and a linking of these elements with the introjects. In the clinical presentation of the patient addicted to amphetamines, the subject was unable to surrender his dependence on the drug until he was able to give up his attachment to his introjects. The drug dependence in his case was secondary; the real addiction was to the introjects. As long as he clung to his invested position as a weak, vulnerable, incompetent baby, his need for the drug was too powerful. Only when he realized that the magical significance of the drug was a reflection of something he denied in himself, and that he no longer needed to deny that more aggressive side of himself, could he give up the drug. The essential connection was the recognition and acceptance of the aggressive, powerful, and narcissistically grandiose elements projected onto the drug as deriving from and reflecting a part of the patient's own self-image. Such patients are usually quite in touch with one side of the introjective configuration, as was my patient, but quite resistant to acceptance of the other side. In my patient, the more aggressive and grandiose side of his character was revealed in an active fantasy and dream life in which he was from time to time the powerful aggressor, the seducer of women who could at his will force them to a variety of perverse sexual acts even against their will. It was this repressed, denied, and threatening part of himself that he invested in the drug, so that it became a magical transforming substance that made it possible for him to write his papers, perform well academically, and even to become potent and phallically competent in bed. Acceptance of this side of himself was threatening precisely because it entailed surrender of the protective and gratifying position of being his mother's special baby, and beckoned him to join the adult world of striving, competition, challenge, and the dual risks of failure and success. Remaining the special baby absolved him from the responsibility for his own limitations and failures, even as the ascription of power and competence to the drug absolved him of the consequences of his more adult performance.

The addictive experience is obviously heterogeneous and complex, and reflects the dynamics peculiar to the individual subject. Therapeutic approaches to the management of drug problems frequently require difficult regimens of detoxification and drug regulation and/or substitution. Our concern in the present effort has not extended to these pharmacological aspects, except to suggest that there is an important interaction between the pharmacological properties and action of specific drugs and the individual dynamics of the drug taker. Our emphasis here has been on the psychological aspects of addiction and correlative psychotherapeutic issues. An important question remains as to the extent to which drug problems can be approached psychotherapeutically. The inference from the above discussion must be that any meaningful approach to treatment of drug problems must rely on an effective integration of pharmacological management and psychotherapeutic intervention. The better our understanding of these respective parameters of the problem of drug dependence and of their interaction, the greater is the promise of effective treatment. The paranoid process might well provide at least one schema facilitating such understanding.

REFERENCES

Berman, L. (1972). The role of amphetamine in a case of hysteria. *Journal of the American Psychoanalytic Association* 20:325–340.

Bychowski, G. (1953). The problem of latent psychosis. *Journal of the American Psychoanalytic Association* 1:484–503.

Calogeras, R., and Camp, N. (1975). Drug use and aggression. *Bulletin of the Menninger Clinic* 39:329–344.

Carrington, P., and Ephron, H. (1975). Meditation as an adjunct to psychotherapy. In *New Dimensions in Psychiatry: A World View*, ed. S. Arieti, pp. 261–291. New York: Wiley.

De Angelis, G. (1975). Theoretical and clinical approaches to the treatment of drug addiction: with special considerations for the adolescent drug abuser. *Journal of Psychedelic Drugs* 7:187–202.

Edwards, G. (1974). Drugs, drug dependence and the concept of plasticity. *Quarterly Journal of Studies on Alcohol* 35:176–195.

Fenichel, O. (1945). *The Psychoanalytic Theory of Neurosis*. New York: Norton.

Frederick, C., Resnik, H., and Wittlin, B. (1973). Self-destructive aspects of hard core addiction. *Archives of General Psychiatry* 28:579–585.

Freud, S. (1895). A reply to criticism of my paper on anxiety neurosis. *Standard Edition* 3:123–139.

——— (1905). Three essays on the theory of sexuality. *Standard Edition* 7:123–245.

——— (1911). Psycho-analytic notes on an autobiographical account of a case of paranoia (dementia paranoides). *Standard Edition* 12:1–82.

——— (1930). Civilization and its discontents. *Standard Edition*, 21:57–145.

Frosch, J. (1970). Psychoanalytic considerations of the psychotic character. *Journal of the American Psychoanalytic Association* 18:24–50.

Frosch, W.A. (1970). Psychoanalytic evaluation of addiction and habituation (panel report). *Journal of the American Psychoanalytic Association* 18:209–218.

Galanter, M. (1976). The "intoxication state of consciousness": a model for alcohol and drug abuse. *American Journal of Psychiatry* 133:635–640.

Gerard, D., and Kornetsky, C. (1954). A social and psychiatric study of adolescent opiate addicts. *Psychoanalytic Quarterly* 28:113–115.

Glover, E. (1928). The etiology of alcoholism. In *On the Early Development of the Mind*. New York: International Universities Press, 1956.

——— (1932). On the etiology of drug-addiction. In *On the Early Development of the Mind*. New York: International Universities Press, 1956.

Greenacre, P. (1969). The fetish and the transitional object. *Psychoanalytic Study of the Child* 24:144–163.

Guarner, E. (1966). Psychodynamic aspects of drug experience. *British Journal of Medical Psychology* 39:157–162.

Hartmann, D. (1969). A study of drug-taking adolescents. *Psychoanalytic Study of the Child* 24:384–398.

Hochman, J., and Brill, N. (1972). Chronic marijuana use and psychosocial adaptation. *American Journal of Psychiatry* 130:132–140.

Jacobson, E. (1961). Adolescent moods and the remodeling of psychic structure in adolescence. *Psychoanalytic Study of the Child* 16:164–183.

Kernberg, O. (1967). Borderline personality organization. *Journal of the American Psychoanalytic Association* 15:641–685.

Khantzian, E. (1974). Opiate addiction: a critique of theory and some implications for treatment. *American Journal of Psychotherapy* 28:59–70.

——— (1975). Self-selection and progression in drug dependence. *Psychiatry Digest* 36:19–22.

Krystal, H., and Raskin, H. (1970). *Drug Dependence: Aspects of Ego Function*. Detroit: Wayne State University Press.

Lewin, B. (1946). Sleep, the mouth, and the dream screen. *Psychoanalytic Quarterly* 15:419–434.

——— (1950). *The Psychoanalysis of Elation*. New York: Norton.

MacAndrew, E., and Edgerton, R. (1969). *Drunken Comportment: A Social Explanation*. Chicago: Aldine.

Marmor, J. (1953). Orality in the hysterical personality. *Journal of the American Psychoanalytic Association* 1:656–671.

Mayfield, D., and Montgomery, D. (1972). Alcoholism, alcohol intoxication, and suicide attempts. *Archives of General Psychiatry* 27:349–353.

Meerloo, J. (1952). Artificial ecstasy: a study of the psychosomatic aspect of drug addiction. *Journal of Nervous and Mental Disease* 115:246–266.

Meissner, W. (1971). Notes on identification: II. Clarification of related concepts. *Psychoanalytic Quarterly* 40:277–302.

——— (1972). Notes on identification: III. The concept of identification. *Psychoanalytic Quarterly* 41:224–260.

——— (1976). Psychotherapeutic schema based on the paranoid process. *International Journal of Psychoanalytic Psychotherapy* 5:87–114.

——— (1977). Psychoanalytic notes on suicide. *International Journal of Psychoanalytic Psychotherapy* 6:415–447.

——— (1978a). Notes on the levels of differentiation within borderline conditions. To be published.

——— (1978b). *The Paranoid Process*. New York: Jason Aronson.

Menninger, K. (1938). *Man Against Himself*. New York: Harcourt Brace.

Mirin, S., Shapiro, L., Meyer, R., Pillard, R., and Fischer, S. (1971). Casual versus heavy use of marijuana: a redefinition of the marijuana problem. *American Journal of Psychiatry* 127:1134–1140.

Pinderhughes, C. (1971). Somatic, psychic, and social sequelae of loss. *Journal of the American Psychoanalytic Association* 19:670–696.

Radford, P., Wiseberg, S., and Yorke, C. (1972). A study of "main-line" heroin addiction: a preliminary report. *Psychoanalytic Study of the Child* 27:156-180.

Rado, S. (1933). Psychoanalysis of pharmacothymia. *Psychoanalytic Quarterly* 2:1–23.

——— (1957). Narcotic bondage: a general theory of the dependence on narcotic drugs. *American Journal of Psychiatry* 114:165–170.

Rosenfeld, H. (1960). On drug addiction. *International Journal of Psycho-Analysis* 41:467–475.

Sandler, J. (1960). On the concept of superego. *Psychoanalytic Study of the Child* 15:128–162.

Savitt, R. (1954). Extramural psychoanalytic treatment of a case of neurotic addiction. *Journal of the American Psychoanalytic Association* 2:494–502.

———— (1963). Psychoanalytic studies on addiction: ego structure in narcotic addiction. *Psychoanalytic Quarterly* 32:43–57.

Schwartzman, J. (1975). The addict, abstinence, and the family. *American Journal of Psychiatry* 132:154–157.

Seitz, P. (1974). "Reality is a stone-cold drag": psychoanalytic observations of hippies, with a selected list and annotated index of references on adolescent problems. *Annual of Psychoanalysis* 2:387–415.

Szasz, T. (1958). The role of the counterphobic mechanism in addiction. *Journal of the American Psychoanalytic Association* 6:309–325.

Tamerin, J., and Mendelson, J. (1969). The psychic dynamics of chronic inebriation: observations of alcoholics during the process of drinking in an experimental group setting. *American Journal of Psychiatry* 125:886–899.

Vaillant, G. (1966a). A 12-year follow up of New York narcotic addicts: I. *American Journal of Psychiatry* 122:727–737.

———— (1966b). A 12-year follow-up of New York narcotic addicts: III. *Archives of General Psychiatry* 15:599–609.

Westermeyer, J., and Walzer, V. (1975). Sociopathy and drug use in a young psychiatric population. *Disease of the Nervous System* 36:673–677.

Wieder, H., and Kaplan, E. (1969). Drug use in adolescents: psychodynamic meaning and pharmacogenic effect. *Psychoanalytic Study of the Child* 24:399–431.

Winnicott, D. (1953). Transitional objects and transitional phenomena. In *Collected Papers*. New York: Basic Books, 1958.

Wurmser, L. (1974). Psychoanalytic considerations of the etiology of compulsive drug use. *Journal of the American Psychoanalytic Association* 22:820–843.

Yorke, C. (1970). A critical review of some psychoanalytic literature on drug addiction. *British Journal of Medical Psychology* 43:141–184.

Zinberg, N. (1975). Addiction and ego function. *Psychoanalytic Study of the Child* 30:567–588.

Phobic Core in the Addictions and the Paranoid Process

LEON WURMSER, M.D.

A discussion of "Addiction and the Paranoid Process," by W. W. Meissner, M.D. Three major strata are
distinguished in the psychodynamic make-up of addicts: (1) a sociopathic-paranoid stratum,
(2) a depressive layer, and (3) a phobic core. The last consists of a claustrophobic constellation, with claustrophobia seen as primary. Parallel to phobic neurosis, and in contradistinction to the personalized paranoid construction, compulsive drug use is seen as an impersonal
condensation system. The drug effect is a type of counterphobic fantasy. While the paranoid
character blames others and the depressive character blames himself, the phobic character
compulsively avoids the claustrum on the outside and the addictive character both searches
for it and destroys it.

> Let me not burst in ignorance, but tell
> Why thy canonized bones, hearsed in death,
> Have burst their cerements, why the sepulcher
> Wherein we saw thee quietly inurned
> Hath oped his ponderous and marble jaws
> To cast thee up again.
> —*Hamlet*, Act I, scene IV

Meissner's lucid, innovative, and deeply meaningful study requires a
comment that does not confine itself to a consideration simply of the
essay at hand, but that deals also with some of the main ideas presented in
his recent *The Paranoid Process* (1978) and his earlier "Notes on Identification" (1970, 1971, 1972).

There is no doubt that paranoid features are clinically prominent in
compulsive drug users. Just glancing over the two dozen case studies

I take this opportunity to express my gratitude to Drs. Leo Rangell, David Beres, Paul Gray,
Ellen McDaniel, Johannes Ginsberg, and Robert Langs for their valuable suggestions.

presented in my own recent book (Wurmser 1978), I am struck by how many of them display severely paranoid character attitudes. These dictate many of their actions and much of their view of the world, and may be seen in the attitude "The world is against me and I have to fight back." This may be exaggerated into a murderous paranoid rage and thus issue in actual or skirted homicide.

But that is far less than Meissner's novel approach entails. He sees the *paranoid process*, rightly I believe, as a ubiquitous phenomenon, shared by more or less everyone, as expressed by such commonplace feelings as jealousy, envy and, perhaps to some extent, shame. Psychodynamically he equates it, as repeated in this essay, with the combination of three essential features: (1) a core of regressive introjects, stamped by archaic narcissism and aggression; (2) derivative projections; and (3) the paranoid construction lending a semblance of stability to the fragile system of self- and object-relations. Drugs sought and incorporated as objects, drug effects, the drug culture, and social ostracism—all fit into this tripartite model of the paranoid process. It is, perhaps not entirely incidentally, remarkably similar to Hegel's model of thesis, antithesis, and synthesis, since for Meissner the rhythmic movement of introjection, projection, and construction is, more generally viewed, a ubiquitous process of psychic development.

The great heuristic value of this model notwithstanding, there remains a lingering question whether concept and definition of paranoid process may not thus become overextended and turn into what Szasz, twenty years ago, called a "panchreston," an overly usable, universally applicable notion that loses with its specificity also much of its usefulness (1957).

I have a concrete reason for this doubt. When collating my own data from the psychotherapies, I became more and more impressed by a quite typical layering of phenomenology in these addicts. The superficial constellation is that of the *sociopath* with all his accoutrements: lying, violence, actions for the sake of undifferentiated tension relief, self-deception, unbridled narcissistic demands of omnipotence and entitlement, fantasies of invulnerability and invincibility, and, particularly, the conviction that all limits and boundaries can be, even must be, violated. This irritating, provocative complex of behaviors evokes universal negative countertransference, manifest almost at once. It is indeed accompanied, quite regularly and not much less manifestly, by the paranoid traits already referred to and so well described in Meissner's essay and his book.

The second important (and the next deeper) layer is what Meissner, with Glover and others, describe as the *depressive system* or depressive core of the addictions. This stratum is much less accessible. While it has more superficially outreaching taproots, especially in abusers of stimulants, the mass of depressive configurations is quite deeply buried and indeed may at times reach the dimensions of a psychotic mood disorder. Typically though, this depression (whether psychotic or nonpsychotic) is rather different from the usual, more guilt-oriented depressions. It has more of a lethargic, apathetic, strongly shame-ridden nature—a narcissistic let-down in the grandiosity of the self rather than in the expectations vested in the idealized other, the self-object (Kohut 1971). Whether this follows the classical outline given by Freud (1917) in "Mourning and Melan-cholia"—ambivalent relationship to the object, loss of or disappointment in the object, introjection of the object, and turning of aggression against the self—or whether it is based primarily in a traumatic loss of self-esteem due to overwhelming helplessness and exposure, I cannot make out for sure. I am, however, much inclined to the second hypothesis, which is suggested by the centrality in these subjects of really very severe (trau-matic) and repeated experiences of extreme aggressive and sexual over-stimulation throughout childhood. Therefore, although the framework of pathogenic introjections is important, it does not suffice as explanation for this depressive layer.

The third level is what I came to call the *phobic core*. It is obviously risky to universalize any statement and to claim its application to *all* cases, but, looking back, I find in nearly all patients, regardless of type of compulsive drug use, a pervasive and massive anxiety at the bottom of the more clamorous pathology. Although often to some extent free-floating, this anxiety was almost always attached to specific objects and situations. In all such cases a fairly clear-cut infantile neurosis of the phobic type could be revealed as a central constellation underlying the adult neurosis. This was combined with other grave developmental impairments, mostly ego and superego defects, whose calamitous effects transcend by far the frame of a well-delimited infantile neurosis (cf. A. Freud 1965, 1970). Still, it is important to stress that the more I work with these patients, the more I am impressed by the heterogeneity of this group, by the great dynamic, structural, genetic variability under the coating of a relatively uniform symptomatology.

Obviously there are many phobic features again quite superficially evident. These are offshoots of the really meaningful ones that reside in great depths and become truly open to the critical working through only after years of therapy. Moreover, in line with the overall developmental failures of most of these patients, it is usually not a well-structured phobia, i.e., one attached to such clearly defined and relatively avoidable objects as animals, thunder, vehicles, or school. Instead it is vague and pervasive, involving many levels of abstraction, and is typified, *par excel-lence*, by *claustrophobia*.

Meissner's *The Paranoid Process* (1978) does not distinguish phobic from paranoid symptoms, phobic from paranoid process, phobic from paranoid character, or, finally, their distinctive psychodynamic formulations, whether generally or as specifically related to drug addiction. In my view, he deals with phobias as part and parcel of the paranoid process since they answer as well to the tripartite definition of (regressively tinged or developmentally stuck) introjection, projection, and paranoid construction; thus, of course, they include the same archaic features of narcissism and aggression (Meissner 1978, pp. 313, 527, 579, 586).

These distinctions would be mere semantic quibbling were it not for the very different affects that present themselves quite prima facie in phobic and paranoid conditions. The affects in each instance bespeak a distinctly different dynamic substrate. We can, in self-observation, clearly and strongly distinguish the group of paranoid affects (jealousy, envy, injured pride, self-righteous indignation) from that of the phobic affects (anxiety attached to certain objects and situations). To be sure: such a phenomenological difference in affect should not be the ultimate arbiter. Such differences may on closer scrutiny appear to vanish, as in the case of repressed sexual wishes and anxiety. These two were originally perceived by Freud in his theory of the actual neurosis as equivalences. Later theory showed these to be related but very different metapsychological processes (Freud 1926, Rangell 1968). Should we then not also hold that the "feel of blame" characteristic of the paranoid process is so distinct from the "feel of fright" in the phobic process that the two need to be sharply distinguished, despite our agreement with Meissner that metapsychologically both share such underlying mechanisms as introjection, projection, repression, regression, and displacement?

I question whether Meissner's definition of the paranoid process is not lacking one or another criterion for the strict exclusion of undue generality. Thus we need to work out the distinction between paranoia and phobia in order to integrate his presentation with what I described as the third and deepest layer of psychodynamics; as far as the other two levels are concerned, I believe his thoughts excellently apposite.

DIFFERENCES BETWEEN PHOBIC AND PARANOID PROCESSES

In the simplest terms, one difference is this. In the phobic state the feeling is: "It is a danger, but I do not know why. It may be for this or that reason." In the paranoid state it is: "It is a danger, *and I know why*, namely such and such is his or her intention." In both forms there is what Freud described in his last works (1940a,b) as a kind of split, a tear *(Riss)* in the ego, a functional disparity between acknowledgment and denial—"The object is really harmless"—versus "A danger is lurking in the object." But this functional discrepancy that splitting really amounts to (Wurmser 1978) has a qualitatively different ring in the paranoid process as compared to the phobic process. It is the animation and personalization, the elaboration of purpose, reason, and intentionality in the paranoid process. An explanation for this must be deferred for the moment.

A second difference lies in the leading affective reactions to the projection. In the paranoid process, rage and its derivatives—anger, hatred, contempt, resentment, grudge—lead either to attack or to provocation of attack. The experience is a defense by *turning passive into active*. This is successful in the attack, only partially so in the provoked state of being confirmed as the persecuted victim. This seems quite the essence of the paranoid process: to blame and to provoke.

By contrast, in the phobic process the leading affects are anxiety and its derivatives—disgust, some form of guilty fears or shame anxiety, somatic equivalents—and these lead to avoidance and flight.

In other words: In the phobic process the defenses of repression, projection, and condensation seem to work. The anxiety due to projected aggression and libido remains focused, vested in, and limited to the object, no matter how broad this "object" may yet turn out to be. It can be coped with by avoidance and ego restriction (sometimes leading to inhibition). In the paranoid process these defenses break down regressively; the anxiety is not contained. An archaic (regressive) attempt of dealing mostly with the uncontrolled aggression by turning passive (anxiety, helplessness) into active (rage, counterattack, provocation) is added to those defenses typical for the phobic process. Were we to deal with the depressive process, another defense would enter here instead of, or in addition to, the one just described: turning against the self. Thus the paranoid process is accompanied by a preponderant identification with the aggressor, while the depressive process is marked by identification with the victim. The prevalent introjections would, I believe, show just the reverse; an introjection, an egodystonic self-part (that is, the victim) in the paranoid process, and the introjection of the aggressor in the superego of the depressive (Meissner 1970, 1971, 1972). Both processes are attempts to deal with an original state of anxiety where phobic efforts at containment have failed.

We may have a further corroboration of this in a third phenomenological difference: In the phobic process the idea is that something might happen, especially an injury. Hence anxiety. In the paranoid process it is that something has already happened. Hence the rage. In the depressive process it is that this has happened because one has caused it himself. Hence the rage at the self.

But what about the element of intentionality described as the first difference, that in the paranoid process the threatening object is always personalized and endowed with willpower, cognition, and planning? How can we understand this addition of the projection of willpower, of intentionality, to that of the menacing drive elements that distinguish the *paranoid construction* from the *phobic condensation?* I believe the intervening step between the phobic and the paranoid projection has to be an introjective step whereby this one crucial element of the self, namely intentionality—self-willedness, the ability to have the power to act by motive and conscious design, the element of decision making and choice—is inserted before the complex is reprojected. This description, however, already contains a very important metapsychological and therefore explanatory implication. In the phobic process id and superego elements are projected; in the paranoid process one centrally important ego function, that of willfulness or decisionmaking (Rangell 1969), is added to the projection. This is manifested by a splitting up of the central self-experience—a crucial part of the core self is now disowned, repudiated. This is a far more regressive, archaic, and deeply threatening event than the splitting off and disowning of more peripheral aspects of the self (Fingarette 1969, Rangell 1969).

This attribution of personal willfulness to the projections is quite reminiscent of what Mahler (1968) describes for symbiotic psychoses: the self becomes mechanical and depersonalized while the inanimate world assumes animated and even personal features. This too is a disowning of this probably most important, most centrally experienced ego function.

Obviously, such a disowning does not always have to be a psychotic phenomenon. Small-scale projections of this paranoid nature are parts of the psychopathology of everyday life; they underlie the paranoid features in neuroses, as Meissner aptly stresses. Moreover, they form the warp and woof of much of mythical thinking (Cassirer 1923). It is their extensive, even global character, their systematized nature, and their defensive compulsiveness that render them immune to correction by new experience and consensual invalidation, and that marks them as psychotic (Meissner 1978).

One may also and finally claim that narcissistic conflicts are central for paranoid (and depressive) processes while object-related ones are the relevant conflicts in the pathogenesis of phobias. Meissner (1978) states that "the paranoid defense is essentially based on the underlying narcissistic trauma" (p. 676), whereas it is rather generally accepted that, as A. Freud (1936) summarizes, "phobic patients repress the impulses associated with the castration complex" (p. 154). Thus, their symptom deals basically with object libidinal wishes on an oedipal level.

Yet this neat distinction may not hold up. While it probably holds true that many typical phobias (especially those directed at animals, at certain locations, or at locomotion) are of "genital" origin (S. Freud 1909), the pregenital types are much more important. Just to take one very important example:

Psychoanalytic studies of patients who used spider symbolism for the expression of their repressed (perverse) impulses and conflicts revealed, as important genetic factors, pregenital, particularly anal, fixations and unresolved preoedipal relationships with their mothers. The spider symbolism as well as the symptoms most frequently found associated with it, such as severe sleep disturbances and phobias, are also an indication of unresolved separation conflicts and a high degree of ambivalence which intensifies bisexuality and the problems of sexual identification. (Sperling 1971, p. 497)

It is precisely these phobias of predominantly pregenital determination that we are particularly interested in here.

To a more careful study of this phobic core in compulsive drug users we turn now, albeit rather cursorily since our task is not to study extensively this phobic core but to give justice to Meissner's work by adding a new and relevant dimension.

THE METAPSYCHOLOGY OF PHOBIA

The basic features of a phobic neurosis have been summarized elsewhere (Wurmser and McDaniel 1978) and need not be recapitulated. The necessary defensive movements leading to various forms of phobias were described there as repression, projection, displacement, reversal (Fenichel 1944), regression, condensation (A. Freud 1977), and externalization (Wurmser 1978). All or most of these defense mechanisms can be found in the full constitution of a phobic symptom.

In a second stage, during the actual development of the phobic neurosis, the phobias themselves may largely disappear and remain as minor vestiges under the shell of several layers of additional defenses. With the help of enduring character traits, e.g., attitudes or activities, the patient protects himself against the underlying fears. One possibility is a spreading, whereby a concrete, limited fear becomes a more and more generalized timorousness; everywhere dangers are seen lurking.

A very important secondary layer of defense against a phobia is the "overcompensation against fear" or what Fenichel (1939) called "the counterphobic attitude," a "never-ending attempt at the belated conquest of an unmastered infantile anxiety" (Fenichel 1939, pp. 163, 167). Instead of fleeing the source of anxiety, the phobic seeks it out again and again.

An even more radical defense is a kind of "identification with the aggressor," specifically, with the frightening, already phobically viewed object: "Instead of my being afraid of the monster (or the dead relative), I play the monster (or the dead) and, in fantasy, I really am it!" This may be done in compulsive games intended to frighten other people, in a basic generalized aggressiveness, defiance, stubbornness, and even in criminal violence. A most fascinating means of coping with a very general phobia, that of death, is the universal custom of mask wearing (Meuli 1975).

It will be noticed that we are here already halfway to the paranoid process. Many other forms of such secondary cover-ups against partly hidden phobias may be found in apparently independent problems: homosexuality, general fear of human intimacy or of distance, and, as our task here bids us focus on, drug or alcohol abuse. It often takes very long work in psychoanalysis or psychotherapy to unravel the complex structure of such phobic neuroses, with their defensive overlays that deceive patient and physician alike. Not too rarely, fear and wish are intermingled. For instance, the claustrophobic may also be claustrophilic in some more secret areas; the one afraid of dead and ghosts is fascinated by tales about them. Fascination and thrill are just anxiety turned around—the "return of the repressed" (Balint 1959).

Claustrophobia—the fear of an enclosed space (*claustrum*)—is in fact the one type pf phobia specifically relevant for us. Since it is often particularly well-shielded by character traits it is often misdiagnosed and unrecognized. This is due to the fact that claustrophobia usually is displaced further to metaphorical enclosures: many feel stifled, smothered, uncomfortably hemmed in by human warmth, by physical or emotional closeness (including intensive psychotherapy), and either have to beat a frightened or angry retreat or to "burst out" as soon as somebody gets too close. (Note the same stem word in "close" and "closed in," the Latin *clausus, from the same root as claustrum*). Any gesture of such closeness is experienced as a suddenly concrete threat of being engulfed and swallowed up by the other.

Another symbolic variant is manifested by procrastination and indecision: every deadline, every chore or task becomes a confining limit, and thus represents a claustrum, evoking both fear and anger; "a definitive decision excludes the possibility of escape" (Fenichel 1944, p. 283; see also Gehl 1964, 1973). This phobia may also eventuate in the fear of death (to be buried alive, to be enclosed in the tomb, to be devoured by the earth) or of being helplessly closed in within vehicles (cars, railroad trains, especially airplanes). Yet another character variation can often be traced back to a hidden claustrophobia. Arlow (1966) speaks of patients who have to escape any commitment. They show insufficient perseverance in tasks and are perpetually peregrinating (compulsive travelers).

claustrum, so much a part of his feelings of depersonalization as well as a central motive in his drug use. He felt the same about separation, structure, and discipline. More specifically, the tie-in between claustrophobia, depression, and paranoid violence was striking.

Without the drug, this patient was overwhelmed by his intense feelings of loneliness, disillusionment, emptiness, and rage. These feelings crystallized into a broad sense of being trapped, a feeling that had to be met by bursting out of the limits—by running away or by violence. With the drug he still had similar feelings of loneliness but was not overwhelmed; instead he felt bored and depersonalized. Again the dependency assumed the quality of enclosure and entrapment he had to break out of. Life seemed a desperate running back and forth between claustrophilia and claustrophobia, regression to mother and flight from mother, and being alive but enraged, calmed but bored and depersonalized.

No matter what he broke out from, the world continued to close in on him. Every new freedom inevitably changed into the old prison.

Case 3. When he was five, Andreas (Wurmser 1978) witnessed a playmate being crushed to death by a truck. Since he slept in his parents' room until he was eight years, he was always present during their intercourse. From early on he was so terrified and enraged by any sense of being pinned to the ground, "crushed," enclosed, that he avoided all sports and any confinement. Once he severely injured a boy who had "crushed" him during a ballgame. At age nineteen, he killed a man who had humiliated him. Guilt and shame were experienced as intolerable limitations he had to burst out from. It was again this already encountered, particularly frequent type of claustrophobia: the pervasive fear of any limitation as a form of confinement which was to be broken at all costs. All external structures and lines became death traps.

The most prominent boundary dilemma was the one between the guiltful expansion of power in success versus the shameful collapse of power in humiliation. In both instances, Andreas used the metaphor of "invisible lines": when his enemies violated his shame boundary he had to kill. And if Andreas scared the other by asserting his power too blatantly, or by not giving him due honor, he feared that he would be killed. These lines of narcissistic prerogative, the boundaries of power, were terrifyingly real and concrete in this man's life. It was always the shame boundary which, if crossed by a foe, absolutely needed to be defended by bloodiest violence. But before this occurred, there was a crash of self-esteem, a stunning, paralyzing sense of humiliation which could only be repaired by revenge, fueled by boundless rage. In analysis, even this feeling reduced itself to the basic state of being closed in.

Thus all threats became concretized: *the stifling, horrifying claustrum,* as personalized by *the archaic mother who tempted and devoured.* For him drugs did away with boundaries, limits, claustra, and yet always led to even more confining ones. In turn, the drug program, the probation on drug-related charges, the study plans—all of them kinds of "good" boundaries, giving him both security and freedom, firmness and flexibility—struck, for a while at least, that balance between wish and dread that allowed him to mature. But eventually these limits had to be beaten again, escaped. Thus there were pertinent aspects in the psychotherapeutic situation which were both desired by him and yet which eventually raised such profound dread that they led to the premature breaking off of treatment. These concerns were seen in his avoiding shame and hence eye contact by exchanging the face-to-face position for the couch. When withdrawn from the narcotic, he fled from the feared independence and unprotectedness into increased dependence upon his therapist by increasing the frequency of sessions. However, this raised the much more profound anxiety, his claustrophobia: to be "close," intimate, dependent meant again to be confined and swallowed up. These were fought off with paranoid rage and flight from treatment. In that sense, the "structure of therapy" assumed very regressive and antitherapeutic aspects when it became too intense and protective. In turn, the cessation of psychotherapy and its replacement by counseling was followed by a remarkable and hitherto continued improvement.

In many other cases, similar fears led to flight from treatment at its inception. It becomes more and more convincing to me that the behavioral manifestations of these patients' phobic flight in the form of "unreliability" make them so particularly intractable—more so than the behavior directly derived from the underlying (and correlated) excessive oral demandingness and dependency needs.

In sum, these cases show pervasive archaic phobias, particularly claustrophobia. Typically, phobias and the entire phobic syndrome are peculiarly shame-laden and thus often reveal their centrality only after years in treatment. It becomes persuasive to view the entire panoply of compulsive drug use, depersonalization, sociopathic acting out, and the often noted depressive and paranoid states as secondary, supraimposed constellations defending against the primacy and massiveness of such archaic phobic constellations.

Yet another element needs brief mention: protective figures and protective fantasies serve as a kind of countervailing structure against any phobia. Anna Freud's description of the daydream about the imaginary tamed lion is paradigmatic. Though the lion was a substitute for the frightening father, the anxiety could be denied, the fantasy lion turned into its pleasurable opposite, that is, into a protective figure for him and a source of terror for others (A. Freud 1936, pp. 74–75). This powerful protective figure or thing, or this entire type of object, can frequently be encountered in the history of phobic patients. Such a countervailing fantasy of a protective object, which has been split off from the hated and frightening anxiety object but still shares in its power, is really the other side of the coin, the direct pendant to the phobia.

It is in this novel sense that we may now see the addictions as the negative of the phobic neuroses. While the phobic neurotic compulsively *avoids* the condensed and projected symbol for his anxiety on the outside, the toxicomanic compulsively *seeks* the condensed and projected symbol of protection against uncontrollable, overwhelming affects, again on the outside. The drug, as symbol (as displacement) for the protective object, exerts its magically shielding power in the form of the pharmacological effect. The patient thus mobilizes with its help a transient and spurious counterforce. I suspect that parallel phenomena of protective fantasy figures may be detected in other phobic neuroses as well.

With both addicts and phobics the therapy can only succeed if this countervailing protective fantasy is reexperienced and analyzed in the transference. It is, in my experience, much more resistant to recognition and working through than the negative transference.

THE ARCHAIC ORIGINS OF CLAUSTROPHOBIA

We can now also be more precise about the core of claustrophobia. According to Lewin (1950), this phobia's content is derived from childhood fantasies about the prenatal state. The enclosure stands for the mother's body, the intruding object for the father's intruding penis. "The idea of being within the closed space is not an anxiety fantasy, but one of safety, of being in hiding. The anxiety arises from the threat of interruption" (Lewin 1950, p. 108). It is by no means certain that this interpretation is valid for all cases or even central for most. Thus, Fenichel's explanation seems more and more apposite and plausible: *"any state of anxiety is physiologically accompanied by feelings of being closed in;* and thus reversely, an *external closeness* (or the idea of it) facilitates the mobilization of the entire anxiety syndrome"* (p. 283, italics mine). This means that every intense affect (excitement, rage, etc.) has become equated with an undifferentiated global tension over which all control has been lost and which has left the person helpless and overwhelmed, a tension reawakening an original truly and severely traumatic state (Krystal 1978a,b).

Thus we are forced to assume that "the idea of a claustrum or of a claustrophobia" may be "behind all other phobias—and even behind all other symptomatic neuroses," as Leo Rangell has suggested to me personally. Even the word *anxiety* expresses a physical constriction and confinement, "angustiae" being a narrow, boxed-in place. Is not the basic experience of anxiety that of being entrapped, smothered, constricted, and quite physically so? Freud (1916–1917), in relating anxiety to the experience of birth, writes: "The name 'Angst'—'angustiae,' 'Enge'— emphasizes the characteristic of restriction in breathing which was then present as a consequence of the real situation and is now almost invariably reinstated in the affect" (pp. 396–397). Leo Rangell has added: "Behind all of the experiences is the physiological-psychological situation of the anxiety state itself being felt as a hemming-in from which one fears but also wants to burst out. Ultimate anxiety or four-plus anxiety in the decompensated state is felt as the danger of bursting asunder" (personal communication).

This basic line of the anxiety experience moves from an all-pervasive, generalized, internal one to a specific body location, one nearer the body surface. The body, particularly the chest, is felt to be a stifling enclosure, and anxiety is then projected to surrounding structures. From there it is displaced onto all forms of limitation, abstract or concrete. On all levels this anxiety series is usually accompanied by a group of aggressive actions that would liberate the self from these various concentric bounds. Yet this liberation and bursting-out raises new specters: condemnation in the form of guilt and shame, aloneness because of separation from the enclosing, protective, shielding claustrum, and ultimately, as Rangell (personal communication) has observed, the fear of the most radical bursting: that into small fragments of body and mind, Jones's "aphánisis (1929).

A further part of this picture of pathogenesis in the history of these patients is massive overstimulation, mostly of an aggressive nature. While I have encountered such traumatic overstimulation in nearly all compulsive drug users, whether in intensive exploratory psychotherapy, analysis, or more superficial therapy, it would be unwarranted to base a universal statement on these extensive but still limited observations.

Theoretically, one could assume that overstimulated children would later on become compulsive seekers of sedative drugs (including narcotics), while understimulated, deprived ones would fill the emptiness with stimulants (particularly amphetamines) or psychedelics. This is not borne out by my observations. Most addicts, of all varieties, have quite uniformly gone through severely traumatic periods from early childhood on through adolescence, traumatic not in common parlance (Krystal 1978b) but in the sense of unusually severe *real* exposures to violence, sexual seduction, and brutal abandonment; of severe unreliability, mendacity, betrayal, and abandonment; or of pervasive secretiveness and shame in the family, usually with *real* parental schism or skewedness (Lidz et al.

1965). This overstimulation is experienced as traumatic anxiety, typically in the form of helpless confusion and loss of felt controls, a vague aimless tension. Probably because of the physiologic concomitants of internal, somatically felt narrowness and stricture, this severe anxiety becomes concretized in and attached to the general idea of confinement, entrapment, and enclosure, and is projected onto all external structures lending themselves to be viewed as claustra. Simultaneously, however, relief from such anxiety can only come from protection, yet this protection would be sought primarily again in external structures, in outside controls and limitations, in the hope that somebody else take over, constrain him, and thus shield him against this dark overwhelming part within him. The tragic paradox, of course, is that all such protection against this devastating anxiety is bound to become once more just a new claustrum and, therefore, a renewed source of terror. Thus the claustrum evokes very intense conflict.

At least as far as these very profoundly disturbed patients are concerned it would make sense to see in claustrophobia the *primary phobia*. It can reach back into the deepest layers of experience, to the substrate of physiologic experiences, but it does not have to have such archaic origins. Anxiety on all levels can give rise much later to the same phenomenon of being constricted (as the German word *zusammengeschnürt,* "tied together," expresses.)

An interesting sideline should be mentioned: Claustrophobia quite often leads to *hyperventilation,* which in turn brings about a state of induced depersonalization or derealization. This state of estrangement is typically reproduced by a good number of drugs, above all hypnotics. Thus drug-evoked depersonalization comes to serve the function of dealing with the basic anxiety. (I was made aware of this fascinating and hitherto neglected sequence by J. Ginsberg in a personal communication.)

THE ROLE OF EXTERNALIZATION

The most solid and intractable way of dealing with this vicious cycle of claustrophobia and claustrophilia is not their paranoid, depressive solutions nor even their compulsive use of drugs, but their externalization of "internal structures and their antecedent archaic self- and object-representations" (Novick and Kelly 1970, Berg 1977). This is a way of using the concept of externalization that differs from Meissner's use and parallels that of Anna Freud (1965). She emphasizes how internal conflict is changed into external action: "by displacement and externalization, the whole internal battleground is changed into an external one" (p. 223). It presupposes the *"denial of the intrapsychic nature of conflict"* (p. 224).

Brodey (1965) has specified further this concept and thus made, I believe, a major conceptual contribution. He described externalization as involving: (1) projection combined with the manipulation of selected, verifying reality, and (2) the misperception of reality that does not verify the projection. Thus information is used "to train or manipulate [others] ... into validating what will then become the realization of the projection." In the shortest form: it is the "patients' effort to manipulate him [the therapist] into validating projections" (1965, pp. 167, 168).

Giovacchini (1975) has described externalization in similar terms, emphasizing how "the environment has to be constructed so that their total ego organization is maintained" (p. 123). Thus, such patients "unconsciously attempt to create an environment in which they feel frustrated" (p. 125).

Some authors have used the term "projective identification," the effort "to force the analyst to behave exactly as the patient needs to see him" (Kernberg 1975, p. 278). This term (which I personally avoid because of its lack of precision) has been circumscribed by Kernberg (1975, p. 80): "Projective identification is a primitive form of projection, mainly called upon to externalize aggressive self- and object-images; 'empathy' is maintained with the real objects onto which the projection has occurred, and is linked with an effort to control the object now feared because of this projection."

Yet in Brodey's, Giovacchini's, and Kernberg's descriptions, we do not deal with a simple defense mechanism but rather with a complex defense, using projection, identification with the aggressor, turning passive into active, and often even denial. The common denominator in all these descriptions and definitions may perhaps be seen in the defensive effort to take external action in order to defend against an internal conflict, that is, to change an internal conflict into an external one. Any of the structures—id, ego, or superego—may thus be vested transiently or permanently in outside figures (projection) with whom the inner conflict is reenacted (externalization) (A. Freud 1965, Novick and Kelly 1970). In severely disturbed patients very primitive ego functions may thus be ascribed to the object world (limit setting and boundary drawing, for example) and continually tested, manipulated, challenged, and undone (Giovacchini 1975).

Indeed, this defense by action seems closest to the archaic defense mechanism of turning passive into active. The difference between these two may really be only that in the latter case we have the reversal of an aggression by the object against the subject into an aggression by the subject against the object, while in the former we have an aggression between one part of the personality against another one turned outward. (It will be noted that I refrain from using terms like "inner objects" or "introjects" since they are unclear and too reified, too static and concrete.

In addition, when a part of an object-representation is incorporated into a self-representation it changes over, to whatever variable degree, from the object world into the subject world. This makes the term *inner objects* self-contradictory. Philosophically, we would be rather hard put to defend the existence of "objects" within the subject. Object derivatives of whatever form, yes; objects, no.)

In sum, this defense by action may be simply a turning outward of intersystemic aggression. Perhaps there is an even more primitive use: massive anxiety (whether as superego anxiety, anxiety concerning outer reality, or anxiety concerning the strength of the instinctual drives) is turned into aggression. Anna Freud made a passing, though very important reference to this: "I guessed that he was turning his anxiety into its opposite, namely, into aggressiveness" (1936, pp. 39–40). More generally we could say that the unbound energy of intense anxiety is discharged by outward-directed aggressive action. It thus could be one type of drive reversal: from self-directed to object-directed. In general it seems to me that such archaic drive reversals are far more important clinically than our literature admits; as such they deserve more study. I would even wonder whether this type of defense by drive reversal might be as central to aggression as repression is to libido.

Certainly it is very difficult to clearly distinguish externalization from projection. I conceive the difference as follows: the emphasis in externalization as a defense lies on action (especially provocation), whereas in the case of projection as defense the emphasis is put on emotionally distorted perception. Obviously they very often accompany each other, but altered perception may certainly play a minimum part in primitive forms of externalization if conceived as defense by action, and projection is often not accompanied by correlated action.

In severely disturbed patients, who are so deeply afraid to be traumatically overwhelmed by unmanageable global affects, externalization leads to drug use. The solution to this inner problem is sought on the outside, by action and in concrete form. It is an action with the aim of taking magical, omnipotent control over the uncontrollable. Everything else appears less specific compared with this peculiar defense. The anxiety is that the various affects—anxiety, pain, rage, and depression—would be overwhelming. This fear of the traumatic state is powerfully warded off by the incorporation of the potent substance: the power—via this magical substance—to "master" the unbearable. It is a specialized form of defense by acting. This is similar to what goes on in analytic patients who feel they solve an inner problem by an outer action (or avoidance of action) instead of by exploring, understanding, and remembering. It is obvious, then, that externalization is not solely a defense mechanism but is also a wish fulfillment, above all the wish for magical power.

If we change the focus from externalization as defense mechanism to its manifestation in numerous, more specific modes of defenses, we encounter in these patients a host of parallel forms. The externalization occurs:

a. by use of a magically powerful, mind altering, especially self-esteem increasing and affect dampening substance or thing;
b. by use of another impersonal agent such as food, as internal problem-solver;
c. by use of an all-powerful, all-giving personal agent in symbiotic bonds or by a fight against a totally evil enemy;
d. by lying, manipulating, and evading all personal commitments;
e. by transgressing in grandiose "acting out" the limits set by nature and society;
f. by provoking retaliation in form of shaming, angry punishment, or diffuse attack;
g. by outright violence—destroying a symbolic representative of part of oneself or bringing about punishment;
h. most typically, by seeing action as exciting risk.

As a general characteristic of all defensive externalization, we discern its dehumanizing quality. With the defensive use of action, the action itself is relevant, not the needs, qualities, or properties of the person "used," unless they happen to fit totally into this action scheme serving denial. It is mainly this dehumanizing use of others that strikes us as so infuriating in all "sociopaths."

An important aspect of externalization, in these patients at least, is obvious. The defense of externalization reestablishes the illusion of narcissistic power and control, a prominent wish in all toxicomanics in reaction to the panicky fear of not being in charge of their destiny, especially of the most ominous "ghosts," the haunting representatives of the inner demons, those overwhelming, never mastered, always newly menacing affects and wishes, the emissaries of the original traumatic state. Further, this defense allows for the expression of aggression through its action properties.[1]

1. There is a particularly beautiful description by a novelist of this process of externalization. I refer to Stendhal's *The Red and the Black.* After having given in to her attraction to the socially inferior Julien Sorel, Mathilde suddenly turned against him: "I do not love you anymore, monsieur; my imagination deceived me." Stendhal continues: "With such high-strung natures there is only a step from self-reproach to violent anger, and Mademoiselle de la Mole began to pour out upon him a veritable torrent of contempt. She displayed a dauntless spirit in torturing his pride. . . . As for herself, she found the greatest pleasure in punishing him, as well as the passion which she had felt for him a few days before. There was no need of inventing the cruel things she addressed to him; she only repeated what her pride had waged against her love for a week past."

To recapitulate: the phobic core of addiction follows a specific dynamic sequence. First, the state of traumatic anxiety is basic. It is experienced as constriction and enclosure, as "angustiae," which needs to be broken through, burst out from, in a concrete, physical form. Other feelings, besides anxiety, are of a similarly global, somaticized, nonverbal nature—especially excitement and rage (Krystal 1974, 1975). This inner sense of confinement and stricture is then projected to all outside structures, which are experienced as frightening claustra one has to burst out from. As outer structures are sought as controls against the inner danger of these overwhelming affects, the threat increases. This oscillation between the view of an object as protective structure and as dreaded and hated engulfment reenacts the original traumatic state with the mother. Thus the merger with the all-powerful, all-giving mother figure is both desired and profoundly feared, furiously striven for, and no less furiously fought off (Jacobson 1964, 1967). From concrete objects, especially the mother, these fears are next displaced to other restrictions. Conscience, time limits, social constraints (such as laws and customs), jail, structure of life, family, marriage, space—all are experienced as unease-evoking enclosures. The confines of all such claustra have to be burst, broken through, violated, transgressed at all costs and by all means of externalization: by criminality and violence, by triumphant victory and exploitation, by magical distortion of reality and self-deception. Countervailing fantasies against basic helplessness and exposure cluster around the two typical narcissistic constellations, undoing and denying the traumatic state: "I am great, invulnerable, invincible, omnipotent" (the grandiose self); and "Mother is all gratifying, fulfills all my demands, is never going to leave or disappoint me" (the idealized self-object—Kernberg 1975, Kohut 1971, 1977). Finally, drugs counter the state of helplessness by giving a feeling of magical power and self-transformation, by "healing" the crushed self-esteem for a little while. Then they reestablish passive union with a maternal figure and endow the person with a sense of invincibility and grandeur. They function as an archaic affect defense against the global emotions and moods. They represent both a claustrophobic transgression of law and reality and a claustrophilic return into a new, even more enslaving dependency.

However: They destroy confining structures while creating new, even more constricting and restrictive ones. They use a concrete means from the outside to solve the inner problem, a magical action-related talisman of protection, guarding against, yet recalling again the phobic situation. They are a concrete implementation of the central countervailing fantasy. They mute guilt and shame and yet cause them anew. They bring about the sudden flipflop in the entire personality, with the attending split in the superego (the periodic disparity in the functioning of conscience and ideals which were described in detail in Wurmser 1978).

Obviously, as with all other neurotic symptom formation, this particularly drastic form of autoplastic alteration ultimately fails; the past cannot be undone, the conflicts cannot be resolved, the structural defects cannot be repaired with the help of drugs and other types of externalization. And behind these patients we see the shadows of their family backgrounds: of massively traumatizing violence or pervasive indulgence, inconsistency and lack of structure, hidden family secrets and family lies.

PHOBIC CORE OR PERSONAL INTROJECTS?

The question then arises anew: How to relate this sequence to the enveloping layers of depression and paranoid constellations that Meissner presented so very well? It is as if we looked at roughly the same material in two completely different perspectives, each a cohesive appraisal that opens up new and indispensable meaning without invalidating the other.

The framework presented here can account for several particularly important phenomena that remain left out in Meissner's model: the flight from closeness, the shiftiness and abrupt flipflops, the radical inner instability, and the insistence on disregarding all types of boundaries and limitations. These phenomena are seen as the search for, and a flight from, a claustrum.

Here the parallels with phobic systems and the contrast with paranoid-depressive configurations becomes more evident. As noted before, the distinctive difference between phobic and paranoid processes is the *impersonal* nature of projections in the former, and the personal, planful character of the latter. In compulsive drug use there is an impersonal condensation system, delimited and not global, that corresponds in mirror-image fashion to the underlying phobic system. In that sense the drug effect is in itself a type of counterphobic fantasy (very similar to sexual perversions) that validates the attempted and hoped-for protection against (and denial of) the phobic fears, a protective, countervailing fantasy against the main anxieties and, with that, also against the major phobias. With stimulants, there is the sense, "I am strong, not vulnerable"; with narcotics and other sedative drugs, "I am blissful, not enraged"; with psychedelics, "I am trustful, not disillusioned"; and with alcohol, "I am accepted, approved, and belonging, not isolated and guilty."

In sum, the crucial steps in drug addiction are phobic projection plus externalization. In the paranoid process these steps are projection plus introjection plus reprojection (and externalization). In the depressive process, there is projection plus introjection. In other words, the passage through an additional layer of archaic introjections, which adds the personalizing element, especially willfulness, is omitted in the phobic-addictive constellation, and is a *conditio sine qua non* for the paranoid-depressive configuration. This introjective passage is a defensive move by regression. It ensues after collapse of the phobic-addictive defense structure. Both are attempts to cope with the underlying global, traumatic anxiety: one by attaching the anxiety to confining structures, the other by attaching it to the ego function of willful, deciding personhood. In the former, the faculty internalizations pertain mainly to structural limits, boundaries, and controls and hence to *functions*, while in the latter they involve object representations of great aggressive content and hence entire composite images. In the phobic-addictive state, the patient fails to identify fully with, and thus to assume as his own, the ego functions of self-control and limit setting; in the paranoid-depressive constellation, he does not identify with the ego functions of goal setting, purposiveness, intentionality. In the former he disowns his separateness and limitedness primarily in regard to id impulses (his own *wish*fulness and subsequent punishment are ascribed to others); in the latter he overrides it on behalf of the one ego function of autonomous decision making (his own *will*fulness and subsequent punishment are ascribed to others.

Therefore the whole concept of personal introjects that forms the pivot of Meissner's model is, I believe, somewhat less central to the understanding of the phobic-addictive syndrome than to the examination of the paranoid-depressive syndrome. Instead we need a new theoretical tool, conceptualizing the system of internalized limits and primordial controls; should we call them *functional introjects, psychosomatic delimitations and confinements* (taking into account the clearly physiologic contributions to the phenomena studied), or *internalization of limit setting as an ego function?*

Still the question has not yet been answered: How can we connect the two sets of phenomena? It will be remembered that three layers can be discovered: a superficial and sociopathic-paranoid one, a depressive one, and the phobic core. I also stressed that Meissner dealt very well with the first two, but left out the third.

My experience points to the state of helplessness and powerless exposure *(Ausgeliefertsein)*—in other words, to the repeated severe traumatization and overstimulation—as the key. One element derived from it is the "primary phobia," a way of seeking both wish fulfillment (protection) and defense (projection) in the compromise solution of the claustrophobic symptom. It can be perpetuated into what has not yet been studied at all: the *phobic character.* Here all limitations or closures are responded to with fear and avoided. Or, as in drug addiction, the engulfment, the submersion, is sought counterphobically.

The second line of development is that of the narcissistic compensation. To repair the shattered self-esteem and the ego fragmentation and, as particularly Kernberg (1975) postulates, to defend against archaic rage and envy, fantasies of grandiosity are employed; they increasingly become crystallized around omnipotent introjects. Typically this experience does not remain static, but develops into a very dynamic interplay: With the continually ongoing traumatizations, a rapid alternation of the stated grandiose fantasies and overwhelming stimuli ensues. With time, this traumatic state loses some of its diffuseness and vagueness and also becomes crystallized around weak, helpless, despised "introjects" (self-images). To use a somewhat different phrasing: an increasing polarity issues between a grandiose, all-powerful, all-entitled, boundaryless self and a despicable, messy, little, weak self. Inner life is polarized around these great contrasts in what Meissner so aptly called the "logic of the extremes" or the "logic of narcissism" (1978).

As mentioned, the sudden flipflops in the entire personality, giving the appearance of a truly split personality, are very characteristic for addicts. According to the logic of the extremes, a compliant, submissive, conforming self is suddenly replaced by a grandiose self that sees no holds barred, that is ready to violate all restraints and boundaries. It is a defense against the total helplessness and its accompanying, undifferentiated contempt, rage, envy, and despair. Out of this emerges a shame-guilt dialectic (Wurmser 1978). The sequence is this: Grandiosity is disappointed, self-esteem utterly shattered; one sees himself exposed as a needy, greedy, weak being, open to humiliation; shame becomes overwhelming; the shaming becomes projected in form of oversensitivity to all real or imaginary slights; in narcissistic rage a position of superiority is reclaimed; the illusion of grandiosity is reestablished; the rights of others are violated, boundaries are transgressed, reality has to be bent in a spree of arrogant demandingness and deceit; profound guilt or at least fear of retaliation arises; these guilty fears are projected either in form of blaming (projection of the aggression) or of feeling persecuted and accused (projection of the punishment). As long as the emphasis is on the introjective resting points—profound shame or equally profound guilt—we deal with depression.

All superego strictures and all limits set by the superego, especially the lines guarded by the feelings of guilt and of shame, are experienced as claustra. The entire claustrophobic conflict centrally affects the introjective system out of which the superego is composed. In short: superego constraints form but another claustrum. The superego is split between a part that abides by and enforces the rules of nature and society, slavishly and with dogged compliance, and a part that sanctions and supports all assertions of arrogant pride and ruthless self-aggrandizement. One side chooses the protection of a claustrum, and the other flees from being boxed in and destroys any enclosing line. The flipflop is thus not primarily that between victim and victimizing selves, as Meissner describes in the paranoid character, but that between the claustrophilic and the claustrophobic selves. Both poles are united in the drug use: The drug effects are a breaking of boundaries that reestablish a new dependency and confinement. Thus, the character of the drug addict is pervaded by the doubleness between weak and grandiose introjects, between seeking protection in the claustrum and avoiding it. The violation of taboos stands against the bringing about of confinement, of outer controls and structures. The rebelling against society is pitted against belonging to the in-group of a subculture. The magic power of grandiose self-transformation with the help of a drug is the very opposite of being the passive recipient of a powerful action. The talisman of the drug as an omnipotent object is, by its proven effectiveness, the grandiose weapon against the ever-present phobic danger. The addict is thus not essentially a paranoid character—one who compulsively blames others—nor a depressive character—one who compulsively blames himself. He is primarily a phobic character turned around: instead of being one who compulsively avoids on the outside, he compulsively *searches* on the outside. Phobic character and addictive character are like photographic negative and positive to each other, as are depressive and paranoid characters.

In conclusion, it seems that Meissner's focus is on the drug as substance and on the cultural medium. He tries to weave both emphases into his intriguing, complex, and often very helpful discussion of introjection and projection. I, on the other hand, tend to stress more of the psychopharmacological effect that specifically fits into the defense structure. Meissner emphasizes that the real addiction is to introjects, that is, to what is feared, devalued, and thus defended against in the self and then projected into the drug and reintrojected into the self. I concur with this, but would rephrase it. I believe that a protective fantasy is maintained with the help of the drug effect and the drug is sought as a powerful counterpoise and antidote against the intense affects. In a very deep sense, we both agree with Homer when he speaks of a *phármakon nepenthés t' ácholónte*—"the drug against grief and rage" (*Odyssey,* Book IV, pp. 220, 221).

But I disagree with Meissner when he states: "One does not need to demonstrate severe psychopathology in order to understand the phenomenon of drug addiction." I still maintain, on the basis of all my experience, that compulsive drug users are without fail very sick patients who struggle in vain against overwhelming anguish, pain, rage, and terror.

In all these discussions we should not lose sight of an overriding principle in psychoanalysis—the *principle of specificity*. Our abstractions and generalities are, though not worthless, still of rather limited value. We need to combine them with as detailed descriptions as possible of the essential unconscious configurations in individual cases, the most specific wishes and defenses, the derivative daydreams and dream associations, the transference of defense in its minutiae, those few really crucial interpretations that lead to clinical breakthroughs. Such in-depth studies of individual but paradigmatic cases are in my opinion long overdue.

The most important question is, therefore, whether we are really able to treat effectively such severe woundedness and imbalance by the most specific and detailed understanding in a relationship of kindness and honesty.

REFERENCES

Arlow, J. (1966). Character and conflict. *Journal of the Hillside Hospital* 15:139–151.

Balint, M. (1959). *Thrills and Regression*. New York: International Universities Press.

Berg, M. (1977). The externalizing transference. *International Journal of Psycho-Analysis* 58:235–244.

Brodey, W. (1965). On the dynamics of narcissism, externalization and early ego development. *Psychoanalytic Study of the Child* 20:165–193.

Cassirer, E. (1923). *The Philosophy of Symbolic Forms*. Vol. II. New Haven: Yale University Press, 1955.

Fenichel, O. (1939). The counter-phobic attitude. In *Collected Papers*, Vol. II, pp. 163–173. New York: Norton, 1954.

——— (1944). Remarks on the common phobias. In *Collected Papers*, Vol. II, pp. 278–287. New York: Norton, 1954.

Fingarette, H. (1969). *Self-Deception*. London: Routledge and Kegan Paul.

Freud, A. (1936). The ego and the mechanisms of defense. In *The Writings of Anna Freud. Vol. II.* New York: International Universities Press, 1971.

——— (1965). Normality and pathology in childhood: assessments of development. In *The Writings of Anna Freud, Vol. VI.* New York: International Universities Press, 1971.

——— (1970). The infantile neurosis: genetic and dynamic considerations. In *The Writings of Anna Freud, Vol. VII*, pp. 189–203. New York: International Universities Press, 1971.

——— (1977). Fears, anxieties, and phobic phenomena. *Psychoanalytic Study of the Child* 32:85–90.

Freud, S. (1909). Analysis of a phobia in a five-year-old boy. *Standard Edition* 10:5–149.

——— (1916–1917). Introductory lectures on psychoanalysis. *Standard Edition* 16.

——— (1917). Mourning and melancholia. *Standard Edition* 14:237–258.

——— (1926). Inhibitions, symptoms, and anxiety. *Standard Edition* 20:75–174.

——— (1940a). An outline of psycho-analysis. *Standard Edition* 23:144–207.

——— (1940b). Splitting of the ego in the process of defense. *Standard Edition* 23:275–278.

Gehl, R. (1964). Depression and claustrophobia. *International Journal of Psycho-Analysis* 45:312–323.

—— (1973). Indecision and claustrophobia. *International Journal of Psycho-Analysis* 54:45–59.

Giovacchini, P. (1975). *Psychoanalysis of Character Disorders.* New York: Jason Aronson.

Jacobson, E. (1964). *The Self and the Object World.* New York: International Universities Press.

—— (1967). *Psychotic Conflict and Reality.* New York: International Universities Press.

Jones, E. (1929). Fear, guilt and hate. In *Papers on Psychoanalysis,* pp. 304–319. Boston: Beacon Press, 1967.

Kernberg, O. (1975). *Borderline Conditions and Pathological Narcissism.* New York: Jason Aronson.

Kohut, H. (1971). *The Analysis of the Self.* New York: International Universities Press.

—— (1977). *The Restoration of the Self.* New York: International Universities Press.

Krystal, H. (1974). The genetic development of affect and affect regression. *Annual of Psychoanalysis* 2:93–126.

—— (1975). Affect tolerance. *Annual of Psychoanalysis* 3:179–219.

—— (1978a). Trauma and affects. *Psychoanalytic Study of the Child* 33:81–116.

—— (1978b). Catastrophic psychic trauma and psychogenic death. In *Psychiatric Foundations of Medicine,* vol. 6, ed. G. Balis, L. Wurmser, and E. McDaniel, pp. 79–97. Woburn, Mass.: Butterworth.

Lewin, B. (1935). Claustrophobia. *Psychoanalytic Quarterly* 4:227–233.

—— (1950). *The Psychoanalysis of Elation.* New York: The Psychoanalytic Quarterly.

Lidz, T., Fleck, S., and Cornelison, A. (1965). *Schizophrenia and the Family.* New York: International Universities Press.

Mahler, M. (1968). *On Human Symbiosis and the Vicissitudes of Individuation.* New York: International Universities Press.

Meissner, W. (1970). Notes on identification, I. Origins in Freud. *Psychoanalytic Quarterly* 39:563–589.

—— (1971). Notes on Identification, II. Clarification of related concepts. *Psychoanalytic Quarterly* 40:277–302.

—— (1972). Notes on identification, III. The concept of identification. *Psychoanalytic Quarterly* 41:224–260.

—— (1978). *The Paranoid Process.* New York: Jason Aronson.

Meuli, K. (1975). *Gesammelte Schriften,* vols. I–II. Basel and Stuttgart: Schwabe.

Novick, J., and Kelly, K. (1970). Projection and externalization. *Psychoanalytic Study of the Child* 25:69–98.

Rangell, L. (1968). A further attempt to resolve the "problem of anxiety." *Journal of the American Psychoanalytic Association* 16:371–404.

—— (1969). Choice-conflict and the decision-making function of the ego: a psychoanalytic contribution to decision theory. *International Journal of Psycho-Analysis* 50:599–602.

—— (1978). On understanding and treating anxiety and its derivatives. *International Journal of Psycho-Analysis* 59:229–236.

Sperling, M. (1971). Spider phobias and spider fantasies: a clinical contribution to the study of symbol and symptom choice. *Journal of the American Psychoanalytic Association* 19:472–498.

Szasz, T. (1957). The problem of psychiatric nosology. *American Journal of Psychiatry* 114:405.

Wurmser, L. (1978). *The Hidden Dimension: Psychodynamics in Compulsive Drug Use.* New York: Jason Aronson.

Wurmser, L., and McDaniel, E. (1978). Phobic neurosis. In *Psychiatric Foundations of Medicine,* vol. 4, ed. G. Balis, L. Wurmser, and E. McDaniel, pp. 243–263. Woburn, Mass.: Butterworth.

Some Clinical Manifestations of Structural Defects in a Borderline Personality

ALAN KROHN, Ph.D.

A case is presented that illustrates specific clinical manifestations of structural deficits and psychopathological complexes characteristic of borderline patients. Following an overview of the patient's presenting problems and history, the patient's personality organization is conceptualized metapsychologically. Then the clinical manifestations of three core problem areas in the patient are explored: (1) deficits in narcissistic cathexis leading to clinically apparent, primitive, self-confirming character traits, (2) fear of helplessness and pathological attempts to establish a sense of control, and (3) arrest of drive development coupled with limited ego capacity for sublimation.

While the seeds of our current understanding of regressed states can be found even in Freud's study of Shreber (1911) and Tausk's paper on the influencing machine (1933), modern conceptualizations of these disorders awaited a study of object relations conducted by Klein (1948), Fairbairn (1952), and Jacobson (1964), among others. The psychoanalytic study of infancy and early childhood (A. Freud 1965, Mahler 1968) also provided new and valuable data on the pregenital phases of development from which severe disturbances arise. Further, a more systematic clinical investigation of the ego and its individual functions opened the way for more refined metapsychological assessment of patients. The projective testing work of Rapaport, Gill, and Schafer (1968) was a significant benchmark in this evolution toward a systematic study of the defensive and adaptive aspects of the ego in individual patients. The study of the development of mental representations (self and object) both through psychoanalytic child observation and through analyses of adults enriched our understanding of psychotic and depressive patients. The studies of

Jacobson (1964) and Greenacre (1953a,b) were truly pioneering in their application of an emerging psychoanalytic understanding of pregenital development to the clinical experience of treating severely regressed patients.

While the conflicts of severely regressed patients have some things in common with those of the neurotic, such as the presence of intrapsychic conflict, the impact of unconscious forces, and the role of pathogenic defensive processes, they are in many respects very different. Among these many differences, some of the most essential are: the regressed patient is not struggling with conflict over phallic wishes toward an incestuous object but rather with a fear of loss of object, loss of cohesion of self, separation panic, and fears of pregenital aggression. The conflicts in the regressed patient devolve not only from the conflicts between wish and defense (as in neurotic patients) but as well from the ego's inadequacy as manifested in the nature of defensive operations (primitive defenses such as projective identification, denial, and splitting), in characteristic object representations (undifferentiated, split, omnipotent, and malevolent images of objects), in poor adaptive functioning (poor capacity for sublimation), in the inability to tolerate anxiety, in the lack of impulse control, and in frequent regression to more primitive modes of thought (intrusion of primary process thinking into areas of functioning demanding secondary process thinking).

Kernberg's work (1967) organized and integrated these new perspectives. While the concept of borderline psychosis had appeared previously in the literature (Knight 1954), it was Kernberg who defined the borderline systematically and comprehensively as a discrete psychopathological entity. He clearly distinguished among a variety of nonneurotic psychopathologies, the most major of which was the distinction between psychotic and borderline personalities. He presented the symptom and character traits generally found in borderline patients and delineated the underlying personality organization found in these patients. He synthesized well the work of previous authors and presented a coherent picture of the characteristic drive development, ego organization, and object representations found in borderline patients. He emphasized the ego and object-relational deficits and distortions found in the borderline, noting nonspecific ego weakness, primitive defense mechanisms, lack of sublimatory channels, and pathology of internalized object relations as the most pervasive deficits. Brodey (1965), Masterson (1976), and Rinsley (1977) have also discussed the nature of these deficits and distortions. Some of the clinical manifestations of these defects have been described by Kernberg in general terms:

The presence of some degree of lack of differentiation of self and object images and the concomitant blurring of ego boundaries can be considered one other "nonspecific" aspect of ego weakness in the borderline field, but this aspect is closely linked to the pathology of internalized object relationships and will be taken up in that context. The rigidity of characterological patterns is sometimes mistakenly considered to be a sign of ego strength; neither excessive rigidity of character pathology nor its "overfluidity" in itself represent ego strength or weakness, but rather both are specific modes of organization of the character pathology. (1966, p. 22)

These manifestations can be viewed as direct effects of the ego defects involved. With poorly developed ego adaptive channels for expression of drives, id impulses cannot be sublimated or channeled by the ego. The impulses erupt relatively undisguised into consciousness and the anxiety generated by the impulses (or the anticipation of the environment's response to their expression) is poorly tolerated by the ego. At the same time such impulses fuel primitive superego processes leading to intense self-hate. There are also, according to Kernberg, many secondary symptomatic and characterological developments that occur as natural outgrowths of these ego deficits. Kernberg considered splitting, for example, to be a defensive mechanism that is secondary to nonspecific ego weakness.

Thus in borderline patients a variety of pathological structures develop (in place of these defective functions) that distort the ego and character structure. This study seeks to illustrate with a single case certain highly pathological symptoms and ego operations that typically function in borderline patients in place of the normal ego functions, which are deficient in such patients. The paper will delineate the central structural defects and distortions and describe some of the pathological structures that emerged in place of the ego deficits.

CASE STUDY

The following is a picture of the patient, Miss L, which emerged during the first six months of intensive psychotherapy (two and three times a week). While this study seeks to analyze the patient as she presented toward the beginning of treatment, it will draw upon material she presented over the course of her five-year treatment. As this is a study of psychopathology, not psychotherapy or therapeutic change, little will be said of the changes that occurred over the course of treatment.

Miss L was a twenty-one-year-old, reasonably attractive, slightly overweight woman of medium height who walked with a brusque gait, held herself very erect, seemed aloof, and appeared to know just where she was going. She had a high, loud, and shaky voice that was experienced by many as grating and demanding. Though she did not deliberately behave dramatically, her body movements and speech habits seemed a bit larger than life, like postures or poses, and tended to draw attention to herself. She wore clothing made of heavy, warm, dark fabrics such as long dark blue wool skirts and bulky sweaters. She said she liked this type of clothing because it hid her body, which she regularly perceived as obese and ugly. The clothes helped her feel snug and protected. She felt such clothing to be "substantial, sturdy, and practical." Her clothing, like all her possessions, was very important to her. They were used to protect, disguise, and, most important, to defend herself from what she felt to be an unsafe, mocking world outside.

An only child, Miss L was born when her mother was in her late thirties and her father in his late forties. Her father was a salesman, mother a housewife and former nurse. The patient's mother was a relatively attractive, quiet, understated, down-to-earth woman who had been intermittently depressed throughout the patient's childhood. Though the mother had wished to pursue her career as a nurse, she gave in easily to pressure from her husband to stay at home with her child. The mother clearly felt victimized by this, remained bitter, and grew more depressed. A few years after a hysterectomy, which occurred when the patient was three and a half, the mother developed chronic peptic ulcers, colitis, and headaches and finally was plagued with arthritis.

The patient viewed her mother as valuing self-reliance, practicality, and asceticism. The patient remembered that as a child as soon as she demonstrated that she was capable of doing anything on her own, she would feel her mother to be insisting that she perform that function independently from then on and would feel her to be very displeased if the patient regressed. When the patient demonstrated that she could act independently in some way and did not need to depend on her mother, she recalled hearing her sigh. She interpreted this as her mother saying "another burden has been lifted from me." The patient felt that with each accomplishment she was burning bridges behind her and that her mother would be annoyed and disappointed to be asked to resume, even temporarily, an old caretaking responsibility.

The patient's father was a small, almost elflike man who spoke very fast, seemed very anxious, and had been described by one evaluator as hypomanic. He seemed constantly to be lecturing, instructing, directing, and judging those around him. During the patient's childhood he was preoccupied with his work, to the extent of reading professional books at the dinner table while demanding absolute silence from his wife and daughter. He tended to stop eating entirely when anxious and was easily disgusted by particular foods or allusions to dirt or disease at the dinner table. He grimaced when injury or body functions arose in conversation. He demanded order and blamed his wife and daughter for interfering with his routines and rituals. At times he would fly into rages, chasing his daughter around the house and hitting her.

The atmosphere of the family seemed generally to have been sober, driven, and compulsive, punctuated by the father's tirades. Mother and father both seemed to have felt overwhelmed by the responsibility of having a child and poorly able to handle their child's needs to depend on them. To comfort the child by saying "there, there" was considered irrational and magical and therefore intolerable to these very intellec-tualized parents. The patient was expected to be a self-sufficient, minia-ture adult and, very important, was expected to be "creative." The parents seemed to have been truly excited when the patient, either as a child or an adult, demonstrated some capacity to be "creative"; their daughter seemed to come alive for them most fully at those times.

Both parents were shy socially, the family having little to do with others in the community. The father would often behave in a submissive, almost apologetic fashion with peers, and the mother, too, was often worried about being accepted by peers. By contrast, in the home there seemed to have been little regard for each other's needs and sensitivities. Self-interest (particularly in the case of the father) came first, and there was continual blaming of others for one's own difficulties. It seemed that no one could admit within the home the insecurities they clearly manifested socially. If there was an obstacle, it was always someone else's fault. (Brodey [1965] has commented on the mutual externalization in families such as this.) The parents' need to see their daughter as "creative" may well also have served to ward off their own sense of worthlessness. To be in any respect ordinary or mundane seemed to have been for the parents, and most surely came to be for the patient in her adulthood, the very worst thing one could be.

Overview of the Patient's Development

In addition to gathering developmental material from the patient and inferring it from her associations, I had the opportunity to interview the parents on several occasions during the course of the patient's treatment and to gather further information about her early life.[1]

---

1. These interviews occurred at the initiative of the parents, who were paying for the treatment. I told the patient that I wished during these interviews to learn more about her early life than she could herself remember; I of course explored her reaction to this with her. I shared with the patient, over a period of time, essentially all the information I obtained from the parents. While I did not feel these contacts to be antitherapeutic for this patient, I am not recommending this as a clinical or research technique.

The course of the patient's development was, as is always the case, intimately connected with the climate of the mother's emotional life and with the mother's own relationship with her mother. The mother reported that the patient was a planned child and that the pregnancy went smoothly. The parents' conflict about having a child can be discerned, however, in their waiting six years into their marriage to have a child. On the day the patient was born, her mother's mother, whom her mother described as emotionally "cool", had her first heart attack. This heart attack was then followed by a gradual deterioration in the grandmother's health until her death when the patient was four years old. In addition, from the patient's first birthday until her third, her mother's only brother developed an inoperable brain tumor and died. Five months after the patient's birth the family moved to a strange city; the year after that the mother developed a fibroid cyst and underwent a partial hysterectomy, when the patient was two years old. During this period, there was a one-week separation from the mother. The patient's father during her first four years was working very long hours and was largely unavailable to mother or daughter.

The mother reacted to these losses and impending losses by withdrawing from her already limited social contacts in the new city and entering an essentially symbiotic relationship with her child. The mother described the child as a "delight" during her first two years and spent virtually all her time with her daughter. She was virtually housebound, read to her child for hours on end and held her most of the time. There was very little encouragement of active, independent play. During these two years the patient had virtually no contact with other children or adults. From the mother's description, the patient was allowed to be frustrated relatively little during her first three years. The mother's report contained strong indications that at the same time as she was rushing to gratify her infant, she was also feeling periodically depressed and detached. As the mother described these years and her own relationship with her own mother, the meaning of this symbiotic relationship became quite clear: The mother seemed to feel with her own mother's first heart attack that she would now never receive the nurturance she had long sought from her own mother. She turned then to her daughter to try to create with her the peaceful symbiosis she unconsciously longed for with her own mother. She encouraged the passive, loving, quiet, and intellectual aspects of her infant and gratified her quickly to avoid the frustration and rage that threatened to disrupt the actualization of her fantasy. She was also trying to vicariously enjoy her daughter's passive pleasure in order to avoid her own impending depression. It can be speculated that the mother was struggling with her rage at her own mother for lack of nurturance and for her impending loss, rage that in classical depressive fashion was experienced as sure to drive the object away or destroy it. Her relationship with her daughter then had to be for defensive purposes entirely devoid of aggression.

To a clinically sophisticated observer, the patient's first signs of abnormal development could have been seen between ages one and a half and three. The mother reported how "comfortable" her child seemed walking up to and talking to strange adults in the street or in shops. She would have to be watched very closely, for she was so "friendly" that she would often walk off and attach herself to a strange adult. The patient had not achieved object constancy. Due probably to the excessively close, exclusive relationship with the mother, the minimal frustration combined with the mother's affective distance, all objects were assumed to be different versions of the mother. All were experienced essentially as need-gratifying objects, with no real distinctions among them.

About the time her daughter was three, the mother first notice that she was in turmoil and was quite different from her peers. The mother at this time was feeling more interested in becoming involved with people in the community. Under some social pressure, she took her child to a play group. At the play group it was immediately obvious that the little girl could not tolerate to be even a few yards away from her mother or to have the mother express even the slightest interest in other women or children in the group. The patient would scream at her mother, cling to her, have temper tantrums, or become combative with any potential rivals. The overwhelming need for the exclusive and uninterrupted attention of the mother led the latter to terminate most of these contacts. Back at home when the symbiosis was restored, the patient was able to be quieted and calmed. Increasingly, however, there were disorganized and disorganizing eruptions of rage, usually in connection with some frustration. The rage included hitting the mother, yelling, and throwing things. The rage was also increasingly combined with self-directed aggression including biting herself, banging her head, and severely criticizing herself for even the most minor mistakes. Both the patient and her mother remember her crying for hours over a glass she had accidentally broken. This severe, ruminative self-criticism occurred regularly when she failed to perform up to her expectations in school.

In elementary school she withdrew from other children out of fear that they were mocking her. Her hostile and suspicious stance toward the other children led them then, in fact, to exclude her. Teachers and other children were the objects of tremendous rage and were, via projection, experienced as persecuting and tormenting. The relationship with the mother became then a haven in which she could complain about these persecutions and where she could feel safe and nurtured. From age six to thirteen little or no hostility was expressed toward the mother. The mother was idealized and depended upon. The patient was described by teachers as withdrawn, selfish, and possessive of things and people. She would be very demanding of adults and children. She was belligerent with other children and unable to share or cooperate with them. She remembered vividly feeling in some horrible, vague way "bad, wrong, and different from the others." She was taken to a child guidance clinic where she was seen briefly, apparently with no improvement.

Following puberty, the patient developed interests in music and writing that quickly became all-consuming preoccupations. She would fantasize about being the world's most outstanding pianist and imagined that people would be in awe of her. In her fantasy, they would feel bad and wrong in comparison to her. Beginning at this period of her life, she began to ruminate interminably about her future, became preoccupied with what others thought of her and became extremely sensitive to the most subtle slights, real or imagined. She grew terribly shy and came to feel that she had to keep up a front continuously to hide from others that she was bad, ugly, and defective. At the same time she developed a fantasy that she could be truly magnificent in her looks, her work, or her artistic pursuits. She became very driven, examining every day her progress or regression in different areas of self-development, scrutinizing meticulously virtually everything she did, a pattern that later, in college, became paralyzing. An experience of herself as a great artist alternated with an image of herself as completely worthless. Disgusted by the prospect of a drab, workaday life, she dreamed of living on an exalted plane, continuously achieving and creating-fantasizing inside herself founts of dazzling creativity that would permit her to write, sing, and perform effortlessly.

Still having difficulties relating to other children, she was sent to a series of private schools for troubled adolescents where teachers felt her to be intelligent and in actuality somewhat creative. She went to a small college, where after her first two months her ruminations about her work led her to grow depressed and to alternate between being convinced that she was worthless and feeling herself too good (or different) for the world to tolerate. She left college precipitously, went to California and joined a group of marginal people, returned to college, and made a serious attempt to kill herself with sleeping pills. She was hospitalized for a year and I began treating her two months after her discharge.

The Patient's Manner

People often initially experienced the patient as pushy and obnoxious.

Her manner made others feel that she was blaming them for her difficulties, that she felt she had been treated unfairly and that she deserved
and needed more. She regularly gave people the feeling that they somehow owed her something. What came through in her manner was a
gnawing hunger, a sense of being deprived, a demand for recompense,
and a haughty demand to be looked up to and respected. The patient
initially felt that she was shy, modest, and unnoticed. In consciously
trying to compensate for this, she often struck others as trying to impress
and boast. It was the plaintive, self-righteous, long-suffering attitude in
her manner that annoyed others, felt like a burden to them, and often led
them to turn away from her. When the patient would feel more secure, a
softer, pleading, infantile quality emerged, including a naive, all-loving,
pervasive awe of others. Though she had some friends, she had very few
who felt capable of gratifying her intense and continuous needs for
support, reassurance, and maternal comfort. She grew enraged even at
those who befriended her, because they could not do enough. She often
felt that those who failed to meet her demands were actively trying to
deprive her and persecute her. At moments when she felt people were
actually depriving her, she felt a "white-hot rage," involving impulses to
murder, smash windows, or throw herself out a window. These rageful
episodes frightened her greatly and would make her feel she should kill
herself. Alternately, she deprecated herself, feeling like a loathsome, ugly,
fat person who contributed nothing to the world, who was a parasite and
therefore deserved to be hated. She felt at such moments as if her
stomach were filled with razor blades and was about to explode. When she
entered treatment, she had little capacity to be interested in others except
as gratifiers or frustrators of her needs. She would develop clinging,
dependent relationships characterized by intense wishes to *have* the
qualities of the other, often including intense envy of the object.

The Patient's Presenting Problems

The presenting problems centered on the patient's view of herself. This
involved rage at herself or others for her not being "better" than she
actually was. She felt certain that she could be a "great writer," comparing
herself to Hemingway and others and was envious of friends who wrote
well. She idealized these friends, felt angry that they possessed "drive" to
actualize their gifts (though she felt her gifts were surely superior) and
blamed her parents, then herself, for her lack of dramatic and supreme
success. She dreaded being mundane and looked down on almost everyone with the exception of great artists or writers. She ruminated for long
periods of time about her talents and potential, but was at the outset of

the treatment unable to direct any of her energies; she could neither work nor go to school, much less be creative. To think of work or study at this juncture was accompanied by fear and rage. She felt many life necessities as unfairly imposed on her. These feelings were countered at times by feelings that she was terribly self-indulgent.

She was preoccupied with her body, its weight, appearance, flaws, and ills. She wanted to look perfect and graceful and felt that earlier in her life she was truly beautiful and happy. Now her body felt ugly, flabby, and she imagined that people in the street were mocking her and were saying behind her back that if she really wanted to lose weight she could stop being such a glutton and eat less. She alternated between feelings of omnipotence and feelings of being profoundly helpless and worthless. Feelings of inadequacy were met with attempts to find people to whom she could attribute great protective power which they would use on her behalf. The feelings of omnipotence, which represented primitive attempts to have everything under her control, led to a haughty, disdainful view of others. She worried she had cancer and had a dread of dying and growing old, she also had a great fear that her body would be "ordinary." She often felt that having been overweight had ruined her body and that this irreparable damage was her punishment for having failed to regulate her appetite. She did have many somatic problems: chronic headaches, irritation of the skin around her eyes (which she constantly rubbed), and eczema. She was capable of maintaining very few relationships, for she continually expected others to meet her needs as if they owed this to her. She would get enraged at them when they responded to their own needs independent of hers and would fear that she would not be able to control this rage. In fact, though she was never violent, her anger would often be quite recognizable to others and they would often feel blamed by her.

Typical Session

A session from the third month of treatment will illustrate many things about the patient. She walked into the session in a rage, fists clenched, teeth gritted, and immediately exploded about how people in the hospital corridor look at her like a sick, strange person. "I hate them," she said. I tried to explore this with her, but she broke into tears, said it is hopeless to think she can live on her own, hold a job, or have friends. She complained that she had no friends, and when I reminded her of our recent attempts to explore the obstacles that interfere with her reciprocating overtures made by others, she barked back that she needed help, not accusations of being bad. She then said, "People don't call me because they can't stand me." When I wondered what indication she had that a particular friend hated her, she said this person had told the patient when the latter asked her to go to a movie that she was busy. She didn't believe her: "She's just trying to avoid hurting my feelings, but she basically feels I'm nothing." Why then, I wondered aloud, would she want to avoid hurting your feelings? "Because she doesn't think I'm even worth an explanation." She then launched into a long rumination about her worth, speaking of herself either positively or negatively in very global, amorphous terms. She feels that she has the potential to be great, but lacks the drive to be. She wants to find out how to develop this drive. "Can't you tell me how?" she demanded. I said that it may well be that her conflicts interfere with her being able to use some of her talents. She responded, "Instead of helping me learn to use these things in myself, these good things, which I think we're here to do, you again blame me." I pointed out to her here that she seems to feel helpless to do what she needs to to make herself feel both worthwhile and in control of her world. "You feel the only way this can happen is if I give you some type of training, advice, or direction; most basically, really, you are asking me to provide in some magical way power you feel I have but which you feel I am sadistically witholding." She said, "I do feel that you could give me much, much more than you do. You seem able to do things and I want to be able to be that way." She then described an often-mentioned woman friend whom she saw as perfect in appearance: "She makes pictures everywhere she is. No matter how she stands she makes beautiful pictures with her body. I want to have that. I hate myself. I want to be completely changed. I have to get out of this fat body." She became very rageful, first at herself for having ruined her body and then at the hospital where she had been an inpatient for feeding her such fattening food. She talked of wishing to be able to break out of her body, break out of herself. Finally she described a feeling that had occurred the night before, a frightening feeling like storm clouds gathering. She said then what she had on many occasions before: "This feeling is entirely different than any feeling that I've told you about before, it is urgent that you understand it just as I experience it, you must." Characteristically, she became severely troubled when I was unable to do so. She felt very angry that I would think she was "crying wolf." A few moments later I said to her that she feels secure here only if I experience her experiences as if thinking with and feeling with her brain. At this point, characteristic of times when she felt understood, she smiled, reported feeling excited and very close, feeling the therapist could in fact know her feelings as he just had, without her even telling him of them in words.

Such a kaleidoscope of wishes, demands and protests were common, particularly at the beginning of the hours, leaving me feeling drained and assaulted. I often felt under tremendous pressure to be for the patient whatever she at the moment wished me to be. Probably most difficult was the patient's utter preoccupation with herself, her demands that I "help," her railing at me for not doing so, and her rarely being concerned about my feelings or those of other people.

During the early portion of the psychotherapy, much contact with the patient occurred on the phone, for she would often call me in the evening in a panic. She called because she had suffered a real or imagined slight and was either murderously rageful at whoever had slighted her or felt that she deserved the slight and therefore felt herself to be awful. She called at other times feeling helpless to cope with some exigency and would frequently become rageful that I could not tell her how to solve the problem or could not magically change her so that she could solve it herself. She would at times call me on the telephone and describe a sense that she did not want to do something; she would demand ragefully that I transform her so that she would want to do the necessary tasks. She often asked to be "taught" how to do something that was unteachable, such as how to find an idea for a poem or how to know what she wants. She wished on a very basic level for me to share her experience completely, as if we were not two separate people. Finally she would call, profusely anxious, even on a day when she had been optimistic about her life and feeling pleasant in the session. What continually emerged was her sense that to feel good was dangerous and that she had to tell the therapist that she felt awful and dreadfully pessimistic. But, as the therapy progressed the patient could recognize in herself that to feel good meant unconsciously to separate from her mother, saying in effect, "I have resources in me to feel good." The calls represented an attempt to say, "I'm not happy, I am suffering as mother does and am as pessimistic as she."

During this period the patient was never very far from an overwhelming feeling of helplessness. She would ragefully demand that I and others do more for her. This usually centered around a wish for other people to magically alleviate her painful feelings; she felt that others were intentionally withholding these supplies from her. While some empathic comment would lead the patient to feel temporarily soothed, this was soon experienced as not enough. Attempts were of course made to interpret her fantasy that the therapist, like a magical mother-protector, could change her, change her world or in some concrete way give her the skills to cope with things. These interpretations were essentially ignored. Much later in the treatment, when changes had occurred in the patient, such interventions began to have some effect.

METAPSYCHOLOGICAL OVERVIEW

Based on the material just presented, as well as five years of material that followed, a reasonably complete picture of the structural and dynamic aspects of the patient could be constructed. Symptoms and character traits can be specified that developed to compensate for deficiencies and weaknesses in the patient's psychic structure and functioning.

The patient clearly presented both the presumptive and meta-psychological criteria considered by Kernberg to be definitional of borderline personality organization: there were many nonspecific manifestations of ego weakness, such as low tolerance for anxiety as reflected in her panic reaction in the face of potential future problems, however minor. The anxiety to which the ego was most vulnerable was objective, not superego anxiety. Her ego would be overwhelmed by the sense of danger associated with her anticipation that vital objects on whom she excessively relied would suddenly abandon her, leaving her utterly helpless to meet even the simplest environmental demands. Her low tolerance for anxiety would lead her to feel that she desperately needed the therapist as an idealized friend to help her. She spent large portions of her day attempting to steer clear of any incidents that might provoke feelings of helplessness or rage in an effort to avoid the anxiety and panic which inevitably followed. She followed a narrow, rigid routine in which shopping for her food was the only activity of the day. She presented often a virtually uncontrollable need to return to bed and to sleep to quiet her anxiety.

She presented lack of impulse control in her frequent eruption of rage. In addition, during crises she would eat impulsively, steal food from roommates, "shove food into my mouth with my hands, no silverware, as fast as I could." When she felt angry at being, in her view, unappreciated or put upon, she would throw things around her room and on occasion smash a window. The most common expression of her lack of impulse control was the urgency and immediacy with which needs had to be fulfilled. One minor expression of this was her need to interrupt therapy sessions to go urinate. It became clear over the course of treatment that this was not a neurotic expression of an unconscious fantasy or identification, but rather a reflection of her ego weakness.

Although the patient was clearly of superior intelligence and was talented as a writer, she was able to gain no real satisfaction from the use of her skills. Most activities had as their purpose to prove time and again her worth to justify to herself that she should be allowed to live. In short, her few activities not directly concerned with obtaining food, shelter, and emotional support, such as writing and drawing, were not truly sublimations but rather were concerned with shoring up her basic narcissistic weakness. Virtually all her time and energy was devoted to feeding herself, comparing herself (usually unfavorably) with idealized others, ruminating about her future, and feeling enraged that reality made any demands on her at all. She thought often of suicide.

The patient presented both on psychological testing and in the treatment the shift toward primary process thinking described by Rapaport, Gill, and Schafer (1968) and Kernberg (1975). These regressions in her thinking processes were connected with her narcissistic pathology. In response to her two basic fears, abandonment and helplessness, she felt as if everyone with whom she had contact behaved in response to her. From a slightly different vantage point, we may say that her object relations were in large part need-satisfying. People existed to gratify or frustrate her and were therefore always involved with her. This basic need to have an object involved only with her, existing only for her, promoted a significant distortion of thinking: the basic source or "cause" of events in her world was always considered to be herself. Capacities to test reality and to think logically were obliterated by this basic ego-distorting need.

She presented the specific defensive operations characteristic of borderline personality organization. Both in her attitudes toward her therapist and toward herself in the sample session presented above, the ease with which the patient fled a true ambivalence by splitting was clear. When the therapist failed to know without being told how the patient felt, he was viewed as worthless and persecuting. When he happened on a depiction of the patient's feeling that seemed to fit with her experience, he was experienced as omniscient and all-caring. The splitting was also apparent in her attitude toward herself as a writer. She would feel that she had it in her to be a truly great writer, but after writing one sentence, she would be overcome with self-loathing and would feel she was entirely without capacity in this area. This tendency to avoid intense anxiety by splitting images of self and objects reflects the ego's deficient capacity to integrate images built up under the influence of aggressive drive derivatives and those built up under libidinal ones. We can see in the patient's early history that her own constitutional proclivities and the mother's behavior colluded to prevent a gradual disillusionment of the mother's omnipotence and gradual frustration of needs by the mother. There was little opportunity it seems for bringing the aggressive and libidinal strivings toward the mother together to form a true ambivalence. This course of development did not permit the maturation of object images and elaboration of the ego resources necessary to handle opposing strivings. Her ego obviously handled her aggressive drives poorly. Little repression could be found. Projection and turning against the self were the dominant defenses associated with aggressive drives. Projection was also seen in connection with sexual drives, though phallic-oedipal strivings were minimal in this patient. A common reaction seen in her illustrates projection of both libidinal and aggressive drives. If she saw a man looking at her, she often felt he was lusting after her, which she consciously experienced not as pleasant but as attacking. While she was aware of her anger at the man, she was much more concerned with her conviction that he was angrily attacking and degrading her. She also projected her own anal arrogance onto others, seeing them as putting her down, mocking her, viewing her as a worm. As noted by Kernberg (1975), this projection has as its essential aim the externalizing of the all-bad self- and object-images and includes a weakening of self-boundaries in a particular area of projection of aggression. The patient became confused at moments of intense rage: she didn't know who the real object of her anger was or whose rage she was experiencing. She would say, "I'm so angry, and I don't know where it's coming from. Is he making me angry or am I angry? Who is making all this rage happen?"

The pathology of internalized object representations is considered by Jacobson (1964), Kernberg (1966), and Klein (1948) to be the most basic pathological feature in the borderline personality. In this patient, objects and the self were experienced pathologically due to splitting, projection, and idealization. In the session reported above, the therapist was experienced as a potentially omnipotent and omniscient object who, in witholding his power, was persecuting. In order to protect herself from a basic sense of helplessness associated with separation from a "powerful" figure, she would desperately seek to establish a self-image or an object-image so powerful that no possible danger could occur. Images of self and objects were infiltrated with pregenital aggression. When an important object frustrated some need, she both projected her rage onto the object and turned it on herself, feeling, for example, that "the bus driver was torturing me when he forgot to stop at my stop, but then I am so fat and worthless anyone would see that I deserve to be treated like this." There were often simultaneously strong wishes to assault others and urges to attack herself by smashing windows or killing herself.

With this overview, we are in a position to examine specifically some of the patient's structural deficiencies and the character traits that developed to function in their stead.

Although this case, as with any, could be approached from many vantage points, this presentation will now consider the patient in terms of pathological structures that devolved from three core complexes: deficiencies of primary and secondary narcissism, fear of helplessness and panic at separation, and the poorly developed channels for regulating and sublimating strong pregenital libidinal and aggressive drives. Many characterological formations presented by the patient can be seen as primitive, pathological developments arising from these three sources. Many authors, most notably Kernberg, have very thoroughly and carefully described the ego and object relations deficits. Yet, defensive pathology, the process by which characterological, symptomatic, and ego attitudinal distortions then arise from these deficits has been relatively less well explored. Boyer's recent article (1977) is a notable exception.

DEFICITS IN PRIMARY AND SECONDARY NARCISSISM AND PRIMITIVE SELF-CONFIRMING CHARACTER TRAITS

There are many indications of a deficit in primary narcissism in this patient. She regularly presented morbid fears that she had cancer and that her insides were rotten and diseased. For example, during one phase early in treatment, she was preoccupied with the feeling that all she was was a "bag full of guts." She manifested the severe pessimism concerning her body (among other areas) indicative of primary narcissistic defects. Any pain or minor injury was immediately followed by conviction that the little she had going for her was now gone. She was often concerned that people would see her body as peculiar. She thought, for example, that her hips were grotesquely large and felt herself to be obese. A conscious or preconscious fear that often emerged was that her body was not under her control. This fear was intimately connected with her fear of her impulses—that she would become so voracious that she would eat forever and become tremendous.

Another expression of the primary narcissistic difficulties could be seen in her deficient cathexis of her own basic ego functioning. She was continually plagued by serious doubts about her capacity to carry out such simple life tasks as buying her groceries, paying her rent, and doing her laundry. She became tremendously anxious that these tasks would be beyond her capacity. At one point she was almost in a frenzy that she would not be able to muster the energy to put on her coat or put one foot in front of the other to walk. It was clear that her ego failed to integrate past successful efforts. If she had yesterday gone to the store to buy groceries, she felt no less doubt about her capacity to accomplish the same task today.

Another expression of deficient self-cathexis was seen in her fear of being mundane. To be ordinary led her to fear that she would be indistinguishable from others. She responded to so-called "supportive interventions," by which it was suggested to her that her experience was natural or universal or similar to someone else's, with rage and fear that the fragile distinction between self and other was implicitly challenged. The patient, for example, had an image of the masses, of women usually characterized as waitresses, maids, or harried housewives—faceless, mindless automatons. She had trouble holding any job because in a job she would suddenly see herself as such a person and would feel drab, grow suicidal, and then quit. To be ordinary, in a profound sense, was for her to be nobody.

Probably the most pathological expression of this primary narcissistic deficit appeared in her interpretation of others' reactions to her. When, after prolonged and reasonably friendly contact with someone, he expressed annoyance at something the patient did, she would feel the hostility was the only real feeling the other person ever had toward her. She would feel the hostility to be the true, basic feeling the other person had toward her, viewing all that preceded it as covering up this true attitude. The experience of objects, of course, arose not only from her narcissistic defects. She also projected her pregenital aggression and her experience of objects as withdrawing from her with hostility when they failed to gratify perfectly and completely.

Many aspects of this patient's character can be seen oriented toward establishing by highly magical means self-definition and self-coherence. These pathological ego-characterological processes can be seen as developing as compensations for deficiencies in the patient's primary narcissism.

In place of a reliable and enduring sense of "owning" her body and being able to rely on it, the patient constantly sought to control any changes in it. She became preoccupied with her weight and her appearance for extended periods of time. Though only ten pounds overweight, she experienced herself as obese. She would refuse to wear a bathing suit, imagining people would think her as fat, ugly, and gluttonous as she herself did. She felt she was doomed to gain weight, gradually, but uncontrollably. She felt that by overeating she had ruined her body permanently.

She joined a dieting group which involved weekly "weigh-ins," group support for weight loss, mild censure for weight gain, and guidance in following a very specific (though not severe) diet. When she began to lose weight, it meant for her more than being pleased with her appearance—it seemed to give her a sense of control over the workings of her body. When she gained even a pound, she would microscopically scrutinize her eating behavior to discover where she had departed from the diet. She expected total and perfectly direct correspondence between what she ate and the amount of weight she would lose or gain, and would often grow extremely frustrated if she could not explain the cause for even a slight weight gain. She would jump from considering it as a result of some minor transgression of the diet to thinking something was wrong with her constitution, to saying she was somehow not meant to lose weight because she was a "failure." She was convinced that if she could only work her way down to fifteen pounds underweight she would never have to worry about anyone calling attention to her fat. Then she would feel completely comfortable walking down the street, for she would be a perfect thing of beauty and be admired for her capacity to control herself.

Perfect control of gains and losses in her weight constituted for her a compensation for her feeling of alienation from her body. Since the "ownership" of the body was not consolidated, it was necessary for her to find some way of *changing* her body. The unconscious idea was, "If I can change my body, it must be my creation and thus it must definitely be mine." The control of weight is reminiscent of the infant's attempts from three to eighteen months to exert control over what he is coming to recognize as part of himself. The poor consolidation of cathexis of the body was also evident in the patient's typical near-panic upon having an unexpected body sensation, such as fever or muscular soreness, or an unexpected feeling state. At these moments she needed to find some clear and direct "cause" for the feeling or body sensation, just as she sought to discover the "cause" for slight weight gains.

She sought to experience her body, and through it herself, as a benign, reliable part of her by seeking to completely control or regulate any change in it. If she could control her weight to the pound or at least in retrospect know what had caused some unexpected change, she felt that much more the master of herself and that much less disorganized and chaotic. She was capable of spending most of her waking time ruminating about the changes in her weight, assessing the impact of this doughnut or that tomato, weighing herself as many as six times a day. As will be seen later, this preoccupation had simultaneously two other aspects: an ego effort to regulate drives experienced as dangerous and a primitive type of superego pressure.

Another primitive self-confirming ego-characterological trait involved her use of possessions and rigid stereotyped images of herself and a preoccupation with ideal self-images. She would think about what kind of person she was and would review her traits, habits, and other people's impressions of her. She would wonder if she was a potential artist, singer, or writer, and would review her accomplishments in these areas, refer-ring back compulsively to her monolithic ideal of being a great writer or artist. Then she would degrade and judge herself. Her attentional pro-cesses at these times were narrowed and directed. The function of this ruminative self-judgmental process was in part to create a sense of self, consolidating everything under the auspices of self-feeling. Experientially this showed itself in an attempt to force all of her traits into a single, often narrow, rigid "label" of the self, e.g., self as writer, singer, mental patient.

She sought to define herself via aspects objectively very peripheral to herself. Clothing, possessions, physical appearance, and status symbols were for her of paramount personal importance. She would become very concerned with her "image," her clothing, and what "type" of person she seemed to be on the basis of her status as a student, playwright, etc. Credentials were also of tremendous importance. A student I.D. card, a degree, a driver's license, all of which she obtained during treatment, each gave her a sense, albeit transient, of self through which she sought to be unique, to distinguish herself from others. She felt she could never really be known as an individual and that she had to settle for the least noxious stereotype. Her posessions and credentials were basic to the effort at definition, though each was quickly assimilated and new trappings became necessary to fuel her quest for definition.

The emphasis on stereotypes reflects another basic feature of the patient's struggle to consolidate an enduring image of herself and others. In the face of great fluidity in self- and object-images, there is a reification of roles and an attempt to limit images of self and objects to a single dimension. She would define someone as a "drama person," herself as a "writer," the therapist as "therapist." To consider multiple functions of an object led to a feeling of confusion and a sense that internal definitions of self and object were dissolving.

This feature of the patient's sense of herself illustrates well a form of altered ego development described by Brodey (1965). Brodey spelled out the consequences for the child's ego development if a mother experiences the child only in strict accord with her own fixed, often monolithic images of the child:

> Only those aspects of the child's inner environment congruent with his mother's cathected hallucination will be organized into his percepts and refined into culturally ordered ways of expression. . . . The energies of the existent child irrelevant to the experience acknowledged by the mother as the *Umwelt* of the child are not organized with parental relationship. They remain random, unorganized, and split off from the pseudo personality, which is structured to match either negatively or positively the parents' projection. . . . His instinctual energies are not patterned by acknowledging experience into sublimated skills and objective learning (Hartmann, 1939). One part of his energy is used to keep reasonable the *Umwelt* he knows. The remainder is untouched by ego work: it is a vague, intense fear, a sense of inner wildness, which is used to fortify the need to hold onto the defenses. . . . (p. 186)

The importance to patients such as this of monolithic, reified stereotypes of self and other creates a vicious cycle. The concrete definition of self and others serves to organize what would otherwise be chaotic impressions of self and object. Yet the effects of such typing leads people to be experienced as types, and consequently to be regularly prejudged and misunderstood. In addition, there grows again a sense that there is nothing truly unique or distinctive about the self. This, in turn, results again in a sense of anonymity and drabness, and a renewed search for a new, usually exalted defining activity or role.

Throughout the early work with this patient, the attempts to make herself over, to go on campaigns to improve herself or change herself were regular occurrences. She recognized that she had a need regularly to change herself especially into a dramatic, impressive person everyone would admire. Often just following an unexpected weight gain, a minor illness, or a period of concern with death or failure, she would set out to become something new—an engineer at one point, a painter at another, a radio announcer at yet another. She was a very bright and quite creative woman and could manage to achieve some initial success in these areas. Unfortunately, the sense of achievement failed to endure. She regularly felt herself quickly taking new accomplishments for granted. Though to some small extent they enriched her sense of self, they failed ultimately to build a sense of her own separateness and uniqueness from others. More fundamentally, "to be" involved a continuous, driven quest to change and "become." Like figure set off against ground, the process of becoming something new would give her a sense of separateness. As soon as one hurdle had been surmounted, another would suddenly emerge, and she would again become preoccupied with fears that she would not succeed, that failure was death; she thought she might just as well actually kill herself. *Most important, the struggle itself seemed to have a self-defining function.* Thus understanding the role of "becoming" for her helped explain the place of creativity. To write fiction or poetry, which felt to her to be consuming activities, made her feel she knew who she was. In the act of painting or writing, she felt she was creating *herself* anew. Finding something unique to write, from within herself, was to make herself unique, to feel herself continuously in the process of change—to be observable and definable to herself. In sum, her sense of self stood out more clearly, as if in relief, only when she was in dramatic transition and change.

FEAR OF HELPLESSNESS AND ITS CONSEQUENCES

A second central issue involved the patient's virtually continuous fear of helplessness. While this experience was connected with her feeling that her own ego operations were not reliable, it also was composed of feelings that the external world and the people in it were unpredictable and dangerous. When she met someone in the street she did not get along with or did not want to see, she would feel she was being attacked by the world and was in some kind of danger. When she would hear music played in an adjacent apartment, she looked extremely angry, but it emerged that she was basically frightened that if she could not control her world in an absolute fashion, it would be in no way reliable and she would be in terrible danger. Her typical response to such events was to be very angry at herself for not controlling things better. What could regularly be inferred from her reactions was a fantasy of herself that she could potentially control everything omnipotently and be safe. Though this fantasy was irrational, it was for all intents and purposes preconscious, not unconscious.

The effort to exert this type of control shows itself indirectly in two character traits: narcissistic cognition and narcissistic rage. These are both seen in the relationship with the therapist in the session described earlier. This pattern was by no means limited to the treatment situation. In a desperate effort to feel the therapist to be in a magically empathic tie with her, a tie that countered her feelings of helplessness in the face of the demands of her world, she assumed (again a preconscious, not unconscious, attitude) that he could know what her main concerns were on any particular day. She assumed too that any lapse in his presumed sensitivity to her had to do with his reaction to her. In fact it emerged that her view of others as existing only for her and only in response to her would intensify when she began to feel that the external world was not in her control. Her feeling that the external world was dangerous would be increased by hearing of an unexpected death, injury, or illness. This would lead her to come into the session in a terrible rage saying, "It is all so unpredictable, why is the world like that? It must be rotten, nothing but rotten if something like that happens." The external world was experienced as perfectly and completely under her control or hopelessly outside it. Her fear of helplessness was such an ever-present concern that any indication that something important was not under her control would lead her to panic and then rage. Another example: if she felt that something unexpected and frightening had happened, she would enter my office, sit for a moment in silence, and then yell, "Why do you sit there, tell me what I need to talk about. I know, so you should know. Tell me!" Exploring this pattern over a period of time revealed that she had a powerful need to have the therapist under her control, for this gave her a sense that the external world was more manageable. It emerged that she felt that if she shouted or threw things, this would literally force the world to do as she demanded.

Both the patient's feelings of being overwhelmed by the environment and her compensatory need to feel in absolute control of it had led her ego to develop a particular mode of thinking. Her thinking was very rigid, linear, concrete, tending to consider many things in all-or-nothing terms. She was singularly incapable of seeing anything in her world as the result of multiple factors. Analyzing this mode of thinking revealed time and again the patient's unconscious fantasy that there was some ultimate cause for events and that in knowing these causes she would in a very basic sense be safe.

To illustrate, Miss L would muse on how people became professionals such as doctors and lawyers. Her conviction was that there was a single force that was the key to their success, such as having the right schooling. If things went badly between people (not necessarily including her), she would think in terms of an error, a *faux pas*, having been made from which all the subsequent difficulties ensued. This pattern of thinking was not just invoked defensively but colored virtually all of her intellectual and synthetic processes. The search for primary causes did not necessarily involve feeling that forces outside the source of power were directed at the self; the self too was often considered the single source of such power. If, in interacting with someone, the other would grow upset, angry, or sad, the patient would often assume that she was the cause. The possibility that there might be other events or people that were brought to mind in the object was difficult for her to consider.

The concern with ultimate causes reflects the degree to which the random events of the world were seen as motivated and directed by someone. There was a subtle animistic view of events that suggested the operation of some controlling force. There was no conscious delusion of power sources, rather the patient affectively responded in accord with an unconscious fantasy of a world under supreme control. It expressed at the same time a fantasy of a watchful, perfectly responsive, empathic, and omnipresent mother only partially distinguished from the self.

The assumption of relatedness of everything to everything else, again not a delusion as in the delusional paranoid, but subtly woven into the fabric of her thought, expressed a wish for connection and union. To develop thinking processes that easily included a concept of independence and randomness of events brought with it for her a greater possibility of feeling helpless and alone. This mode of thinking is molded around a desperately needed fantasy that no one is ever alone and out of reach. Brodey (1965), again through his observations of schizophrenic families, has shed some light on this sort of thinking style. He observed in these families a "hyperrealism which, if unbounded, encompasses a world unmodified by fantasy or humor or awareness of multiple points of view."

This narcissistic mode of cognition arose too from the patient's struggle with her projected aggression, deficient ego resources, and primitive severe superego to which we turn shortly.

In working with this patient over a period of time, it became very clear to me that her need to have the world in absolute control (and her rage at it or herself when she could not) derived most basically from a need to be in the perfect, binding embrace of an omnipotent mother. Viewed slightly differently, it represented an attempt to have the world (mother) be an extension of the self, to be one with it. Characteristic of the borderline and in distinction to the psychotic, the patient longed for this merger but forever felt rageful that it could not be completely achieved. In short, she sought to see everything in her world as occurring in some necessary relation to her. This world view was intended to avoid the separation panic aroused in her when she recognized that she and others existed as independent people.

While this stance brought some security for the patient, making her feel her mother was with her, it also brought tremendous guilt, for she felt whenever something she was even marginally connected with went badly that she deserved to be criticized or punished. To illustrate: when a woman she was working with was one day brusque and out of sorts, the patient immediately concluded that an innocuous disagreement that had occurred between them a week before was responsible for the woman's mood. The patient felt intense self-hatred (she rarely experienced modulated guilt) and felt that the woman's brusqueness was the punishment she deserved for her "argument" with the woman. Though on this occasion, as on others, the patient later learned that there had been other events to which the other person was much more likely responding, she nevertheless repeatedly felt that she alone had caused the reaction.

ARREST OF DRIVE DEVELOPMENT, LACK OF EGO CAPACITY TO SUBLIMATE, AND PRIMITIVE COMPENSATIONS

Essential to this patient's underlying personality organization was the arrest of most of her drive development at the oral and early anal phases, and a paucity of sublimations. The arrested drive development was apparent in many ways. Eating, the timing of meals, and the conditions of her meals were all terribly important to her. Her relationships with others were also characterized by a directly oral, demanding, hungry quality. Her predominant affect was intense, oral envy, a wish to have as part of herself the traits and characteristics of others. She described feelings of ecstasy when she "swallowed" the beauty of the world around her and felt it was "inside." Conversely, she experienced disgust at being near repulsive things, for seeing them was felt as if she were eating them, making her feel nauseous, as if she wanted to spit them out. She considered herself greedy, selfish, and hungry, and felt that others saw this and hated her for it. To have pleasure was associated with eating up and destroying the object of her pleasure. Following an ecstatic experience of seeing trees in bloom, she had the fantasy that she had somehow killed them and that they were enraged at her; following virtually any intense pleasure, intense self-hate would follow. This self-hate would often be accompanied by feeling "like there are razor blades in my stomach tearing at the sides." It became very clear that this was an expression of an unconscious fantasy that the world was equivalent to food and that enjoying it was equivalent to attacking and murdering it. The razor blades were the retaliation by the world for being devoured.

It is apparent here too that her aggressive and libidinal drives were very poorly differentiated. To have pleasure was inextricably bound up with destroying and being punished. She unconsciously imagined that the punishment would be that she herself would be devoured. Expressions of this included very vivid fantasies that "storm clouds are gathering and will engulf me"; "I feel today that something is out to get me, to kill me"; "I look at the street and it's dull and depressing and suddenly I feel it is swallowing me up." Once, while sitting in front of a cake, she joked that it was teasing her, that it was saying, "Come and eat me and you'll get fat and be sorry." On another occasion she said that when she enjoyed food she had eaten she felt as if it was "coming up to meet me." A general expression of this unconscious fantasy was a pervasive, subtle animism in her outlook. If things went well, the "world" had punished her enough for the time being and would spare her the greater retaliation of disease or death. The oral impulse directed outward and inward toward the self (which constituted a superego precursor, but by no means a coherent superego) would regularly overwhelm the ego, leading the patient to withdraw into her home to follow a rigidly prescribed routine and to avoid any possibility of pleasure.

In this area, just as in those discussed above, pathological compensations could be seen to have developed. The patient's stance toward food and weight reflected primitive compensations for the defective ego and superego processes. Her concern with weight constituted a way of trying to focus and thereby overcome her feeling of her own murderous voraciousness. She experienced her weight gains or losses very concretely as expressions of wild voraciousness or control of her hunger. Her weight had become a register of her greediness. To lose weight was felt to be a certain proof that she had, at least for the moment, curbed her oral drives. Controlling her weight seemed to her more possible than being able to control her oral, cannibalistic impulses.

The patient would also invoke her fear of being obese, ugly, and repulsive in order to control these drives. Thus her concern with weight reflected both her concern with the primitive and unmodulated character of her impulses and the limited ego resources available to transform and modify these drives. Surveillance of her weight was an effort at control from the periphery, and the narcissistic preoccupation with how she looked seemed to a significant degree to help the patient control her sometimes desperate oral impulses.

When we look at this function of weight, we can discern some significant ego distortions. She presented a pseudo-logical thinking process that concluded that eating led *directly* to weight gain or loss. There was also a fixed idea that fat people without exception are globally greedy and selfish. The meaning of weight for Miss L also reflected a concretistic aspect of her thinking. The weight was seen as a tangible "thing" to prove to an imagined critic (externalization of primitive self-critical attitudes) that impulses had been effectively tamed. This substituted for an ego capacity to modulate the expression of impulses and for a superego capacity to guide benevolently.

REFERENCES

Boyer, L. B. (1977). Working with a borderline patient. *Psychoanalytic Quarterly* 46:386–424.

Brodey, W. (1965). On the dynamics of narcissism. *Psychoanalytic Study of the Child* 20:165–193.

Eisnitz, A. (1974). On the metapsychology of narcissistic pathology. *Journal of the American Psychoanalytic Association* 22:279–291.

Fairbairn, W.R.D. (1952). *An Object Relations Theory of the Personality*. New York: Basic Books.

Fraiberg, S. (1969). Libidinal object constancy and mental representation. *Psychoanalytic Study of the Child* 24:9–47.

Freud, A. (1963). The concept of developmental lines. *Psychoanalytic Study of the Child* 18:245–265.

——— (1965). *Normality and Pathology of Development in Childhood*. New York: International Universities Press.

Freud, S. (1911). Psychoanalytic notes on an autobiographical account of a case of paranoia (dementia paranoides). *Standard Edition* 12:3–82.

Goldberg, A. (1974). On the prognosis and treatment of narcissism. *Journal of the American Psychoanalytic Association* 22:243–254.

Greenacre, P. (1953a). Certain relationships between fetishism and faulty development of the body image. *Psychoanalytic Study of the Child* 8:65–78.

——— (1953b). *Trauma, Growth and Personality*. London: Hogarth Press.

Hartmann, H. (1939). *Ego Psychology and the Problem of Adaptation*. New York: International Universities Press.

Jacobson, E. (1964). *The Self and the Object World*. New York: International Universities Press.

Kernberg, O. (1966). Structural derivatives of object relationship. *International Journal of Psycho-Analysis* 47:236–253.

——— (1967). Borderline personality organization. *Journal of the American Psychoanalytic Association* 15:641–685.

——— (1970). Factors in the psychoanalytic treatment of narcissistic personalities. *Journal of the American Psychoanalytic Association* 18: 51–85.

——— (1974). Contrasting viewpoints regarding the nature and psychoanalytic treatment of narcissistic personalities: a preliminary communication. *Journal of the American Psychoanalytic Association* 22:255–266.

——— (1975). *Borderline Conditions and Pathological Narcissism.* New York: Jason Aronson.

Klein, M. (1948). *Contributions to Psychoanalysis.* London: Hogarth Press.

Knight, R. (1954). Borderline states. In *Psychoanalytic Psychiatry and Psychology,* eds. R. Knight and C. Friedman, pp. 52–64. New York: International Universities Press.

Kohut, H. (1971). *Analysis of the Self.* New York: International Universities Press.

Krohn, A. (1974). Borderline "empathy" and differentiation of object representations: a contribution to the psychology of object relations. *International Journal of Psychoanalytic Psychotherapy* 3:142–165.

Mahler, M. (1968). *On Human Symbiosis and the Viscissitudes of Individuation. Volume I. Infantile Psychosis.* New York: International Universities Press.

Masterson, J.F. (1976). *The Psychotherapy of the Borderline Adult.* New York: Brunner-Mazel.

Nagera, H. (1963). The developmental profile: notes on some practical considerations regarding its use. *Psychoanalytic Study of the Child* 18:511–540.

Rapaport, D., Gill, M., and Schafer, R. (1968). *Diagnostic Psychological Testing,* rev. ed., ed. R.R. Holt. New York: International Universities Press.

Rinsley, D.B. (1977). An object relations view of borderline personality. In *Borderline Disorders: The Concept, the Syndrome, the Patient,* ed. P. Hartocollis. New York: International Universities Press.

Spruiell, V. (1974). Theories of the treatment of narcissistic personalities. *Journal of the American Psychoanalytic Association* 22:268–278.

Tausk, V. (1933). On the origin of the "influencing machine" in schizophrenia. Trans. Dorien Feifenbaum. *Psychoanalytic Quarterly* 2:519–556.

Some Comments on the Treatment of the Borderline Personality

THOMAS A. PETTY, M. D.

A discussion of "Some Clinical Manifestations of Structural Defects in a Borderline Personality," by Alan Krohn, M. D. Because the borderline patient presents the gamut of symptomatology and therapeutic responses, diagnosis and treatment have been problems since the beginning of psychoanalysis. With her key conceptualization of the "as if" personality, Helene Deutsch, in the 1930s (1942), stimulated the clarification of both the diagnostic and therapeutic problems. The primitive ego defenses were delineated by Klein (1946), and Mahler's studies (1968) of symbiosis, separation, and individuation provided the developmental framework for the growing understanding of these conditions. Since then, many have contributed, none more than Kernberg (1975). He has proposed limiting the term *borderline* to a relatively specific, more or less stable personality with typical symptom constellations, defensive operations, pathology of internal object relations, and instinctual vicissitudes. These conditions dictate a modification of therapeutic technique practiced by many but formulated by Kernberg, Masterson (1972, 1976), Boyer (1977), and others. Essential to the implementation of this modified technique is the understanding of the defensive operations and the pathology of the internal object relations. Particular emphasis is given to two defensive operations, splitting and projective identification, and to aspects of the other concepts especially pertinent to the therapy of the borderline. The work of Kernberg has been drawn on extensively.

Understanding symptomatology within the framework of psycho-analytic concepts affords an effective basis for the treatment of the borderline personality organization (Boyer and Giovacchini 1967, Boyer 1977, Frosch 1971, Giovacchini 1972, Kohut 1971, Kernberg 1975, Knight 1953 a, b, Masterson 1972, 1976). Dr. Krohn has presented an insightful, in-depth study of the psychopathology of a case of borderline personality organization. For the time being, he has opted to defer comment on the course of treatment and the changes that took place during the five-year period of intensive psychoanalytic therapy. Thus, he has provided an opportunity to consider some of the implications of treating such patients.

Because the BPO may present symptoms from either the neurotic or the psychotic end of the symptom spectrum, or from both, the patient usually has been diagnosed neurotic, depressive, schizophrenic, borderline, borderline psychotic, or psychotic and treated accordingly before referral to the analytic therapist. Thus a very careful evaluation over an extended period of time may be required for the diagnosis to be established. The previous diagnosis and treatment frequently complicate the psychoanalytic therapy to follow. By the time the diagnosis has been settled, treatment may already have progressed for weeks or months and supportive and/or analytic techniques may have been tried.

It is advantageous to both the patient and the analytic therapist if he has been able to maintain a flexible, expectant attitude and has not prematurely committed the treatment to a particular technique. In his presentation, Dr. Krohn indicates that he used both supportive and analytic techniques, with the latter becoming the modus operandi. It is worth emphasizing: The therapist does well by the patient to accept such an unfolding of diagnosis and treatment. Dr. Krohn's patient came to him two months after being released from the hospital. She had been hospitalized for one year following a "serious attempt to kill herself with sleeping pills." Presumably he arrived at his diagnosis and treatment technique only after working with her for a while.

To be effective, "supportive psychotherapy," the popular psychotherapy for "borderline cases," requires utmost skill and a thorough knowledge of the genetic dynamics of the patient. Otherwise, what is being "supported" may run counter to the therapist's intention. The supportive technique ostensibly supports the defenses and tries to avoid primitive transferences and the emergence of the transference psychosis, while promoting the practical working relationship with the therapist and the reality adjustment of the patient. This approach emphasizes intensifying but not interpreting the positive transference and disregarding or suppressing the negative transference. Either can bring the treatment to a premature end.

Kernberg (1975) has warned that the supportive technique can fail because the predominant defenses of the patient might interfere with building up a working relationship or "therapeutic alliance"; the negative transference might mobilize even further the pathological defenses, and the outcome might be acting out outside of treatment and emotional shallowness within it. The final result might be a therapeutic stalemate.

An additional warning: because supportive therapy is not psychoanalysis or psychoanalytic therapy does not mean that the therapist can forget or disregard the peculiarities of ego functions, especially the defensive operations, negative transference, and the genetic-dynamic orientation, or get by indefinitely with serving up Pablum, i. e., constant soothing and encouraging comments and interpretations. To be most effective, supportive therapy should blend or, even better, fade into psychoanalytic therapy up to the patient's capacity to tolerate it. This is an exciting subject that cannot be pursued here.

Currently, a modified psychoanalytic procedure is the treatment of choice for most BPO patients. Because these patients do not tolerate well the regression associated with psychoanalysis—they tend to act out their instinctual conflicts, use the transference to gratify their pathological needs, and develop transference psychoses—a modified technique is employed. Modifications of technique have in fact always been practiced by the effective analytic therapist with such patients, but this is acknowledged only with utmost discretion lest the therapist be stigmatized among colleagues for "nonanalytic practices."

Kernberg's proposal (1975) for a modification in psychoanalytic procedure in treating the BPO has become a generally accepted model. It consists of the following:

1) Systematic elaboration of the negative transference only in the "Here and now," without attempting to achieve full genetic reconstructions; 2) interpretation of the defensive constellations of these patients as they enter the negative transference; 3) limit-setting in order to block acting-out of the transference, with as much structuring of the patient's life outside the hours as necessary to protect the neutrality of the analyst; 4) noninterpretation of the less primitively-determined, modulated aspects of the positive transference to foster the gradual development of the therapeutic alliance; 5) formulation of interpretations so that the patient's distortions of the analyst's interventions and of present reality (especially of his perceptions in the hour) can be systematically clarified; 6) working through first the highly distorted transference (at times of an almost psychotic nature) reflecting fantastic internal object relationships related to early ego disturbances, in order to reach later the transference related to real childhood experiences of these patients. (p. 185)

Boyer (1977), with minor differences, concurs. He interprets the defenses as they are seen in positive and negative transference rather than limiting the interpretations to the defenses entering the *negative* transference. He considers "the understanding and pertinent interpretation of the unfolding transference to be of the utmost importance." He has "come to contemplate each interview as though it might have been a dream and material from recent interviews as part of the day residue" (p. 389). I have found this technique helpful especially with inarticulate patients. My own articulation of what I knew transpired and sometimes guessed (admitting this to the patient) served as a model and as encouragement to the patient to articulate.

The differences between Boyer and Kernberg may be more apparent than real. For Kernberg, the recognition that BPO patients are prone to employ splitting to dissociate negative and positive transferences underscores the importance of undoing the artificial separation. He points out that the positive aspects of the transference have to be highlighted along with ventilation of the negative aspects. Thus the difference seems to be one of degree or emphasis.

Essential to the effective application of the modified psychoanalytic procedure is the understanding of two of the basic defense operations of the BPO, i. e., splitting and projective identification.

Splitting is defined in a limited sense "as the active process of keeping apart identification systems of opposite quality" (Kernberg 1975, p. 69). It is a primitive dissociation which takes place at the basic level of ego function and becomes the crucial mechanism for the ego's defensive organization. Freud (1938) first used the term in referring to splitting of the ego in the creation of a fetish as a defense against the castration threat. Klein (1946) and her followers used the term to designate an active process by which the primitive ego dispersed destructive tendencies. Following Klein (1946) and Fairbairn (1952), Masterson (1976), in addition to using the term as Kernberg (1975) does, adds: "the ego is itself split into two parts, one of which functions according to the pleasure principle, the other according to the reality principle" (p. 57). While Kernberg's limiting definition simplifies the use of the concept with some borderline patients, with others the broader definitions are more applicable.

The concepts of projective identification and introjective identification are potentially confusing and difficult to understand. Kernberg (1975) has clarified Klein's definition (1946) and enhanced the clinical usefulness of the concepts by including the term *empathy* to describe the relationship to the real object as a result of the primitive projection. Kernberg's instructive discussion deserves emphasis and extensive citation here. He says:

> Projective identification is a primitive form of projection, mainly called upon to externalize aggressive self- and object-images; "empathy" is maintained with the real objects onto which the projection has occurred, and is linked with an effort to control the object now feared because of this projection. . . .
> In the transference this is typically manifest as intense distrust and

fear of the therapist, who is experienced as attacking the patient, while the patient himself feels empathy with that projected intense aggression and tries to control the therapist in a sadistic, overpowering way. The patient may be partially aware of his own hostility but feels that he is . . . justified in being angry and aggressive. It is as if the patient's life depended on his keeping the therapist under control. The patient's aggressive behavior, at the same time, tends to provoke from the therapist counteraggressive feelings and attitudes. It is as if the patient were pushing the aggressive part of his self onto the therapist and as if the countertransference represented the emergence of this part of the patient from within the therapist. . . .

It has to be stressed that what is projected in a very inefficient and self-defeating way is not "pure aggression," but a self-representation or an object-representation linked with that drive derivative. Primitive self- and primitive object-representations are actually linked together as basic units of primitive object relationships . . . , and what appears characteristic of borderline patients is that there is a rapid oscillation between moments of projection of a self-representation while the patient remains identified with the corresponding object representation, and other moments in which it is the object-representation that is projected while the patient identifies with the corresponding self-representation. For example, a primitive, sadistic mother image may be projected onto the therapist while the patient experiences himself as the frightened, attacked, panic-stricken little child; moments later, the patient may experience himself as the stern, prohibitive, moralistic (and extremely sadistic) primitive mother image, while the therapist is seen as the guilty, defensive, frightened but rebellious little child. (Kernberg 1975, pp. 80–81)

Emphasizing splitting and projective identification is not intended to minimize the significance of the other primitive mechanisms of defense, i.e., idealization, denial, and omnipotence. Clinically, the latter appear simultaneously and in the treatment may from moment to moment preempt the attention of the therapist and the interpretive process. The other primitive mechanisms of defense reinforce the effect of the splitting and protect the ego from having to deal with conflicts between love and hate, good and bad, right and wrong, and permit action that would otherwise be impossible. The ego function of integration, however, is sacrificed.

With this background, let us consider some of the therapeutic implications of the persistence of the primitive defenses and the primary level of ego function of which they are a manifestation. While initially allowing psychic development to take place under adverse conditions, they have also compromised healthy development and the integration of the structures of the personality and have predisposed the individual to regression. Once regression has set in, they facilitate it and contribute to the resulting disintegration of structures. In treatment, projective identification contributes to transference regression via the rapid oscillation of projection of self- and object-images that undermines the patient's ego boundaries (Kernberg 1975, p. 83).

The therapeutic alliance (Sterba 1934, Greenacre 1959), a concept that encompasses the more limiting concept of working alliance (Greenson 1965, Greenacre 1959, Zetzel 1956, Dickes 1967), is dependent upon the patient's capacity to develop and tolerate the split between the observing self and the participating self. Developing the therapeutic alliance with the BPO presents the therapist with a special problem: The observing self of the patient may be barely developed or absent. And the necessary split between the participating self and the observing self may promote a regressive disintegration of the self and primitive splitting, which in turn may result in submerging fantasies of a dreadful nature. Further, "to establish a therapeutic alliance with the therapist becomes equal to submission to him as a dangerous, powerful enemy, and this further reduces the capacity for the activation of the observing ego" or self (Kernberg 1975, p. 82). Finding the optimal closeness and distance to the therapist may preoccupy the patient and determine progress.

The observing self and consequently the therapeutic alliance may be enhanced by a consistent interpretation of the manifest and latent negative transference and the projective-introjective cycles which in turn will result in a broadening of the conflict-free ego sphere. Kernberg (1975, p. 81) refers to Strachey's description (1934) of the mutative interpretation by which modification in the superego and a differentiation between the patient's fantasied object and the therapist as a different object are wrought.

Once treatment has been undertaken, transference initially may be warded off vigorously, especially if the patient previously had been in an intensive form of psychotherapy and experienced some of the chaotic potential of transference. When the transference has developed: "Perhaps the most striking characteristic of the transference manifestations of patients with borderline personality organization is the premature activation in the transference of very early conflict-laden object relationships in the context of ego states that are dissociated from each other. It is as if each of these ego states represents a full-fledged transference paradigm, a highly developed, regressive transference reaction within which a specific internalized object relationship is activated in the transference" (Kernberg 1975, p. 77).

The conflicts that emerge are usually condensations of pregenital and genital aims predominantly under the influence of pregenital aggression. However, clear oedipal material under the influence of libidinal surges may appear early in treatment, partly as a defense against regression. Failing to recognize its defensive nature and interpreting the oedipal content may precipitate a severe regression and the emergence of the transference psychosis.

Kernberg (1975) says: "Excessive pregenital, and especially oral, aggression tends to be projected and determines the paranoid distortion of the early parental images, particularly those of the mother. . . . the mother is seen as potentially dangerous, and hatred of the mother extends to a hatred of both parents when later they are experienced as a 'united group' by the child. A 'contamination' of the father image by aggression primarily projected onto mother and lack of differentiation between mother and father tend to produce a combined dangerous father-mother image" (p. 78). When the resulting transference, of the projection of this father-mother image, is displaced onto a spouse or other member of a family, the consequent discord and danger may require the intervention of the therapist.

Transference psychosis (Reider 1957, Romm 1957) or delusional transference (Little 1958) develops when the patient experiences the therapist as identical with the image of the transference object. The therapist may be identified with a parental image or with a split-off self-image via projection. The reaction may be confined within the therapy or may extend into the patient's life at large. In either case, the reaction may be of brief duration or prolonged. It may be indistinguishable from any other psychotic reaction. It is usually a reaction dreaded by both the patient and the therapist. The patient has usually heard stories about people who went insane in treatment and fears the loss of control. The therapist is blamed, and gossip is started even by colleagues who should know better. Searles (1963) has commented on this:

"Transference psychosis" usually connotes a dramatic but dreaded development in which an analysand who at the beginning of analysis was overtly sane but who had in actuality a borderline ego-structure becomes overtly psychotic in the course of the evolving transference-relationship. We generally blame the analyst for such a development and prefer not to think any more about such matters, because of our own personal fear that we, like the poor misbegotten analysand, might become, or did narrowly avoid becoming, psychotic in our own analysis. (pp. 250–251)

Kernberg (1975) attributes to Klein the view that "the transference psychosis represents a condensation of actual experiences, a gross elab-

oration of them in fantasy, and efforts to modify or turn away from them"
(p. 89). Klein's view (1952) constitutes a therapeutic aid. Bearing in mind
these facets facilitates the therapist's interpretation of the transference
psychosis and helps him deal with it.

While it is true that, in contrast to the psychotic patient, the capacity to
test reality is preserved in the BPO (Frosch 1960, 1964, 1970), the patient's
relationship to reality and sense of reality may be impaired, though the
level of impairment may fluctuate. Consequently, reality testing may be
secondarily affected and take on a vague and tentative quality. I have
found awareness of the interplay of the facets of reality useful as in
indicator for therapeutic focus. Kernberg (1975) also refers to a more
general and more subtle use of the term *reality testing:*

> Subtle alterations in the behavior of borderline patients within their
> ordinary social context (such as their frequent lack of perception of
> subtle "messages" from other persons, their unawareness of inap-
> propriate appearance, of the emotional reality of others, of the
> influence of value judgments on the behavior of other persons, of
> how they themselves are perceived by others, and tactlessness), all
> reflect loss of the more subtle discriminatory aspects of reality
> testing determined by ego and superego pathology. (p. 137)

Countertransference demands the therapist's constant vigilance.
Whether defined in the classical sense (Fliess 1953, S. Freud 1910, 1912,
Glover 1955, Reich 1951, 1960) as the therapist's unconscious reaction
(transference) to the patient's transference, or as the therapist's total
emotional response to the patient (which includes the therapist's realistic
needs and transference reaction to the patient's transference and reality;
Fromm-Reichmann 1950, Little 1951, 1960, Weigert 1952, Winnicott 1949,
1960), the countertransference provides crucial data. Diagnostically: Patients with the potential for a severe regression tend to elicit strong
countertransference responses. When the therapist finds himself preoccupied and/or experiencing intense emotions in relation to a patient, he
should be alert to an impending severe regression in the patient. The
countertransference response may be due more to intense chaotic transferences of the patient and to the stress it constitutes for the therapist
than to the therapist's transference. If the therapist's reaction is determined by those emotions, his neutrality and therapeutic effectiveness
may be endangered. Further, underlying attitudes of the patient toward
the therapist may first be reflected in countertransference. The therapist
may become aware of his own reaction in countertransference before
perceiving in transference what a patient's response is.

A repeated recurrence or prolongation of a particular countertransference is likely to lead to a therapeutic impasse. The therapist should confront himself with one or more of the following options: (a) consultation, (b) additional treatment for the therapist, (c) discontinuing treatment and referring the case to another therapist, and (d) not treating that type of case.

Kernberg (1975) writes: "What the therapist does when he becomes unable to 'snap out' of his countertransference bind is to re-establish the vicious circle of the patient's interaction with the parental image" (p. 60). Under the circumstances, a therapeutic impasse may be the least serious of possible consequences.

Perhaps the most severe test for the therapist is dealing with the countertransference response to the patient's pregenital aggression. "Aggression and aggression against the self are fused in the patient's effort to destroy the [therapist's] capacity to help him, and both elements are also present in the [therapist's] emotional response to this situation" (Kernberg 1975, p. 61).

The therapist's most skillful efforts may be defeated, resulting in the loss of confidence in therapy and technique and a tendency to masochistic submission and fear of the criticism of colleagues and relatives of the patient. When the patient is a close relative of another therapist or someone engaged in the mental health profession, the fear of criticism and its consequence for the therapist may become acute. As defenses against such countertransference Kernberg (1975) mentions three possiblities: (a) the reappearance of the old neurotic character structure of the therapist in a peculiar complementary integration with the patient's characterological pathology; (b) a narcissistic withdrawal or detachment of the therapist from the patient so that empathy is lost; and (c) a narcissistic withdrawal of the therapist from reality, with the appearance of unrealistic certainty of being able to help this patient—"The therapist now tends to establish himself in a kind of island with such a particular patient, helps the patient to deflect his aggression from the [therapist] to external objects, and absorbs some of this aggression in masochistic submission to the patient, rationalized as 'total dedication,' which also provides some narcissistic gratification" (p. 62).

The third reaction is a potential problem for the skilled and sophisticated therapist. Usually the knowledge, skill, and confidence of a competent therapist are required to get into such a bind in the first place and even more to get out of it.

The therapist's capacity to experience concern is one important force in neutralizing and overcoming the effect of aggression and self-aggression in the countertransference (Kernberg 1975). Kernberg describes concern in connection with the immediate reality of the treatment situation of a patient:

In concrete terms, concern implies ongoing self-criticism by the [therapist], unwillingness to accept impossible situations in a passive way, and, continuous search for new ways of handling a prolonged crisis. It implies active involvement of the therapist as opposed to narcissistic withdrawal, and realization of the ongoing need of consultation with and help from one's colleagues. (p. 64)

I prefer my own view of how the concerned therapist should react with himself. This is no time for equivocating and temporizing.

Sparkling insights that impress the therapist are usual among adolescent and young adult BPOs. Among older BPOs, the insights have less sparkle and are less impressive, partly because they are the same as the adolescent insight. Kernberg (1975) expresses it aptly:

Unfortunately, one frequently finds that what at first looks like insight into "deep" layers of the mind and into unconscious dynamics on the part of some borderline patients is actually an expression of the ready availability of primary process functioning as part of the general regression of ego structures. . . . "Authentic" insight is a combination of the intellectual and emotional understanding of deeper sources of one's psychic experience, accompanied by concern for and an urge to change the pathological aspects of that experience. (pp. 92–93)

While I agree with Kernberg on this point, I have often found these "insights," even among sixty-year-old adolescents, an excellent point of departure for the development of "authentic insight." The sparkling insight frequently represents defensive regression to primary process functioning to avoid the implications of secondary process functioning and of realities. Interpreting "in-depth insights" in terms of secondary process and realities can lead to "authentic insight."

The neutrality of the therapist, i. e., the maintenance of a perspective equidistant from the patient's reality, superego, instinctual needs, and acting out (A. Freud 1946), may be severely tested. For instance: The therapist's calling attention to the difference between the patient's distorted perception of him as an archaic fantasy object and the therapist as a real object in the external world may convince the patient that the therapist is not neutral, that he actually favors one or another of the structures mentioned above. Indeed, at any given moment the therapist may evince such a preference, although not necessarily the one the patient perceives as operative. Another instance: the therapist's activating the patient's ego functions, such as integration, anticipation, or judgment, by exercising his own on behalf of the patient (that is, up to the point that enables the patient to exercise those ego functions for himself) can be difficult to achieve without favoring ego, superego, or id. The usual structuring of the setting of treatment, e.g., hospitalization, limitations on acting out, to protect the neutrality of the therapist is of no help in such instances. I know of no alternative to proceeding with tact and keen awareness of countertransference implications.

As the BPO patient develops the capacity to experience depression in the course of treatment, depression may be the reaction to progress. As primitive idealization and omnipotence yield to improving reality functions, the patient mourns the loss of the grandiose expectations and fantasies that make the newly found realities dull by contrast. At such moments the patient may reproach the therapist only half in jest with: "You've ruined my life" or "You have spoiled things for me; I know too much." Both patient and therapist may be disappointed in the concomitants of therapeutic progress.

REFERENCES

Boyer, L. B. (1977). Working with a borderline patient. *Psychoanalytic Quarterly* 46:386–424.
Boyer, L. B., and Giovacchini, P. L. (1967). *Psychoanalytic Treatment of Characterological and Schizophrenic Disorders.* New York: Jason Aronson.
Deutsch, H. (1942). Some forms of emotional disturbance and their relationship to schizophrenia. *Psychoanalytic Quarterly* 11:301–321.
Dickes, R. (1967). Severe regressive disruptions of the therapeutic alliance. *Journal of the American Psychoanalytic Association* 15:508–533.
Fairbairn, W. R. D. (1952). A revised psychopathology of the psychoses and psychoneuroses. In *Psychoanalytic Studies of the Personality: An Object Relations Theory of Personality.* London: Tavistock.
Fliess, R. (1953). Countertransference and counteridentification. *Journal of the American Psychoanalytic Association* 1:268–284.
Freud, A. (1946). *The Ego and the Mechanisms of Defense.* New York: International Universities Press.
Freud, S. (1910). The future prospects of psychoanalytic therapy. *Standard Edition* 11:139–151.
——— (1912). Recommendations to physicians practising psycho-analysis. *Standard Edition* 12:109–120.
Fromm-Reichmann, F. (1950). *Principles of Intensive Psychotherapy.* Chicago: University of Chicago Press.
Frosch, J. (1960). A specific problem in nosology: the psychotic character disorder. *Journal of the American Psychoanalytic Association* 8:544–547.
——— (1964). The psychotic character: clinical psychiatric considerations. *Psychiatric Quarterly* 38:81–96.
——— (1970). Psychoanalytic considerations of the psychotic character. *Journal of the American Psychoanalytic Association* 18:24–50.
——— (1971). Technique in regard to some specific ego defects in the treatment of borderline patients. *Psychoanalytic Quarterly* 45:216–220.
Giovacchini, P. L., ed. (1972). *Tactics and Techniques in Psychoanalytic Therapy.* New York: Jason Aronson.

Glover, E. (1955). *The Technique of Psycho-Analysis*. New York: International Universities Press.

Greenacre, P. (1959). Certain technical problems in the transference relationship. *Journal of the American Psychoanalytic Association* 7:484–502.

Greenson, R. R. (1965). The working alliance and the transference neurosis. *Psychoanalytic Quarterly* 34:155–181.

Kernberg, O. (1975). *Borderline Conditions and Pathological Narcissism*. New York: Jason Aronson.

Klein, M. (1946). Notes on some schizoid mechanisms. *International Journal of Psycho-Analysis* 27:99–110.

——— (1952). The origins of transference. *International Journal of Psycho-Analysis* 33:433–443.

Knight, R. P. (1953a). Borderline states. In *Psychoanalytic Psychiatry and Psychology*, ed. R. P. Knight and C. R. Friedman, pp. 97–109. New York: International Universities Press, 1954.

——— (1953b). Management and psychotherapy of the borderline schizophrenic patient. In *Psychoanalytic Psychiatry and Psychology*, ed. R. P. Knight and C. R. Friedman, pp. 110–122. New York: International Universities Press, 1954.

Kohut, H. (1971). *The Analysis of the Self*. New York: International Universities Press.

Little, M. (1951). Countertransference and the patient's response to it. *International Journal of Psycho-Analysis* 32:32–40.

——— (1958). On delusional transference (transference psychosis). *International Journal of Psycho-Analysis* 39:131–138.

——— (1960). Countertransference. *British Journal of Medical Psychology* 33:29–31.

Mahler, M. S., and Furer, M. (1968). *On Human Symbiosis and the Vicissitudes of Individuation: Vol. 1: Infantile Psychosis*. New York: International Universities Press.

Masterson, J. F. (1972). *Treatment of the Borderline Adolescent: A Developmental Approach*. New York: John Wiley.

——— (1976). *Psychotherapy of the Borderline Adult: A Developmental Approach*. New York: Brunner-Mazel.

Reich, A. (1951). On countertransference. *International Journal of Psycho-Analysis* 32:25–31.

——— (1960). Further remarks on countertransference. *International Journal of Psycho-Analysis* 41:389–395.

Reider, N. (1957). Transference psychosis. *Journal of the Hillside Hospital* 6:131–149.

Romm, M. (1957). Transient psychotic episodes during psychoanalysis. *Journal of the American Psychoanalytic Association* 5:325–341.

Searles, H. F. (1963). Transference psychosis in the psychotherapy of chronic schizophrenia. *International Journal of Psycho-Analysis* 44:249–281.

Sterba, R. (1934). The fate of the ego in analytic therapy. *International Journal of Psycho-Analysis* 15:117–126.

Strachey, J. (1934). The nature of the therapeutic action of psycho-analysis. *International Journal of Psycho-Analysis* 15:142–143, 159.

Weigert, E. (1952). Contribution to the problem of terminating psychoanalyses. *Psychoanalytic Quarterly* 21:465–480.

Winnicott, D. W. (1949). Hate in the countertransference. *International Journal of Psycho-Analysis* 30:69–75.

——— (1960). Countertransference. *British Journal of Medical Psychology* 33:17–21.

Zetzel, E. R. (1956). Current concepts of transference. *International Journal of Psycho-Analysis* 37:369–376.

The Significance of Kleinian Contributions to Psychoanalysis I. Kleinian Instinct Theory

JAMES GROTSTEIN, M.D.

The history of Freud's instinct theory shows that it ambiguously contains two separate roots of development; one, the nutritional-transactional, and the other, the autoerotic discharge model. The former is the forerunner of Klein's instinct theory and the latter is considered classical theory. Kleinians and Freudians have not fully understood that each holds an instinct theory which is quite different from the other. The consequences of this theoretical dialectic are of great importance in distinguishing the Kleinian theory of fantasy from the Freudian theory of fantasy, the theory of repression, the theory of the unconscious, and ultimately the theory of the internal world.

Freud's first theory of psychoanalysis was characterized by a censorship of a traumatic memory of reality (Breuer and Freud 1893–1895). Evidence eventually contradicted this theory, enabling Freud (1899) to discover fantasy, rather than reality, as the content of the repressed. In searching for the origin of fantasy, he returned to his neurological background to discover the sexual instincts. He believed that the sexual instincts emanated autoerotically from the mucous membranes of the body generally, and from the genital organs particularly, from the very beginning. Infantile sexuality and the pleasure principle were born. The penis became the totem ancestor of all psychic energy, and a male patriarchy administered the cathectic cosmos. Infantile sexuality had a male orientation and there occurred a genitalization of sexuality applied to the pleasure obtained at the erogenous zones. Ultimately, the id was to house the instincts and was to function through impulse discharge of tension.

I should like to develop Freud's instinct theory a little more to demonstrate that his conceptualizations themselves contained divergent views which helped to spawn the discrepancies between classical and Kleinian notions of instincts. In *Three Contributions to the Theory of Sexuality* (1905) Freud states, concerning autoerotism:

> It must be insisted that the most striking feature of this sexual activity [infantile sexuality] is that the instinct is not directed towards other people, but obtains satisfaction from the subject's own body. It is "auto-erotic," to call it by a happily chosen term introduced by Havelock Ellis. . . . (p. 188).

And yet, in "Transformation of Puberty," he adds:

> At a time at which the first beginnings of sexual satisfactions are still linked with the taking of nourishment, the sexual instinct has a sexual object outside the infant's own body in the shape of his mother's breast. It is only later that the instinct loses that object, just at the time, perhaps, when the child is able to form a total idea of the person to whom the organ that is giving him satisfaction belongs. As a rule the sexual instinct then becomes auto-erotic. . . . There are thus good reasons why a child sucking at his mother's breast has become the prototype of every relation of love. The finding of an object is in fact a refinding of it. (p. 222)

In the first quotation we can clearly see the autoerotic discharge foundation of the classical Freudian instinctual infrastructure. In the second quotation we can see a hint of a different instinct theory—one that is object-directed from the beginning and then, because of separation and loss, becomes, by default, *seemingly* autoerotic. But the autoerotic nature of the instinct is clearly due to object loss and thus constitutes a defense against the frustration of object attachment. It is this latter theory which is the infrastructure of Kleinian psychology and of the British object relations movement.

Freud (1923) soon tired of oversimplistic instinct analysis and came to realize that the ego repressing the instincts was also unconscious even though it was unrepressed. This was the beginning of his emphasis on defense in lieu of the repressed. Meanwhile he had established the importance of fantasy but in his conceptualizations emphasized the instinctualization of reality to produce a fantasied reality: the instincts were the agent which modified the image of reality rather than vice versa. A child's father was misperceived because of a fear of him generated by projections of the child's instinctual impulses. Once the authentic origin of the instincts were uncovered, the rest of the analysis was occupied with the "working through" of their derivatives.

My own belief is that he came up against a *reductio ad absurdum*. Once he analyzed symptoms into their conflictual components and their libidinal zone origins, he found himself in an instinctual *cul de sac*. His theory was stymied in a genetic reconstruction beginning with a realistic external event which had been turned into fantasy by instinctualization. For instance, the sight of the female vagina would be the reality event which the instinctual nature of the boy would turn into castration fantasies because of fear of punishment for autoerotic pleasure. Something similar obtained in obsessive-compulsive neurosis, in which case the analysis sought to trace the origin of the neurosis down to anal libido and its conflict with an environmental censor. The important point is that once the instinctual zone and its energy were located, that was the deepest penetration which the analysis could make. The rest of the analysis was left to the working through of the descendants of the libido. Libidinal energy is, therefore, what created the fantasy.

It is important to realize that Freud thought of fantasy as the alteration of the view of external reality created by the prejudiced intercession of our biologically acquired instinctual drives. In other words, Freud reasoned that sexual traumata were not necessarily induced by parental seductions of children into reality so much as they were the child's *imagination* that he was being seduced. Imagination was another way of stating sexual fantasies. Because of feelings and impulses emanating from the initially autoerotic sexual zones of the child, he began to perceive his objects as if they too were sexual. This was Freud's foundation for his theory of infantile sexuality and is based obviously on the theory of projective identification from the child onto the parent. Id analysis, when successful, restores the more nearly accurate, that is, less instinctualized and therefore less fantastic, picture of reality.

Instinct theory and psychic energy are currently being fundamentally reappraised by classical analysts. Gill (1963) and Schur (1966) find that the id, rather than being dialectical with the ego, is a functional entity possessing structure and that its functions are on a gradient with ego functions. Rosenblatt and Thickston (1970) have gone so far as to negate the importance of psychic energy as a separate economic issue, fulfilling the prophecy of Fairbairn (1952). More recently G. Klein (1976), Schafer (1976), Holzman (1976), Rubinstein (1976), and others, all of whom have been fundamentally affected by their mentor, David Rapaport, have concluded that ego psychology is unsuitable to explain mental life and are taking issue with Freud's biological model. As I have read the above authors in the monograph, *Psychology Versus Metapsychology: Psychoanalytic Essays in Memory of George S. Klein* (Gill and Holzman 1976), I see them opting for a primary psychology of mind independent of biological instinctual drives. I think this tendency is very congruent with Kohut's (1971) emphasis on the development of the narcissistic personality. While these authors laudably realize the difficulties inherent in the attempt by traditional psychoanalysis to assume a mind-brain isomorphism—and that in its present state of psychoanalytic theory may therefore comprise incompatible paradigms—I should have been more sanguine about their efforts had they familiarized themselves with the instinct theories of Melanie Klein (1952a, b, c, d, 1957, 1959, 1960), Isaacs (1952), Fairbairn (1940, 1941, 1943, 1944, 1946, 1949, 1951), Bion (1962a,b, 1963, 1965, 1970), and Money-Kyrle (1961, 1971). All these authors tend to be more holistic, ethological, ego-centered, and object oriented from the beginning; instincts represent an integral, nonseparated aspect of ego (self) which is always striving for contact with an object. Fairbairn was clearer then Melanie Klein in pointing out that she was really ignoring the id as a separate entity. Moreover, it would appear that her object-oriented conception of instincts also included Freud's other instinct theory—that of autoerotism-discharge, as the destiny of the pleasure-unpleasure principle—in her conception of projective identification. In other words, Klein and her followers believed that instincts were always object-seeking primarily in a nutritive, nonsexual mode. Excitation or frustration mobilized autoerotism as a defense against the frustration. Projective identification could then be employed by the infant to evacuate his tension into mother as a toilet-container-breast—as the manifestation of evacuative aspects of the pleasure-unpleasure principle.

The Thirtieth International Psychoanalytic Congress in Jerusalem in 1977 brought forth a particularly acute distinction between the Kleinian and the Freudian ways of understanding instinct theory. It demonstrated an equally interesting aspect of the respective psychoanalytic techniques devolving from each of the school's understanding of that instinct theory. A distinction was drawn of such importance that I should like to dwell on it at some length. Leo Rangell, in his criticism of Betty Joseph's espousal of some aspects of Kleinian technique, reminded the audience that Freudians wait for the analytic situation to develop (Gaddini and Kuchenbuch 1978). Furthermore, he pointed out, they interpret from the surface. Fundamentally, he added, they try not to interfere with the patient's flow of association, but rather seek to remove the impediments to the flow. He was pointing out, in other words, that classical analysis is largely the analysis of resistance.

The instinct theory to which Rangell was alluding is that of the discharge model of the pleasure-unpleasure principle. In this consideration truth lies oracularly in the patient's unconscious instincts awaiting discharge. Instincts are veritably synonymous with the id, or with unconscious memories that have been repressed and are reinstinctualized. The classical analyst regards this instinctual, unconscious layer with such reverence that he does not wish impede its epiphany and does all he can to facilitate it. Forbearance will thus be the watchword of the classical analyst who would facilitate the patient's unfolding but would do nothing to interfere with it. The transference which develops is that of past object relationships, he reminded the audience.

Betty Joseph, in presenting the Kleinian point of view, kept referring to "establishing contact" with the infantile aspects of the patient. This suggested going beneath the surface and into the depths and also seemed to convey a transactional context; the patient's associations were always related directly or indirectly to the therapist, reflecting the breadth and ubiquitous activity subsumed under the Kleinian notion of transference (Gaddini and Kuchenbuch 1978).

What was most striking to me as an observer at this congress was my ultimate realization that each took for granted that the other understood his own instinct theory as a common ground between them. Neither one realized, in my estimation, that each was using an instinct theory entirely different from that held by the other. The classical instinct theory is that of an instinctual drive which is impelling towards discharge and contains the message to be released and revealed in the analytic session. The success of the analyst and the analysis is in the removal of the impediments to this discharge. The Kleinian point of view, on the other hand, borrows more from Abraham's (1924) concept in which instinctual development was coexistent with the development of object relations. Abraham's object relations theory reflects the immediacy of connection between the instinct and the object. Abraham, like Freud (1905), believed that the source of the instincts was in the mucous membranes of the autoerotic zones and that the impulses emanating from these zones were object-directed as well as aiming at discharge from the very beginning. The Kleinian notion of instincts constitutes a transformation of Abraham's theory, removing the autoerotic mucous membrane zones as the source of the instinct, and changing its aim. Instead, Kleinians believe the instinct to be a holistic urge or need on the part of the whole infant, not just of the mucous membranes, which is oriented toward objects who are meaningful rather than primarily sexually oriented. Fairbairn's (1952) statement to the effect that the infant is oral, not because he is erotic, but because he needs a breast, is very much to the point. The Kleinian infant is a whole infant who *urgently* needs mother for nutrition, evacuation, and for holding. These are primary biological survival needs. In no conceivable way is sex one of them. "Sexualization" comes about more as a defensively precocious state of excitement in order to alter the awareness of frustration so as primitively to master it.

Thus the notion of infantile sexuality to a Freudian would be translated as infantile omnipotence to a Kleinian, and would be a defensive rather than a primary urge or need. The Kleinian analyst, as a result, always feels impelled to reach out towards a needy infant who is trying at the same time to reach through a veil of splitting or projective identification in order to establish contact between his authentic needy infantile self and the proper mate: mother's breast. As the Freudian analyst feels justified in not interfering with the flow of associations, the Kleinian analyst feels technically justified in continuing to reach out to contact the infant by designating the maximum unconscious anxiety at any given moment. He is looking for need, not libido or aggression. He recognizes libido and aggression in the context of the needs of the infant as defenses or as later expressions of need during the phallic-oedipal phase. The Kleinian notion of instinct, therefore, is one that more closely resembles that which has been studied by such ethologists as Lorenz (1957), Tinbergen (1951), Bowlby (1969), and others—a holistic, innate behavioral coordinator reaction pattern which contains a built-in transactional dialectic—within the conception of Kleinian instinct as an infantile self always in a relationship to an object. There is no such thing as an infant without some relationship to an object. The autoerotic theory of the instinctual drives of Freudian classical analysis disagrees entirely.

Impulses occur in an object relations context from the beginning, as I have stated, and thus are not primarily autoerotic but rather object-directed from the beginning. The infant is looking essentially for nurture, a breast, not for sex or for discharge of impulses. Precocious sexual excitation, which Freud called infantile sexuality, is a defense against the awareness of separation from the needed object and is not sexual per se (Klein 1929a, b, 1932, 1940, 1945, 1952d, 1959, 1960). Where Freud talked about *infantile sexuality*, Mrs. Klein talked about *infantile omnipotence* and *infantile states of confusion*. The emphasis was nutrition, not sex, and primarily from a mother not a father—two major shifts in theory. Freud had also known about the nutritional instincts but he never gave them priority in a psychoanalytic theory. *Therefore, to Freud, sex was primary and nutrition was secondary, and to Klein, nutrition was primary and sex was secondary.*

Classical authors were not unaware of the male, patriarchal orientation Freud gave early instinctual life. Ferenczi (1930) and Abraham (1924) consequently investigated the importance of the maternal relationship to the child. In more recent times Spitz (1965), Benjamin (1965), Brody and Axelrad (1970), Elkisch and Mahler (1959), Erikson (1950, 1959), Fries and

Woolf (1971), Gediman (1971), Mahler (1971), Tolpin (1970), Weil (1970), and Wolff (1960) have closed the gap and made significant contributions to the importance of the infant's nurturing relationship to it's mother. Bowlby (1969) has emphasized the ethological aspects of the infant's bonding with his mother and he, like Winnicott, Fairbairn, and Balint, has had considerable influence in establishing the primary importance of the infant-mother bond. Although each writer uses his own metaphor, I do believe that a rapprochement with Klein is being forged in this area, but again, without acknowledgment. Bowlby, Winnicott, and Fairbairn are the only notable exceptions to this.

The classical notion of instinctual drive, moreover, corresponds to that aspect of Kleinian instinctual theory which accounts for the evacuation of tension through the projective identification of needs and affects into an object, as mentioned earlier. In other words, Kleinian instinct theory, that of communication, is more elaborate than the classical but also can be seen to contain it within its theoretical framework.

The Kleinian theory of instincts remained relatively unchanged until Bion's (1962a, b, 1963, 1965, 1970) recent modifications. Although Kleinians generally speak of instinctual impulses, they seem really to mean infantile egos exerting will over objects. In another publication (Grotstein 1977) I develop the notion, following Bion, that Klein's instincts more nearly resemble ethological instincts than they do Freud's sexual drives. I posit a libidinal instinctual organization, an inherent undifferentiated defense organization (death instinct or aggressive instinct), and an epistemophilic instinct. My theory suggests the following: (a) the libidinal instinctual organization includes all the mental-biological urges and tropisms which orient and direct the infant toward the needed nutritional object (clinging, following, etc., are activities belonging to this organization); (b) the death instinct organization (which I have termed the inherent undifferentiated defense organization) is the inherent preconceptual apparatus which warns us of the danger of death, of the predator or stranger who can effect this death, and the prey upon whom we are to visit this death for our own defensive purposes. It includes all the defensive possibilities in which we fight or take flight from a danger situation. It is the origin of what Freud has termed signal-alarm anxiety; (c) the epistemophilic organization which is the drive of the infant toward stimulation for wakefulness and exploration to satisfy an inherent capacity for curiosity and growth. It is my impression that they are all potentially adaptive to the welfare of the human being and are not necessarily in dialectical opposition. I believe it is a serious shortcoming of Klein and of her followers to have neglected the adaptive and cooperative function of the death instinct—a protector of the infant against danger in general and against the predator in particular.

THE IMPORTANCE OF FANTASY

Melanie Klein, who issued from the heritage of Ferenczi and Abraham and the patronage of Jones, came forth to rescue Freud's id by elaborating and extending his concept of fantasy. Freud believed that fantasies issued from instincts, that is, he believed that instincts, the mental equivalents or representations of biological processes, were experienced as fantasies; they were transformation of instincts (Freud 1905). Klein, on the other hand, reasoned that fantasies were not merely the transformations of instincts but that *instincts were themselves fantasies in the first place*. Whereas Freud (1933, p. 98) stated, "We suppose that it [the id] is somewhere in direct contact with somatic processes and takes over from them instinctual needs and gives them *mental expression*" (italics mine). Isaacs (1952) states, "Now in the view of the present writers, this 'mental expression' of instinct *is* unconscious fantasy. Fantasy is (in the first instance) the mental corollary, the psychic representative, of instinct. There is no impulse, no instinctual urge or response which is not experienced as unconscious fantasy" (p. 83). My own understanding of this dichotomy is that Freud primarily believed that instincts were somatic excitations from the periphery of the body whose aim was discharge in order to dispell discomfort according to the pleasure-unpleasure principle. An object is ultimately needed in order to facilitate the discharge. The Kleinian instinct is itself a fantasy and is, as such, the autobiographical narrative of the infant's neediness. Instinctual impulses are a priori obtrusions into the infant's awareness and are experienced as fantasies. The infant is not clear whether they come from within or from without because the distinction between inside and outside must await for the development of a sense of a skin-boundary-frontier representation which allow him to determine inside from outside. All one can say at this stage is that there is a perturbation of the sense of the state of bliss from the outside. These fantasies are experienced as narratives which attempt to tell a story which helps to organize the impinging data of experience in an attempt to account for it and therefore to master it.

In order to illuminate the difference in emphasis that Klein's conception that instinct *is* fantasy conveys in theory and clinical practice, let me employ the example of the destructive drive (death instinct to a Kleinian, aggressive drive to a classical Freudian). To most classical analysts, the aggressive drive is separate instinctual energy in a potentially conflict laden cauldron known as the id. Until it is sublimated or neutralized, it is purely destructive. To a Kleinian, the death instinct is itself a fantasy, reified by the infant's feelings, motoric capacity, affects, etc., which allows him to overcome a persecutor which stands between him and the good object. In other words, it is omnipotently (magically) reparative insofar as it aims to restore the goodness of the idealized object by fantasizing away the obstructive or intimidating bad object which stands between the infant and the good object.

The reasoning is similar for the libidinal instinct and for the epistemophilic instinct as well, both of which enable the infant to possess the good object sensually (concretely) and psychically so as to restore primary identification. As maturation occurs, the aims of these instincts change. The destructive instinct protects the infant and his relationship to libidinal objects. The epistemophilic instinct acquires knowledge to vouchsafe the infant's survival. The libidinal instinct helps to acquire the nurture upon which the survival directly depends. All in all, the Kleinian version of instincts as fantasies implies, from the very beginning, the absence of an id and the presence of an instinctual ego which has magical—but magically adaptive—attitudes towards its objects in order to achieve survival.

Yet it must be stated that Kleinians have failed to exploit this very important difference in their instinct theory, especially when they talk about the conflict between the life and the death instincts (Klein and Riviere 1964) and the danger of the preeminence of the latter. When Kleinians talk about the death instinct as "the thing in itself," they are, in my opinion, realigning themselves with the classical view of instinctual drives without realizing it. Kleinians are, therefore, inconsistent in their clinical use of instincts, particularly the death instinct, when they ascribe to it a separate and destructive will or purpose. This only slightly detracts, however, from what I believe to be the inherent superiority of their basic concept of instincts. Deserting the concept of instinct as adaptive fantasy, they may not realize (in their unfortunate shorthand) that they are dealing with a split-off separate self which has its own will. Thus, when they speak of a "destructive part of the self" (such as envy) they are probably talking about a split-off separate *entity within the self* which has separate enfranchisement and independent imaginative existence, in other words, a separate self acting as a peremptory parasite. This is not to be confused with the normal instinctual self in which the three instincts— the libidinal, the death instinct, and the epistemophilic instinct—work in harmony. When Kleinians depart from their basic conception, they are committing the sin of deserting the adaptive point of view—a problem which many classical analysts have been forced to recognize, as seen in the current apologia vis-à-vis the biological instinct theory.

Bion (1962b, 1963, 1965, 1967, 1970) expanded upon the Kleinian conception of instincts by relating them to even deeper fantasies than the personifications elaborated by Klein. He offered the notion of inherent preconceptions—that is, *a priori* knowledge in the Platonic sense—which exist as potential, inherited imagery, awaiting experience with their external counterpart (their realizations) in order to form those compounds of experience known as conceptions. Thus, according to Bion, the experience of the "hole" of hunger can anticipate something like a breast to fill it before the infant has actually known the breast in reality. When hunger locates the breast, the inherent preconception meets with its counterpart, and a conception is formed. Thus, Bion's inherent preconceptions would constitute something of first order instincts, and Klein's conception of personifications constitutes second order. The conception of fantasy is implicit to both.

Instinctual impulses are experienced *a priori* as fantasies, insofar as any perturbation of the infant's awareness, whether from within or from without (and this difference is not clear in the infant), is experienced, Kleinians believe, as primitive narratives. Inchoate splitting and projective identification render all preceptions into "instinctual stories" which are split-off likenesses of self or components of self. The infant's awareness of his hunger might be experienced by him as a devouring breast within because of the splitting off and projective identification of painful sensations into the breast followed by its introjective return as a hungry breast-experience within. The "instinctual" need known as hunger is then believed to have come from a source, though now inside the infant, also from the outside. His hunger is knowable, in other words, only through its prime reference point, the breast. The other way of saying all of the above is that the infant always *personifies* his experiences, and he can personify only in terms of himself and the narcissistic objects around him. Instincts themselves present sensations to the sense organ of unconscious awareness which is later to be known as the id (Freud 1923). It is in the first instance painful and unknowable until personified in terms of its first experience with the external object which comes in contact with it to become a constant conjunction (Bion 1962b). Thus, hunger is inextricably and permanently bound with the devouring breast as an inchoate fantasy. According to Kleinian thinking, all experience that comes from unconscious or instinctual sources is fantasy and all data of experience is first experienced as fantasy.

ENVY AND GREED

I have already alluded to the different way in which Mrs. Klein used instincts. She believed that they, rather than being primarily discharging and sexual in nature, were primarily object oriented (breast) and communicative. Excesses of the libidinal instinct may result in (a) greed and (b) precocious sexual excitation (the genital being confused with the breast). In considering greed, Mrs. Klein (1952b) noted that the hunger component of the libidinal drive may be so responsive to a sense of frustration or danger that a fantasy develops in which the infant experiences himself invading the breast, scooping it out, and possessing it and its milk for himself. The aim is not to do damage to the breast; damage is a consequence of the desperation of the invasive act born of a sense of danger. The consequences in fantasy are the internalization of a damaged breast with which the infant is identified and of a split-off greedy or demanding breast which becomes a superego object. It must be remembered that Klein's use of fantasy is her denotation of *her* inference about the infant's inner experience, and that she infers this inner experience to be a series of linkages between himself and his object in his imagination arranged in a narrative manner in order to give *ad hoc* meaning and organization to his chaotic world. Fantasies, in other words, are the most elemental means of giving meaning to the data of experience.

Klein arrived at these inferences about the fantasy life of infants from the reconstruction of the inner psychic life of children who were as young as two years of age. At this time they had achieved sufficient verbal capacity to be able to understand interpretations and produce responses which convinced Klein and her followers that they were on the right track (Isaacs 1952).

Klein (1957) believed that the affect of envy was a consequence of the mental representation of the death instinct itself. The fantasy of envy, in other words, is the infant's hatred of the very goodness of the breast regardless of it being present or absent, gratifying or frustrating. This paradox is due to the fact that the perception of mother's having the needed breast is believed in infantile fantasy to arouse a greater sense of danger to the infant's psyche (because of the mobilization of hatred inside) than would be aroused by a refusal to accept helplessness and feeding at the breast. In other words, the death instinct attacks any perception which reinforces the awareness of helplessness and lack of omnipotence. Again, it must be remembered that these concepts are inferential and are reconstructions of what Klein believed to be the infant's inner experience.

Insofar as envy is a universal phenomenon in infantile mental life, Klein was able to demonstrate its far-reaching consequences in mental development. Unlike greed, damage to the breast in fantasy is purposeful, not accidental. Envious attacks against the breast result in the internalization of a damaged or mutilated breast and of an envious or belittling superego, the forerunner of a malevolent and omnipotent internal object which sadistically attacks the infant's ego.

Envious feelings towards mother's breasts are normally attenuated by the experience of gratitude towards mother and the breasts for survival and thriving. When gratitude continues, the attainment of the depressive position helps the infant to experience a sense of conquest over his own destructive impulses and allows him to have confidence in the power of his grateful and reparative ones (Klein 1957).

The classical literature has also dealt with the phenomenon of envy but mainly in the phallic stage of development where the female child is believed to be envious of her father's or brother's penis. In his "Critical Review of the Status of the Envy Concept," Joffe (1969) criticizes Klein and her followers for assigning a basis for envy so early and relates it instead to later stages of development. Joffe's criticism is based upon the classical model of infant development which suggests a later and more delayed achievement of psychic individuality. The classical infant, it must be remembered, does not even have mental status until he has achieved the threshold of the hatching subphase of separation-individuation, whereas the Kleinian infant has achieved this independence of mind from the very beginning of life, if not before, and achieves a definite awareness of it by virtue of that cluster of anxiety known as the paranoid-schizoid position at age three weeks. Joffe's definition of the beginning of psychic life *seemingly* justifies this criticism of Klein; but, as I have stated earlier and elsewhere in this presentation, more recent data suggest that Klein has been correct all along in her assumptions of early mental life. Nevertheless, her assumption of such elaborate mentation, such as fantasies of greed and envy in early infantile mental life, must still be considered hypothetical inferences, as yet unproved though highly suggestive.

THE NATURE OF THE CONTENT OF THE UNCONSCIOUS

The major differences between the Kleinian and the classical Freudian conceptions of instincts devolve into their respective theories about the nature of the content of the repressed and the repressing. The classical school believes the unconscious consists of *a priori* libidinal and aggressive instinctual drive impulses which optimally undergo a change of function to become drive representations and other neutralized derivatives in the ego. It also contains all those memories of events with objects which are both "pushed" and "pulled" into it: pulled secondarily by virtue of the attraction of the drives in association with linkages to memory of conflict; pushed when "damned" by this association by repression into the same labyrinth with the drives. Further, the unconscious also consists of the countercathectic defense mechanisms themselves.

The Kleinian unconscious consists of internal objects and the egos located within them identificatorily. The instinctual drives, the selves experiencing them, and the objects which are the targets are all indistinguishable from each other. A Kleinian would experience no embarrassment in stating (when appropriate) that the patient is "shoving exciting penises into the therapist" to interpret the patient's attempt at seduction. To the Kleinian conception that internal objects form the composition of the unconscious, Bion has added inherent *preconceptions*, by which I infer he means some kind of inherent prototypes for anticipating each and every experience before one has encountered it (Bion 1962a, 1963, 1965, 1967, 1970).

Thus, the Kleinians's unconscious is synonomous with their concept of the internal world. Rather than a conception of a "seething cauldron" of formless instinctual drives, they conceive of split-off inchoate selves linked with internal objects in a gradient from dominating or controlling objects to passive, helpless objects, all of which are associated with egos. The Kleinian unconscious, in other words, is always personified and never otherwise.

REPRESSION

The theory of repression also differs between Kleinians and classical Freudians. At the Jerusalem Congress of 1977, Betty Joseph alluded to "porous repression," by which she meant the achievement of a healthy repression which could allow appropriate instinctual elements into awareness. The classical analysts Brian Bird, Leo Rangell, and Harold Blum took issue with her conception and reminded her that repression was pathological and that the goal of analysis was to overcome it (Gaddini and Kuchenbuch 1978). The Kleinian views repression as the successful outcome of the depressive position and values the transformation it achieves of primitive and more rigid defenses. Therefore, a Kleinian would be more sanguine about repression. If a child has confidence in his capacity to *re*press, then he can have confidence in his ability to *ex*press.

It has been my impression that the classical conception of repression has never freed itself from a pathological model. Brenner (1966) points out, for instance:

Repression is one of the several defense mechanisms which the ego may employ against an instinctual drive which is the source of anxiety. Thus the *occasion* or *motive* for repression is anxiety, usually anxiety aroused by a derivative of an instinctual drive. The *target* of repression is ordinary libidinal drive but it is possible that repression may also be employed on occasion against an aggressive or destructive drive . . . and it certainly may be employed against the superego demand. . . .

The mechanism of the earliest, infantile repressions is the same as that of later ones, i.e., the establishment of a counter-cathexis by the ego. However the infantile repressions are the basic ones. Later repressions are by-and-large repetitions or consequences of the infantile ones. (p. 391)

Brenner seems to be restating the classical position about repression being the defense against infantile anxieties and its derivatives. By infantile anxiety, I presume he means primal repression, although he does not specifically state so. He also states in the same paragraph: "Repression is thus possible only after a substantial degree of ego development has taken place." The fact that this is inconsistent with the notion of infantile repression is a point not to be considered here but does lend itself to ambiguity. In classical conception, repression is due to anxiety which is basically pathological, insofar as anxiety is conceived to be the break-through or disruption of instinctual drives into the ego overwhelming—it were not repression intact.

Although the Kleinian conception of repression subsumes this classical notion, as Gaddini and Kuchenbuch (1978) suggests, in more common usage it seems to be a quite different one. Owing to the fact that Kleinians, although not specifically so stating, treat the id as if it were indistinguishable from infantile ego, they therefore have developed a conception of the psychic apparatus as one which is slightly different from the classical. Rather than an id, ego, and superego, I believe that Kleinians see the id as an infantile aspect of the self which is striving for nurturing contact with an object. The nurturing infant is not seen as pathological or as primarily irrupting, destructive, or pathological in its own right. It is only excesses of the instinctual equipment of the infantile ego due to frustration which may press against a repressive barrier. The repressive barrier to a Kleinian, in other words, is more like a sphincter or a valve which functions two ways. Unlike the Freudian id which requires no protection against the ego (whereas the ego requires all the protection it can get against the id), the Kleinian "id" requires as much protection against the ego as otherwise. In other words, the repressive barrier to a Kleinian is one which regulates the traffic between the two entities much as a gating mechanism. It can be closely analogized to the relationship between the two cerebral hemisphere organizations and functions. The right hemispheric organization corresponds much more clearly to the Kleinian id and the left hemispheric organization to the Kleinian ego. Each has a relationship to the other through the gating mechanism of repression which allows selective communication and selective exclusion for the *ecological* protection of each organization. I find this conception in clinical practice far more sophisticated and workable clinically than the classical one.

Klein herself tended more than classical authors to relate splitting to later repression and discrimination. She saw splitting as the forerunner of normal discrimination perceptually and cognitively and also saw splitting as the forerunner of normal repression defensively. Although she did not state so in so many words, I think that Klein believed repression to be something like a sublimation of splitting. This formulation seems to me to be of enormous importance: it suggests a psychic apparatus long ago adumbrated by Fairbairn (1940, 1941, 1943, 1944, 1946, 1949, 1951). By postulating that instincts were themselves fantasies, Klein was clearly implying that the separation between the impulsive id and the containing ego was effectively nonexistent.

Rather than a separation of formless energy and structure, which was Freud's concept, Klein was actually positing that energy and structure were inseparable, as Fairbairn explicitly stated, and that the impulsive character assigned to the instinctual drives by Freud was really a statement of a communication to oneself and to one's object in a communicative or transactional context. Thus, a sexual impulse as posited by Freud would arise from the mucous membranes of the autoerotic zone associated with that impulse, namely, the genital zone. In Klein's thinking, a sexual "impulse" would be a fantasy which is stimulated by some frustration whether from within or without but not from the mucous membranes of the autoerotic zones. The stimulation of frustration immediately becomes a fantasy to the infant and, if sexual feelings be the result, these fantasies are attempts to link up with the object to his optimum benefit. In other words, the Freudian impulse theory is neurophysiological more than psychological, and the Kleinian conception is all psychological.

Splitting of the ego and of its objects has been a hallmark in Mrs. Klein's conception of the infant internal world. Classical authors were slow to realize its enormous importance. I review the classical literature on splitting in another contribution (Grotstein, in press). Most noteworthy among classical authors who have emphasized splitting of egos and objects are Jacobson (1964), Kohut (1971), and Kernberg (1975, 1976). Kernberg in particular has applied Fairbairn's and Klein's conceptions of splitting most cogently. Kernberg's conception of splitting ranges all the way from the splitting of egos and objects to the splitting of personalities altogether, a phenomenon which he associates with the borderline personality disorder. Mahler (1971) has also called attention to splitting of the self and of objects in early mental life during the stage of symbiosis. Thus there seems to be a developing reconciliation between classical authors and Mrs. Klein's formulations on splitting and its relationship to early mental life.

SUMMARY

The classical instinctual theory is based upon biological instinctual drives which impel towards discharge and ultimately utilize objects in the facilitation of this discharge. Later, as drive representations, they are able to undergo a change of function under the aegis of neutralization. On the other hand, to Kleinians, instincts are holistic aspects of the infant's psyche and are object-directed and object oriented from the very beginning. They are inherently narrative from the beginning and seek to bind the infant's needs, frustrations, and anxieties by uniting the chaos into a narrative structure which offers the indispensible illusion of omnipotent control over the object by controlling the internal image of that object. Thus, the Kleinian internal world is comprised of egos and objects in countless phantasmagoria, whereas the classical unconscious is comprised of instinctual impulses divorced from structure along with ego and superego aspects which have been pulled into the unconscious by the instincts.

REFERENCES

Abraham, K. (1924). A short study of the development of libido, viewed in the light of mental disorders. In *Selected Papers on Psycho-Analysis*. London: Hogarth Press, 1927.

Benjamin, J. (1965). Developmental biology and psychoanalysis. In *Psychoanalysis and Current Biological Thought*, ed. N. Greenfield and W. Lewis. Madison, Wisconsin: University of Wisconsin Press.

Bion, W. (1962a). A theory of thinking. In *Second Thoughts*. New York: Jason Aronson, 1967.

——— (1962b). *Learning From Experience*. In *Seven Servants*. New York: Jason Aronson, 1977.

——— (1963). *Elements of Psycho-Analysis*. In *Seven Servants*.

——— (1965). *Transformations*. In *Seven Servants*.

——— (1967). *Second Thoughts*. New York. Jason Aronson.

——— (1970). *Attention and Interpretation*. In *Seven Servants*.

Bowlby, J. (1969). *Attachment and Loss*, vol. 1. New York: Basic Books.

Brenner, C. (1966). The mechanism of repression. In *Psychoanalysis: A General Psychology. Essays in Honor of Heinz Hartmann*, ed. R. Loewenstein, L. Newman, M. Schur and A. Solnit, pp. 390–399. New York: International Universities Press.

Breuer, J., and Freud, S. (1893–1895) Studies in hysteria. *Standard Edition* 2.

Brody, S., and Axelrad, S. (1970). *Anxiety and Ego Formation*. New York: International Universities Press.

Elkisch, P., and Mahler, M. (1959). On infantile precursors of the "influencing machine" (Tausk). *Psychoanalytic Study of the Child* 14:219–236.

Erikson, E. (1950). *Childhood and Society*. New York: Norton.

—— (1959). *Identity and the Life Cycle*. New York: International Universities Press.

Fairbairn, W. (1940). Schizoid factors in the personality. *Psychoanalytic Study of the Personality*, pp. 3–27. London: Tavistock.

—— (1941). A revised psychopathology of the psychoses and psychoneuroses. In *Psychoanalytic Study of the Personality*, pp. 28–58.

—— (1943). The repression and the return of bad objects (with special reference to the 'war neuroses'). In *Psychoanalytic Study of the Personality*, pp. 59–82.

—— (1944). Endopsychic structure considered in terms of object-relationships. In *Psychoanalytic Study of the Personality*, pp. 82–136.

—— (1946). Object-relationships and dynamic structure. In *Psychoanalytic Study of the Personality*, pp. 137–151.

—— (1949). Steps in the development of an object-relations theory of the personality. In *Psychoanalytic Study of the Personality*, pp. 152–161.

—— (1951). A synopsis of the development of the author's views regarding the structure of the personality. In *Psychoanalytic Study of the Personality*, pp. 162–183.

—— (1952). *Psychoanalytic Study of the Personality*. London: Tavistock.

Ferenczi, S. (1930). Each adaptation is preceded by an inhibited attempt at splitting. In *Final Contributions to the Problems and Methods of Psychoanalysis*, p. 220. New York: Basic Books, 1955.

Freud, S. (1899). Screen memories. *Standard Edition* 3:301–322.

—— (1905). Three contributions to the theory of sexuality. *Standard Edition* 7:125–148.

—— (1923). The ego and the id. *Standard Edition* 19:3–66.

—— (1933). New introductory lectures in psycho-analysis. *Standard Edition* 22:3–182.

Fries, M., and Woolf, P. (1971). The influence of constitutional complex on developmental phases. In *Separation-Individuation: Essays in Honor of Margaret S. Mahler*, ed. J. McDevitt and C. Settlage. New York: International Universities Press.

Gaddini, E., and Kuchenbuch, A. [rep.] (1978). Dialogue on different types of anxiety and their handling in the psychoanalytic situation. *International Journal of Psycho-Analysis* 59:237–243.

Gediman, H. (1971). The concept of stimulus barrier: its review and reformulation as an adaptive ego function. *International Journal of Psycho-Analysis* 52:243–257.

Gill, M. (1963). *Topography and Systems in Psychoanalytic Theory*. New York: International Universities Press.

Gill, M., and Holzman, P. (eds.) (1976). *Psychology Versus Metapsychology: Psychoanalytic Essays in Memory of George S. Klein*. New York: International Universities Press.

Grotstein, J. (1977). The psychoanalytic concept of schizophrenia: I. The dilemma. *International Journal of Psycho-Analysis*. 58:403–425.

—— (in press). *Splitting and Projective Identification*. New York: Jason Aronson.

Holzman, P. (1976). Theoretical models and the treatment of the schizophrenias. In *Psychology Versus Metapsychology: Psychoanalytic Essays in Memory of George S. Klein*, ed. M. Gill and P. Holzman, pp. 134–158. New York: International Universities Press.

Isaacs, S. (1952). The nature and function of phantasy. In *Developments in Psycho-Analysis*, ed. M. Klein, P. Heimann, S. Isaacs, and J. Riviere, pp. 67–122. London: Hogarth Press.

Jacobson, E. (1964). *The Self and the Object World*. New York: International Universities Press.

Joffe, W. (1969). A critical review of the status of the envy concept. *International Journal of Psycho-Analysis* 50:533–545.

Kernberg, O. (1975). *Borderline Conditions and Pathological Narcissism*. New York: Jason Aronson.

—— (1976). *Object Relations Theory and Clinical Psychoanalysis*. New York: Jason Aronson.

Klein, G. (1976). Freud's two theories of sexuality. In *Psychology Versus Metapsychology: Psychoanalytic Essays In Memory of George S. Klein*, ed. M. Gill and P. Holzman, pp. 14–71. New York: International Universities Press.

Klein, M. (1929a). Infantile anxiety-situations reflected in a work of art and in the creative impulse. In *Contributions to Psycho-Analysis, 1921–1945*, pp. 227–235. London: Hogarth Press, 1948.

—— (1929b). Personification in the play of children. In *Contributions*, pp. 215–226.

—— (1932). Early stages of the Oedipus complex and of super-ego formation. In *Contributions*, pp. 179–209.

—— (1940). Mourning and its relation to manic-depressive states. In *Contributions*, pp. 311–338.

—— (1945). The Oedipus complex in the light of early anxiety. In *Contributions*, pp. 339–390.

—— (1948). On the theory of anxiety and guilt. In *Developments in Psychoanalysis*, ed. M. Klein, P. Heimann, S. Isaacs, and J. Riviere, pp. 271–291. London: Hogarth Press, 1952.

—— (1952a). Some theoretical conclusions regarding the emotional life of the infant. In *Developments*, pp. 198–236.

—— (1952b). On observing the behavior of young infants. In *Developments*, pp. 237–270.

—— (1952c). On the theory of anxiety and guilt. In *Developments*, pp. 279–291.

—— (1952d). Notes on some schizoid mechanisms. In *Developments*, pp. 292–320.

—— (1957). *Envy and Gratitude*. New York: Basic Books.

—— (1959). *The Psychoanalysis of Children*. London: Hogarth.

—— (1960). *Narrative of a Child Analysis*. New York: Basic Books.

Klein, M., and Riviere, J. (1964). *Love, Hate, and Reparation*. New York: Norton.

Kohut, H. (1971). *The Analysis of the Self*. New York: International Universities Press.

Lorenz, K. (1957). The nature of instinct. In *Instinctive Behavior*, ed. C. Schiller. New York: International Universities Press.

Mahler, M. (1971). A study of the separation-individuation process: and its possible application to borderline phenomena in the psychoanalytic situation. *Psychoanalytic Study of the Child* 26:403–424.

Money-Kyrle, R. (1961). *Man's Picture of His World*. New York: International Universities Press.

—— (1971). On cognitive development. *International Journal of Psycho-Analysis* 49:691–698.

Rosenblatt, A., and Thickston, J. (1970). A study of the concept of psychic energy. *International Journal of Psycho-Analysis* 51:265–278.

Rubinstein, B. (1976). On the possibility of a strictly clinical psychoanalytic theory: an essay in the philosophy of psychoanalysis. In *Psychology Versus Metapsychology: Psychoanalytic Essays in Memory of George S. Klein*, ed. M. Gill and P. Holzman, pp. 229–264. New York: International Universities Press.

Schafer, R. (1976). Emotion in the language of action. In *Psychology Versus Metapsychology: Psychoanalytic Essays in Memory of George S. Klein*, eds. M. Gill and P. Holzman, pp. 106–134. New York: International Universities Press.

Schur, M. (1966). *The Id and the Regulatory Principles of Mental Functioning*. New York: International Universities Press.

Spitz, R. (1965). *The First Year of Life*. New York: International Universities Press.

Tinbergen, N. (1951). *The Study of Instinct*. Oxford: Clarendon Press.

Tolpin, M. (1970). The infantile neurosis. *Psychoanalytic Study of the Child*. 25:273–309.

Weil, A. (1970). The basic core. *Psychoanalytic Study of the Child* 25:442–461.

Wolff, P. (1960). *The Developmental Psychologies of Jean Piaget and Psychoanalysis*. New York: International Universities Press.

The Significance of Kleinian Contributions to Psychoanalysis II. Freudian and Kleinian Conceptions of Early Mental Development

JAMES GROTSTEIN, M.D.

This paper discusses and compares Freudian and Kleinian conceptions of the development of early mental life from the vertices of the genetic hypothesis (and reconstruction), the infantile neurosis, the conception of the evolution of the infant, the issue of reality, and the oedipus complex. In so doing, some of the newer findings of infant development are considered. We can now correlate Kleinian conceptions of early infantile reconstruction in light of these new developments; this paper seeks further to demonstrate that the classical notion of primary narcissism, which is laterally known as the conception of the self-object representation, is incompatible with notions of infantile psychology and therefore leaves the classical conception of early mental life in an ambiguous state. An attempt is made to redress this by reconciling the classical and Kleinian notions via a "dual-track" theory.

THE GENETIC HYPOTHESES AND RECONSTRUCTION

I should like to support the Kleinian assumptions of early infantile mental life in the following ways. First, recent infant developmental literature, by such contributors as Bower (1971, 1974), Trevarthen (1974), Boston (1975), Lipsitt (1977), Brazelton (1969, 1973), and Condon (1974), is beginning to show a trend of earlier infantile mental sophistication than hitherto thought possible. Bower in particular points out that the sophistication of such measuring techniques as the slow-motion camera have caused a breakthrough in this area. Second, Mrs. Klein was able to reconstruct fantasies of infantile staging areas by inferences drawn from the analyses of very young children, one of whom was two years of age (yet it must be pointed out that Klein's inferences were based upon the reconstructions of earlier fantasies). Finally, there seems to be a confusion among many analysts about the difference between "early" and "deep." I speculate that the infant experiences himself as being separate as well as nonseparate from the very beginning of life, according to what I call a dual-track conception, and, insofar as there is some perception by virtue of this separation, this infant does have capacity to perceive and to think, no matter how rudimentarily.

Reconstruction, as a way of gaining a picture of early mental life, also differs between classical and Kleinian authors. To classical analysts it seems to mean the establishment of linkages to past memories of key childhood events and one's responses to them. In other words, some classical therapists attempt to reconstruct past events which are buried by repression, and consequently seek to reconstruct the past much in the manner of a detective. Other classical analysts may seek to use reconstructions in the present as well as in the past. My own impression is that Kleinian authors tend to use data about the past in order to reconstruct the present rather than the past. For instance, information coming from the patient about his parents would be thought of by a Kleinian as important genetic material on the one hand, but on the other hand, would be use of historic residues (corresponding to day residues in free association) in order to illustrate a transference point of the present. To Mrs. Klein, reconstruction meant the attempt to link up with one's infantile self as a continuing entity into the past. Bower (1974) has done immense research in this area to show how a child achieves verbal capacity and then tries to assign his verbal knowledge to preverbal structures.

Reconstruction to a Kleinian is the attempt to undo primal repression as well as secondary repression and to achieve integrative unity with one's self. Insofar as primal repression includes those areas of self which were never conscious in the first place, reconstruction seeks to contact them in order to persuade them into consciousness so as to achieve greater psychic expansion and maturity. Many patients, for instance, will seek to recreate their own birth in fantasy. This can often be seen as a series of fantasies beginning with a parthenogenetic notion of birth, followed by a birth from mother without a father being involved, then being born from father without a mother being involved. Finally, with the acceptance of the oedipus complex, the parental genital birth is accepted.

While this notion is not incompatible with Freud's frequent speculations about early infantile fantasies, most classical authors seem more freely to commingle early childhood or infantile fantasies with notions of early childhood reality, whereas Kleinians tend to adhere to the reconstruction of early infantile fantasies exclusively.

The Kleinian infant therefore seems to be one of the continuing biography of what to classical analysts would be the id but to Kleinian analysts would be an id-ego in "joint tenancy." Hartmann (1939, 1964) has gone a long way to demonstrate that ego functions exist along with instinctual functions in the undifferentiated state. Therefore, we might say that the continuing Kleinian infant resembles a continuation of Hartmann's undifferentiated state. The portraiture of this deep infant undergoes changes due to the modifications which maturation and experience impose upon it. It is no longer the infant of a calendar but rather it is the infant of the depths. This infant is the organizer of the primitive mental mechanisms of primary process, dream work, projective identification, splitting, idealization, magic omnipotent denial, manic defenses, and the whole gamut of primitive narcissistic relations. Its portraiture, I believe, is constantly being modified via unconscious reconstructions. It is my belief, based on my understanding of Erikson (1950, 1959), that this is the truest function of reconstruction, the reestablishing of communication with our earliest past and then extending this past forward.

In conducting the reconstruction of infantile fantasies Mrs. Klein was able to allow the infant to have complete ownership of himself from the very beginning. Moreover, a sense of genetic continuity from the very beginning of life was established by her concept of fantasy. Freud (1926) was himself aware of this concept of genetic continuity when he alluded to the progression of anxiety from the separation anxiety of birth to castration anxiety, which takes place by displacing cathexis from the object to the organ which reassures reunion with the object. Yet Freud did not have a theory to support the notion of early infantile mental life capable of experiencing the anxiety of separation.

Mrs. Klein's theory becomes, I believe, that fulfillment of Freud's genetic hypothesis which he himself could not establish. The castration anxiety of a boy in the phallic period could now be related to earlier fantasies of invasion of mother's breast and scooping it out, leaving a big castrated hole which is then equated with a threatening vagina. Difficulties in toilet training could now be seen to be due to the second stage of weaning from omnipotence—the first being from the breast and the second being from the omnipotent value given to one's own feces. The mother who is conducting the toilet training is viewed by the infant as one who is robbing him of his valuable products, as once upon a time he believed himself to have robbed her of her valuable breasts.

Thus, Klein was able to transcend the Freudian notion of autoerotism and construct a psychology of a relationship between self and object even earlier. This enabled reconstruction of infantile sexuality as autoerotism in particular and of infantile sexuality in general as due to frustrations of an even earlier object relationship. In other words, Freud considered the castration complex as due, for instance, to the boy's perception of the female vagina. Klein added step one to what now appears as (Freud's) step two in the following manner: the infant's greedy and envious attacks on the breast create, via projective identification, the image of a greedily and enviously destroyed breast as well as of a breast which is infused with the greedy, envious infant himself. The vagina may appear to the male infant as the condensed and compressed residue from these earlier infantile attacks and may be experienced as a vagina dentata as a result. Thus the first castrator is the infant who castrates mother's breast and then perceives the castrated vagina as his nemesis. Alternatively, he may project this castrating infant-breast (internal object) into his father and perceive the father as castrator, much as the child damaged father's wife once upon a time.

Certainly it is true that parental influences in the phallic-oedipal period can be very important in the development of the castration complex in the child by virtue of reinforcing his fears about his own instinctual impulses of incestuous desire for mother and competitive feelings towards father. It is my impression, and I believe the impression of Kleinians generally, that this is rarely if ever the entire case, however. The child at the phallic-oedipal stage perceives mother in strikingly oral dependent terms as well as in incestuous sexual terms and, more often than not, the very incestuous drive is but an attempt to master the frustrating object of oral dependency of yesteryear. Fantasies of phallic penetration of mother are, after all, but the latest in an ontogenetic series of attempts at projective identification used in an attempt to enter mother in order to possess her exclusively. Castration anxiety is, after all, but a specific example of separation anxiety. It denotes, in other words, the anxiety the infant develops when confronted by the absence of the beloved dependent object, his mother. It may very well be more of a mistake to analyze castration anxiety strictly in terms of the phallic stage then it is to analyze the full epigenetic significance of its separation theme.

It is not easy to say what is the classical position on this link between early oral and later infantile sexual zonal phenomena. This is due to the great variations in emphases and styles which, in my opinion, characterize the clinical work of classical analysts as best as one can infer from a broad reading of the literature. Kleinian therapists tend to adhere more strictly to the definitive analysis of the archaic self in its projective identificatory and splitting transformations in the paranoid-schizoid and depressive positions. While the pleomorphism of classical analysts would allow on one extreme those who might essay the analysis of infantile fantasies transactionally (as Klein does) and then link them with later childhood events, others at the other extreme might be content with what they believe to be realistic memory traces which they then believe to be repeated per se as symptoms and character structure in the patient's later development.

Kleinian analysis technically differs from the classical psychoanalytic technique insofar as it emphasizes dealing with this continuing infantile id-ego as active in the present as opposed to being a historic memory. In short, the three-week-old infantile self (the hegemony of the paranoid-schizoid position) is a fantasied representation of one's three-week-old self transformed from a calendar reference point to a psychic depth point of primitivization: the primitive infant is a fantasy that a patient today might have about his own depth. Analysis with Kleinians therefore is predominantely of the present rather than of the past. It was Freud (1899) who bequeathed to us the knowledge that reality, past or present, is unanalyzable. The past can be analyzed only in terms of the fantasies about it which are still actively present and lingering dynamically. In order to continue, they are linked with primary processes in the id (Freud 1900).

Freudian analysts, recently Kohut in particular, often take patient's statements about their past histories at face value and seem to accept the heresay evidence of their patients as accurate in regard to their treatment at the hands of their parents. Kohut (1971, 1977) goes so far as to incriminate parents as defective in their capacities to offer normal gran-diosity to their infants and, further, as defective in their own capacity to be idealized by the infant-child, and all this is ascertained by virtue of the patient's productions. This principle of the acceptance of the patient's verdict of his own reality is then often conjoined with the repetition compulsion so as to construct a theorem that the patient is repeating a past trauma. What is left out of this by many classical analysts, in my experience, is the notion of the fantasy which the reality precipitated. Kleinians seem closer to the more conservative psychoanalytic point of view that reality is a precipitant of fantasy, and its fantasy precipitant is the only analyzable element, not reality itself.

THE INFANTILE NEUROSIS

Another important aspect of early Freudian theory was the ambiguity Freud bequeathed to us in his use of the term *infantile*. Freud (1909a) seems to have been convinced of an infantile genesis to personality and symptom development but was at a loss to account for it earlier than the oedipal complex of later *childhood*. He could not definitively establish infantile way stations for neurosis because he could not account for object relations or conflictual organization prior to the oedipus complex. Stages of libidinal development prior to the oedipus complex were autoerotic and were conflictual only with reality rather than internally conflictual. The id had no conflicts within itself. Internal conflict could not develop until the ego developed, and the ego did not develop fully enough to have a conflict until the oedipus complex because objects could not be internalized until this time.

Since Freud's introduction of the conception of the infantile neurosis, that is, since his analysis of the Wolf Man (1918), psychoanalysis has paid homage and tribute to the central importance of infantile neurosis as an underlying, constellating, organizing principle of early mental life. This concept was to include the oedipus complex on the one hand and the pregenital components on the other as regressive elaborations of the oedipus complex. Infantile neurosis came to be equated with the oedipus complex and to displace it as a centralizing conception. Since the terms "infantile" and "neurosis" are central to the discussion of the differences between Kleinian and classical authors, I should therefore like to dwell at some length on some important contributions to the understanding of this important phenomenon.

In 1954, Kris conducted a symposium on "Problems of Infantile Neurosis." Anna Freud, one of the participants, questioned whether the infantile neurosis could really be called a neurosis before a pathogenic conflict was fully internalized. Preferring to use a structural approach in defining the infantile neurosis, she stated, "But since there is today a very wide divergence of opinion as to when the personality structure is set up, this will still leave many authors with the concept of neuroses occurring in the first year of life" (p. 43). Spitz, in the same symposium, negated the idea of a neurosis occurring in the first year of life, seemingly questioning the use of the word infantile. Greenacre divided infantile neurosis into two separate concepts: "one, meaning the outbreak of overt neurotic symptoms in the period of infancy, i.e., approximately before the age of six; second, meaning the inner structure of infantile development, with or without manifest symptoms, which forms, however, the basis of a *later neurosis*" (p. 18). She preferred the second meaning of the term.

Nagera (1966) states that the infantile neurosis appears when the child has reached the phallic-oedipal level of development. "The infantile neurosis is, in my view, an attempt to organize all the previous and perhaps manifold neurotic conflicts and developmental shortcomings, with all the conflicts typical of phallic-oedipal phase, into a single organization, into a single unit of the highest economic significance" (p. 57). Yet he states later in the same contribution, "It is not yet completely clear to us which factors are decisive in determining the level at which the neurotic struggle would take place or the neurosis organize itself—at least temporarily—at this stage. A significant factor in this connection is the presence or absence in any given case of important early fixations at the oral and anal phases. The more important the early fixations, the stronger is the backward pull on the drives that have reached the higher levels of development" (p. 59). Although Nagera does not state so explicitly, I understand him to mean that the infantile neurosis predicates the phallic-oedipal stage of development, but at the same time is itself predetermined by early preoedipal factors. In so stating, he is in effect allowing for a continuity of mental life from an earlier time with the phallic-oedipal stage.

Rangell (1972) has offered the conception that the oedipus complex can be viewed as a psychic organizer in the sense that Spitz has employed the term. Mahler (1975) finally has done justice to a necessary reconsideration of the infantile neurosis by questioning whether it really occurs as late as the phallic-oedipal stage. She tries to link it up with her explorations of the autistic, symbiotic, and separation-individuation phases of development. Mahler would assign infantile neurosis to the rapprochement phase of separation-individuation, that is, to the second half of the second year. One has the impression, however, that the origins of the rapprochement stage are being pushed back even earlier.

Tolpin (1970) reviews the psychoanalytic literature on the infantile neurosis and points out that

> unfortunately, Freud blurred the clarity of this metapsychological concept when he loosely referred to clinically manifest disorders associated with the oedipal stage as infantile neurosis. . . . Freud's confusing use of the same term to designate two distinct, although related, psychological phenomena, which are on fundamentally different levels of conceptualization (the force and the symptomatic manifestations of that force), as been continued in the literature to the detriment of the clarity of the concept of infantile neurosis. (p. 274)

> I would recommend that clinical disorders, regardless of their stage of origin or their underlying organization, not be referred to as infantile neurosis. These would be described as childhood disorders, neurotic or otherwise, or simply as mental disorders in children. The term infantile neurosis should be reserved for the metapsychological concept that designates the repressed potentially pathogenic oedipal conflict (associated with the phallic-oedipal phase) which is central in the pathology of the transference neurosis. (p. 278)

Although Tolpin does yeoman duty in her attempts to clarify the ambiguities of the concept of the infantile neurosis, she undermines her own efforts. First she calls attention to the fact that the infantile neurosis is an unsuitable term for the phallic-oedipal stage and then undoes this objection by redefining it in exactly those terms, a pitfall from which, in my opinion, no classical analyst prior to Mahler has disengaged.

Ritvo (1974) and Loewald (1970) have also written on the current status of the concept of the infantile neurosis and have come to conclusions similar to those of Tolpin. The current status, in short, is that infantile neurosis should be used as a metapsychological concept to denote a configuration of psychic structure rather than, as in its older usage, a clinical illness occurring in the infantile period. Again, none of the authors seems to be impressed by the fact that the oedipus complex on the phallic level is not infantile; and if it is on the infantile level, it is not a neurosis. Moreover, the classical trend is more in the direction of redefining the "infantile neurosis" in terms of a metapsychological concept and is farther away from the denotation of its phenomenology.

Klein's conception of the paranoid-schizoid and depressive positions and the fantasies which are their content expresses better, in my opinion, the phenomenology, that is, the experience, of the truly infantile neurosis. Although Klein and her followers have not specifically stated so, it is my own belief that *their* concept of the infantile neurosis is one of a continuing "infant of the depths," not merely the "calendar infant"—a concept that I shall deal with at some length later in this presentation. As a consequence, if my theory is correct, the Kleinian infantile neurosis is always being reconstructed in *statu nascendi*. It is the essence of constant reconstruction in phantasy extending over a lifetime.

In another contribution (Grotstein 1977) I have challenged the classical conception of the infantile neurosis in the following way. I have suggested that Freud employed two separate tracks of genetic conceptualizations for development; one was the truly infantile which he discussed in his paper "On Narcissism" (1914); and the other was his conception of an oedipus complex due to instinctual development specific to the phallic stage. Certainly the classical notion of the infantile neurosis, except for the modifications which Mahler has suggested, does not qualify for serious consideration as "infantile" since infantile describes a period of development which, in the older classification, was largely oral and maybe slightly anal but never phallic. The anal stage of development characterizes the toddler stage, and the phallic stage of development would correspond to early childhood. It was, after all, only Klein who posited that the oedipus complex occurred in the early infantile stage. Classical analysts went to great lengths to attempt to discredit this idea. And thus, to me, the classical notion of the infantile neurosis really corresponds to a childhood neurosis. Moreover, Anna Freud questions even the possibility of neurosis at *this* stage because of her belief that psychic structures are not fully intact.

It is my belief that the *infantile neurosis* is a term which should be placed on a continuum, beginning with infantile psychosis and continuing as infantile neurosis at a later stage (Grotstein 1978b). It, in turn, is followed by a childhood neurosis. Klein has hypothesized internal psychic structures created through projective identification and introjection occurring at an exceedingly early period of life. These correspond to what I believe should be called an infantile psychosis, not an infantile psychotic state but rather a period in which psychotic mechanisms such as splitting, projective identification, magic omnipotent denial, and idealization dominate the infant's mental life. These comprise the hegemony of the paranoid-schizoid position which peaks at approximately three weeks of postnatal life. The depressive position, which Klein posits at approximately three to four months of age (currently thought to be the first beginnings of the hatching stage of separation-individuation) corresponds, in my opinion, to the infantile neurosis. A childhood neurosis would, in my opinion, more logically occur at the time of the phallic-oedipal stage.

One of the problems which has complicated our conception of the infantile neurosis is the confusion about the conception of the oedipus complex itself. To classical analysts the oedipus complex is a phallic, that is, an early genital phenomenon. In Klein's conception, the oedipus complex begins virtually at birth, not so much as phallic-genital phenomenon, but as a denotation of an intrusion by a third mysterious factor into the bonding between the infant and the breast/mother, so that the experience of envy, greed, and jealousy can be thought of as yet a third factor which attacks this linking. This becomes the progenitor of sibling and parental rivalry. In other words, Klein and her followers believe the oedipus complex to be on a continuum, the final phase being phallic-gential. She also posits the infant's inborn pre-knowledge of parental intercourse in a conception more in keeping with ethologists.

NARCISSISM AND INTERNAL OBJECTS

Freud's paper "On Narcissism" (1914) seems to have opened the door for speculation about very early infantile development on an alternative track to the object drive track implied by instincts. In this paper, he dealt with the way of relating to objects known as identification, which was antecedent to anaclitic or dependent object relations. This notion of the infant's relation to objects via identification prior to anaclitic object choice was to be a major springboard for Melanie Klein's concept of projective identification.

In "Mourning and Melancholia," Freud (1917) tried again to fill in the infantile gap by postulating a narcissistic object loss resulting in the internalization of objects which were in conflict with one another at this stage of development. In short, he postulated that in depression the narcissistic loss which precipitated the depression seeks to be magically nullified by the introjection of the lost object in two locales, one in the ego-ideal (later superego) and the other in the ego. Splitting of the object is implied as is splitting of the ego. A maximum of sadism, according to Freud, is assigned to the ego-ideal and the object to which it is attached; these, in turn, attack the ego in its identification with the lost object. Internal objects and their conflictual organizations were thus born.

With the concept of projective identification as elaborated in "On Narcissism" and the establishment of the presence of internal objects (and egos) as established in "Mourning and Melancholia," Klein then conceived of the possibility that infants relate to objects through projective identification, and, in so doing, reintroject a projectively altered image of that object to constitute a new internal object within the ego. Further, because of the splitting mechanisms which Freud demonstrated in melancholic illness, the infant could now be seen to comprise many split-off objects and subsidiary egos. They were, in short, much like miniature personalities dissociated from one another but all within the ego. Klein did not make clear, unfortunately, that she was using such terms as impulse, greed, envy, and object relationship almost interchangeably at times. Thus, when an infant is thought to have a hostile or loving impulse towards an object, he transforms that object in his imaginative experience by his *communicative relationship* to that object (a transactional concept) rather than discharging an impulse into an object—the latter being the way Freud generally used the term impulse. Yet Klein's use of the communicative aspects of impulse were taken from Freud's clearly implied transactional conception of identification in his paper "On Narcissism."

In epitomizing Klein's notion of the development of infantile narcissism, I should like to make use of the paradigm of Biblical *Genesis*. When God, the Infant, first opened His eyes after descending from the face of the deep, He believed He had discovered everything His eyes opened up to. When He saw the light, He believed He had created it. When He saw a good mother and a father who gave Him good feelings, He believed that His own good feelings created a good Adam and Eve in the Garden of Eden. Eden was the paradise He had come from. He knew it only in retrospect after He was forced to leave it. Thanks to projective identification, He could imagine Himself back inside this marvelous paradise, and His envasseled objects, his parents, Adam and Eve, were to maintain this illusion of paradise by their special way of handling Him. Bad or frustrating feelings were to develop Cain, the anthropomorphization of the death instinct. Thus we can see how Biblical paradise is created by a projective identification.

The first rent in Biblical paradise is the snake's offering of the apple to Eve. The invitation to bite into the apple represents the normal desire of the Infant to avail himself of His epistemophilic instinct in order to grow, to search and to be curious.[1] Because it is inimical or conflictual to His desire to stay in paradise, the God/Infant projects His epistemophilic instinct into His parents and then curses them for their desire to know each other, the first contact with the primal scene. The curse upon the primal scene causes the expulsion from paradise and the crime of Cain.

I am emphasizing not just projective identification but also the concept of fantasy in general, which helps the child to create his own first internal world, his narcissistic world, by imagining omnipotently that external or alien objects are themselves projected fantasies from himself.

Frustration in conjunction with the conceptualization of the primal scene punctures the omnipotent narcissistic world and simultaneously confronts the infant with what appears at first to be *other* narcissistic worlds. These later develop into external and separate realities which are no longer believed to be created and controlled by one's own omnipotent narcissism. This is the threshold of the depressive position. In an attempt to continue omnipotent narcissism and postpone the depressive position, the infant has relegated his omnipotent power to his former vassals, Adam and Eve, by idealizing them. This becomes the second stage of narcissism in the descent of omnipotence. Here again projective identification is of key importance. The infant transfers his omnipotence to his objects via projective identification but imagines himself to be inseparable or confused with them as well as separate at the same time—a paradox which characterizes the second narcissistic stage. It can be seen as the object relations characterizing symbiosis. The parents are idealized in proportion as maturation takes place and the infant's own infantile omnipotence becomes gradually perforated. Freud (1914) himself was in total agreement with this.

According to Klein (1952), the narcissistic infant idealizes the parent in order to maintain omnipotence and to protect his own welfare. A frustrating object is also narcissistic, however, because it has become invested with the will to frustrate the child. Since the child can imagine himself wanting to frustrate the parents until they do exactly what he wants for his benefit, he can, at the same time, imagine them doing the same thing

1. I am indebted to Dr. Albert Mason for his discovery of the epistemophilic conception implicit in Eve's biting of the apple.

to him because of projective identification. All actions, therefore, are solipsistic and omnipotent.

Kohut (1971, 1977) and Kernberg (1975, 1976), long after Klein, Winnicott, and Rosenfeld, also explored narcissism, and have come up with their own views which seem like amalgams of the theories of the earlier workers, together with unique contributions of their own. Kohut, after Winnicott (1962), believes that the central difficulty in narcissistic personality disorders is a developmental defect in the formation of self-esteem that is precipitated by a bad parental environment. The resultant narcissistic sensitivity manifests itself as a defectively grandiose self yielding an inadequate mirror transference (in analysis) and an inadequately idealized object which develops a poorly idealized transference. Kohut does not explain the development of the idealized transference as due to projective identification via idealization from the self into the object. He also does not explain the development of the omnipotent self as an introjection of the idealized grandiose self.

While seeming to eschew or to minimize the importance of the structural theory and its associated instinctual associations, Kohut's latest work strikes me as the use of Freud's exhibitionistic and voyeuristic part instincts in a sophisticated and quasi-sublimated way to account for the grandiose and mirror transference phenomena. Kohut believes, in other words, that the child suffers a loss of developmental self-esteem if he is not allowed to develop a normally grandiose self which is mirrored by an adoring parental audience. Likewise, the child suffers from a lack of self-esteem if his parents are not able to be normally idealized by him so that he can use them as models for the establishment of his sense of pride in parentage. Like so many classical formulations since Freud, this theory falls more into the overall conception of Hartmann's theory of adaptation and the average expectable environment, and Erikson's concept of the cog-wheeling of the sense of identity, as well as Winnicott's conception of maternal care and concern. In other words, this trend seems to be more in keeping with the notion of the prime importance of reality in fashioning the infant's life. Good models produce an infant with good self-esteem, and bad models establish a defective sense of self-esteem in the narcissistic portion of the personality, according to Kohut. In all this there is little if any mention of fantasies, let alone unconscious fantasies. Yet one of Kohut's most striking contributions is the conception of separate tracks for the development of the self and of object relations on the one hand, and of the grandiose versus the idealizing self on the other. The attention he directs to the differentiation of these tracks is of great importance, I believe. Kleinian analysis does not emphasize the self in contrast to the object. Kleinian analysts, for instance, seldom deal with the phenomenon of *shame*.

Kernberg (1975), on the other hand, who seems to be somewhat familiar with Kleinian concepts and who seems to use them quite freely in his own formulations, has conceived of the pathological narcissism in terms of a mad omnipotent self comprised of an ego-ideal, a superego, and a mad omnipotent infant. His conceptions *suggest*, but do not state, that the mad omnipotent infant projects himself into the ego-ideal and the superego to make them mad also, thereby establishing grandiose internal objects. At least he is employing Klein's conception of projective identification in so doing—unlike Kohut, in my estimation. Kernberg's conception is much in keeping with that of Rosenfeld and of other early Kleinian authors.

Both Kohut's (1971, 1977) and Kernberg's (1975) conceptions of narcissism have been anticipated by Klein's conception of projective identification. Kohut emphasizes the mirroring and idealizing aspects of the infant's development in establishing a grandiose self and an idealized object. He believes furthermore that narcissistic defects occur when the caretaking environment is unable to supply this reinforcement of omnipotence. Kernberg follows Rosenfeld's notion of the "mad omnipotent child" and combines it with the ego and superego to account for the psychopathology of narcissism. He leaves obscure the origin of the mad omnipotent child and, although he refers to projective identification, he does not adequately link it up, in my opinion, with the projective-introjection of the infant's destructive (envious) and hyperlibidinal (greedy) impulses.

Klein's conception of narcissism has escaped notice because most classical authors have been distracted by her emphasis on *objects* and not on the *self*. I do believe this is a fault in the way Klein and her followers have expressed themselves. My own reading of Klein's work—and that of her followers—has afforded me the following picture of the Kleinian theory of narcissism. It is almost as if the external world of the narcissistic infant has the main purpose of reflecting good impulses and of discrediting bad ones. The infant loves himself not only because mother loves him and because he later internalizes this maternal love; the infant loves himself primarily because his objects are a mirror of his goodness and therefore demonstrate his capacity to love. The mirror aspects of the object's opinion of the self is, therefore, of crucial importance. The emphasis of Klein's theory is in starting with fantasies which help the patient understand his own autochthonous and syncretistic (imagined) power to create objects which reflect either his good or bad qualities. Without so stating, therefore, Klein seems to implicate a dual-track theory, much like Kohut's, which reflects the separate development of the object relations of the self and of the self alone. It is to Kohut's credit that he specified what Klein implied.

My own conception of the infantile narcissistic state is that each author (that is, Kohut and Kernberg and, for that matter, the Kleinian and other classical writers) has made valuable contributions which complement each other. In studying the phenomenon of narcissism, I became impressed by the need for a dual-track conception in order to account for two separate kinds of phenomena. In other words, not only do I conceive of the infant as being born separate and nonseparate at the same time, but I believe that the phantasies to which Kernberg and the Kleinians are alluding to be correct insofar as the pathologically narcissistic infant wishes to idealize his objects in order to be identified with such omnipotent objects, or, conversely, wishes to enslave or to envassel his objects so that they can mirror his own omnipotent greatness. Both states of mind are achieved through the infant's phantasies of an invasive projective identification into the object. In the former case, possessive and omnipotently idealized feelings are thrust onto the object and the newly installed idealized object is mysteriously and magically connected with the self— thus, the infantile idealizing transference. In the second state the idealized object is invaded and his/her idealized qualities are purloined by the invasive self and thus split-off from the object and repossessed by the invasive self.

Kohut, on the other hand, conceives of two separate tracks for infantile development: one for instinctual development, leading toward fantasies, and the other, although involved in fantasies of idealization and grandiosity, involving the conception of the reality of the parents' idealizability and his mirroring of the infant's grandiosity. Thus, Kohut can be seen as sponsoring a form of a dual-track theorem which counterbalances reality and fantasy, which renders him in proper lineal descent from Fairbairn (1952), Winnicott (1958, 1965), and Bion (1962, 1963, 1965, 1970). The infant may truly suffer from a sense of loss or from a defect in his capacity to emerge and to flower in the development of his self-esteem if he has parents who are unable to give him that care and concern which his birthright seems to demand. What Kohut seems not to be clear about is the limitation of the infant's capacity to perceive his objects other than in fantasy. Thus, my dual-track theory suggests that the separate infant (track one) may seek to develop his healthy narcissistic core by developing a sense of regard and respect for the objects who nurture him. Alternatively, the nonseparate infant of track two is experienced as a continuation of primary narcissism and therefore may expect the adulation and fealty of his subjects, his parents. Insofar as he can give credit and gratitude to his nurturing objects for his survival, he internalizes objects with which he identifies to give the end result of *self-esteem*. That is the Kleinian conception of normal narcissism. Abnormal narcissism is the infant's attempt to maraud his image of his needed object so as to possess its goodness, thereby remaining grandiose, omnipotent and unborn. This latter conception would affect the second track conception, that is, the continuation of primary narcissism or the state of primary identification. According to Tustin (1978), a Kleinian, abnormal narcissism probably begins oftentimes as a premature rent or rupture in the inchoate oneness of primary identification.

SPLITTING OF THE EGO AND OF INTERNAL OBJECTS

After strongly implying that splitting of the ego corresponds to a splitting of the internalized objects, in "Analysis Terminable and Interminable" (1938) and "Splitting of the Ego in the Process of Defence" (1940), Freud dealt more firmly with conflicts between internal objects. His paper, "Fetishism," (1927), more fully explored splitting of the ego and presaged the later papers. Despite these investigations into the internalization of objects which were the results of narcissistic and therefore preoedipal conflicts, psychoanalysis nevertheless seemed to veer away from the notion of early internalization and conflictualization. Difficulty in understanding the formation of the superego prior to the resolution of the oedipus complex proved insurmountable. Psychoanalysis was therefore fated to continue to deal largely with an amalgam of Freud's three major theories of psychoanalysis: namely, the traumatic memory, infantile sexuality, and the repetition compulsion. The internal world classical authors were thereafter to deal with was an introjected external world which had been colored and transformed either by traumatic experience or sexual impulses and was then to be repeated in later life in symptoms and in character formation.

The Kleinian internal world, on the other hand, was first created by projective identification from within the infant, which was then modified by the external world before it was reintrojected.

Kernberg's (1975) conception of splitting in the borderline personality and in the development of normal object relations comes closest to a classical parallel with Klein's (1952) use of splitting. Although Kernberg uses nonphenomenological terms for the early infantile stage (such terms as self-object representations orchestrated by the affects so that there can then exist a good self-object representation and a bad self-object representation based upon the experiences of pleasurable and unpleasurable affects), he nevertheless is denoting a split between one self attached to a corresponding object and another self attached to another corresponding object so that the phenomenon of a miniature dissociation is clearly delineated by him. According to Klein (1952), splitting of the ego corresponds to a splitting of the objects. The purpose of splitting the objects is to protect the necessary good object from the destructive aspects of the bad object. Thus, splitting is initially a protective device.

SPLITTING AND PROJECTIVE IDENTIFICATION: THE PARANOID-SCHIZOID POSITION

I do not believe that the full impact of Mrs. Klein's extension of Freud's concept of fantasy has been fully appreciated. By conceptualizing that instincts themselves were also fantasies and by employing two mechanisms alluded to by Freud—*splitting* and *projective identification*—she reasoned that the infant could create objects as phantoms via generalizations from himself and from his feelings (Freud 1909b, 1912, 1917, 1919, Klein 1929, 1933, 1935, 1940, and Klein et al. 1952, 1957). By generalization I am referring to the tendency in primitive infantile thinking for the object to be generalized via assignment of similarities from the infant's own repertoire of his limited experience of himself. He assigns his familiar self to the object and discovers it by making friends with it, so to speak. When objects are brought together, the common elements which unite them can be located and generalized upon. Freud (1900) called this phenomenon *condensation*. The principle of distinction accounts for the mechanism known as splitting whereby the infant is able to mitigate generalization and allow good and bad or pleasant and unpleasant to be separated. Freud called this *displacement*.

Klein was thus able to account for an earlier, more archaic internal, conflictual world than was Freud. The formation of this world was due largely to projective identification, acting with splitting to create an internal fantasy world which was, in the first instance, a reification of the infant's own instinct-fantasies.

When the infant God of *Genesis* was first born, it would seem that He opened His eyes and believed He had created everything His eyes had opened up to. This *is* projective identification. The world of Eden which He created was the result of the projective identification of His instinctual impulses (preconceptions). The objects of the external world are perceived only in terms of the modifications they make upon His impulses. Klein infers that when mother gives the infant a good feeding, the infant believes he has created this experience. Likewise, frustration or deprivation is a confirmation of his own feelings of badness. Klein has often been criticized because of her neglect of external reality. I believe this criticism to be quite unfair. Melanie Klein speaks of reality as she believes the infant experiences it. The infant's first reality is the externalization and then reinternalization of his own insides, so to speak. The external world modifies this experience, but the awareness of this modification does not dawn on the infant until he is able to withstand and comprehend separation and individuation in the depressive position, she believes. Causality is solipsistic, that is, from within. The awareness of causality from the outside must await further maturation of the ego.

Freud's internal world, by contrast, is that of external objects who are initially perceived hyperlibidinally or hyperaggressively. Thus, the external mother is the object of incestuous wishes for the male child, as the father is for the female, and the contralateral parent is the object of rivalrous hostility. As I explained earlier, the rivalrous hostility in the contralateral parent is due to projective identification, but this projective identification is much more sophisticated than its infantile precursor and involves more realistically perceived external objects.

Only lately have classical analysts attempted to deal with the psychology of the object relations of pregenitality. Jacobson (1964) has discussed object images occurring in the oral period; Erikson (1950, 1959), basic trust and distrust; Kohut (1971), the development of the grandiose self and the mirror transference in narcissistic disorders; and Kernberg (1976), the mad omnipotent self in narcissistic disorders and splitting of selves and of objects in borderline personality disorders. Of these, only Kernberg seems to be familiar with the mechanism of archaic projective identification.

Projective identification is the instrument of the solipsistic, narcissistic primary process which characterizes the infant's discovery of his own world via mirror projections, as Klein seems to use the term. In the primal void of postnatal separation, the infant seeks to explore himself in his new world and to slip back into fusion with his mother in the state of sleep. Exploration of the new world hopefully will develop into his desire to differentiate and to grow, whereas his desire for sleep may become the forerunner of repression and states of defense against feelings. The latter is a regressive dedifferentiation and is an example of projective identification used as a defense. The former is an example of explorative projective identification in which the infant seeks to discover new or alien objects by their feel on his sense organs.

In contradiction to Freud's theory, Mrs. Klein seems to have believed that the pleasure principle and the reality principle were operant simultaneously and from the very beginning. The Kleinian infant seems to be integrally separated from the primal object (mother) at the very beginning of extrauterine life although he or she simultaneously experiences varying states of nonseparation. The classical Freudian infant is primarily undifferentiated gradually, differentiating from a state of autism (Mahler 1971) into symbiosis and later into separation-individuation. Mahler's concepts, a refinement of the earlier classical conceptions of infancy, in contrast to Mrs. Klein, place differentiation quite late. Until my own recent efforts, no attempts had been made to reconcile these disparate views.

I have tried to reconcile the Kleinian inference of initial separation with the classical inference of primary confusion by offering the concept of a dual-track theory to account for two different simultaneous infantile experiences. One experience is that of initial separation and the other is one of continuing postnatal oneness or primary narcissistic undifferentiation. The separated self functions so as to grow and develop through explorative projective identification but may elect to regress back into a state of secondary undifferentiation through defensive projective identification (Grotstein 1978a). The continuing primary undifferentiated track gradually develops into a separated or separating self as infancy, childhood, and adolescence are abandoned. I think the dual-track theory helps to account for Klein's phenomenological inferences and for the more observational findings of classical theorists. It also helps to reconcile the views of Kernberg and Kohut, for that matter, although the latter has a different kind of dual-track theory, as I discussed earlier.

Projective identification, in conjunction with splitting, seems to be a Rosetta stone to the hieroglyphic of inchoate, primitive, preverbal communication and is the architect as well of the internal objects which populate this early world. Freud's concept of primary process and its prime characteristic components, condensation and displacement, can now be seen to be the first vicissitudes of projective identification. In other words, projective identification, in conjunction with splitting, is the mechanism or vehicle by which Freud's instinctual drives express themselves. A patient who felt that he was being suffocated by the very act of riding in his car was able to see that the car was a necessary vehicle for his getting somewhere and was therefore a metaphoric displacement from another object, namely, the analyst on whom he also depended in order to get somewhere in life. Thus, displacement from the analyst to the car was an instinctual vicissitude based upon the projection or assignment of significance from the patient's instinctual needs to the object which was needed. All phobias follow a similar pattern insofar as needs and affects are projected into objects and then are split-off (displaced) into, generally, inanimate objects.

Condensation, on the other hand, is the experience of multiple projective identifications into a single object which may seem to alter the fundamental nature of the object or its fundamental significance. Any object in a dream which can be used for condensation will express the overdetermined (multiply projected) aspects of one's needs into this condensed object. For example, dreams of the analyst may reflect the imputing to (projecting upon) the analyst infantile needs as if he were mother or father, brother or sister, teacher or wife or husband, etc. Insofar as the analyst (or anyone, or anything for that matter) stands for all of these projections at the same time, projective identification can be seen to be the vehicle of condensation. In other words, projective identification, in conjunction with splitting, constitutes displacement and condensation, particularly after the splits have undergone precocious closure ("after-splitting"). (Precocious closure is a result of massive, seemingly permanent splitting-off of psychic elements which are no longer responsive to the rest of the personality.)

Now that Klein had established instincts as fantasies, they were no longer reductionistic, neurophysiological processes. Many new avenues of conceptualization then opened. For instance, orality could then be seen to be no longer an autoerotic impulse discharging tension from an oral mucous membrane when in contact with a breast. It became the relationship between an infant and his mother in which his mouth searched for her breast for nurture. Klein in effect established the transactional principle of object relations—that the infant is implicitly part of a dyad. Fairbairn (1952), Winnicott (1958, 1965), and Balint (1953, 1968) were to take up this issue more specifically in their contributions. Freud's theory of autoerotism seems to have negated this important biological truth. It was not until Erikson (1959) that this transactional dyad was to find a theoretical haven in classical theory. To return to the oral paradigm, however, the hungry infant in looking for the breast might fantasy his hunger as an internal bad breast biting him. That is, some internal object awakens him from his beatific slumber and causes him pain and also causes him to search for the good object to get rid of the bad object. It is this *feeling* of getting rid of the bad object by finding the good object which constitutes the fantasy of taking in something good and getting rid of something bad, a phenomenon which corresponds to Freud's discharge of impulse.

The badness of the internal object can be seen as a projective generalization from bad feelings associated with the self to the object which is believed to be the cause of one's bad feelings. A mother who is experienced by the infant as being frustrating becomes a bad mother by projective identification of his own destructiveness into her because of her seeming to confirm his bad impulses. This distinction is based upon the infant's capacity to recognize the external world and the limitations of this exploration because of the strictures upon his exploring psyche due to projective identification. A truly bad mother, however that be judged, becomes bad by virtue of confirming bad impulses. A good mother is good because she confirms good impulses. Yet a good mother can also confirm bad impulses since Klein advises us that the infant's envy or greed can attack the goodness of the breast and transform it into a bad breast. Yet even envy of the breast and its malevolent consequences can be mitigated by sufficient love, according to Klein.

A truly bad external mother, on the other hand, exaggerates envy and greed all the more because of the deficient supply of goodness which she offers. It must be remembered that the infant cannot perceive external reality with any degree of accuracy because of the limitations imposed upon his infantile psyche by its primitive instrumentality. It is only in the depressive position that he begins to develop the notion that mother can be bad in her own right.

One of the advantages of Mrs. Klein's employment of projective identification as the instrument of exploration (fantasy) was that she could avail herself of Freud's conception of the part instinct, epistemophilia, and detail the early aspects of its epigenesis and ontogenesis into the ego modality known as perception. The infant's exploratory fantasies are very concrete, Klein felt, and seek to possess concretely the very anatomy of the object. For instance, in the anal stage of development one would no longer be limited to explaining obsessive-compulsive neurosis as due to anal erotism but could hypothesize psychodynamically elaborate fantasies having to do with the infant's notion of wanting to invade the rear of his mother to take possession of the goodness he believes to be inside. Thus, playing with his own anus in infantile anal masturbation is believed by the infant, according to Meltzer (1966), one of Klein's followers, to be identical with touching mother's body in the same area and mastering separation by fusing with her in an omnipotent manner. Incestuous fantasies in the phallic-oedipal phase of development, moreover, reflect a more sophisticated aspect of projective identification in which the infant desires to get inside of mother in a more zonally advanced method.

Therefore, by positing instincts as fantasies, Mrs. Klein was able to allow for the construction of a very archaic, yet intricate language of communication between parts of the self and internal objects. Instead of instincts discharging, they were communicating with internal and external objects. Instincts were no longer reductionistic insofar as they would end at the mucous membranes where they could go no farther. Now they could be part of an endless series of fantasies which were trying to account for all the states of asymmetry which exist postnatally between the infantile ego and its objects of nurture. I should like to state a word more at this point to explain how this communication takes place—and how it results in the development of the infant's conception of external objects.

Once internal objects are formed on the basis of projective identification and subsequent introjection, they are installed as internal objects in two separate ways. According to Freud's melancholic paradigm (Freud 1917): *(a)* the infant internalizes what he believes he has done to the object, so that if he greedily attacks the object, he then internalizes a greedily mutilated breast which is identified with the ego; *(b)* insofar as the infant's greedy self (or envious self) is felt to invade the breast and becomes confused with it, he internalizes a greedy breast which then becomes a demanding, insatiable superego object.

Thus, at least two object internalizations occur in gradients in the ego due to projective identification, splitting, and subsequent reintrojection. Then, the infant reprojects not only his impulses, but also these variegated internal objects into objects in the external world so that his perceptions of external objects become even more complexly colored by these reprojections of their first modifications. Only gradually are these projections withdrawn from the external object as the depressive position ensues and reality becomes increasingly apparent.

THE DEPRESSIVE POSITION OF
SEPARATION-INDIVIDUATION

The solipsistic world is soon enough to butt up against another conception of the world, one which is not of one's own making: the world of infinite solipsisms, individuals, and of happenings beyond one's control and creation. This is the world of separation-individuation, or as Mrs. Klein (1952) called it, the depressive position. The road between the first internal world and the second conception of the world can be seen as the *via dolorosa* of the depressive position. According to Mrs. Klein, separation-individuation is achieved by the infant's surrendering fantasies of omnipotent possession of his objects. An internal object is a possessed object. That is the meaning of a narcissistic object; it is the fantasy of an object really being inside of the self.

In the depressive position, the infant begins to realize the awareness of an external world over which he has no control. He therefore surrenders the illusion or the fantasy of control of the external and internal objects. In lieu of fantasies of controlling the needed external object, he then develops thoughts or symbols in connection with the object. At the same time, he also seeks to withdraw sadistic fantasies from these objects and to repair the damage he believes he has done to them in the past. As this happens, the earlier splittings between good and bad now begin to come together in that rapprochement of ambivalence known as integration into wholeness of the object. In all, I would say that at the present juncture,

Mahler's and Klein's conceptions are complementary, although Mahler's subphase theory has given considerably more descriptive breadth to this stage. Klein's depressive position implies all the subphases but ignores the discreet delineations implicit in their differences, including them together in one phenomenological sweep. The importance of this stage for her and her followers is the establishment of the "gap," the space of separateness between self and object so that each can then be allowed to be human rather than omnipotent and can occupy separate and separating agendas. Weaning has been carried one significant step forward as omnipotent projections and splittings are recalled and "demobilized." The infant as well as the analysand who is at the threshold of the depressive position now begins to pine for the missing, separate object rather than for the part object (breast or its equivalent). This actually means phenomenologically and phantasmally that the infant (and patient) now allow the mother of separation to possess the breasts which offer goodness to the infant. Until this time, the possession of the breasts had been a contested issue. This acceptance of ownership amounts to a *reconciliation* or rapprochement with reality, internal as well as external. In other words, the infant owns his or her neediness and allows mother to own the breasts which nuture it.

This reconciliation or rapprochement with internal and external reality heralds the evolution of internal objects (self-objects in a state of fusion because of possessive projective identification) into object representations, the latter of which are phantoms or symbols occupying the place left vacant by the object in its absence after its release from within, thanks to reconciliation over the ownership of the breasts. Now representational object constancy begins.

INTROJECTION VERSUS PROJECTION

Classical theorists have constructed a schema of infantile development in which the infant grows largely through introjection of external experiences which are modified by the instinctual drives (early classical) and by the affects (Kernberg 1976). The emphasis on the importance of the introjection of the external world is a major characteristic of classical formulations which differs from Kleinian formulations. Klein implied (1960), and Bion explicitly stated (1970), that the external world is unknowable. We approach it by a constant series of projective identifications acting like radar to correct our images of it. Moreover, the Kleinian view of perception of external reality depends upon the release of an internal object to become an object representation. In short, the Kleinian point of view is that the external world develops only after the achievement of the depressive position, that is, after internal objects which axiomatically exist in a state of projective identification with the ego (self) are released by the self to become nonidentificatory objects and, instead, object representations. The Kleinian representational world is a release from an internal world, not the introjection of an external world. This is one of the most noteworthy differences between the two points of view. I myself would go much farther than Klein and state the proposition as follows: the human being's perception of his external world is based primarily upon his preconceptions of it from his world of early infantile projective identifications. He releases information (which he takes in) from their identificatory status and assigns them to a representational status. I believe this to be true for all data entering the central nervous system, and in terms of current neurological research, all data become sorted out by the (intuitive, emotional) right brain and then related to the left brain organization for abstractive computations (Galin 1974).

The classical position, in my estimation, is exactly the opposite. Classical authors seem to emphasize the importance of introjection and minimize the role of projective identification in the processing of data. Perhaps it would make it even easier if I stated that projective identification is simply another way of talking about the proposition that all data is first "worked over" by primary process (or as Bion [1963] prefers to call it, alpha function) in order to be processed by the instinctual world before this data can become aliment for the organ of thinking known as the mind. Introjection, initially, is a coverall for a complicated process in which the infant invades the image of an external object through projective identification. By this invasion, he assigns his own preconceptions and sensations to the object and experiences the object's modification of his preconceptions and sensations. It is this modification which is internalized. Thus, all objects of the external world become knowable first as sensual = concrete = internal objects; that is, the infant invades them with his own sense perceptions linked with memories of similar events and objects. They are then normally released into re-presentations, having acquired a symbolic essence usable as re-creations of the object for thinking, knowing, and storage (memory). The classical object representation emerges as an introjection of an external object without going through the aforementioned stages despite the fact that drives and affects are known to modify them.

The conflict between the reality and unreality of the ultrasensual object parallels a great epistemological debate among philosophers. Plato, Berkeley, Hume, and Kant have in various ways held the view that the mental object does not correspond exactly to the material object, whereas Descartes and Locke opted for the reality of the object of the senses as being true. The classical notion of the psychoanalytic object of the psyche—the representations, either of self or of object and for part objects—depends very heavily on the Lockeian notion of the verisimilitude of the representation to the object it represents. Hartmann (1964) and Jacobson (1964) in particular are identified with this point of view. Freud (1930) himself never altered his view that external reality emerged as a projection from the internal world.[2]

THE EVOLUTION OF THE "INFANT"

The evolution of an internal object into an object representation is a paradigm for the evolution of the infant from the paranoid-schizoid position to the depressive position and is thus a model for the following transformations: (a) of omnipotent narcissism into a normal narcissistic self separated from object representations; (b) of internal objects into object representations; and (c) of concrete sensations into perceptions and thoughts. From the Kleinian point of view, the maturation of the ego parallels the maturation of the conception of objects and of sensations so that, as narcissism proceeds from primary (omnipotent) narcissism, which is a state of identification with an ideal object, it devolves into a narcissistic self shorn of omnipotence and separated from an object. A dual track of nonomnipotent narcissistic self is counterposed to a nonomnipotent object representation. At the same time, internal objects, that is, objects which are experienced as being partially fused with the self (self-objects), are released from the possessive stranglehold of the omnipotent, narcissistic self. These internal objects are allowed to be free and separate, thereby evolving into object re-presentations. In other words, they are no longer objects concretely held within the psyche but are rather the souls or spirits of objects in the absence of the object. At the same time, the essential and concrete relationship to the object becomes a relationship to the essence of an object. In the object's absence, this relationship is ultrasensual and therefore spiritual.

Recent infantile observational research, as reviewed by Boston (1975) is beginning to provide evidence for an exceedingly early active infantile mental life which can be inferred to corroborate Klein's intuition of an organization of early infantile mental life. The experiments of Meltzoff and Moore (1977) show that the infant's imitative competence had been underestimated. They found that twelve-to twenty-day-old infants can

2. I am indebted to Dr. Melvin Lansky for reminding me of the philosophical-epistemological fallacies in the classical concept of the representational world.

imitate both facial and manual gestures. Their recent observations of facial imitation in six newborns—one only sixty minutes old—suggested that the ability to use intermodal equivalences is an innate ability of humans. They believe that we must revise our current conceptions of infancy, which hold that such capacity is the product of many months' of postnatal development, and believe instead that the ability to act on the basis of an abstract (spiritually hallucinated so as to achieve the essence of the object in its absence) representation of a perceptually absent stimulus becomes the starting point for psychological development in infancy and not its culmination.

Another distinguished researcher, Lewis Lipsitt (1977) has shown that there is extremely early functioning of all sensory modalities, particularly those for color discrimination, detail discrimination, depth perception, hearing, smell, touch, habituation, balance, and of early ego autonomies. Lipsitt states, "The newborn comes into the world with all sensory systems functional" (p. 180). Instead of pursuing this data, however, I should like to pursue a related avenue of approach, namely the evolution of the early infant into the continuing infant.

It is my belief, as I stated earlier, that the chronological infant evolves into the infant of the depths which perpetuates the continuity of the primitive experience: *early* becomes *deep*. Klein's concept of the three-week-old hegemony of the paranoid-schizoid position and the infant suffering it now can be seen from a different perspective.

The three vicissitudes of infantile experience are as follows: (a) maturation and development into an older and growing person who casts off the awareness of his infantile self or relegates it to memory; (b) maturational arrests or fixations which are states of splitting and of projective identification of an infant into an image of an object where he is now lost from his further maturational sequence. This is another way of saying that the roots of psychopathology, which have formerly been assigned to the conception of developmental fixations, belong to areas in one's infantile past which have been formed through splitting-off aspects of the self and its relationship to objects, and projective identification into a split-off conception of an object that persists separately from the rest of normal development. Also, (c) a continuing notion of the infantile self in terms of the awareness of one's sense of basic neediness and desire. This latter is the once-and-forever infant, the id. In all probability this "id" would be more accurately described as a primitive ego which has intimate contact with its instinctual self and is therefore in touch with its needs.

Klein's calendar dating of the paranoid-schizoid position at approximately three weeks of age finds some corroboration by Wolff (1966):

In [a] pilot study (1959) I referred to this state (waking activity) as *alert activity*; the term now seems inappropriate for the neonatal period since the infant gives no behavioral evidence of "alertness" (for example, he makes no visual and auditory pursuit movements); *at four weeks, however, the infant will respond selectively to visual stimuli even while he is active* [italics mine]. *I have therefore used the term "waking activity" for the neonatal period, and reserve the term "alert activity" for the more highly differentiated state that begins at about three and one half weeks, when the infant attends to environmental events at the same time as he is motorically active* [italics mine].

The observation by Wolff of a marked difference in neonatal activity at four weeks of age is supplemented by Benjamin's equivalent observation. Benjamin (1965), in discussing the "stimulus barrier hypothesis," discussed what he called the "maturational crisis" in infants which occurred at three to four weeks of age. He states:

[As previously reported] we noted that full-term infants showed a marked and relatively sudden increase in sensitivity to external and internal stimulation at the age of three-four weeks. The behavioral criteria are increased crying and other motor manifestations of negative affect, of unpleasure. The phenomenon is most easily accessible to naturalistic observation whenever, for one reason or another, the usual physiological needs of the infant are not well met. In all other cases, it is clearly demonstrable only when sensory stimulation in different modalities is experimentally introduced. [p. 58]

Thus Wolff and Benjamin are documenting what more and more infant observers are finding—that there is a definitive maturational crisis in infant development at three to four weeks of age, a finding which Klein clinically intuited almost two generations ago.

Lichtenberg (1979), a classical analyst, has recently reviewed the neonatal research data in depth and has tried to bring it into approximation with classical analytical theory. He finds that the neonatal research data is so sufficiently challenging to many of the precepts of psychoanalytic theory that revisions are in order. For instance, he states that the bulk of evidence derived from neonatal research is contradictory to the economic points of view and the drive discharge theory of classical psychoanalysis.

Lichtenberg has done psychoanalysis a great service in reviewing all the pertinent neonate research literature and bringing it to bear on psychoanalytic theory with the hope of a revision of the psychoanalytic conception of the neonate's state of being. At risk in psychoanalytic theory are not only drive theory and the economic principle, as Lichtenberg beautifully brings out, but also the psychoanalytic notion of when "being human" begins. Clearly, Mahler's conception of the beginning of mind during the hatching phase is obviously jeopardized by neonatal research. Neonatal research, according to Lichtenberg, seems to demonstrate very clearly that the neonatal infant has almost immediate humanness, mentation, consciousness, etc., and is preadapted to his mother from the start. In short, the research data suggest that the infant is immediately a personality upon birth. If so, this would lend greater credence to Klein's conception of early infantile development which has so long been at odds with the classical theory, which maintained a theory of the infant in the continuing postnatal slumber and quiescence of primary narcissism and "incubational bliss." Again, I think a better way of resolving this dilemma is to discredit neither Klein's or Mahler's approach but rather to place them both in a meta-theory which I have called the dual-track conception.

In summarizing much contemporary work, Lichtenberg concludes that neonatal infants are not necessarily quiescent and, furthermore, that prolonged quiescence is abnormal. Infantile research reveals that there is a high degree of stimulus hunger and search. He also concludes that the old conception of the oral infant needing an object for discharge and hunger satisfaction is obsolete and is to be replaced by a conception of an infant whose responsiveness is centered on and geared to a perceptual-motor-affective dialogue with his or her mother. Study after study, he points out, documents the neonate's preadaptive potential for a direct interaction, human to human, with his mother. The infant is responsive selectively and actively to sound frequencies within the range of his mother's voice. Lichtenberg points out that neonates react in a specifically responsive manner to their mother's chattering at them in a way that suggests active participation in a dialogue. Lichtenberg concludes, "it has been suggested that the neonate begins life with responses that are patterned differently for stimuli arising from human and inanimate objects" (p. 6).

Further, in summarizing the work of Bower, Lichtenberg adds that by the second week, infants prefer an actual three-dimensional object to a photograph of the same object. This suggests that, with minimal learning, the infant can respond differently to an object and its two-dimensional representation. Lichtenberg points out that

beginning about the third week and declining at about three months, all infants exhibited 'fussiness' (Emde et al. 1976). The puzzling aspect of this fussiness is that it seems relatively independent of mothering and is not in response to either pain or hunger. The period of decline of non-specific fussiness coincides with the occurrence of the social smile. (pp. 24–25)

In another portion of his monograph Lichtenberg states:

> At two-and-a-half to three months dramatic changes occur. There is
> a shift of perceptual organization in which the eight-inch gaze focus
> has expanded to a range almost extensive as adults. The infant can
> track his mother as she leaves, approaches, and moves about the
> room. . . . This dramatic change tends to confirm Spitz's (1959)
> hypothesis that development occurs in irregular spurts with an
> affective sign such as the social smile serving as an indicator that an
> organizing change has occurred. This theory lends weight to a
> developmental hypothesis whereby a predictable genetic ground plan
> must coordinate with environmental responses. (pp. 15–16)

The last two quotations from Lichtenberg emphasize two distinct
phases of development, one characterized by "fussiness" and the other
characterized by a dramatic change in which the infant's mother is clearly
recognized as a separate personality of importance to him. I believe that
Lichtenberg is confirming Melanie Klein's postulations of the paranoid-
schizoid position (which peaks at approximately three weeks of age) and
of its successor, the depressive position, which normally succeeds the
paranoid-schizoid position at approximately three to four months of age,
and at which time infant and mother, according to Klein, achieve a sense
of separation from one another and become individuals in their own right.
Further, Lichtenberg states,

> The marked sensitivity of the maternal response to having immedi-
> ate contact with her newborn may surprise the clinical analyst, but
> certainly the significance of the mother's empathic caretaking is
> entirely familiar. What has been less well appreciated in the psycho-
> analytic literature is the role of the infant as an active force in the
> dyadic interaction. One study discovered that more than half of the
> observed interactions were initiated by the infant [citing Moss and
> Robson 1968]. Moreover, many of the researchers believe that the
> behaviors of the neonate are "built in" in order to function as elicitors
> of maternal responsiveness. . . . Infant differences in the requirement
> for soothing [of mother] may play a larger role in development than
> has hitherto been recognized. (pp. 21–22)

Lichtenberg goes on to suggest that the neonatal research also confirms
that the neonate makes a distinction between an "environmental mother"
and an "object mother." He states:

> Winnicott (1963) stated that the infant experiences his mother in two
> ways: the environmental and the "object" mother. As the environ-

mental mother, she constitutes the whole background world in which the infant exists: the air he breathes, the force of gravity that holds him to his crib, the emotional climate in which he feels. As the "object" mother, she is the mother with whom the infant interacts in a response to all of his drive urgencies, the mother who feeds, the mother he cries to have come, the mother whose face he explores, the mother against whom his rage is directed. . . . Experiencing the mother as environment is the paradigm of the tendency to generalize, experiencing the mother as "object" . . . is the paradigm of the tendency to particularize. Particularizing establishes the sense of borders and boundaries; generalizing crosses boundaries within the sense of self in between self and object. . . . The concept of an environment mother receives support from the neonate researcher's reference to a background or non-specific stimulus environment (Wolff 1969, Sandler et al. 1976) and the object mother becoming particularized out of the background receives support from the account of social smiling. (p. 32)

I believe the above quotation from Lichtenberg's monograph is especially interesting in terms of the conception of a background object. This is adumbrated by Winnicott (1963), and I have discussed this in greater detail as the *background object of primary identification*, suggesting the first phenomenological experience of an object surrounding one and governing one's sense of mental space from the very beginning of psychological birth.

It is very interesting to note that more and more infant observers of late are noting earlier and earlier traces of infantile personality development. Not only is this due to the development of newer and more sophisticated techniques for detecting early personality existence but may also be due to yet another factor. Infant developmental observation has frequently been carried out by people who seemingly have been trained in the behaviorist tradition. Their own methods of observation perhaps paralleled the methods of observation by analysts who became behavioristically empirical when they were not behind a couch experiencing empathically, intuitively, and imaginatively what the patient is stating. In other words, I believe there are two observational techniques: the empirical and the rationalistic. Empirical, Aristotelian technique utilizes the senses to detect that which is within the sensual band of recognition, whereas the rationalistic is capable of adding intuitive, empathic and imaginative links and addenda to the sensual data. In other words, the rational or Platonic method is ultra-sensual and/or infra-sensual as well as sensual. Thus Aristotelian empiricists missed an important conclusion which rationalistic Platonists, such as Freud and Klein, did not miss, namely, that there may be a difference between the observable behavior of the infant on the one hand and his capacity on the other hand to experience states of mind which he cannot yet demonstrate behavioristically because the behavior-demonstrating apparatus may not be myelinated enough to manifest to the senses of adult observers.

I believe it is of crucial importance to distinguish between the capacity to experience states of mind on the one hand and the capacity to demonstrate its existence to an external observer on the other. Until recently, all our "scientific" conclusions about infants were based upon behavioristic inferences which did not make this distinction. Piaget is noteworthy in this respect insofar as his conception of "sensorimotor" totally ignores that which occurs between the incoming sensory impulses and the outgoing motor impulses, namely, mind itself. It is obviously more apparent that the infant from the very beginning is not merely a "heart-lung apparatus" but rather a sensitive human being who is stuck inside of an unmyelinated behavioral skeleton which will take weeks, months, and years to master to his satisfaction and to the satisfaction of his observers. He is not unlike the tragic victim of a stroke who is struggling within his endeadened skeletal-muscular system to strive for the expressiveness which paralysis denies him.

THE OEDIPUS COMPLEX

The tendency of classical analysts to opt for the analysis of the oedipus complex prior to analyzing preoedipal structures ironically endangers the optimal formation of the normal oedipus structure. It must be remembered that the oedipus complex is a staging area which regressively organizes and elaborates all previous zonal fixations and transforms archaic internal objects into usable object representations to form a permanent structural scaffolding in the psyche. To analyze the oedipus complex before it optimally forms and consolidates endangers its structure and functions. Greenson (1967) seems to state the opposite. Most people who come to analysis have insufficient rather than excessive oedipal development. The capacity to establish a normal oedipus complex depends upon the successful maturation of antecedent objects, that is, of transformations of internal objects to object representations. There must be a smooth flow from the beginning. The oedipal father must be trustworthy enough to allow ambivalent expressions from the child, and also, he must be stalwart enough to thwart the omnipotence of his child's ambitions. In this way, exploration, self-discovery, limitation and sublimation are discovered by the child.

In order to have this optimal parent, one must produce him or her. He or she must evolve in the child's capacity to regard the importance of his objects and to release them for *their* maturational development vis-à-vis himself. The releasing begins very early. The infant must learn how to suck the content of the breast (milk, experience) without swallowing the breast, the container itself. He must learn how to bite and to chew what he has separated into more separate bits. He must learn to swallow the milk from the breast and to suffer its loss. This loss of the milk may be equated with the loss of the breast or the loss of the experience with the breast. The infant must learn to defecate and thereby be able to separate the relevant from the nonrelevant. He must control himself and not his objects, and he must give back once he has confidence in his capacity for retention. Weaning from omnipotence takes place all along the line. Once our infantile pilgrim has made enough progress through sucking and defecating, then and only then is he properly ready to explore sex.

Thus, using the Kleinian point of view, interpretations which contact the infantile aspects of the self on what is commonly called the oral level seem to promote a gradual integration of these early phantasmal objects and to allow them to become less split, more ambivalent, more whole and integrated with their external counterparts, the real parents. In other words, the Kleinian principle of genetic continuity and progression is a way of talking about the epigenetic descent of infantile omnipotence. This integration takes place in the depressive position of which the genital oedipus complex is a component. The oedipus complex which evolves anew from the interpretations of its genetic antecedents is a far different one, in my experience, than the one initially presented by the patient. This new oedipus complex begins to emerge later in analysis and has an enormously full flowering. I can now see, for instance, that the incestuous male child, if he has undergone this transition from the beginning, may desire intercourse with his mother in order to give her good reparative penises so that she may thrive, rather than to give her cruel sadistic anal penises, or penetrating hostile penises, or greedy ones, and so on.

I should like to make brief mention of a case I saw some time ago in analysis in order to demonstrate some of these points so as to emphasize the bridge between the two internal worlds previously described. A twenty-six-year-old woman came in because of frigidity—a phenomenon which I would now call genital anorexia. In the first few hours, the material seemed to cluster into oedipal phenomena. Dependency on me took on a sexual hue and, after a while, material which could easily be seen as penis envy seemed to emerge. Finally it developed that her envy of my penis had two components: (1) the traditional one of fantasies of male superiority; and (2) envy of an organ she was emotionally dependent upon. This led to fantasies about me as a father, upon whom she was dependent in a nonsexual way.

In this case, the penis was less a sexual organ than an organ for nutrition from a parent on whom she was dependent. This reminded the patient of her dependency on her mother and thus breast envy quickly came into the analysis. Later, her frigidity, which had been unsuccessfully dealt with in a previous analysis, began slowly to yield as she began to realize that it represented preventing two internal parents from having intercourse. She was treating external objects as if they were internal objects, "constipating" them, "freezing" them, and controlling them. The attack on the parental intercourse had been internalized and, as she had omnipotently kept them separate, they also kept her from intercourse.

Moreover, she described her mother as a very aggressive, domineering woman and her father as a very passive, unreliable person. Eventually the patient was able to see that both these portraitures, in addition to being accurate reflections of reality, were also projective identifications of separate aspects of herself. She did not like herself as a domineering infantlike person, nor did she like her weak helplessness. The weak helplessness became associated with her passive father and her domineering self became associated with her mother via projection (projective identification). When she was able to resolve her projective identifications and to resolve the envy of her dependency on each of them, individually and as a couple, she was able to have a full oedipus complex with the resolution of her symptoms.

The Kleinian concept of the oedipus complex is a far more extensive one than the classical one. It takes into consideration that the oedipal myth is a birth myth in the first place and, like all dreams and myths, uses alterations and distortions to narrate intensely affectual life situations. The crimes of Oedipus can be seen on many different levels. In being born he was to bring a curse upon his family—not unlike the curse that his own father, Laius, had caused (Laius, according to legend, brought homosexuality to Greece). This idea of a curse is similar to the later Judaeo-Christian notion of being born from original sin. Oedipus's being sent into the wilderness to die is but another version of the fantasy of birth as viewed retrospectively by an infant—being exiled from Eden and abandoned, so to speak. His belief in his destiny to return to Thebes is but a metaphor about his desire to return to mother's body, the phenomenon the Kleinians refer to as projective identification.

Bion (1957) has discovered a triumvirate of invariants in borderline and schizophrenic patients which owe their origin to an awareness of an infantile catastrophe. The triumvirate consists of *arrogance, stupidity,* and *curiosity.* The blindness of Tiresias corresponds to the desire to be stupid— as does Oedipus' later enucleation of his own eyes. This blindness corre-

Mahler, M. (1971). A study of the separation-individuation process: and its possible application to borderline phenomena in the psychoanalytic situation. *Psychoanalytic Study of the Child*
26:403-424.

—— (1975). On the current status of the infantile neurosis. *Journal of the American
Psychoanalytic Association* 23:327-333.

Meltzer, D. (1966). *The Psycho-Analytic Process*. London: Heinemann.

Nagera, H. (1966). *Early Childhood Disturbances, the Infantile Neurosis, and the Adulthood Disturbances*.
New York: International Universities Press.

Rangell, L. (1972). Aggression, oedipal, and historical perspective. *International Journal of
Psycho-Analysis* 53:3-11.

Ritvo, S. (1974). Current status of the concept of the infantile neurosis. *Psychoanalytic Study of
the Child* 29:159-188.

Sandler, L., Stechler, G., Julia, H., and Burns, P. (1976). Primary prevention and some aspects
of temporal organization in early infant-caretaker interaction. In *Infant Psychiatry*, pp.
187-204. New Haven: Yale University Press.

Spitz, R. (1959). *A Genetic Field Theory of Ego Formation*. New York: International Universities
Press.

Tolpin, M. (1970). The infantile neurosis. *Psychoanalytic Study of the Child* 25:273-309.

Trevarthen, C. (1974). Conversations with a two-year-old. *New Scientist* 62:230-235.

Tustin, F. (1978). Psychological birth and psychological catastrophe. In *Do I Dare Disturb the
Universe*, ed. J. Grotstein. In press.

Winnicott, D. (1962). A personal view of the Kleinian contribution. In *The Maturational
Processes and the Facilitating Environment*. New York: International Universities Press, 1965.

—— (1963). Communicating and not communicating leading to a study of certain
opposites. In *The Maturational Processes and the Facilitating Environment*, pp. 179-192. New York:
International Universities Press.

—— (1965). *The Maturational Processes and the Facilitating Environment*. New York: International
Universities Press.

Wolff, P. (1966). *The Causes, Controls, and Organization of Behavior in the Neonate*. Psychological
Issues Monograph 17. New York: International Universities Press.

—— (1969). The natural history of crying and other vocalizations in early infancy. In
Determinants of Infant Behavior, vol. IV. ed., B. M. Foss, pp. 81-109. London: Methuen.

sponds to a self-imposed stupefaction of the senses and the mind for
having the arrogance of curiosity to "find out." The arrogance of curiosity
(the greedy desire to "know" mother) is then transformed into the
arrogance of stupidity, which amounts to the arrogance of being able to
rid the mind of thoughts and even the self of the mind which thinks the
thoughts, via abnormal projective identification. The blinded Oedipus,
with a cane and with his daughter Antigone to care for him on his way to
Colonnus, constitutes the real Oedipal tragedy. His curiosity destroyed
him (the infantile catastrophe) so that he was then reduced to being a
helpless, crippled infant in need of a mother (daughter) to help him on his
way through life. His crippling represents the downfall of his omnipotence and omniscience and the curiosity associated with it. The Kleinian
Oedipus, therefore, is more a Faust than a petty infantile lover. His crimes
are his desire to "know" mother—and father—in many different ways,
libidinal and destructive.

The ultimate meaningfulness of Bion's conception of the oedipus
complex is a sophisticated modification both of Freud and of Klein. The
oedipus complex to Bion, therefore, represents the infantile catastrophic
fear of the premature awareness of significance. The content of the
repressed, therefore, would be not so much instinctual drives pressing
towards incestuous and patricidal discharge, but rather the awarenesses
of the significance of birth itself when parental intercourse is understood
in dimension. For instance, in the birth myth of *Genesis* the God-Infant
cannot tolerate that He is the product of the intercourse by Adam and
Eve, His parents. He generates an autochthonous myth in order to
account for His creation of Himself, His parents, and His cosmos. The
birth myth of Oedipus is less autochthonous and more in the direction of
the depressive position. Oedipus is born into the cold abandonment of
isolation and then seeks to return inside of the womb to repossess the
internal world of his conception, having first to penetrate the Sphynx at
the Gate of Thebes. (Sphynx is the root word for sphincter in Greek and
means "she who squeezes.") He must also get rid of the paternal penis
which stands between him and his beloved womb—thus, the patricide.

The ultimate catastrophe, Bion states, is the infant's desire to "know"
his parents in the Biblical sense, which means not only the greedy
acquisition of mother's body and of father's penis but also the destructive
aspects of knowing, a phenomenon more in keeping with the concept of
the "evil eye." In other words, the infant's omnipotence is experienced as
being destroyed by the significance of having been born by parental
intercourse and by the significance of the fact that mother first of all
belongs to father. Their intercourse also has the capacity to produce other
babies every time there is a mating. The oedipus complex is, therefore, a

mythic paradigm for the introduction to the third dimension of depth perspective in reality, where the infant realizes that the outside world, the world he did not create, is one in which he is relatively insignificant.

Thus the conception of the oedipus complex as modified by Bion and his followers would be that of a developmental point in the infant's and child's maturational progression in which he is confronted by a world beyond his own capacity to create. If he can reconcile with the significance of this external world and can allow his internal world to reconcile with his external world, then he is in touch with "thirdness" (the oedipal triangle) and can allow for the relativity of objects in third dimensional space to matriculate. He has achieved the threshold of significance.

Bion has lifted the significance of the oedipus complex from Freud's and Klein's body psychology and elevated it to fundamental epistemology in which it represents the "thirdness" of psychic space, that is, the subject, the object and the relationship between them. I believe that there is no comparable conception of the oedipus complex by classical writers.

REFERENCES

Balint, M. (1953). *Primary Love and Psycho-Analytic Technique*. New York: Liveright.
——— (1968). *The Basic Fault*. London: Tavistock.
Benjamin, J. (1965). Developmental biology and psychoanalysis. In *Psychoanalysis and Current Biological Thought*, ed. N. Greenfield and W. Lewis, pp. 57–80. Madison: University of Wisconsin Press.
Bion, W. (1957). Differentiation of the psychotic from the non-psychotic personalities. In *Second Thoughts*. New York: Jason Aronson, 1977.
——— (1962). *Learning from Experience*. In W. Bion, *Seven Servants*. New York, Jason Aronson, 1977.
——— (1963). *Elements of Psycho-Analysis*. In *Seven Servants*.
——— (1965). *Transformations*. In *Seven Servants*.
——— (1970). *Attention and Interpretation*. In *Seven Servants*.
Boston, M. (1975). Recent research in developmental psychology. *Journal of Child Psychotherapy* 4:15–39.
Bower, T. (1971). The object in the world of the infant. *Scientific American*, October, pp. 30–38.
——— (1974). *Development in Infancy*. San Francisco: Freeman.
Brazelton, T. (1969). *Mothers and Infants*. New York: Delta.
——— (1973). *Neonatal Behavioral Assessment Scale*. London: Heinemann.
Condon, W. (1974). Speech makes babies move. *New Scientist* 62:624–627.
Erikson, E. (1950). *Childhood and Society*. New York: Norton.
——— (1959). *Identity and the Life Cycle*. New York: International Universities Press.
Fairbairn, W. (1952). *Psychoanalytic Study of the Personality*. London: Tavistock.
Freud, S. (1891) Hypnosis. *Standard Edition* 1:103–114.
——— (1899). Screen memories. *Standard Edition* 3:301–322.
——— (1900). The interpretation of dreams. *Standard Edition* 4, 5.
——— (1909a). Analysis of a phobia in a five-year-old boy. *Standard Edition* 10:3–152.
——— (1909b). Family romances. *Standard Edition* 9:235–244.
——— (1912). A note on the unconscious in psycho-analysis. *Standard Edition* 12:255–266.

——— (1914). On narcissism: an introduction. *Standard Edition* 14:67–104.
——— (1917). Mourning and melancholia. *Standard Edition* 14:237–260.
——— (1918). From the history of an infantile neurosis. *Standard Edition* 17
——— (1919). The uncanny. *Standard Edition* 17:217–256.
——— (1926). Inhibitions, symptoms, and anxiety. *Standard Edition* 20:77–1
——— (1927). Fetishism. *Standard Edition* 21:235–239.
——— (1930). Civilization and its discontents. *Standard Edition* 21:59–145.
——— (1938). Analysis terminable and interminable. *Standard Edition* 23:20
——— (1940). Splitting of the ego in the process of defence. *Standard Editi*
Galin, D. (1974). Implications for psychiatry of left and right cerebral s neurophysiological context for unconscious processes. *Archives of C* 31:572–583.
Greenson, R. (1967). *The Technique and Practice of Psychoanalysis*. New Yor Universities Press.
Grotstein, J. (1977). The psychoanalytic concept of schizophrenia: I. the dilen *Journal of Psycho-Analysis* 58:403–425.
——— (1978a). Who is the dreamer who dreams the dream and who is th understands it? A psychoanalytic inquiry into the ultimate nature of be *Disturb the Universe?* ed. J. Grotstein. In press.
——— (1978b). The infantile psychosis and the dual-track principle. Submi tion.
Hartmann, H. (1939). *Ego Psychology and the Problem of Adaptation*. New Yor Universities Press, 1958.
——— (1964). *Essays on Ego Psychology*. New York: International Universitie
Jacobson, E. (1964). *The Self and the Object World*. New York: International Un
Kernberg, O. (1975). *Borderline Conditions and Pathological Narcissism*. New York:
——— (1976). *Object Relations Theory and Clinical Psychoanalysis*. New York: Ja
Klein, M. (1929). Infantile anxiety situations reflected in a work of art an impulse. In *Contributions to Psycho-Analysis 1921–1945*. London: Hogarth.
——— (1933). The early development of conscience in a child. In *Contribut*
——— (1935). A contribution to the psychogenesis of manic-depressive sta tions.
——— (1940). Mourning and its relation to manic-depressive states. In *C*
——— (1945). The oedipus complex in the light of early anxiety. In *Contri*
——— (1952). Notes on some schizoid mechanisms. In *Developments in Psycho* Klein, P. Heimann, S. Isaacs, and J. Riviere, pp. 292–321. London: Hoga
——— (1960). *Narrative of a Child Analysis*. New York: Basic Books.
Klein, M., Heimann, P., and Money-Kyrle, R. (1957). *New Directions in Psych* York: Basic Books.
Klein, M., Heimann, P., Isaacs, S., and Riviere, J. (1952). *Developments in Psych* York: Basic Books.
Kohut, H. (1971). *The Analysis of the Self*. New York: International Universit
——— (1977). *The Restoration of the Self*. New York: International Universitie
Kris, E. [rep.] (1954). Problems of infantile neurosis: a discussion. *Psychoan Child* 9:16–71.
Lichtenberg, J. (1979). Implications for psychoanalytic theory of research o Lecture given at the Los Angeles Psychoanalytic Institute and Society, l
Lipsitt, L. (1977). The study of sensory and learning processes of the newbo on neonatial neurology. In *Clinics in Perinatology* 4:163–186.
Loewald, H. (1970). Psychoanalytic theory and the psychoanalytic process. *Ps* *of the Child* 25:45–68.

On Blame

MELVIN R. LANSKY, M.D.

Blaming transactions can be dominant in the lives of couples for years, but blame is usually discussed in terms of the mechanism it is thought to exemplify. "Projection" captures the notion of exculpation but misses features that hold the relationship system together. "Sadomasochism," to the extent that it explains anything, implies that sexual excitement accompanies the giving and receiving of punishment and ignores the fact that blaming is, of its essence, verbal. "Projective Identification," as a transpersonal defensive operation, encompasses a systems level of thought but may not be used in a way that stresses the disowning of parts carried by the other. None of these mechanisms captures the richness of the symptom which serves to express and contain disowned inadequacy in the persons in the system. The endurance of marriages organized around blaming underscores the collusive nature of the seemingly aversive transaction. When such marriages do break up psychosis or aggression directed at self or others points to blaming as a restitutive phenomenon. Therapeutic understanding of blame must go beyond manifest content and encompass the appreciation of blame as mechanism, symptom, and restitution.

Progress in the conjoint psychotherapy of couples frequently comes to a standstill with accusatory episodes at the forefront of the couple's transactions. The unpleasantness of these episodes and the superficiality of the manifest issue being argued might suggest that the couple is dealing with an issue in crisis or conflict and is headed toward resolution. But experience shows that blaming transactions may continue to be dominant not only in therapy, which may never progress beyond such issues, but throughout years and even decades of the couple's lives together. Blaming tends to exclude not only the resolution of the issues being contested, it also prevents the emergence of other issues in the therapy and other attachments in the couple's lives together. In the context of therapy this is a resistance; in the larger sense, a life style.

Couples do not usually enter treatment for blaming. Such situations are seen in the midst of treatment for some other complaint that usually arises out of a change in equilibrium in the family system: troublesome conduct or underachievement on the part of a child; depression, drinking, or work difficulties on the part of one spouse, so that the family homeostasis has been disrupted. However, even with severely dysfunctional blaming marriages, it is the rule for couples to readily admit that blaming pervades the entire relationship, especially if that question is asked while blaming behavior is observed during conjoint sessions. The couples admit readily that it is not productive in resolving difficulties. Nonetheless, to point to the defensive nature of blaming in this sort of couple is especially difficult. Therapeutic techniques that consider the issue in question at face value miss deeper issues and the significance of the symptom. Those techniques that go beneath the surface issue to underlying issues or mechanisms have to face the rather primitive defensive operations going on in such transactions. These are much more difficult to handle than higher level, more neurotic mechanisms such as displacement, isolation, or simple repression.

Both the distortion involved and the vehemence of the primitive defensive operations make it most difficult to secure a therapeutic alliance while blaming is going on. When one spouse appears alone or when the blaming states are not present, one gets the sense that a different state of consciousness is present and one is not dealing immediately with the blaming situation, no matter how the patient (or patients) may try to reflect on it.

Case 1

Mrs. A, in conjoint treatment, proclaimed, "I'm a yeller. I get upset and yell. Then it's all over and I'm all right. I don't store it up. I just yell and get it over with. But if I don't, he walks all over me." This was early in her awareness of ego states not integrated with each other (Kernberg 1976a). In the angry blaming state, she could vent anger and ward off domination vehemently but unthinkingly. In her more usual, calmer state, she was reflective and reasonable, but she felt prey to domination by her husband and powerless to ward off his influence. In this more relaxed usual state, she compared herself to her mother and sister, whom she saw as dominated by their husbands. Both states reflected fear of domination and inadequacy to manage life independently.

Thus, in addition to a relatively consistent syndrome, there is a fairly typical technical difficulty that the blaming couple presents: the collusive use of primitive projective defensive operations such that reflection on the process while it is going on is almost impossible and reflection on the process at some other time is ineffective.

The phenomenon of blame, as such, has received very little attention. Although discussion of such patients is frequent in the literature, blame is usually discussed as something else: anger, hostility, conflict, marital disharmony, or in terms of a particular mechanism involved in the blaming—such as projection, sadomasochism or projective identification. Frequently the features of the blaming couple are discussed as individual pathology in terms of what has come to be called borderline phenomena: those defensive operations organized around the maintenance of splitting (as opposed to repression) and organized around the primacy of oral-aggressive rage. Such defensive operations derive primarily from dyadic, preoedipal disturbances and involve the mechanism of splitting and those mechanisms reinforcing splitting: idealization, devaluation, primitive forms of projecting and projective identification, in particular (Kernberg 1967, 1975).

Discussion of blame subsumed simplistically under various intra-psychic mechanisms may miss the richness of the clinical picture of the blaming couple. Such blaming situations have stable structures that may endure for decades. The couple may be chronically miserable, yet stay together. Divorce is not nearly as common as one would think in view of the evident and continual misery. Disputes do not resolve either cog-nitively or emotionally. One or both in the marriage may threaten divorce without making convincing moves either to get out of the marriage or to make it better. It is this striking cohesiveness that makes necessary a full explanation of blame that goes beyond the surface experience, beyond a simple conflict model of verbal behavior called blaming and beyond explanation entirely in terms of intrapsychic mechanisms.

This paper attempts to underscore the significance of the blaming couple as a clinical syndrome. The principal focus is on the therapeutic understanding of the phenomenon of blame. The difficulties in those who form such relationships can be seen as constitutional neediness and aggressiveness (Kernberg 1975) or as resulting from developmental failures (Mahler 1971, Masterson 1976) or some combination thereof. Parties in such relationships may be seen as having affective disorders, characterologic difficulties, neuroses, or as part of the vast category of borderline disorders. They may be treated separately or together, with drugs or without. Our present state of knowledge does not allow for definitive conclusions about etiology, diagnosis, or treatment. Assuming this amount of uncertainty, one can best proceed to deal with such difficulties only with a proper understanding of the significance of the syndrome. The main focus of this paper is blaming within a dyadic relationship. Accordingly, details of the attribution of blame in multiple party relationships or in scapegoating phenomena across generation boundaries will not be emphasized.

Since it is my contention that the full richness of blaming is often missed because blaming is called something else, I shall begin by considering blame in terms of projection, sadomasochism, and projective identification. Early usages of each of these terms suggest mechanistic and intrapsychic explanatory models. These have, of course, given way to richer usages mindful of the adaptational and interactional significance of the processes involved (Brenner 1959, Langs 1976). Since early and later usages are often confused, I will try to get beyond the conceptual entrapment superimposed by the terminology by tracing the development of more sophisticated models from earlier ones. Hopefully, this will allow for a fuller discussion of the blame as a symptom, as a restitution, and in the therapeutic situation.

The clinical material from which this study was done is, for the most part, from the conjoint treatment of couples in many settings and with patients with varying degrees of psychopathology. That which is offered as evidence, therefore, is not the associations of individual patients. Associative material, depending as it does on the sustained intrapsychic focus in one patient, is not the basis of the observations from which this study derives. Rather, the material deals with the phenomenology of the blaming situation from the perspective of the treatment of the entire system of which blame is the predominant transaction.

MECHANISMS OF BLAMING

Projection

Of the many uses of the word projection, I shall stick to the narrow sense of projection as a defense whereby traits, the recognition in oneself of which would cause distress, are disowned and noted or imputed to be in others. This sense locates its strictly defensive usage and by the use of the word "disowned" logically links projection to blame. Specifically, the avoidance of the displeasure of blame is a motive for projection.

To understand the role of projection in the blaming transaction, one must understand the conscience of the blamer. It is a more primitive regulatory device than the mature conscience and, as Klein (1934) pointed out, much more savage. Disruptions in personal well-being are met with savage attacks, whether those disruptions be an inner awareness of impulses, of shortcomings of the adaptive capacities, or of shortcomings in those with whom primitive, symbiotic relationships serve to keep ego deficits and uncontrolled drive manifestations from awareness. The experience of disequilibration attached to the inability to contain repressed contents or the inability to meet responsibilities are responded to with a mortifying sense of humiliation that can be evacuated by attribution of the shortcoming to one in such a symbiotic relationship. On such occasions when clear manifestations of the conscience are evident in treatment, one senses a mortifying sense of responsibility for defects. Spouses may function at a fairly mature level of responsibility outside of the relationship but require the blamed for the evacuation of what are essentially self-reproaches. In that process, there may be a therapeutic impasse because, in the blamer, even the most nonjudgmental interpretation locating responsibility in himself is experienced as a reversal of the projective process—hence, as blame itself.

Case 2

Mrs. B, a middle-aged wife, appeared reluctantly for a conjoint interview after her husband was told that treatment for his potency disorder would have to involve her. She appeared angry and caustic, speaking only of his inadequacy and inability to satisfy her, his disgusting personal attributes, his failure as a breadwinner, and his lack of respect for her relationship with her mother which had dominated the household for decades of married life. A query from the therapist, concerning her views of any part she might play in the unhappy situation, was seen as an accusation exactly like the ones she leveled at her husband. She flew into a rage at the (felt) attack and left the first session never to return.

It does not exhaust the function of either blame or of projection to say that projection is in the service of attributing to another what would be blamed in oneself. This may be examined convincingly by looking at a three-party transaction; gossip, where one talks to another about the blameworthy traits of a third. In evidence here is not only blame of the third party but a strengthening of the bond between the two conversants by virtue of sharing and reaffirming the standards by which the criticized trait is blameworthy. The disowned traits are always envied ones at some level: sexual or aggressive actions, aggressive behavior, assertiveness, competitiveness, or special status of some sort. All are such that they would threaten interpersonal bonds. Disowning the threatening traits makes such bonds possible and the blame (to some extent, the envy) is felt towards those who seem to be able to have it both ways. Returning to the two-party blame system, one can see the same factors operative, albeit in some different ways. Blaming is a phenomenon that goes beyond exculpation and relocation of culpability. It constitutes, in some part, an envious attack on the activities which threaten the dyadic bond of a significant relationship. The blamed activities may be sexual, aggressive, competitive; but they may also be anything, including simple independence or going one's own way—freedom from the dependent and restrictive dyadic relationship. One can hear in the reproaches of the accuser not only projection of culpability, but also the intense dependency and need that the accused not show those traits being disowned because of the type of bond between the two.

Case 3

The following is from the transcript of the first few minutes of a taped session in which the wife, Mrs. C, was a few minutes late:

H: But at three o'clock you should have been here.

W: I got out of there about five minutes after three.

H: (vehemently) You should have been done and at your car at three o'clock and all that other stuff should have been done and over with.

TH: I don't understand why you couldn't meet right in the office.

H: Because she's afraid, I guess, of being by herself with some of the people around here, I guess. I don't know. She seems to be helpless sometimes and so able at other times.

TH: You're angry.

H: (furious) I'm *goddamned* angry!

TH: What about?

H: (screaming) At this unreliable . . . asshole . . . I come up here depending on her being here at a certain time and she ain't there. She's off doing her own thing . . . like this ain't the first time. It's the story of her life. I cannot depend on her to do a simple little function.

Here is the fear of either the dissolution of the relationship or the loss of the expected reliability and specialness. Although this is almost always manifest in the actual content of what is said, it may be overlooked because of the self-righteousness and attacking quality in the blamer (Kernberg 1975, Lax 1975). The surface issues are often not distorted so much as magnified in importance and the magnification bespeaks the attacker's dependency, fear of separation, and fury about being let down.

Case 4

A few moments later in the same session:

W: Every time I make a mistake he blows it out of proportion.

H: I don't. I get madder and madder and madder when you stand there and defend yourself when you're a hundred percent wrong. If you'd just said, "Honey, I'm sorry," I could forget the whole thing, but you stand there like a fool and try to defend yourself.

W: I guess maybe it's because you come at me and, well, as if I, and start fussing at me and jumping down my throat.

H: Well, I have reason to . . .

W: And, so . . .

H: See, you're defending yourself some more. Goddammit, if you're in the wrong, can't you, haven't you got the guts to, to say, "Honey, I'm sorry."

TH: What should she have done?

H: She should have either sat in her car from three o'clock on waiting for me to arrive.

W: Most of the time when *he* says meet him some place, sometimes he hasn't thought it out exactly what he . . . uh . . . all the fine details evidently. Or he comes little bit earlier than what he . . . uh . . . should be coming. He shows up and then he decides that he can actually find me in a place. Well, he can't find me so he gets angry with the fact that he can't find me.

H: Well, a ten-year-old girl, you would have to have to give Mommy or Daddy and lead them around by the nose for them to get someplace and I think that's just about where you're at because nobody else . . . I don't think . . . you have to tell that to. Anybody else would have enough sense to be able to figure, "Well, now, he's gonna come down here looking for me. I better make myself available."

In contrast, patients in psychotic paranoid states with fixed delusions may gain some measure of self-esteem by disowning traits, usually impulses, but no relations other than delusional ones are secured (Lansky 1977). Projection plays a prominent role in blaming transactions, but the phenomenon of the blaming couple cannot be explained by projection entirely. The concept fails to account for the collusive nature of the blaming transaction—why such relationships endure, why they do not correct themselves, and why they are so prominent in the couple's activities together to the exclusion of all else.

Sadomasochism

Blaming involves aggressiveness towards the blamed, and to the extent that punishment is inflicted or received in a repetitive fashion, there may be the temptation to subsume blaming under the model of sadomasochistic relationships. Mutually accusatory relationships fit such a model less than relationships in which one person blames and the other typically receives the blame; I shall confine my remarks to this sort of blaming relationship, where one party typically blames, accuses, bullies, or berates the other, who does not protest or does so only feebly.

In the dynamic sense the term sadomasochism, as well as the terms sadism and masochism, have a history that renders their usage confusing if not incomprehensible. Prior to the consideration of aggression in Freud's "Beyond the Pleasure Principle" (Freud 1905, 1917), sadism was regarded as an instinctual vicissitude, in particular, as erotism of the muscular apparatus, consisting in sexual excitation in the infliction of punishment on another. Sexual perversion is sexual excitation enhanced by or permissible only in the presence of inflicting punishment on the other. Early theories of masochism saw it as the passive and complementary counterpart of sadism, in particular, sexual excitation at being the object of punishment, again a derivative of erotism of the neuromuscular apparatus.

Since 1920, with attention to the structural theory and to aggression, psychoanalytic theory has gone considerably beyond this explanatory mode (Brenner 1959). As used today, the term has the disadvantage either of implying that actual sexual excitation accompanies the inflicting and receiving of punishment, or of losing most of the explanatory advantages altogether. Attention to the erotic lives of blaming couples shows that both sexual excitation and intercourse are almost nonexistent. What is implied by the noninstinctual "ego-psychological" use of the term, "sado-masochism," is that there is some sort of gratification underlying the apparent unpleasantness. The notion of collusion is implicit but no real mechanism is spelled out, and, with the term alone out of context, no real explanation of phenomena is given.

Case 5

Mr. C complained bitterly that his wife was unreceptive to intercourse and that he was perpetually frustrated sexually. His sexual needs were voiced petulantly, belligerently, and reproachfully, while adding that she was disloyal, unkempt, stupid, and undependable. While the aggressive attack served as an expression of his feeling sexual arousal, it served also to insure that sexual activity did not happen. That is, the collusiveness in giving and receiving punishment served to avoid genital contact, rather than enabling it.

Case 6

Mrs. D constantly berated her husband for drinking and being unemployed, often siding with her daughter from a previous marriage in contemptuous attacks on her husband. She was sexually excitable, but in the presence of his resentment, drunkenness, depression, and impotence seldom got satisfaction. On one occasion, when she reported satisfying intercourse, her husband reported thankfully that he had "done his duty" for the first time in months.

Describing blaming relationships as sadomasochistic also fails to distinguish the verbal act of blaming—the inflicting of punishment via verbal assaults, accusations, criticism, contempt, or belittling remarks—from other forms of punishment, be they physical abuse, open infidelities, impulsive or addictive behavior, job difficulties, taking sides with children or in-laws, or others. The essence of blame is that it is verbal as opposed to other actions that may inflict punishment or even communicate the act of blaming.

The verbal behavior of blaming asserts a relationship, discharges aggression, makes charges, and at the same time covers over or gainsays the intense dependency and low self-regard that one might imagine from the neediness made manifest in the blaming transaction. In the act of blaming, this neediness is covered over with a facade of self-righteousness and mastery (Lax 1975). This exhilarated sense of self-righteousness and mastery lasts only during the act of blaming and serves a defensive function in those in whom humiliation or desertion is a major issue.

In men, the content of blaming is frequently the wife's caretaking, cooking, affection, or cleaning house. It thus expresses intense dependency, in addition to creating a facade of superiority, mastery, and independence. In women, such behavior may represent narcissistic defenses against envy of a strong male by destroying his masculinity while simultaneously expressing the same need not to be let down, deserted, or neglected.

Case 7

Mrs. D' (also Case 6 above), whose father and first husband were drinkers, savagely blamed her husband for his drinking even during long periods of time when he was sober. With the aid of conjoint and couples group therapy, she was made to see that her anxieties were activated by issues other than her husband's drinking. She explored her past and how much her upbringing in a marriage similar to her own had colored both her marriages. Her strong attachment to and fear of being like her mother, that is fearing and attacking men, came to the fore so strongly that she went to visit her mother in a distant city to explore the "unfinished business" she had brought into her marriages. Her husband's drinking, job difficulties, and depression abated when the anxieties underlying her blaming behavior were recognized and dealt with. He remained both sober and employed after a lengthy follow-up period.

Blame may also represent the revolt against a previous and long standing attitude of subservience. Women in such relationships are quite commonly slovenly by their own admission—poor housekeepers with almost no interest in sexual relationships.

For the blamed, there is a loss of self-respect and resentment of the humiliation as well as the perpetration of the degraded status by inviting demeaning accusations.

Case 8

Mrs. C consented infrequently to intercourse. She consented to and even invited punishment from her husband. When her parents' marriage had dissolved, she went with her mother while her older sisters went with another relative. When mother and daughters were reunited, she assuaged the wrath of her sisters by masochistic submission by which she secured the relationship. She did so again in her marriage but at the cost of all self-respect. Her resentment was seldom expressed actively, but her perpetual disinterest in sex served to distance her husband, retaliate for his attacks, and invite more blame. Mr. C, on the contrary, felt in constant need of sexual gratification and perpetually frustrated.

Frequently there is an outright clinical depression present in the recipient of blame. Men in such relationships are often alcoholics or have aloof distant and preoccupied relationships with wives who early or late rebel against distancing maneuvers of their mates. In my clinical experience, history of a significant loss early in life is characteristic for both sexes. This loss is quite frequently the loss of a parent, or an easily ascertainable history of a precarious relationship with one or both parents early in life. Not uncommonly, both of these situations hold.

Both parties in such relationships are intensely dependent and both have narcissistic preoccupations that make it impossible for them to feel that they have entered the marital relationship completely. For the one inflicting punishment, avoidance of humiliation is of paramount concern, and can never be put to rest in the relationship except during the act of blaming. For the one accepting (or inviting) the punishment, preservation of the relationship at the cost of self-respect has been a *modus operandi* in the past so much so that a degraded form of relating is less anxiety provoking than one in which mutual respect is to be had.

Case 9

Mr. E was hospitalized numerous times for depression stemming, in part, from the consequences of his characterologic difficulties. His wife berated him for drinking even when, by her admission, he had been sober for many months. At length, his fury mounted and he did drink, losing a job and his self-respect and inviting more blame from his wife. The drinking served to justify his wife's blaming and to lower her anxiety about commitment to him and to the marriage. The cost, however, was his self-respect; and chronic impotence, vocational difficulties, and serious depression resulted.

The collusiveness takes place as follows: one spouse has a need to degrade or feel self-respect in the act of bullying and the other has a need to use humiliation to lock the other into a relationship. Both are intensely dependent and need an exclusive relationship, no matter what the cost, and both have a terror of intimacy which the collusive giving and receiving of blame, painful in its own right, serve to avoid. The spouse receiving the blame is almost always clinically depressed, frequently with attendent neurovegetative signs, such as sleep difficulty, loss of libido, diurnal variation of mood and, less frequently, increased or decreased appetite. There is rarely gratification outside of the relationship. Work and business relationships are described in a colorless affectless way. If there are extramarital affairs, they often serve to inflict more humiliation and punishment on the receiving spouse, who is almost always made aware of these relationships. The inflictor of punishment is as incapable of autonomous gratification as is the receiver.

Calling such relationships sadomasochistic because of the repetitive and, in some ways, gratifying giving and receiving of punishment departs from consideration of sadism and masochism as organ pleasures of the neuromuscular apparatus. There is a certain amount of security, and even exhilaration, in the aggressive discharge that secures a relationship and avoids humiliation at the same time, but this must not be confused with genital and sexual excitation. Furthermore, blame is of its very essence verbal and although physical punishment may accompany blame, it is a peripheral phenomenon. The issues of self-respect, loss, and the inflicting and receiving of verbal punishment (verbal expression of what has been called a preverbal disaster [Chessick 1974]) are paramount in the blaming relationship.

Projective Identification

The term projective identification has a great number of usages, each emphasizing different points. The term was introduced in 1946 by Melanie Klein to refer to the primitive defensive operation whereby in fantasy part of the self is split-off and projected into another who is sadistically controlled and who carries that part. Melanie Klein intended this as a primitive variant of a phenomenon of vicariousness first observed in detail by Freud and discussed by him as "identification" (Breuer and Freud 1893–1895, Freud 1921). Robert Knight (1940, 1953) was one of the earliest investigators to discuss the interplay of identification, projection, and introjection in primitive defensive operations, especially those that characterize the oral fixation in borderline states and alcoholics. It is beyond the scope of this paper to arrive at a consistent workable and agreed upon notion of projective identification and all that is conveyed by that term. But it is important to point out that the word is frequently used to describe a primitive mechanism reinforcing splitting, specifically a split-off part of the self, treated in fantasy as though it were carried by another. Hence, projective identification finds its location in lower level defensive operations, particularly those reinforcing splitting (Kernberg 1967, 1975).

From the standpoint of the present paper, it is necessary to add to the strictly intrapsychic dimension of projective identification, that is to say, of projective identification as fantasy. In addition to the fantasy of splitting off part of oneself and projecting it into another, there is frequently the invitation and provocation to collude, that is, for the other to act as though he carried that part. This point has been most often emphasized in the discussion of transference and countertransference phenomena with borderline patients (Bion 1957, Frosch 1970, Giovacchini 1973, Kernberg 1975, Klein 1946). The provocation to collude and the acceptance of collusion—almost coercion to collude—then make projective identification much more complicated than an intrapsychic defense. The term, in its more sophisticated usage (Langs 1976), referring to a complex collusive defensive and gratifying interactional system, far supersedes the original intrapsychic usage and goes a great deal further in explaining the blaming situation.

But to understand blame, more has to be added to explain the notion of projective identification as Melanie Klein described it, and the acceptance of such invitation, provocation, or coercion to carry "parts" for another. In the blaming couple and in the blaming collusive defense, which the term, projective identification, may describe in part, there is also a *disowning* both of the projected part and of the collusive process itself. Unless this is appreciated, neither projective identification as a mechanism, transpersonal or otherwise, nor the phenomenon of blaming, which may be seen as a specific type of projective identification, can be understood.

The concept of projective identification bridges the gap between the intrapsychic point of view and the systems point of view. The specifics of the vicariousness in the blaming system is that it involves simultaneous expression and disowning of the same traits in the marital system. It is not necessarily pathological to act in collusion with others such that they carry parts not compatible with one's identity. This normally happens, especially in close relationships and invariably in the family. The absence of the ability to live through people vicariously by identification is, itself, a sign of serious narcissistic pathology. In a family, in particular, the traits of any of the members are available for all to identify with and to use, not only typical instrumental, integrative, expressive and nurturing qualities in the parents but childish and omnipotential ones in the children. What is of importance in relationships dominated by lower level defensive operations is exactly what is noteworthy in the blaming relationship. Not only the vicariously experienced parts but also the act of colluding is disowned. In more normal close relationships, collusion may be inexplicit, but it is not disowned. The charges in the blaming attack are almost all variants of desertion, unreliability, abandonment, failure to reach perfection—of letting the blamer down in one form or another. Close attention to what the blamer actually says will often reveal in a very obvious way allusions to desertion, failure to take care of the blamer, being undependable, letting the blamer have no one to rely on, and similar complaints. To the extent to which these are traits of the blamer carried by the blamed, one may say that projective identification in the Kleinian sense is operative. But the act of blame also carries with it some coercion to be blameworthy in the exact manner of the reproach.

Case 10

Mr. B, a fifty-five-year-old man, entered the hospital voluntarily for observation. An admitting note observed that he was a deteriorated, psychotic alcoholic with uncontrollable rage attacks whose wife had taken legal steps to commit him. The same story was corroborated by numerous previous therapists. On initial interview he was coherent with intact sensorium without psychosis, dementia, or depression. For the first time in his long history, he gave a clear account of his use of alcohol to enable rageful rebuttals to his wife's blaming attacks. His counterattacks served not only to retaliate, but also to confirm, and, therefore to invite, his wife's reproaches.

In view of the content of the transactions and the history of the patients, there is some temptation to see the blaming transaction in terms of the repetition of an actual traumatic relationship in the past. This is the view of the object relations school (Dicks 1963, 1966). Disowned "parts" as well as the failure to meet needs in general are seen as attributes of the person being blamed. A two-fold identification takes place—the disowned and projected needs are identified with the blamed person; and the blamer may also identify himself with an internal representation of someone whom he saw in the past as critical (A. Freud 1936, Fairbairn 1952). The assumption here is that early and basically unsatisfying object relationships have been dealt with intrapsychically in a way that involves the internalizing and identifying acceptable parts of oneself with one object, a critical one, and externalizing parts of oneself that are not acceptable onto another who, however stimulating he may be, is ultimately disappointing. This "identification with the aggressor" may involve both projection and a primitive variant of projective identification. The unacceptable parts of the self are projected onto or into the object being blamed and the acceptable part of the self unconsciously identified with a bad internalized or critical object. The exhilaration and feeling of self-righteousness result from the identification with a critical rejecting bad internal object whose loss is feared. The blamed behavior, always one's own traits by this schema, is experienced as coming entirely from the other. The contribution of the object relations theorists to the notion of projective identification is basically a theory of preoccupation with past traumata and their residual developmental consequences which are replayed in the process of projective identification.

Blaming relationships involving projective identification do not reach resolution. There are constant replays of internalized past traumata that interfere with the integration of the self and with which there is constant preoccupation. The repetition should not be thought of as a simple repetition of something that actually happened. Perception of frustrating relationships is modified internally by the vicissitudes of the individual's aggression and reprojected in altered form. Projections may be available for some alteration before being reintrojected (Klein 1946, Malin and Grotstein 1966). Likewise, perpetuation of the repeated relationship requires the collusion, coerced or willing, of the acceptor of the disowned traits. Such collusion may be by doing something active to confirm the blamer's expectations or by being provoked to do something that may be so interpreted, such as responding angrily or leaving the field physically or emotionally.

Case 11

Mr. F, a man in his fifties, gave a history of overstimulation and abandonment by his mother. His father died when he was four. Thereafter, he slept in his mother's bed until she suddenly remarried three years later and placed him in an orphanage. In later life, he went from job to job, usually quitting and leaving town after he impregnated his latest girl friend. He subsequently married one of the women and continued to berate her verbally with threats of abandonment. His wife, in turn, was left by her own mother to her grandmother's care, taken back by the mother, and left with her grandmother again several years later after sexual advances were made by her stepfather. In the relationship and subsequent marriage both "replayed," in modified form, preoccupations with overstimulation and abandonment.

As noted above, what is pathological about projective identification is the disowning and the high cost of the pathological object relationship. In normal relationships, the projection of traits incompatible with one's identity into another who carries them is a use of vicariousness as a liberating and gratifying experience conducive to freedom and growth. In regressive, collusive relationships there is only a collusive permission to replay psychic trauma to the exclusion of everything else. This replay of predominantly traumatic object relationships involving splitting may represent not only a set of expectations and anxieties concerning dependency issues and modification of these by internal aggression, but also attempts at the establishment of omnipotent control. What was internalized is a traumatic, intensely dependent and, above all, precarious relationship. Subject to constant withdrawal and abandonment, it is replayed as a masterful act of self-righteousness. Presumably, what was experienced in a passive victimized role is replayed actively in a verbal role involving blame. Mastery, self-righteousness, and omnipotent control are quite the opposite of the presumed original affects of helplessness and anxiety and, in that sense, the defensive function of projective identification is partly successful in overcoming anxiety, helplessness, and culpability by the reworking of the original situation that is experienced in the act of blame. The sense of entitlement noted by Murray (1964) indicates collusive permission to discharge verbally the aggression resulting from such situations and awareness of their consequent developmental deficits.

Infantile fears of loss of the relationship, loss of omnipotence, being let down, and being helpless are still in evidence in the background but in the forefront are well-ordered verbal attacks, with the self-assuredness and exhilaration that one sees in the accusatory state. The mastery and self-righteousness, as well as the omnipotence, are to be had only in the act of blaming when the dyad is held in place, and so there is the necessity to repeat the blaming transaction constantly. Without recourse to blaming, the old infantile anxieties reappear, especially when the collusive other embarks upon some independent activity. Collusion (as the reciprocal fantasy of omnipotent control) is the hallmark of relationships characterized by projective identification. This is, of course, evident in the blaming couple. One can only understand the tenacity of these relationships in terms of collusiveness.

Accounts based on brief therapeutic models (Greenspan and Marino 1974) and those based on countertransference feelings of the therapist miss the complexity of the blaming system, of which projective identification is a part. The full complexity is evident only in the natural setting where collusive activity is unrestrained, particularly where there is regression to a dyadic relationship and an inability to integrate split-off and projected parts of the self as they unfold in the dyad. What is often missed in models not derived from a full understanding of the depth of collusion is a full range of the expression of anger, the intense feelings of mastery and well-being attendant on self-righteous verbal attack. Here there is the terror at the other's independence, the verbalization of one's own dependence, the triggering of such attacks by independent activities on the part of the other or by the vicissitudes of a precarious relationship with yet another person (whether this be relative, employer, or friend) that forms a further preoccupation. Taken out of the context of the psychoanalytic situation, the notion of projective identification may be used in the simplest way that fails to give a complete picture of a blaming marital system. It becomes just another mechanism, albeit slightly more useful because it is transpersonal, and because it is a significant mechanism operative in persons with preoedipal disturbances where there is a preponderance of mechanisms reinforcing splitting.

Detailed exploration of technical problems posed by this mode of defense is beyond the scope of this discussion. It has already been noted that while the defense is operative, it is most difficult to point to the defensive nature of the activity because of the collusiveness and the primitive projective qualities of the defenses (Kernberg 1975). When the defense is not in operation, there is frequently a separate state of consciousness which is completely split off from the state of consciousness during blame and does not influence it. In the midst of the blaming transaction the issue of being let down is usually experienced as of such overriding and immediate importance that therapeutic intervention that can be utilized at the point of "immediacy" (Strachey 1934) may be impossible to attain.

THE SYMPTOM

Hopefully, brief consideration of the concepts under which blaming phenomena have been subsumed will get beyond conceptual confusion to allow an appreciation of some of the infantile roots and forms of defensive

operations often seen in blaming without cutting short a full investigation of the phenomenology of the blaming situation.

Blaming is aggressive and the accuser attacks as he blames. There is
direct instinctual gratification from such an attack and the gratification
accompanies the expression of anger at being deserted, at being let down,
not being able to be dependent on the blamed; that is to say, it is oral
aggressive (Kernberg 1975). The attack may also consist of attributing
disowned traits to another. In this way, exculpation of the self is involved
as well as the inculpation of the other in the aggressive discharge. The
blaming is in essence verbal behavior, and allows verbal attention to an
expression of anxieties that stem from frustrations in the past or represent incompletely dealt-with relationships, central and tenuous ones, that
are repeated in the person of the blamed. The repetition is not presumed
to be the same as the original experience and the difference is usually
manifest in the increased sense of mastery and self-worth that accompanies the verbal facility, exhilarated sense of self-righteousness, and the
omnipotent expectations of the other. The blamer may, and usually does,
feel competent and relieved, even exhilarated during the act of blaming.
Sexual excitement may occur in the blamer, but the act of blaming usually
precludes rather than enables sexual satisfaction. The feeling of mastery
and exhilaration is not present at times other than when blaming occurs.
Blaming as a symptom works, so to speak, only when it is going on; and,
while it is going on, there is an altered state of consciousness—an angry,
labile, omnipotently-expectant entitled self. At other times it is not so
much repressed as it is split-off as a different consciousness manifesting a
preoccupation with traumata in early life.

Real intimacy is avoided, yet there is also in the act of blaming a
cohesiveness and collusion in the relationship with the one who accepts
blaming behavior (whether or not the culpability is accepted), that accepts
the dependency of the blamer on the blamed, that grants a certain
entitlement to be special in the relationship. The entitlement is always to
be heard beneath the show of confidence and mastery that the verbal
behavior purports to exhibit. This verbal ego strength apparent in the act
of blaming, as has been noted, is not generalized and applies only to that
relationship and only when blaming is going on. The masterful quality of
blaming serves to gainsay the weakness and helplessness that the dependency on the blamed presupposes. The helplessness and dependency are
usually considerably less evident than the verbal dexterity and masterful
attack, although the examination of a verbal transcript of a blaming
transaction will show this dependency quite obviously (see, e.g., cases 3
and 4). Blame preserves self-esteem, particularly when weakness, dependency and helplessness have been humiliating issues in the past and have

been faced in the presence of precarious object relationships reprojected in the present onto the blamed.

Blaming has complex effects on the relationship of the blamer and the blamed. The blaming couple or family must be seen as a system of complementary and interlocking pathologies in persons whose behaviors serve to perpetuate, maintain, and protect the system, which is organized around expression and containment of primitive rage and fear of abandonment while at the same time keeping the parts in the system from being flooded with the awareness of inadequacy. The parties keep at some distance by inflicting punishment and disappointment on each other but at the same time there is presupposed and preserved an intensely dependent dyadic relationship that confers on both a special all-encompassing, omnipotent status within the relationship. By distancing the blamer from the blamed, the blaming transaction removes both parties from consciously experiencing real obligations to the other and from real commitment to the relationship and to the risks and uncertainties that commitment entails. Indeed, both may be securely locked into such a relationship for decades, yet experience themselves as on the verge of divorce, on the verge of leaving, as entirely out of the relationship. The entitlement presupposed by blaming preserves omnipotent possibilities for both in fantasy, usually *conscious* fantasy, and this frees both from emotional involvement with the actual other person. The feeling of entitlement is the basis for reproach that the other is less than perfect. The imperfections of the world and the complaints of the blamer against the world are embodied in arguments with the blamed. The blamed thus stands for the whole of the reality, which the blamer hates (Odier 1956, Bion 1954).

The voiced entitlement presumes a collusion; and the collusion is in keeping with the specialness, exclusiveness and omnipotence of the relationship. Voiced angrily, it is thereby free from self-consciousness that might undermine it. Blame may appear at times when one party in a relationship is seeking autonomous gratification; blaming serves to reestablish the dyadic equilibrium and to lock the other back into the relationship when he threatens to go his own way. The awareness of the autonomy of the other may trigger a flood of anxiety about one's own aloneness, weakness, and inability to manage in the world. Such anxiety may be warded off by reestablishing the blaming situation whereby the anxiety and attendant rage are experienced as coming from the shortcomings of the other. At such times as the blaming defense can be foregone, anxiety of this type can be overwhelming.

During the act of blame, the blamer does not experience blame as damaging and there is generally no consciously experienced guilt on the part of the blamer toward the blamed. Blaming may, in fact, defend against the type of involvement that would give rise to feelings of guilt attendant on harming another whose independent existence is valued.

Case 12

Mrs. G, a woman in her early fifties, appeared for conjoint sessions with her husband, who was hospitalized for psychotic depression and a serious suicide attempt. She berated him for irresponsibility, minimized his incapacity, and demanded that he return to work in their small business. He attempted to do so, became overwhelmed and was rehospitalized. He requested vocational training, agreeing with a recommendation that he get a less-pressured, salaried job. After hospitalization, Mrs. G made the same demands and he was again depressed. His wife could see only the gains from illness which, although they were present, were not the central reason for his incapacity.

The blamed person may not feel damaged, hurt, or guilty. This apparent oblivion to the attack is indicative of the underlying collusion. There may, however, be anger about whatever healthy in the relationship is sacrificed to maintain the blame system—especially social, sexual, or recreational parts of the couple's lives that become impoverished. This feeling—that if it weren't for the relationship, one could have a happier, more enjoyable life—may serve to protect both partners from acknowledging overwhelming inadequacies in relation to social, sexual, recreational or vocational enterprises. In general, it is more comfortable to use the inadequacy of the spouse as an alibi.

If the blamed partner does not blame back, there is usually a clinical depression in that person. Conversely, depression may be seen in this situation as the lack of sufficient entitlement to blame. The blaming transaction then may engineer and cover a regression from a mature type of relationship, not only of spouses to each other, but in relationships that involve multiple parties. There is an avoidance of risk, mutuality, guilt, estimates of power, estimates of one's own force in the world, coping with exploitation, enjoyment of sexuality, the necessity of cooperation, and a host of other possibilities that necessitate viewing the other as a whole person. This may be verified by reference to what may be called the negative symptomatology of the blaming couple, that is, not so much the stated conflict but what is avoided. Here one notices that the conflict somewhat covers up and holds in place what may be called an almost schizoid dyad: one without any meaningful connections to the outside world, a stable unit of two despite the appearance of perpetual instability, invoking quarreling as a schizoid withdrawal mechanism to shield them from the rest of the world.

More chaotic blaming relationships may be stabilized by a third party in a number of ways. Attention may be paid to a child who is the object of blame, on whom both of the spouses focus. Unfortunately, as Odier (1956) has noticed, this predisposes the object of such attention to the same inadequacies and, in many instances, the same sort of marriage and the same subsequent fate as both parents. There may be also an attachment to jobs or to relatives whose presence, actual or felt by obligations, may intrude on the relationship. These overinvolvements with bosses, with work, with in-laws, with other people of the same sex may be indications of faulty identifications and ego-ideal formations (Blos 1974). The inadequacies underlying the wish to regress to a dyadic relationship may often be ameliorated with actual relationships with a person of the same sex. The more regressive but similar activities of self-pity (Milrod 1972) and preoccupation may serve the same function. Self-pity and attendant self-consolation are usually attempts to reestablish, at least in fantasy, a dyad with someone who pities, consoles, and makes better. Preoccupation manifests the same insecure identity formation in the failure to leave work behind and in a constant obsessiveness with coping with the external world at the expense of all intimate relationships. There is an inability to put aside those tasks when they are not really being attended to. With both self-pity and preoccuption there is an enhancement of the sense of special status and entitlement that is so much a part of the blaming relationship. Such feelings of self-pity and preoccupation usually concern areas of genuine inadequacy or developmental arrest and give rise to feelings of compensatory entitlement and self-righteousness if they can be embodied in a blaming relationship.

The conflict manifested in the content of the verbal behavior in the split-off blaming state is a regression from mature relationships inside the dyad and out. It preserves a fixation at a preoedipal and essentially omnipotent level of entitled specialness, dyadic collusion, and somewhat magically object-related specialness whereby all the world's imperfections may be objectified in the person of the blamed. In the blamer there is ubiquitously a feeling of being cheated that is objectified in the oral aggressive outbursts and with permission expressed tacitly in the relation to the blamed. The ambivalence toward the blamed is manifest in a magical expectation that relief from all frustration should come from this person and that, at the same time, this person should have no autonomous life of his own. Any attempt for one party in the relationship to go his or her own way is usually followed by some incident that results in a blaming situation that reestablishes the dyad.

Recent emphasis on the preoedipal with the implication that it is more fundamental than the oedipal in considering this sort of pathology misses the point entirely. The oedipal or multiple party situation is not reducible to the preoedipal or dyadic situation. Neither is explainable in terms of the other. To properly explain the symptomatolgy and the family system, one must understand that the blaming relationship serves as a regression from multiple-party anxieties and uncertainties to a situation where dyadic anxieties are also dealt with. It is with these patients, as with most neurotics, simplistic to consider the situation exclusively in terms of oedipal or preoedipal pathology when, in fact, considerations of both types of relationships (and the relationship of the parties to both) are necessary to understand the clinical picture.

RESTITUTION

Conflict in the blaming situation must be seen as something much more serious, enduring, and deep than the issue manifest in the verbal content of the blaming behavior. The conflict represented in the blaming situation essentially holds the fixation in place. It allows the couple to avoid intimacy, involvement and risk, and at the same time serves to replay anxieties about object loss and loss of fantasied special entitlement. The fixation in the blaming relationship is usually shared by both partners. It has been noted (Bowen 1966) that married couples are frequently of surprisingly similar levels of differentiation of self, despite any outward appearance, even where one of the spouses appears functional and the other dysfunctional.

At a deep level there is usally a similar psychological structure in spouses in any enduring marriage. Both tend to come from the same kinds of families and the marriages of parents of both tend to be quite similar to the marriage that the spouses have entered. This marriage usually involves offspring in a manner that predisposes them to similar marriages. When two such offspring select each other for marriage, Odier (1956) has pointed out that the situation which he has called "the neurosis of abandonment"—perhaps a better term than any other—tends to be self-perpetuating. Such people may attract each other by early recognition that both are afraid of the same sorts of things. This is, of course, usually experienced as a great comfort with the other person. What is experienced initially as comfort may be experienced as inadequacies disowned and blamed on the other for precisely the same reasons that the attraction took place. The initial comfort and the subsequent blaming both take cognizance of the same inadequacies. At a deep level of relating an attempt is made to establish a dyadic relationship to one who objectifies all the shortcomings of an imperfect world that the blamer cannot face.

Marriages of such people do break up, but not nearly as often as one would expect in view of the enduring pathology, obvious disagreement, and discomfort. The unhappiness with each other is offset by more basic underlying issues that hold the marriage together. Once such marriages do break up, one may see psychosis, hyperingestive or addictive behavior (Chessick 1974) that expresses the tension previously released in the act of blaming. There is also explosive aggression directed outward when possible, but otherwise inward in the form of suicidal or self-mutilating acts.

Case 13

In the course of treatment, Mrs. C's depression began to lift and, in the process, her inviting punishment (see Cases 3, 4, 5, 8) diminished. Her husband's depression transiently lightened but as her improvement continued, he got drunk, and was imprisoned after being caught in an attempted burglary. His lengthy prison sentence interrupted the threat of his wife's improving in treatment.

Case 14

Mr. F. (see Case 11) replaced a long series of relationships in which he impregnated and deserted his lovers with a marriage in which he constantly berated his wife for shortcomings and threatened to leave her. In the course of concurrent individual and conjoint therapy she made a significant move out of the victim role. This served to undercut his compulsively repeated attempt to deal with the trauma of overstimulation and abandonment by blaming. He became seriously depressed and was hospitalized.

Alternatively, there may be a colorless life characterized by pervasive emptiness.

The inability to maintain entitlement in the relationship with another person who will then serve as a channel for oral aggressive rage may lead to feelings of futility and emptiness (Kernberg 1975), destructive juggernaut attempts at suicide or successful suicides in many cases. The fact that this potential chaos is prevented, the cost notwithstanding, by the blaming relationship places blaming among the restitutional phenomena—the way back to objects—most prominently seen as flagrant symptoms in neurotic and psychotic states. Such restitutional symptoms include the secondary symptoms of psychosis, such as delusions and hallucinations, and in the neurotic compromise formations, phobias, obsessions, or conversion reactions. Although it may be said that any symptom may be understood as a restitution, the blaming relationship is more poignantly so. It is a transpersonal compromise formation that serves as a restitution and has both expressive and defensive properties. As such times when preverbal experiences (Chessick 1974) have rendered the effects of past trauma so prominent that there is always preoccupation with them, the blaming relationship serves as blending angry preoedipal with the more mature multiple-party relationship. Within the dyadic situation of a marriage, there is an attempt to have a genital relationship while at the same time avoiding the complex and uncertain oedipal possibilities that require greater ego strength in dealing with exploitation, risk, power, personal force, and estimates of personal worth that depend on stable self-esteem. This is done by reestablishing in fantasy a reversal of the experienced early trauma: the secure dyad that can only involve one other person to the exclusion of everything else, on whom all the shortcomings of a less than ideal world are blamed.

No account of blaming can really be complete without stressing the importance of restitution. Although this term usually implies a flagrant psychotic mechanism, it may apply to other symptomatology as well. It is an old therapeutic saw that one must get depressive patients angry or that anger must be mobilized in treatment. This may be an incomplete way of formulating what is an initial step in the understanding of depression. The patient with clincial depression does not have the feeling of entitlement sufficient to get into a blaming dyad with the therapist. Depressives, while they are depressed, do not blame, and, while they are in the act of blaming, are usually not depressed. Depression may, in the sense pointed out by this reciprocal relationship with expressed anger, be seen in the inability to blame. Delusional depressives, in my experience, never blame, and those more seriously depressed persons, delusional or not, that are psychotically depressed, do not either. It is almost as though their ver- balizable idea of the world does not include the possibility of entitlement to blame. Schizophrenics, while they may at times have labile accusatory outbursts (Lansky 1977), never have a feeling of entitlement sufficient to use blame as a steady *modus operandi*. Schizophrenic outbursts are either labile projective states or delusional restitution that is not transpersonal, that does not involve a way back to specific objects.

From this point of view, the entitlement presumed in the act of blaming serves as justification for relations to others. However turbulent those relations may be, they present a much more optimistic therapeutic situation than is found in psychotic states where no entitlement is present.

BLAMING IN THE THERAPEUTIC SITUATION

The treatment of the blaming couple is a matter for a separate study—one that ought not to presuppose that dyadic therapy is the necessary treatment, the possible treatment, or even the first step in treatment for people in such relationships. Nonetheless, the consideration of the complexities of defense, symptom, and restitution in the blaming couple allows a perspicacious view of blaming in the therapeutic situation. I shall discuss this in terms suggesting a therapist-patient dyad, though the same considerations apply *mutadis mutandis* to the therapist's (or therapists') relationship to couple, family, or group.

For reasons already elaborated, it is important to see blame as such within the dyad to maximize its conflict-mastering and restitutive features and minimize its constrictive and destructive ones. Quite different problems in therapeutic understanding occur if blame is explicit—if the patient openly blames—than if it is inexplicit. If blame is explicit, a situation may occur that is quite typical of the blaming couple. The patient berates the therapist for disappointments and perpetually threatens to leave. If the therapist can appreciate the collusive bond in the blaming situation and not be put off by the unpleasantness of the perpetual berating and talk of leaving, a quite successful therapy often progresses in the presence of surface chaos.

Case 15

A twenty-three-year-old woman entered treatment for suicidal tendencies and depression. Treatment began and continued with the patient berating the therapist and threatening to stop. This behavior continued unabated several times weekly for several years. Quite by chance the therapist learned that the patient's recent marriage had dramatically improved, as well as her school, current career, and interpersonal relationships. The blaming and threatening within the (quite strikingly successful) therapy continued until the therapy ended.

Blaming may be inexplicit for a variety of reasons. The patient may be too self-conscious of the relationship as a professional one to blame, or there may have been no indication from the therapist that blaming can be tolerated. Implicit reproach may be seen in various ways: the blaming of others, self reproaches; certain forms of silence felt to be reproachful; a sharp attacking tone in the voice when talking about misfortunes as though they were the therapist's fault; and many others. In such cases, the therapist would do well to see the indirectness of the reproach as an opportunity to indicate to the patient (interpretively) that he can take the blame that is expressed indirectly.

Case 16

A woman in treatment complained of an auto accident on the way to the therapist's office. A sharp, sarcastic tone to her voice betrayed a veiled reproach for the failure of the relationship to really protect her. Interpretation to that effect was met with vigorous denial but with abatement of similar anxieties as a result of which she sought protection or contricted her activities.

Case 17

A young woman, quite delinquent in payment of the therapist's fee, returned from vacation silent, depressed, and saying that she couldn't engage in activities or relationships as she had hoped she might. The therapist noted that she reproached her therapist as she had reproached her parents for not equipping her to cope with the world and that the reproach showed up (in both relationships) as a contemptuous neglect of financial responsibilities. This interpretation resulted in explicit reproach, more exploration, and the beginnings of replacement of depressive reproachful preoccupation by explicit anxieties about her own social shortcomings.

Understanding blaming as an interactional symptom highlights certain features of the therapist's part in the relationship. A feature common to virtually every type of therapy is the location of responsibility in the patient for what he does, what he feels, and what he thinks. In blaming couples this therapeutic effort is received by a primitive conscience that experiences failure to meet a responsibility as mortifling blame and evacuates that responsibility by low-level defensive operations. Accordingly (see Case 2), there is the risk that any location of responsibility in the patient for what happens to him—however tactfully and mildly presented—may be experienced as intolerable blame. This may be experienced with a therapist in whom no unconscious collusion is evident.

In other cases, unconscious or unwitting collusion may be in evidence. Emotional withholding by the therapist that goes beyond the need for maintenance of a bipersonal field (Langs 1976) may represent an unconscious infliction of punishment or provocation to blame in the therapeutic dyad. In other cases, the therapist may be provoked to blame the patient by something the patient actually does. This is often in the form of violations of the boundaries of the therapy, acting out, or situations in which the patient senses that the therapist is tense or when the therapist's attention is elsewhere.

Case 18

A young man with severe characterological difficulties, embroiled in a three-party blame system with his parents, regularly missed sessions with his hospital therapist. He would frequently catch the therapist between meetings with ward staff or in tense moments on the ward and make annoying requests to leave, to get extra sessions, or to have vague somatic complaints investigated. The therapist's mounting fury was shared by the staff in the form of ridiculing and unkind comments at meetings. On a suggestion from a colleague, the therapist brought up not only the fact of provocation but the timing of it with the patient. Interpretation based on the therapist's response led to considerable evidence that similar provocation served to divert the angry attention of his (mutually blaming) parents onto him and so dealt with both the fear that the marriage would break up and that he would be totally excluded by the parents' attention to each other if it didn't.

Blame by the therapist may be the result of past experiences brought into the therapy and only minimally due to the particulars of the situation. This is countertransference proper. Excessive emotional withholding is a case in point as are interpretations that are actually in the service of blaming the patient.

Finally, the restitutive qualities of blaming must be seen lest the process of maintaining the dyad be seen exclusively in terms of resistance. Blaming is a way of maintaining a precariously held relationship despite preoccupations with feelings of defectiveness, anger, and dubious self-worth. Such restitution may fail if there is too much self-consciousness on the part of the patient, either because of the professional nature of the relationship or because the therapist has indicated inability to tolerate the stormy symbiosis that the patient requires. Such intolerance may be a manifestation of the therapist's deep anxieties about the intensity of the fusion and may be rationalized by reference to principles of good techniques or by blaming the patient.

To follow the restitutive path inherent in the act of blaming, the therapist must indicate at some level that he can tolerate the patient's blaming. If this is done at the level of unconscious collusion, there is the risk that unresolved feelings of omnipotence on the therapist's part may collude with complementary unconscious expectations on the patient's part; and there may be collusion in assuming that the therapist is responsible for the patient's well-being. A collusion of this type invites disorganizing regressions on the part of the patient to sustain such a dyad and deflects the therapist from the task of helping the patient work through the anxieties that keep his attention on the relationship at the cost of everything else.

More optimally, restitution—of which blaming is often the significant first step—may be permitted consciously by interpretation that indicates that the therapist is aware of and can tolerate reproach that has been less than explicit. By accepting the symbiotic restitutive aspects of blame without colluding in the regressive and restrictive aspects, the therapist maximizes the opportunity to secure the protective features of the dyad and to work toward resolution of deep anxieties—especially those concerning neediness, defectiveness, and abandonment that appear in the manifest blaming transaction and hitherto have formed an insurmountable preoccupation.

REFERENCES

Bion, W. (1954). Notes on the theory of schizophrenia. *International Journal of Psycho-Analysis* 35:113–118.

——— (1957). Differentiation of psychotic from the non-psychotic personalities. *International Journal of Psycho-Analysis* 38:266–275.

Blos, P. (1974). The genealogy of the ego ideal. *Psychoanalytic Study of the Child* 29:43–88.

Bowen, M. (1966). The use of family theory in clinical practice. *Comprehensive Psychiatry* 7:345–374.

Brenner, C. (1959). The masochistic character: genesis and treatment. *Journal of the American Psychoanalytic Association* 7:197–225.

Breuer, J., and Freud, S. (1893–1895). Studies in hysteria. *Standard Edition 2.*

Chessick, R. (1974). The borderline patient. In *American Handbook of Psychiatry*, 2nd ed., vol. 3. New York: Basic Books.

Dicks, H. (1963). Object relations theory and marital studies. *British Journal of Medical Psychology* 36:125–129.

——— (1966). *Marital Tensions.* New York: Basic Books.

Fairbairn, W. (1952). *Psychoanalytic Studies of the Personality.* London: Tavistock.

Freud, A. (1936). *The Ego and the Mechanisms of Defenses.* New York: International Universities Press, 1946.

Freud, S. (1905). Three essays on the theory of sexuality. *Standard Edition* 7:125–243.

——— (1917). Instincts and their vicissitudes. *Standard Edition* 14:109–140.

——— (1920). Beyond the pleasure principle. *Standard Edition* 18:7–6Y.

——— (1921). Group psychology and the analysis of the ego. *Standard Edition* 18:67–143.

Frosch, J. (1970). Psychoanalytic considerations of the psychotic character. *Journal of the American Psychoanalytic Association* 18:24–50.

Giovacchini, P. (1973). Character disorders: with special reference to the borderline state. *International Journal of Psychoanalytic Psychotherapy* 2:7–36.

Greenspan, S., and Marino (1974). A model for brief intervention with couples based on projective identification. *American Journal of Psychiatry* 131:1103–1106.

Kernberg, O. (1967). Borderline personality organization. *Journal of the American Psychoanalytic Association* 15:641–685.

——— (1975). *Borderline Conditions and Pathological Narcissism*. New York: Jason Aronson.

——— (1976a). *Object Relations Theory and Clinical Psychoanalysis*. New York: Jason Aronson.

——— (1976b). Technical considerations in the treatment of borderline personality organization. *Journal of the American Psychoanalytic Association* 24:795–830.

Klein, M. (1934). On the early development of conscience in the child. In *Contributions to Psychoanalysis* London: Hogarth, 1968.

——— (1946). Notes on some schizoid mechanisms. In *Developments in Psycho-Analysis*, ed. M. Klein, P. Heimann, S. Issacs. London: Hogarth, 1952.

Knight, R. (1940). Projection, introjection and identification. *Psychoanalytic Quarterly* 9:334–341.

——— (1953). Borderline states. *Bulletin of the Menninger Clinic* 17:1–12.

Langs, R. (1976.) *The Bipersonal Field*. New York: Jason Aronson.

Lansky, M. (1977). Schizophrenic delusional phenomena. *Comprehensive Psychiatry* 18:157–168.

Lax, R. (1975). Some comments on the narcissistic aspects of self-righteousness: defensive and structural aspects. *International Journal of Psycho-Analysis* 56:283–292.

Mahler, M. (1971). A study of the separation individuation process: and its possible application to borderline phenomena in the psychoanalytic situation. *Psychoanalytic Study of the Child* 26:403– 424.

Malin, A., and Grotstein, J. (1966). Projective identification in the therapeutic process. *International Journal of Psycho-Analysis* 47:26–31.

Masterson, J. (1976). *The Psychotherapy of the Borderline Adult*. New York: Brunner-Mazel.

Milrod, D. (1972). Self-pity, self-comforting and the superego. *Psychoanalytic Study of the Child* 27:505–528.

Murray, J. (1964). Narcissism and the ego ideal. *Journal of the American Psychoanalytic Association* 12:477–511.

Odier, C. (1956). *Anxiety and Magic Thinking*. New York: International Universities Press.

Strachey, J. (1934). The nature of the therapeutic action of psycho-analysis. *International Journal of Psycho-Analysis* 15:127–159.

Vogel, E., and Vell, N. (1967). The emotionally disturbed child as the family scapegoat. In *Psychosocial Interior of the Family*, ed. G. Handel. Chicago: Aldine.

Collusive Blaming: A Commentary

LYMAN C. WYNNE, M.D. Ph.D.

A discussion of "On Blame," by Melvin R. Lansky, M.D.

In presenting his formulations about blaming couples, Melvin Lansky has stimulated me to focus on a clinical phenomenon that could be noted daily in the practice of most psychoanalysts and psychotherapists but has been remarkably neglected in the literature. One reason for this neglect must be that treatment of blaming couples quite consistently has ended in failure. In individual therapy, engagement about the specific issue of reciprocal blaming rarely, if ever, becomes established. The therapeutic goals center on individually-defined problems of one or both partners and the blaming never *mutually* becomes clarified or resolved even after separation or divorce. Marital therapists, of course, are constantly confronted with blaming couples; though a particular battle may be terminated, the encrusted blaming tendency tends to reappear again and again.

Aside from treatment difficulties, a more fundamental basis for neglect of this problem is that its conceptualization calls for the integration of intrapsychic and transactional, systemic considerations, an objective that is not commonly sought and even less frequently achieved. Lansky has moved admirably toward such an integration, though the scope of the issues he has raised inevitably goes beyond his paper or this commentary.

Lansky places blaming in the context of dyadic systems, primarily marital couples. He also comments briefly on multiple-party patterns of blaming and the involvement of others at times. I believe that a next step in conceptualizing patterns of blaming is to move more fully to triangular relationships in families and other primary group systems. In my experience, *any* patterned, recurrent marital blaming, not only a chaotic blaming relationship, is routinely stabilized by a third party. The "third party" may be a parent, a sibling, an offspring, a previous or potential spouse, a personification found in work or other special interest, or, finally, a psychotherapist. Often the relationship with the party that is seen as "third" in relation to a marital couple is perceived as primary from another vantage point, with the spouse then regarded as the source of difficulty. Even when reciprocal blaming appears at first to be confined to a marital dyad, this narrow focus for the fury often facilitates denial of a guilt-ridden third-party attachment held by one or both partners. Hence, the blaming about being let down, neglected, abandoned, unloved, or betrayed by the other typically contains more than a kernel of truth. Conceptually and therapeutically, this means that a broadened frame of reference, beyond the blaming couple, may be crucial to problem understanding and resolution.

Lansky has usefully emphasized "the provocation to collude and the acceptance of collusion" as a powerful process going beyond intrapsychic defenses and maintaining the relationship—even when separation seems desired by both. In 1965, I formulated such collusive entanglements in terms of a "trading of dissociations":

> The general forms of these problems is the following: Each person sees himself as having a specific limited difficulty which he feels derives from another family member and which he announces can only be alleviated by the other family member. While the claims appear to have *some* basis in fact, the person about whom they are made does not recognize the possiblity that he himself makes *any* contribution to the problem. However, this other family member may be highly perceptive about corresponding difficulties which are similarly unacknowledged (dissociated) by the first, or in still another family member. Thus, there is an intricate network of perceptions about others and dissociations about oneself in which each person "locates" the totality of a particular quality or feeling in another family member. . . . What is distinctive about this pattern, and therapeutically difficult, is the trading of dissociations: The fixed view that each person has of the other is unconsciously exchanged for a fixed view of himself held by the other. . . .
>
> It should be stressed that the reciprocal and shared trading of dissociations both serves to *keep out* of each individual's awareness of himself the dreaded qualities and ideas, but also serves to *retain* these qualities within his purview—at a fixed distance from his ego. . . .
>
> The trading of dissociations means that each person deals most focally with that in the other which the other cannot acknowledge. Thus, there can be no "meeting," no confirmation, no mutuality, no shared validation of feelings or experience.

I agree with Lansky that such collusive trade-offs are powerfully sustained through "fear of either the dissolution of the relationship or the loss of the expected reliability and specialness," while at the same time threats of real intimacy are avoided. Elsewhere (1961) I have labeled as "pseudo-hostile" these kinds of family relationships that are held together by endless, but binding, bickering. The hostility (and blaming) is "pseudo" in the sense that it is a shared defense that blurs the threats of affection and psychological fusion, on the one hand, and of lasting separation on the other. Perhaps, following Lansky's lead, pseudohostility should be renamed collusive hostility.

A secondary point by Lansky that I question is his statement that "the essence of blame is that it is verbal." Actually, when he discusses therapy, he gives clear examples of implicit blaming. My observation is that the forms of blaming that are most difficult to treat are nonverbal. Unresponsive silence, forgetting, alterations in tone of voice, and physical avoidance are often experienced as devastating reproaches, as guilt-inducing covert blame that induces retaliative blaming. The nonverbal blamer is, in turn, blamed for being devious and inexplicit, but can easily respond with the charge that the other is "always" looking for hidden meanings that are not there. The mutual belief that each is being devalued, neglected, or let down can be powerfully induced and reinforced by a nonverbal component in a blaming dialogue. Direct observations in conjoint therapy are especially valuable, sometimes essential, in working with nonverbal messages whose existence is usually hotly disputed.

A highly interesting suggestion by Lansky is that the act of blaming involves "a separate state of consciousness" with "a feeling of mastery and exhilaration" not present at other times. Blaming, Lansky notes insightfully, works as a symptom only while it is going on; "reflection on the process while it is going on is almost impossible and reflection on the process at some other time is ineffective." I strongly agree, and would add that this observation points up one basis for the difficulties of reflective and interpretive forms of intervention in psychotherapy with blaming couples. In my view, behavioral, "educational," and paradoxical forms of intervention with all relevant participants present often are needed to break through the impasses of collusive blaming. Far more work is needed to develop consistently effective therapeutic techniques for resolving these thorny difficulties. Meanwhile, Melvin Lansky has made a significant contribution to an improved conceptualization of the nature of this formidable problem.

REFERENCES

Wynne, L. (1961). The study of intrafamilial alignments and splits in exploratory family therapy. In *Exploring the Base for Family Therapy*, ed. N. Ackerman, F. Beatman, and S. Sherman, pp. 95–115. New York: Family Service Association of America.

——— (1965). Some indications and contra-indications for exploratory family therapy. In *Intensive Family Therapy: Theoretical and Practical Aspects*, ed. I. Boxzormenyi-Nagy and J. Framo, pp. 289–322. New York: Harper and Row.

The Creative Process and the Narcissistic Personality Disorder

BEN RUBENSTEIN, Ph.D.
MORTON LEVITT, Ph.D.

This paper describes the emergence of the creative process during the psychoanalysis of a patient suffering from a narcissistic personality disorder. Infantile history revealed an unending series of failures in the maternal holding environment to which the patient had reacted by withdrawal into fantasy, apathy, and hypochondriasis. The transference material made affective reconstructions of early life possible, and a creative communication was initiated. The newly liberated creative capacity permitted an important sublimatory release for the blocking which had hitherto threatened the patient's emotional health. As infantile fantasies were reexamined and their role as a reaction against threatening experience was understood, the creative arrest was slowly lifted. By creation of artifacts concerned with distorted scoptophiliac derivatives, the patient brought into consciousness material which reflected a broadening of his perceptual field.

> Disease at bottom brought about
> Creative urgence—for creating
> I soon could feel the pain abating,
> Creating, I could work it out.
> —Heine

This article illuminates some aspects of the creative process in the analysis of an individual suffering from a narcissistic personality disorder.

Shortly before this volume went to press, the editors were saddened to receive word of Morton Levitt's untimely death, at the age of fifty-nine, on January 13, 1980. This paper and the more than eighty others he contributed to the literature in the course of a distinguished career attest to the creative energy he brought to all aspects of his life, both professional and personal. It is with a deep sense of loss that we mourn his passing.

The patient's artistic productions were a series of copper spectacles and a face mask which represented the resulting internal personality reorganization as archaic narcissistic configurations appeared. It is our intent to place the dynamic issues leading to the appearance of the creative process within the mainstream of a psychology of normal behavior. We are particularly interested in considering those elements that interfered with separation and individuation in the self self-object relationship.

The products of imagination are the data of the psychoanalyst's work. David Beres (1959) pointed out that symbols, fantasies, thoughts, and dreams are to the analyst what the tracing of the electrocardiograph is to the cardiologist or the microscopic specimen is to the pathologist. Imagination has been defined as the capacity to form a representation of an absent object. It is part of a continuum in a progressive series of thoughts from image to idea to abstraction. The decisive distinction between imagination and other mental activities, complex as the latter may be, is the former's capacity to evoke an image or idea in the absence of a direct, perceptive stimulus.

Imagination is surely a component of what is generally accepted as the creative process. In this regard, we hold that creativity is a special capacity which may or may not be associated with great ability. It is usually of significance when it is a part of a constellation of special abilities and drives which make for the creative individual.

In a general sense, Freud's monumental contributions to dream formation and particularly his description of how unconscious material is transformed as it enters the preconscious provide the best foundation for understanding the creative process. Freud wrote of the flexibility of repression and the incidence of passive attitudes and abandonment as the matrix of the artist's inspiration.

Writing in 1950, Ernst Kris drew attention to an important similarity between ego functioning in psychotherapy and in creative experiences. Kris stated, "Our interpretations may stimulate linkages between the various strata of the mind which reawaken the flow of primary process connections." Kris wrote in 1953 that issues of talent, gift, and fate of endowment are determined by the mother's responses to the specific individuality of her infant's fantasy life, particularly in relation to threatening experience. Fantasy plays an important role in defending against danger, and Kris felt that artistic work resulted from the interplay of libidinous and destructive impulses. He further noted that early trauma played an unusually strong role in the life history of creative individuals.

Kris referred to a temporary nonpermeable barrier between id and ego as the basis for creative inhibition and felt that a creative experience could become part of the therapeutic procedure when free associations were not too threatening and did not lead to an uncontrollable, regressive rush. The creative communications between patient and therapist (perhaps those which were not experienced in the original dyad) then could be channeled into consciousness and shaped by the ego.

Melanie Klein (1929) argued that infantile danger could be equated with fear regarding the loss of the beloved object. Because of this fear, the infant was forced to repress destructive impulses. In a remarkably moving story, Klein described a woman who became depressed when her artist brother removed from her wall a painting he had loaned. Driven to do something about the empty space on her wall (synonymous with her own infantile "emptiness"), she painted a picture although she had never painted before. She was no longer depressed, but instead felt fulfilled. When her brother saw the painting, he was incredulous that his un-tutored sister had been able to create a high quality painting.

Speaking of creativity more concisely, Greenacre (1957) considered the basic characteristics of creative talent as being: (1) greater sensitivity to sensory stimulation; (2) unusual capacity for awareness of relations between various stimuli; (3) predisposition to an empathy of wider range and deeper vibration than usual; and (4) intactness of sufficient sensorimotor equipment to allow the building up of projective motor discharges for expressive functions. These considerations will be reviewed below in the discussion section.

More recently, Heinz Kohut (1966a) suggested that creativity—ranging from new-found ability to perform a restricted range of tasks with zestful initiative to the emergence of brilliantly inventive artistic schemes—may appear spontaneously during treatment. Its appearance is specifically related to the remobilization of "frozen narcissistic cathexes" of both the grandiose self and the idealized parental imago. The recrudescence of these activities appears to arise and subside spontaneously as a consequence of dynamic shifts brought about during analysis, and represents transformations of the patient's archaic narcissism. It may well be that Kohut's conceptions provide another link-pin in the synthesis of certain aspects of mental processes as they relate to the creative function.

The creative process possibly develops as part of a "normal" regression to the archaic self. When such movement is experienced as disintegrative (or fragmenting), immense anxiety may well be dealt with by massive repression. When such individuals come into analysis and are able to reestablish the idealizing transference, they can safely regress to the archaic self. At this time, the patient may be able to reclaim his lost creative energies.[1]

An exchange between James Joyce and Jung at the time Joyce consulted Jung about his daughter highlights the above discussion. Joyce was reported to say defensively, "Don't tell me about the unconscious. I swim in it every day." Jung replied, "Yes, but you are not drowning in it." Trilling (1950) may well have had the last word when he pictured the difference between the creative artist and the neurotic; the former in command of his fantasies and the latter possessed by them.

Over the past decade, Heinz Kohut (1971) and others have begun to develop a theory based upon a relatively independent line of development for narcissism which passes through two crucial infantile way stations: the grandiose self and the idealized parental imago. In the first state, the young child has a grandiose and exhibitionistic image of himself, while in the second state, his early self-idealization is replaced by an admired, omnipotent, and transitional self-object.

In typical development, the equilibrium of primary narcissism is disturbed by unavoidable shortcomings in maternal care. The child replaces the sense of personal perfection previously made up of isolated experiences and united in the images of the approving parent by (1) establishing grandiose and exhibitionistic images of himself (the grandiose self); and (2) by giving over the previous perfection to an admired omnipotent transitional self-object (the idealized parental imago).

Normally, movement from the grandiose self leads to an ideal state called the mature cohesive self, characterized by narcissistic cathexes or various ego activities. As the Ornsteins (1975, p. 232) have written, "Further development of the idealized parental imago leads to an idealization of the superego and to the capacity for mature enthusiasm for greatness and devotion to important tasks."

Kohut (1971) argues that narcissistic disturbances are precipitated by

1. From a slightly different vantage point, Louis Sander (1977) refers to an original "given self" (biological inheritance) and a later "constructed self" (a self that emerges out of "negotiations" between infant and environment). The way these two selves merge depends upon the match between one's fantasies and one's actual experience. Infants who are assured of their mother's love can experiment with behavior which evokes a negative response from the mother. When the maternal "no" is neither overwhelming nor destructive and when the baby is able to find his way back into the love relationship by initiating activities on his own, he can maintain his own continuity of self. This movement from "good" relations to "bad" and back again to "good" can be regarded as a "creative" use of options on the infant's part. His willingness to experiment with different modalities of behavior takes place only when he has discovered that he can behave in oppositional fashion to his mother's wishes. The baby's willingness to experiment with displeasing behavior reflects both exhibitionistic and autonomous precursors, and the relationship between these activities and the development of the child's creative potential will be discussed in greater detail in another paper.

very early narcissistic injury in the matrix of the mother-infant relationship, usually in the form of empathic failure. Later life symptoms are depressive anxiety, depression, emptiness, perverse sexual behavior, hypochondriacal brooding, and fear of fragmentation. A common secondary complaint is work inhibition. In treatment, the therapist's major attention must be focused on keeping the old needs mobilized. The analyst's empathic responses gradually help to transform the archaic narcissistic needs into normal devotion to ideals and self-assertiveness.

CASE PRESENTATION

The following case capsule makes explicit some of the theoretical issues alluded to above. The patient, an artisan, suffered from a narcissistic deficit in infancy aggravated by elements of desertion and neglect which led to a fragility of self-concept. As a consequence, every threat of humiliation, empathic failure, or loss reevoked an archaic threat of disintegration. Maternal failure to respond helpfully to the infant's needs increased his state of disorganization and also inhibited the child from experimenting with the active creation and ordering of new perceptual and sensori motor patterns. As discussed earlier, the above process is thought to be an early precursor of creativity.

The poor developmental milieu delayed the resolution of oedipal conflicts, and the patient was caught up in a lifelong struggle with primary objects. These blocks were finally dissolved when the analytic transference provided for the transmuting internalizations within its empathic holding environment. The freeing process allowed the creativity of the patient to express itself in the production of a series of spectacles; and the connection between the choice of creative objects and the sensory apparatus involved (sight) is central to the entire discussion.

Presenting history. J, a tall, emaciated man, was in his early forties when he came seeking therapy. He was born and brought up in a Pacific Northwest coastal village and was now working independently as a designer. He was married and the father of four children. J was experiencing difficulty working, felt desolate and empty, was depressed and anxious and doing a great deal of solitary drinking. At times, he destroyed domestic pets of other people, usually dropping them from bridges at night.

J's father had been a very successful novelist, sportsman, and a prominent World War I military hero. J's mother was twenty years his father's junior. His father was impatient with young children, and his mother appeared only episodically, usually dressed for parties, to kiss J goodnight. She was fearful of her husband and submitted to his wishes.

On those few occasions when J was in his mother's care, she seemed distant, preoccupied, and uncomfortable with her maternal responsibilities. J perceived his mother as an inaccessible, beautiful goddess. The patient and his older sister were consigned to a basement apartment in the care of a succession of "nannies," most of whom treated him in neglectful fashion. One with whom he spent his earliest years pinched him in sadistic fashion when he displeased her. Interestingly enough, J never complained of this practice to his own mother, saying hopelessly, "There was nothing I could do about it." J's sense of the house was that luxury and happiness existed on the upper floors with only bleakness in the basement.

Being with his father frightened him. Once while boating, his father put him on a small island and sailed away, pretending to leave him. On another occasion when he was five, he was taken by his father to visit a military base. The entire battalion stood at attention when J appeared with his father. The immensity of the field, the weaponry, and the respect accorded his father so terrorized J that he lost sphincter and bladder control.

Shortly thereafter, a series of traumatic events occurred. His father was killed in a plane accident and his mother gave birth to his younger brother. His mother withdrew into mourning and depression for a year. J was moved into his parents' bedroom and his emotional problems proliferated. He became more sickly, and spent much time in bed being cared for by his mother. J's mother was forcibly advised by an uncle to separate herself from her child when he was eight years old, and J was sent protestingly to private schools until college. During this period, his self-image as sickly, cowardly, and isolated became fixed.

After college, he married a girl he had accidentally impregnated. He absented himself when she delivered the child, and on other occasions as well, without informing his wife of his whereabouts. In the face of many provocations, J's wife never complained. Their relationship had a mother-child quality to it. His wife managed the money and earned the major income although he was a competent designer and craftsman. Having little energy for work, he would lie in bed, smoke, and masturbate.

The patient and his wife appeared sexually compatible but further discussion revealed that he rarely ejaculated during intercourse. Later in the night, he masturbated, fantasizing about other women with whom he had slept. When he began analysis on a four-times-per-week basis, he left his wife, but endemic panic and anxiety would lead him to return home, only to leave once again.

Clinical material. In the beginning phase, J quickly established a merger transference. When he left the office, he went through elaborate rituals with his clothing (as though girding his loins) before he walked out. When he became threatened by his growing dependency on the analyst, J distanced himself by complaints of disinterest in treatment, impulsive trips, and sexual affairs.

At this time, J fantasized that the analyst led a glamorous existence, knew everything about J, and even had prior knowledge of his mental contents. It became evident that J made the analyst an idealized omnipotent object. There was no suggestion at this point of a grandiose self. The equation created by his need—"I am perfect, and you are perfect because I am part of you"—conveyed other threats, including the loss of his self in the merger along with the fear of the loss of the idealized object upon whom his security depended. (In this equation, narcissism is not defined by the target-self or object but by the nature of the instinctual charge, i.e., the child invests other people with a narcissistic cathexis which contains the quality of control of that object.)

Empathic comments about his fears and needs in the above regard served to produce dreams which expressed the archaic quality of the self-object. An example follows:

"I am in the harbor in a small punt fishing with a jig (a device that determines the distance of the hook from the ocean bottom). I hooked a fish but knew immediately that it was the wrong kind of fish. It was slimy and had scratchy scales. I'm upset that I had no equipment to unhook it. The fish didn't fight; it just lay on the floor of the punt and looked at me. I felt trapped because I didn't want to cut the line and thereby lose my jig.

"I am visiting a university town [not his school] with my youngest daughter, and looking for a friend. I meet a porter and make inquiries of him. When we part, I am saying 'Sir' to the porter. I'm aware that the roles are reversed. The town is crowded and I feel left out, isolated. If I found my friend, I would not feel left out. I would be part of the crowd."

Both the imagery and the manifest content of the dream are in keeping with J's psychic circumstance. He hooks objects at a precise distance, but he is rendered defenseless because the fish retains his jig, and he remains tied to the object. In the dream, he is the part of a self-object which lowers his self-esteem and from which he cannot escape.

The two dreams were precipitated by the fact that J's mistress had left on a trip, and the analyst had also been away. The first dream expresses his shamed feelings when the idealized self-object has left. The second dream is a continuation of the first dream and reflects a real life event. In his associations, J recalled that while in prep school, where he was lonely for his mother, he was befriended by a popular student (the one he seeks in the dream). While in his company, J felt esteemed and protected and part of the crowd. When they were apart, J felt like a "fish out of water" and "slimy." He remembers being called "creepie."

The devalued self-representation in the second dream was also related in J's associations to his younger brother, six years his junior and born after his father's death. J reported that his younger brother exploited and persecuted him with impunity. J failed to recognize that his brother was a very young child during the period of presumed scapegoating because his view of himself as helpless and detested persisted throughout his entire childhood. The absent analyst became linked with J's parents who valued him little and whose absence also left him lonely and afraid. J was also angry that therapy still failed to provide him with enough strength to resist a depressive reaction to his mistress's departure. After some reflection, J accepted the above interpretation.

In succeeding hours, there was a gradual shift in the analytic material to descriptions, hesitantly recounted, of his sadistic treatment of helpless animals. Some of the animals belonged to neighbors while others were his own cats whom he failed to feed. An interpretation was then offered that J perceived the analyst as failing to understand him and the failure placed the analyst among the many others in his life who held themselves apart from him. Feeling himself devalued, J withheld sustenance from his own domestic animals. His self-image as weak and helpless required that he use the analysis to secure the protection and care that he so badly needed in the early life.

The analysis now took a different course. Because of a newly emerging exhibitionism, J's behavior outside the office began to display a potential for self-destruction in the form of narrowly averted accidents in his work. J next reported a recurrent dream which contained the theme of "brinkmanship":

"I am sailing on a rough sea and there was a frightening moment when either the wind had shifted or I had lost the wind as I came about. The unresolved issue was whether I and the craft would be destroyed on the reef while it was out of control."

Here in the manifest content, J sees himself at the mercy of forces outside of himself and as master of a ship he cannot control. If he stays clear of the land (the object) he is lost; if he comes too close (merger), he will be destroyed on the reef. In his associations, J related the dream to his growing tendency to push limits. In truth, he was a good sailor, as was his father. However, when J sensed that his passengers during an afternoon sail were reflecting admiration for his skills, he experienced a depressive anxiety. At the same time, he was threatened by a feeling of growing power in his work and fantasized that he might be ridiculed for his artistic pretensions by his workers.

J then spoke of his flying lessons. As he approached a plane, he feared the attendant would say, "Who do you think you are? Get out of here!"

Once in the air, he lost all fear and guilt, and was excited and sarcastic. He played with the clouds by flying over and around them. When the plane rolled to a stop, J felt guilty and ashamed and slunk off. J then asked directly, "Would you tell me if you really felt I was going to be suicidal?"

The analyst replied that he understood that J felt neither strength nor energy outside their relationship and was therefore uncertain of control when the two were apart. It was further suggested that J had been deprived of the excitement of exhibitionistic feelings of power as a young child and consequently needed to believe then as well as now that he was helpless. J agreed and said in confirmatory fashion that he had wanted to give his knife (a large jackknife which he always carried with him) to the analyst because he was convinced he might hurt himself. He knew that this thought was a strange one, and then recognized that it must have been a childhood residue. He then offered the following associations: As a young child, he had believed that he was very timid and did not require limiting. After his father's death, J remembered sitting on an uncle's lap and playing with the uncle's finger. J pushed the man's cuticle further and further back anticipating the uncle would curtail the activity, but nothing was said, and J became terrified because he feared he had no control over his own aggressive feelings. In these associations, there was additional evidence of J's struggle with aggression; he was fearful that his infantile rage would be uncontrollable unless there was external help.

As these early configurations of the self were mobilized within the analysis, there was increased anxiety, but his sense of the analyst as a calm and understanding presence provided some regulatory influence. J then met a young woman, K, whose character formed a twinship with his own, and the relationship exposed his need to both idealize the object and to fight the merger by struggling for control. When an issue over control surfaced during the analysis, J said:

"I can feel what you tell me about K. If I control her, why do I then fight her? I think that she wants every bit of me. I think that's what I also want, but she also wants it. That's frightening."

K perfectly recreated the archaic self-object configuration. While with her, J feared his need for her; when she left, he felt empty and was convinced she was leading a glamorous life elsewhere. Aware of his strange comfort with the familiar sense of desolation and injury, he said, "I believed that I could always get what I wanted from my mother, my wife, or these other women by being sick and wounded. It reminds me of the mother sea gull who behaves as though she has a broken wing to lead predators away from her brood." Space does not permit a complete analysis of this imaginative metaphor which illuminates issues of control as both self and object. Suffice it to say that in J's associations, he saw himself as both the protecting mother and the helpless child.

J experienced unavoidable interruptions (vacations, meetings, etc.) of the analysis at this time as lack of empathic appreciation by the analyst, and this brought material into the transference which helped J to understand his feelings of powerlessness and emptiness. On one occasion as the analyst was about to leave on a trip, J announced:

"I want to throw things like a child. I want to throw forks and knives. I want to know why you are going and with whom. I think you are going to have a gay old time."

At the door he stopped and said: "I have a fantasy about hitting you," and he hit the analyst lightly on the cheek with a glove. After the therapist returned from his trip, J stated, "I could have hit you much harder. I could feel it." Idealizing the analyst made J feel both perfect and whole but also utterly dependent. Left behind, J experienced the sense of abandonment which revived old anxieties and intensified his problem of maintaining homeostasis.

As can be seen from the above, J began experiencing difficulty in defending himself against his narcissistic rage. He kept many cats which he neglected. One night, he coldly shot one but offered an unclear rationalization for this strange act. Another time, after his mistress had pressed him to do something that was difficult for him, J took his pistol and aimed it at another cat and pretended to kill it. The face of his mistress came to mind when he had his finger on the trigger.

The analyst then offered the following interpretation: When J felt he was being deserted (not valued by the analyst), it evoked feelings of rage analogous to those experienced in his early relations with his mother. His wish to destroy the parent brought the frightening recognition that he would then be absolutely alone. It was also suggested to the patient that he was able to destroy cats because there were always more around, that is, the loss of one was not catastrophic. J now could understand why it was less threatening for him and K to hurt each other within what he colorfully described as a "barbed wire embrace," since to destroy a loved object was to risk self-destruction as well. A dream confirmed this interpretation:

"A cat is drowning in a brook. It is weakly mewing. It is one I like. It will die if I don't save it. I do and hold it with compassion. But I was reluctant to step in to save it."

J commented: "As a child, my mother gave my toy pets to a hospital. I told her she gave away my best friends. It was a family joke but I was filled with hatred. Later at school, I felt covered by a repugnant cloud of guilt. Always certain I'd be caught for something. It had to do with what I do to cats. I don't know how but I see the frightened eyes of gray cats as being myself."

The transient objects (toys) represented that part of J that is ideal, good, and kind, while he continued to experience himself as devalued, bad, and "slimy." He could only value himself when he was in union with a self-object upon whom he could project the good self. The self self-object configuration underwent increasing strain as rage was slowly being experienced in the transference relationship.

Other associations to the cat dream helped in understanding that J was having difficulty managing rage. He wished to believe that the analyst cared about him as though J were his child; J even expressed the desire to be embraced. He said, "Maybe you only pretend to be interested in me." The patient was frightened that both his sense of growing competence and his rage would be discovered. It is within this context that J had dreamed of the dying cat which was a symbolic representation of himself.

More open anger followed. It was experienced within the transference and was also expressed in two dreams, then a memory, and finally the beginning of the exotic creative process alluded to above. The first dream follows:

"I am on the beach with a woman friend. As I walk, I sink into the soft sand which has sharp pieces of glass in it. I walk and the glass cuts into my feet, and it feels both pleasurable and painful. I think I will get tough feet from doing this sort of thing."

The memory stimulated by the dream was from a period when he attended an art school. He had been asked by an instructor to put together two materials in a manner in which one material would bring out the qualities of the second. The patient took his mother's old fur neckpiece, made it into a fish shape, and inserted hundreds of fine steel points into the fur. If anyone caressed the soft fur, their hands would be shredded. J also took a toothbrush and replicated the above circumstance by inserting steel points into the quills.

The above material offered a partial explanation of why artistic designs and constructions were heretofore sterile and cold. The "soft" fur (representing early perceptions of and wishes for maternal warmth) disguised a painful "hard" and rejecting reality. In J's early life, there was little likelihood of echoing or confirming responses on his mother's part for his exhibitionistic activities. Growing consciousness of this phenomena and its impact upon his creative faculties were made known to him through interpretation. As the patient became less fearful of his grandiose fantasies because of the mirroring transference, he began to experience his own work with enthusiasm. However, as his projects approached completion, he felt, much as in flying, ashamed and self-conscious.

It was at this point in the analysis that the specific qualities of the self-object representation in both the dream and memory could be elucidated.

The imagery of hard and soft (fur and needle, sand and glass) and of cats persisted as central themes in the material until a genetic explanation emerged. In an associative link, J offered the following:

"It's odd about cats. I really like geese and rabbits better. The first because they are so pushy and noisy and the other because they are so soft and helpless. I don't know why I am so uncomfortable with thoughts being nasty like geese."

A dream dealing with vision heralded the appearance of the series of spectacles:

"I am with a girl at a stream. It is very beautiful. I see a reptile approaching with a head like a turtle on a dinosaurlike body. It had a bland expression in its eyes as it moved toward me, and I became apprehensive. K said it was all right, but I could see it was after me, not her. I noticed a gate that I could get through if I had time. It was a creature of intelligence and it knew what I had in mind."

The associations from this dream led to his younger brother, Julian, who had terrorized him as a child. J said: "Julian always screamed when I set after him. The monster symbolizes his brute, unaccessible power. Nothing I can do about it!" Next, the lines from *Macbeth* flashed through his mind:

Avaunt! And quit my sight! Let the earth hide thee! Thy bones are marrowless, thy blood is cold; thou hast no speculation in those eyes which thou dost glare with!

The association to the lines spoken by Macbeth confirms that the repression barrier has been breached. The dramatic contrast between the muted quality of the dream, that is, the "bland expression" as opposed to "quit my sight" and "dost glare with," is ample evidence that previously frightening feelings are now beginning to surface.

J's other associations to the reptile dream and the lines from *Macbeth* were diffuse but still illuminating. They all attested to increased self-esteem. At various times during this period, J said:

"Yesterday I bought books and records openly that I would have bought surreptitiously in the past. Book on geology, Joni Mitchell, *Joy of Sex*. . . .

"I'm going to solo [in the plane] soon. . . . The frightening fantasies have disappeared. I have to wear an old shirt with the tail cut off. . . .

"K tells me how handsome I am. I feel both good and ridiculous. . . .

"I almost cut my hand off today in the shop. I was taking a chance. I'm getting too proficient. . . .

"I can ski now like my father did. I no longer use his old boots. I have been asked to design another building. . . . My brother's mistress called; she's interested in me, and I invited her up."

J recognized that he was a victim as always in the reptile dream, but that he was also K and the monster as well. Maternal reassurances remain of little help ("K said it was all right"), and he was not fooled by the monster's "bland expression." The eyes—like on a real life turtle—were the compelling facial features, and J's efforts to escape were doomed, for the creature has already perceived what he had in mind. The dual themes of seeing and being seen were encountered in the verse from *Macbeth* as well. He wanted the dreaded object out of his sight ("quit my sight!"), but was terrified at being observed ("eyes thou dost glare with!").

While working in his shop, J formed in copper, with no clear intention and almost absently, a pair of spectacles. The production has solid copper discs which permitted no vision. On impulse, J wore the spectacles to a children's party at his daughter's school. Sporting a bowler hat and a wig, he presented the appearance of a strange magician which both frightened and excited the children. J appeared for his analytic session wearing the spectacles and smiling like a pleased child. He acknowledged the analyst's surprise with another smile and took them off and walked to the couch. Apart from detailing the reception accorded to his production at the children's party, no further mention was made. Although the analyst said nothing directly, he was sure that J was impressed by his accepting attitude and openness.

The first pair of spectacles present an all-season defense. J can neither see nor can he be seen, and his perception of himself as a magician reflected an early childhood preoccupation with magic associated with his father's violent death in a plane accident. J had spent many hours examining the electronic parts of planes. In a way, they were his main intellectual preoccupation and it seemed restrospectively that he was determined to both find a way to manage his sense of loss through this process, as well as to try to find an explanation in the plane's parts, as it were, for his father's strange death.

The public and private reception accorded the first pair of spectacles—the children were excited and the analyst paid some attention to them—led to the creation of a second pair.

This time there was a minute hole drilled in the beaten copper discs which were covered on the external side by fragments of plastic and crystal joined in a ring. They allowed only the most protected glance through what were most likely "peep-holes" and were notably unlifelike in appearance. These spectacles required quick little movements of the head to find a point of clear vision in the crystal fragments. Looking is tolerated, but barely, and the genetic significance of the "seeing and being seen" problem in the mother-infant interchange will be discussed shortly.

A third production now appeared. It was a partial face mask covering his eyes and nose. J had modeled it, once again without thinking, from the death mask of a mummy. He could barely see through the minute slits for the eyes. J pointed out that the edges of the mask were very sharp and the mask could poke out one's eyes.

This mask was related to a dream which was stimulated by sexual interest in his most recent mistress's girl friend:

"There is an expedition going through a mountain range and all but me are tied by lead ropes. A man with the necessary map cannot be found. I am reminded that an expedition searched in the mountains for my father's body when his plane crashed."

The patient identified the analyst as the man who has the map, but the dream suggested that J was not yet ready to accept his father's death. His recognition that the death mask might represent both his father's face and his own as well brought mounting bladder pressure. J was hiding behind the mask for protection, but it was also his father's death mask, and the sharp edges contain the threat of blindness.

As his conscious fear of his anger grew, J said of the analyst, "You will never change. You will always be the same. I can always depend on you." "But," he added as he left the office and pointed to the spectacles which he had left behind on a book shelf, "they will keep you in line. They will watch you like the eye of the magician."

The reptile dream, the production of the spectacles, the expedition dream, the changes in J's management of reality, and the character of the transference raise interesting technical and theoretical questions at this point. Two arguments can be made: One, J had earlier viewed himself as having limited vision, and later as treatment helped him to feel more esteem and less vulnerability, he became frightened at the prospect of what he might discover by opening his eyes fully. The second argument is the converse: J regarded the analyst as either blind or unavailable, or both, and the glasses were an effort to communicate this information, that is, to express a response to the blindness of the analyst who had been missing important unconscious communications.

As beguiling as it is, the misalliance argument fails for a variety of reasons. The demonstrable forward movement rested upon the empathic therapeutic response to J's difficulties in maintaining a cohesive self. The increased openness of J's creative productions was consistent with his sense of the analyst as an ever-present figure. The above observation is confirmed by the fact that each time he entered the office he scanned the analyst's face while commenting that "seeing you makes me feel good."

Further support for the first hypothesis can be found in responses which generally verify the correctness of interpretations (i.e., correct interpretations lead to confirmatory responses and to the enlargement of the associative field). Ample evidence of this phenomena has been presented above. Clearly, each new set of spectacles represented an enlargement of the patient's ego boundaries. His awareness of the transference as a holding action is verified by both dreams, associations, and simple declarative statements ("Would you tell me if you really felt I was going to be suicidal?") and actions (wanting the analyst to take a knife away from him). At this time, J continued to need to control the therapeutic experience in order to avoid losing himself in a merging experience. This latter issue came into focus when the analyst allowed the glasses to remain behind in his office.

Thinking about the spectacles he had left in the office produced an urge to make several new pairs. J now recognized that the problem that he was struggling with was the fear of unprotected vision. He asked, "How far can I go in protecting my eyes and still have some vision [knowledge]?" The newest spectacles had a live .22 caliber bullet in the center of each copper disc. As he discussed them, he remarked, "If looks could kill someone else, I, too, could be killed by the reaction [recoil] to the explosion." The production of the spectacles stimulated another dream:

"I am observing a huge suspension bridge swaying under a strong wind. It increasingly sways in an undulating motion until the bridge disintegrates. A portion of the bridge hangs from the approach where I stand with a faceless someone. The end of the protruding portion resembles a creature with eyes. They remind me of colored lights on the tunnel approaches that blink on and off as though they have a presence. That part made after me. I ran. There is no sense of fright. The creature's intention is not clear, yet there is an inevitability about it in its eyes."

On the manifest level of the dream, there was the patient's usual preoccupation with visual imagery, but although J was forced to finally break and run, he experienced "no sense of fright." Since he no longer stood alone [he now had a "faceless" friend with him], terror was reduced. Still, the unhappy ending seemed unavoidable. In association, J recalled that after his father's death, he was convinced that he could "see" a vision of his mother, dead and mutilated, if she were late returning home after a social evening. At such times, the patient suffered excruciating spasms of bladder pressure. The experience of bladder pressure occurred then in the context of anxiety about the mother's tardiness; it was also seen earlier as a response to his father's grandiose omnipotence in the battalion incident already described.

J recalled that he kept his father's mirrored dressing table. As he dressed and looked at the mirror, he was mindful that his father looked at that mirror thousands of times. J fantasized that his father was behind the mirror, looking back at him. The theme of *Orpheus* came to mind. His father was not doing anything. Was he waiting to take J to the under-world? The double focus of the association is immediately apparent; it related to the analyst as well. When the interpretation was offered, J's reaction confirmed it. He said, "I've had the feeling that when you are back of me, it creates the same feeling of apprehension that I had as a child at home when I lived in the basement with my father above me and observing me."

New versions of spectacles which appeared followed two trends. When J was depressed and anxious, that is, narcissistically vulnerable, almost no vision was allowed. When he felt heightened self-esteem, there was increased vision.[2] The latter, however, continued to involve intricate constructions of prisms, crystals, and plastic, and allowed for only indirect vision.

J now made spectacles with dimes covering the eye openings, making clear his hostility about the money he paid for treatment. Although his relationships outside the analysis had improved somewhat, J described being upset at the seemingly simple request by K to take a picture of her with his new camera. He suffered a spasm of bowel pressure, and the familiar symptom underlined the analytic construction that seeing (taking pictures) was frightening to J since it exposed his repressed infantile grandiosity.

J's increasing awareness of the analyst's acceptance of his aggressive fantasies within the transference now produced spectacles with larger openings. These were spectacles which were half lens and half reflector. He dreamed that he was ripping pages off a book or calendar, like dead skin or matter. The evening before, he had cleaned out his basement which was "filled with cat shit and stank." It was now in order. J had lived in a basement as a child. Now his basement was pleasant, and he could allow himself wider vision as the analysis reintegrated the present with the past.

Fear of loss of control of the object now became more central in the treatment process. Transference interpretations (it was suggested that J idiosyncratically attributed omnipotence to the analyst and then tried to become part of him) helped him to recognize that as a helpless child, he had invested people around him with his own feelings of grandiosity, and consequently experienced them narcissistically as self-objects. Kohut (1971) reminds us that such control over others is closer to the sense of the control that adults expect to have over their own minds and bodies. For J,

2. Scoptophilia, like its counterpart, exhibitionism, is subject to many restrictions. Freud said, "The eyes perceive not only those modifications in the external world which are of import for the preservation of life, but also the attributes of objects by means of which these may be exalted as objects of erotic selection, i.e., their 'charms'" (Freud 1910, p. 216).

the threat of loss of control of the object triggered fear and rage as though he had lost control of his own mind and body. Here, however, the model was his angry and depressive reactions to any break in the analytic regime.

J's growing consciousness of these issues permitted him to approach reality problems with more self-esteem. Two new pairs of spectacles surfaced which expressed growing freedom. One permitted full vision, but there were flaps which could be dropped down for protection. The patient identified the second pair as being "for pleasure"; they allowed clear vision and resembled sunflowers.

After realistically settling an arrangement for payment of fees, which were badly in arrears, J began speaking of working on another set of spectacles. One day, an unmarked package was delivered to the analyst. It contained a set of glasses which allowed vision but which had heavy meshing over the lens area. When J arrived for his next appointment, he associated to the fact that he had thought the analyst would be apprehensive and might think the package was an explosive. There is little question of mixed motivation here; the therapeutic frame may well be damaged by J's failure to pay his bill. It is also clear that the corrective confrontation regarding fees dislodged explosive rage. J had difficulty with his latest creation because he wanted to convey a sense of a powerful projectile breaking through the metal to the outside. For the first time, he consciously thought of how he had to scorch the jagged rim of each opening. He also found that he had to put a wire grating over each hole for his own protection.

Conscious ego activities such as cleaning up, organizing, and cataloging now came to the forefront. J was preoccupied with geology, and he said repetitively, "I want to know everything."[3] As J became more independent, he made plans for a final grandiose pair of spectacles, electronic in nature, with a receiver which would activate the lenses. He envisioned them as responding to extraterrestrial communication. He planned to send it to K and said: "It will be a fantastical mechanism by which she will control me. Vision will be directed by what it receives." There was a pause and then he shouted: "No, my God, I will control her! That's it!"

He worked enthusiastically on the project, collecting old clock works,

3. Freud had noted that the child in its primitive curiosity needs to see in order to maintain contact with the desired objects as well as for his own self-preservation. "To *know*" implies that the scoptophilia has already undergone restraint. The desire for knowledge, the impulse toward investigation, the observation of nature, and the artistic treatment of things are phenomena which owe their origin to the above process. In pathological development, further sublimation of the scoptophiliac instinct is inhibited. With reference to the patient, J's statement, "I want to know everything", stands in mixed contrast to the flatness of interest which was characteristic of his preanalytic behavior.

radios, and reexperiencing a childhood preoccupation with electronic components of planes in the process. He commented: "As a child, I had to disassemble them. I had to get inside each part in order to experience it. I had no 'practical' interest in them."

He fantasized sending the spectacles to K. They were to be placed on the head of a clothes model, which, in turn, would be placed in a box with windows surrounding the head. The concealed clock works operated by batteries would cause the lenses to open and close. The box was to contain intricate but meaningless directions abstracted from the jargon of flying manuals.

This last creation, which was never completed or sent, marked the beginning of the final phase of the analysis. The imaginative construction expressed: (1) the recovery of the infantile exhibitionistic and grandiose self and (2) the magical thinking engendered by these states. In regard to the recovery of early exhibitionism and grandiosity, J believed that the analyst knew everything that was in J's mind. This belief was not accompanied by anxiety since the patient experienced himself as fused with the analyst, sharing both grandiosity and power. With reference to magical thinking, an incident occurred at this time which brought into the analysis material which proved very illuminating.

The patient received a phone call late at night from a woman who did not identify herself but spoke as if he knew her. Her voice terrorized him. When asked why he did not ask her name, the patient said that he was too frightened. As he continued to speak, it developed that on some level he knew it was K, with whom he was then breaking up. J remarked that he had been experiencing guilt in relation to her before the call, and he clearly stated that he believed her call was both a magical response brought about by his guilt and a confirmation as well of his impending doom for leaving her. J could not ask for her name because the ensuing reality confrontation would dispel the magic which also served as a source of power for him. That is, if J dissipated the "magical" aura which allowed K to call as if in response to his need for punishment, he would simultaneously risk losing his own magical power through which he felt he managed her. When K hung up, J imagined hearing the sound of bat wings rustling against the eaves of the house, a sound associated with magical beliefs in his early childhood. He recognized then that he used magical ideas with the analyst, as with K, in order to control the relationship.

The final spectacle production brought two things to consciousness: (1) J's overwhelming need to merge with his mother ("My God, I will control her!") in order to avoid a sense of helplessness, and (2) his efforts to allay his fear of losing control of his narcissistic anger. In J's earlier creations, where there was ambiguity between inside and outside, the wearer was protected but also endangered by sharp edges, the explosive recoil, etc. In the same sense, the object posing the external threat is similarly threatened. As the life-taking aspect—his mother's shortcomings—expressed in the self-object configuration diminished in affective intensity, so did J's need to exert control.

J's omnipotent narcissistic rage, which was layered first in relation to the unempathic mother, then to the humiliating omnipotent father, ultimately dissipated in the analysis. Because J was unable in early life to achieve a successful resolution of the grandiose self and the idealized parental imago, he entered the oedipal phase with a variety of self-object disabilities. Clinical material described supports the thesis that the aloof and rejecting father prevented a leavening paternal identification by failing to mirror approval of J's movements toward maturity. His experience with new objects was thereafter characterized by an archaic need for conquest and adoration, as well as by a fear of his own reactive rage when such needs were not met.

Discussion

This paper describes the emergence of the creative process during the psychoanalysis of a patient suffering from a narcissistic personality disorder. In the analysis of narcissistic personalities, changes in creative potential may occur during the terminal phase. When it is possible to discover retrospectively that the narcissistic forces now directed toward new objects were active earlier in the patient's life but then became bound up in narcissistic tension states, there is good reason to believe that the patient is achieving a true dissolution of his narcissistic transference engagement with the analyst, and the breakthrough of creativity no longer serves a defensive purpose.

In J's case, the newly liberated creative capacity permitted an important sublimatory release for the narcissistic blocking which had hitherto threatened his emotional health. In this regard, we quote Kohut, who wrote that

> it is my opinion that many creative activities in the terminal phases of the analyses of narcissistic personalities (analogous to the flowering of the empathic ability in the end phases of some training analyses) constitute the favorable result of the preceding analytic work and that they are true transformations of the former pathogenic narcissistic positions. For this reason they do not constitute material that requires psychoanalytic interpretations in the usual sense. (1966a, p. 203).

Formulations regarding the consequences of early narcissistic injury resulting from empathic failure in the matrix of the mother-infant relationship have been of particular value in conceptualizing this case. J's infantile history revealed an unending series of failures in the maternal holding environment to which J reacted by withdrawal into fantasy, apathy, and hypochondriasis. As an adult, he experienced work difficulty, was lonely, depressed, and felt alienated.

Kohut (1971, p. 117) has written:

The most significant relevant basic interactions between mother and child lie usually in the visual area. The child's bodily display is responded to by the gleam in the mother's eyes.

This statement has particular reference to the sterility of J's early work and the later creative breakthrough. There was certainly no gleam in his mother's eye at the sight of him; how then could he risk exposure of his grandiosity when it had failed to elicit any echoing in confirming maternal response in its *de novo* state? From this viewpoint, J's preoccupation with the analyst's facial expression, his avowed wish to touch the analyst's face, and his statement that "seeing" the analyst made him feel good all represent a forward movement in the therapeutic frame.

From the very beginning of his life, J was left in the hands of a succession of nannies, and the best remembered one was the woman who pinched him whenever he did anything wrong. It is clear that J's mother herself hardly qualified as the "good enough mother," a concept first described by Freud (1923) and later elaborated by Winnicott (1953). Consequently, J came to view himself as a weak, injured bird, and this restricted and closed image precluded the healthy freedom (exhibitionism) to try to find new responses in his mother's eyes.

Maternal failure to respond helpfully to the infant's needs increased his state of disorganization and also inhibited the child from experimenting with the active creation and ordering of new perceptual and sensorimotor patterns. The transference material made affective reconstructions of early life possible, and a creative communication was initiated. As infantile fantasies were reexamined and their role as a reaction against threatening experiences was understood, the creative arrest was slowly lifted. The heretofore intensely threatening destructive and libidinous impulses became sufficiently moderated to permit the creative interplay that is fundamental to both play and artistic work. As the patient became more free in his struggle with fantasy, his sense of urgency lessened and he could more effectively "manage" his mental imagery. The regressive rush was thereby weakened.

Therapeutic empathy facilitated the narcissistic transference which provided the genetically missing mirroring environment. Interpretations within the transference aided the patient's ego in mediating unconscious processes emerging through shifts in now freed narcissistic and exhibitionistic energy. The controlled therapeutic regression which temporarily utilized primary process thinking was, we believe, responsible for the appearance of the creative process, in this case in particular, and in the narcissistic character disorders generally.

The creative communications were channeled into production by new ego structures. Interpretations of clinical data related to the spectacle production increased J's awareness of the rage provoked by the self-object tie. When the anger slowly weakened, J came to feel himself more in control of his own destiny, and the loosening of archaic structures permitted the play with new figure-ground perceptions. As the healthy infant responds with pleasure to light and shadow on the nursery walls, so we see J freed to create imaginative objects in a psychological rebirth.

By the creation of artifacts concerned with distorted scoptophiliac derivatives, J brought into consciousness material through which speculation could take place. As the patient's creations moved to more open vision, there was less fear of exposing his rage. At the same time, he became excited by learning, and the search for knowledge allowed J to deal with his father's death. Construction of a magical electronic device controlled by an astral source which drew upon materials relating to his father's death—i.e., the mummy mask and the electronic equipment—finally helped J to resolve his neurotic conflicts.

When J's characteristics are matched with Greenacre's (1957) earlier delineation of creative talent, there is considerable correspondence. In J's case, there was indeed greater sensitivity to sensory stimulus, unusual capacity for awareness of relations between various stimuli, a predisposition to an empathy of a wider range and deeper vibration than usual, and finally an intactness of sufficient sensorimotor apparatus to allow the building up of projective motor discharges for expressive functions.

The third and fourth points above require special emphasis. Issues of empathy were of particular relevance in J's intermingling of the inanimate and animate in his artistic productions. Greenacre (1957) stated that

the increased empathy associated with creative talent would seemingly depend on the sensory responsiveness to the individual's own body state as well as to the external object, and appears as a peculiar degree of empathic animation of inanimate objects as well as a heightened responsiveness and anthropomorphosizing of living objects. The difference between empathy and sympathy is here especially conspicuous. Such animation of the inanimate and anthropomorphosizing ordinarily is lost after early childhood, but in gifted individuals remains active either in its own right or appears in the form of the ease and wealth of symbolization.

The fourth point ("intactness of sufficient sensorimotor equipment to allow for building up of projective motor discharges for expressive function") relates to the most significant way in which the patient's creativity was inhibited. His sense of being physically injured, handicapped, and impaired (the "sickly" childhood, forcible separation from his mother when sent off to school where he was called "creepie," his self-description as "slimy," and his attachment to the metaphoric representation of himself as a wounded bird) was of long duration. Physical competence could be expressed only in counterphobic fashion—flying in the clouds or operating a sailboat in dangerous waters. As J's feelings of omnipotence and rage diminished and as the threat of injury lessened, he was able to experience his body in a more pleasurable way and he could carry on creative work with a sense of freedom and pleasure.

REFERENCES

Beres, D. (1959). Chairman's report, panel on the psychology of imagination. Annual Meeting, Philadelphia, April.

Freud, S. (1910). The psycho-analytic view of psychogenic disturbances of vision. *Standard Edition* 11:209–218.

—— (1923). The ego and the id. *Standard Edition* 19:3–66.

Greenacre, P. (1957). The childhood of the artist. *Psychoanalytic Study of the Child* 12:47–72.

Klein, M. (1929). Infantile anxiety situations reflected in a work of art and in the creative impulse. *International Journal of Psycho-Analysis* 10:436–443.

Kohut, H. (1966a). Forms and transformations of narcissism. *Journal of the American Psychoanalytic Association* 14:243–272.

—— (1966b). Discussion of M. Schur's paper: Some additional "day residues" of the specimen dream of psychoanalysis. Presented at Meeting, Chicago Psychoanalytic Society.

—— (1971). *The Analysis of the Self.* New York: International Universities Press.

Kris, E. (1950). On preconscious mental processes. *Psychoanalytic Quarterly* 19:540–560.

—— (1953). Psychoanalysis and the study of creative imagination. *Bulletin of the New York Academy of Medicine* 29:334–351.

Ornstein, A., and Ornstein, P. (1975). On the interpretive process in psychoanalysis. *International Journal of Psychoanalytic Psychotherapy* 4:219–271.

Sander, L. (1977). Workshop on the psychoanalytic process and narcissism. Boston Psychoanalytic Society and Institute. February 28, 1977.

Trilling, L. (1950). Freud and literature. In *The Liberal Imagination.* New York: The Viking Press.

Winnicott, D. W. (1953). Transitional objects and transitional phenomena. *International Journal of Psycho-Analysis* 34:89–97.

On the Creative Process and the Human Capacity to Construe

KURT SCHLESINGER, M.D.

A discussion of "The Creative Process and the Narcissistic Personality Disorder," by Ben Rubenstein, Ph.D., and Morton Levitt, Ph.D. The human capacity for *construal* is emphasized as a basic process characterizing mental activity. Motivational and developmental phenomena can be better understood when construal is emphasized. The development of the capacity to construe is intimately linked in feedback fashion with the development of the subjective self which uses enactive, imagistic, and lexical modes of conceptualization. Construal is characterized as conflictual and as concomitantly involving powerful affective components. Examples are given in which the role of construal in artistic work, action, acting out, anxiety and object relatedness are emphasized. The basic creative act is the gradual construal of the subjective self on which all later creativity will have to be based.

> In paintings of the apples Cézanne was able to express through their varied colors and groupings a wide range of moods, from the gravely contemplative to the sensual and ecstatic. In this carefully arranged society of perfectly submissive things the painter could project typical relations of human beings as well as qualities of the larger visible world—solitude, contact, accord, conflict, serenity, abundance and luxury—and even states of elation and enjoyment.
> —Meyer Schapiro

This work originates as a discussion of Drs. Rubenstein's and Levitt's paper, "The Creative Process and the Narcissistic Personality Disorder." They are superb teachers for they have made me think. For this I am grateful. The discussion grew like Topsy and I was led to examine and articulate my own ideas on creativity and its relationship to clinical problems. I am in substantial agreement with their thesis but have elaborated my own version.

It has not been possible to review or integrate the psychoanalytic literature on creativity, narcissism, the development of the self, and the psychology of meaning—areas I deem applicable to this topic. I may well be slighting important work, more specifically, work that has shaped my own thinking.

In lieu of one person analyzed in depth over extended time, so expertly presented by the authors, I have had to piece together reactions to their work, foreshortened vignettes of case material, inferences from public events, and a brief self-analytic sequence as the data base for my discussion.

Drs. Rubenstein and Levitt present us with a paper which makes significant points about narcissistic personality disorders, and their analytic treatment. They emphasize aspects of creativity and how the patient's creative endeavors were released by, and integrated into, the analytic work. They most appropriately place the dynamic issues leading to the appearance of the creative process "within the mainstream of a psychology of normal behavior."

CREATIVITY, SELF-CONSTRUAL AND NARCISSISTIC CONFLICT

At the heart of creativity lies the human capacity to construe. This faculty plays a key role in the development of the self. The subjective sense of self is in itself a construction which is determined by early relationships and which in feedback fashion functions to construe the relations to others even as it is determined by them.

The sense of self is a landmark creative process which in turn plays a key role in determining how the psychosexual stages, the oedipal conflict, and object relations will be endowed with meaning. Mahler's (1975) work is an important presentation of observations and theory about the individuation of the self.

The development of the construing self is not a linear unfolding. A series of antithetical polarities or incongruencies need to be resolved in the process of developing a subjective self-concept. Such a resolution is dynamic, and the self-concept is born of conflict and continuously functions with the intensities arising out of the clash of meanings.

Requiring resolution-integration are the needs of the self so as to feel whole when countered by the fear of fragmentation; to feel safe with the antithesis of vulnerability; to feel individually related to others countered on one side by the fear of isolation and on the other by the fear of being taken over; to feel effective rather than helpless; to feel chosen and affirmed rather than bypassed. There are creative possibilities in construing these conflicts and the list cannot be exhaustive any more than there can be an exhaustive list of metaphors or concepts.

The problem of narcissism has its inception as the subjective self develops and resolves such antitheses in the matrix of early self and self-object construal. Normal narcissism is the process in which the subjective self has internalized a relative sense of coherence, identity, integrity and self-esteem. Such a person does not require massive continuing defensive reassurance through behavior and fantasy against the anxiety of fragmentation, of loss of self, of isolation and unlovability. Pathologic narcissism is defined as a relative failure to adequately resolve these and analogous conflicts in the development of the subjective self. Such unresolved issues thus permeate the more adult levels of object relations, work, play, creative function, sensuality, etc., with gross to subtle affects on construal and action. Thus, a narcissistic core is operative as a dynamic issue in well-adapted persons, and at the other end, in those individuals with continuing, engrossing preoccupation with self-conflict at the expense of all other endeavor. We need to refine our clinical theory to adequately construe those problems lying between and encompassing these extremes.

The creative individual has an innately heightened sensitivity to the kinds of contradictions mentioned and combines this with a greater capacity for resolving them in creative forms. The authors quote Kris (1952), who emphasizes the role of early trauma in the life history of creative individuals. The traumatic component embodied in early caretaking interactions interacts with the heightened sensitivity so that intensified incongruencies require resolution. This may appear then as a linear causal relationship between early trauma and creativity. It is more complex than that. The developing self exercises a need for mastery to counter feelings of being overwhelmed. The sense of loss, an ineluctable concomitant of human development, is experienced as an incongruity between the wished for and the attainable. Attempts at construal of a resolution can motivate creativity. Mastery takes the form of construal into the kinesthetic, imagistic, lexical and action modalities consonant with attained developmental levels and innate abilities. These are defensive construals. Subsequent defenses against aggression and libidinal wishes in the context of object relations will participate in the process of creativity in ways modeled by the earlier developmental issues and the degree and quality of their resolution. This broadens the definition of defenses beyond the classic one of defenses against drive. Defenses against drives or wishes also use the construing capacity of the self and can analogously participate in the creative process. Kris considers aggressive and libidinal drives the motive force of creativity, while I stress as the basic motivation, the human capacity to construe incongruence.

The concept of psychological conflict needs corresponding redefinition, and conflict is probably best expressed as a conflict of meanings when two or more ways of construal are in contradiction to each other. The so called "energies" deployed in such conflict and the concomitant anxiety and other affects are the cognitive-affective responses engendered in the person in the face of contending unresolved meanings.

THEORETICAL IMPLICATIONS OF THE CLINICAL MATERIAL

The clinical discussion by Drs. Rubenstein and Levitt emphasizes the manner in which the transference unfolds and how the analytic handling of the transference allows the patient to break out of a self-concept which was imposed by his earliest experiences in the cognitive-affective dyad. Mildly disconcerting is the occasional invocation of metapsychologic theory when the clinical theory has adequately explained the observations. For example, we read: "the narcissistic forces now directed toward new objects were active earlier in the patient's life but then became bound up in narcissistic tension states." This invokes the classical U-tube theory of narcissism as psychological forces/energies reciprocally alternating between being directed outward or invested in the self. The clinical theoretical statements which show how this patient's earliest manifestations of interest, curiosity, joyous recognition of other and self were thwarted and how this distorted the sense of self and thus all of his relationships, explain quite as much without invoking psychologic energies. The paper adequately provides clinical theoretical explanation, and the metapsychologic ones are superfluous. As Gill (1976) has pointed out, "metapsychology is not psychology."

As a result of analysis, the patient undergoes a shift in subjective self-experience from feeling predominantly slimy, rejectable, vulnerable, and a danger to others. Such a subjective self-experience is experienced as so frustrating to relatedness and induces so much rage that the self has to be continually preoccupied with defending against the threat of these conceptions and their concomitant affects. As a consequence, whatever object relations are possible will be permeated by this conflict and self-preoccupation. Any artisanship, if it is at all functional, will be similarly suffused with self-preoccupations. Now with the alteration in the subjective sense of self, the construal of the world as frustrating and enraging gives way to alternate meanings with diminished concomitant rage. The cognitive-affective capacities for interest, curiosity and joy (Basch 1976) can play a greater role in the self-concept.

There has been creativity right along. To metaphorize oneself as a slimy fish, to think of intimate contact with others as being like stroking a soft fur with hidden barbs—these are creative modes of experiencing oneself and others. The core construence of self and of others is historically determined and will decisively shape the quality of the creativity. With a construal less focused on the vulnerability of the self and the frustrating, anguishing character of others, earlier cognitive affective modes, enactive and imagistic (Horowitz 1971), are more readily available in addition to verbal ones for a kind of play or practicing which are part of the ongoing development of the self. An important aspect of creativity at its best is the freedom to range between the enactive, imagistic, and lexical modes, translate problems from one modality to the other, and integrate these transformations into new wholes, metaphors of varying originality.

A capacity to resolve incongruence and a tolerance for ambiguity are important descriptive aspects of creative work as they are for the development of a self. I am characterizing this as the basic human creative act, the development of the subjective self and the subjective perception of others.

In connection with a discussion of humor, I have emphasized the resolution of incongruence in the development of the self (Schlesinger 1979).

The development of the self depends from its earliest inception on the reconciliation of incongruities. The self needs to reconcile the contradiction between its perception of the fragility of human relations with its need for establishing and maintaining relations with others. Another incongruity perceived is the problem of how emotionally close to another being one can be without experiencing it as dangerous fusion and loss of self; and antithetically, how separate and emotionally distant one can place oneself from others without feelings of abandonment and isolation. . . . The need to live with the awareness of finiteness and helplessness and yet hold on to a sense of continuity and competence is a ubiquitous problem of the subjective self. (p. 145)

Whether experience is construed as overwhelming or, alternatively, basic cognitive-affective reactions to it such as distress, shame, anger, fear, surprise, interest, and enjoyment (Basch 1976) will be relatively resolved is linked in feedback fashion to the unfolding of the subjective sense of self. This is in turn linked to the manner in which caretakers are capable of construing and responsing to the communicative aspect of the infant's cognitive-affective reactions.

Let us turn to some of the dynamics of the patient. With the uncovering of his devalued self-representation, his vulnerability as a slimy, creepy thing who can only overcome this sense of himself through relationship to others—his girlfriend, his college friend, his analyst—he "display [s] a potential for self-destruction in the form of narrowly averted accidents. . . ".

I would place the main dynamic emphasis on his need to act out a defense against his sense of vulnerability and helplessness by skirting close to self-destruction without being destroyed. There is need to reestablish an ongoing sense of invulnerability which has been undermined. Suicide can occur in such situations; it is subordinate to the need to prove invulnerable through some testing action—which may misfire.

DEFENSES AGAINST SUBJECTIVE VULNERABILITY

In the aftermath of the 1978 Guyana massacre and the subsequent assassination of the Mayor and Supervisor of San Francisco—events which had a greater emotional impact in that city—I have observed in a number of my patients, patients of supervisees, as well as in myself, the following reaction. A markedly increased amount of risk-taking in driving which appears on closer examination to be primarily an acted out search for the self-concept of invulnerability which these events have undermined—the risk-taking functions as an ordeal which, as it is passed through, reestablishes the self as inviolate. It is not a particularly successful defense since what one attempts to drive out of awareness is actually brought into sharper focus through the risking behavior. In the clinical material of patients, as well as through self-analysis, I find it is not oedipal guilt and the search for punishment through self-destructive behavior which is the major determinant, but rather the need to counter helpless feelings.

A self-analytic clinical vignette is appropriate. The night of the assassinations I was driving home, highly reckless, and narrowly avoided two potentially serious accidents within a few minutes of each other. I felt great relief after each close shave. Further reflection that evening traced the motivation for my uncharacteristic driving to the vulnerability I had experienced on hearing the news. The phrase, "Who is next?" flashed through my mind. A similar phrase, "Well, we are next in line," had been exchanged with one of my brothers on my father's death. I had acted out a test of my own vulnerability and acquired reassurance when I passed through unscathed. Oedipal conceptions with reference to defenses against castration anxiety are one appropriate level of construal. Such meanings interact with earlier meanings of threats to self-integrity. The genetic considerations and full associational network for this view can not be elaborated here.

The evening of the news of the Guyana massacre, a patient of a supervisee, on impulse, chose a notoriously dangerous coastal road to drive on and eschewed her customary safer route. It was raining which made the choice of roads even more striking. She was involved in a rear end collision and immediately felt great relief at "the minor damage" (some five hundred dollars) incurred. The therapeutic material revealed the pressing need for reassurance that she could pass through danger without "major damage." Important dynamic and genetic meanings about self-vulnerability were paradigmatically represented here.

Several other patients manifested analogous reactions, based on the need to defend against the threat to the self which such disasters aroused. In borderline characters the sequence variant appeared to go as follows. The traumatic events are experienced as threatening, as piercing the self-concept of invulnerability, or as futher augmenting consciousness of relative helplessness and vulnerability. The increased threat of vulnerability invokes a defensive derealization necessitating an increased risk-taking which serves as a defensive counteraction to the derealization. It is an attempt to feel real by passing through the intensely felt dangerous experience so that raising the ante through increased subjection to danger invokes increased affect which feels more real.

The patient's so-called sadistic destructive treatment of animals fits in with this dynamic of an ongoing struggle against his vulnerability. Helpless animals are embodied anthropomorphic representations, metaphors of the inner subjective helplessness against which he struggles. Such animals can represent creatures he can dominate and thus he can deny in action his own helplessness. When the denial of his helplessness and vulnerability breaks down, the animals become threatening reminders. In this mental set they have to be destroyed because they bring him again to the threatening awareness of his vulnerability. The act of destruction can also temporarily be experienced as an act of power and a statement of "not I but the animal is vulnerable." His action in threatening to shoot and then not shooting the cat can be seen as acting out of a sense of power which has been restrained. The alteration before, during, and after flying, fits into a similar interpretive framework. "I am nothing. I don't belong." Succeeded by a powerful sense of omnipotence while flying, then reverting to the vulnerable self afterward. The dynamic is spelled out here in capsule form.

SENSORY MODALITIES IN CREATIVITY

The significance of early eye contact between mother and infant, the infant's perception of the mother's face, the significance of vision as an integrator of the other sensory modalities and of the body self, has been well described and elaborated (Spitz 1965, Kohut 1971, Erikson 1972, Mahler 1975). Erikson felicitously puts it:

The motherly person by letting her face, as it were, shine upon the newborn's searching eyes, and by letting herself be verified as a comprehensible image, thus may be called the first reality. . . . This vision becomes the leading perceptual modality for the organization of the sensory space, for reality testing and for adaptation. (p. 46)

The bland, threatening, knowing glances of the dinosaur-turtle are probably the creatively transformed archaic memory of the manner in which his early visual contact with his mother did not provide an optimal affective-cognitive support system, out of which a less vulnerable self-concept might have emerged.

Based on the clinical observations of the analysis in which slimy, vulnerable self-images alternate with pathetic, defensive cruelty toward helpless animals, the authors resolve the question about the oedipal threat of the father as resting on a preoedipal base in which the patient has acquired a sense of self so rejectable and vulnerable in his earlier developmental phases that the memory of the threatening visage of the father is due to the early self-concept of being vulnerable. Any later oedipal significance will be superimposed in overdetermined fashion on this basic self-conflict.

The construed visual threats and other trauma did not overwhelm the imagistic capacity of the patient to metaphorize them. They did not totally impair the child-based capacity to empathize and identify with animals. The analysis of the negative metaphors of his self-concept set the stage for recombinations in new less self-deprecatory ways, with less consequent rage.

The first spectacles prevent his seeing, and in a small child there are magical implications of not being seen, and of thus being invulnerable, as one example. His ongoing preoccupation with his vulnerability, the meanings vision has as manifested in his production of and associations to the spectacles are grounded, as the authors make clear, in unresolved problems at those developmental levels when interpersonal eye contact is of significance to the developing infant in fostering cognitive-affective responses. At about the age of fifteen months, peek-a-boo becomes a game in which self and separate other are playfully defined (Mahler 1975, Schlesinger 1976). With the aid of his artisanship, the patient focuses on and creatively replays aspects of the incomplete separation-individuation drama of his childhood, using his crafted prop in his creative variant on the peek-a-boo game.

Subsequent crafted spectacles deal with the vicissitudes of his sense of self and of his relatedness to others ranging in subjective meaning from danger, vulnerability, being controlled, needing to control, wanting to be lovable and loving. The mask may be a graphic metaphor for alterations in the sense of self. The patient found a way of expressing his transference feelings in artisanship and even as he expressed them found mastery through a combination of interpretation and action.

For some people the representation of ideas in enactive and image forms is a crucial aspect of mastery.

Michelangelo had to learn to read by tracing the letters with his fingers (Papini 1952). Michelangelo's difficulty is evidently not an uncommon experience among sculptors (Steinberg 1979). This is how dyslexics learn and aphasics relearn reading by moving hand and head. The words become meaningful to the mind when kinesthetically and proprioceptively experienced.

Sculpting for Michelangelo was a means of externally transforming his own conflicts into tangible forms from the enactive mode in which he construed them. In his creations there was an attempted resolution to conflicts experienced by the artist primarily in an enactive modality.

Begging the difficult question of genesis which lies in the grey area between the influence of the early maternal-infant interaction and the innate predispositions of the infant, infants derive subjectively significant positive and negative experience from maternal handling and their own body movements. The subjectively experienced body states are not a conflict-free sphere but express cognitive-affective self and self-other conflicts in body terms. In various forms this continues throughout the person's life.

I believe this patient made the feelings of the transference relationship transmutingly meaningful to himself through the creation of the spectacles. As Rubinstein and Levitt put it: "The production of the spectacles and the issue of vision which immediately followed then can be seen as a statement of J's acute vulnerability to sight as a bridge between self and object." As with Michelangelo and the sculptors Steinberg has studied, the route to articulated meaning in this patient is through the creation of the material object.

CREATIVITY IN ACTING OUT

The following vignette illustrates how another patient translated conflict issues into more tangible forms, which had creative aspects to them and oscillated between acting and acting out polarities.

Acting out is defined as an organized piece of behavior, involving others, in which a conflict issue of contending meanings is dramatically and tangibly represented in imagistic, enactive, and lexical symbolic behaviors. The line between acting and acting out may be difficult to draw. Acting out occurring during psychoanalytic therapy has important transference meanings, and represents a statement to the therapist. Acting out can be seen as an inverted dream process and dreaming can be seen as the reciprocal of acting out. Consonant with this analogy can be defined a manifest acting-out process, a latent acting-out process, an intervening piece of construal and an external reality analogous to the day residue in dreams, which is utilized in the acting-out organization. Acting-out episodes focused on in the therapy can be handled like dreams. They can be associated to and interpreted for their unconscious dynamic core and for the manner in which they have been creatively processed (Schlesinger 1962).

A thirty-two-year-old woman working in real estate, married for two years to a professional, was in therapy, complaining of mild, chronic depression and an inability to feel as emotionally close to her husband as she would like. After six months in therapy she felt somewhat closer to him and less depressed. She became pregnant. This was a planned pregnancy and she was appropriately responsive and positively expectant. In the fifth month of her pregnancy the patient began to feel fetal movements and commented on this, without any obvious anxiety.

At the same time the patient was doing something highly unusual in her work. She and her husband had purchased a large apartment complex, on a small down payment and a huge mortgage. It was a highly speculative but potentially very rewarding investment if payments could be met. From month to month the patient had to collect several thousand dollars in rents and by the tenth of the month had to convey these to the bank that held the mortgage on the property. During the first three weeks of the month she kept repeating, "I don't know if I'm going to make it." Ostensibly she meant that she would not be able to meet her mortgage obligation. She was somewhat upset but reported how increasingly frantic the various loan officials were becoming as the deadline passed and she repeated to them, "I don't know if I'm going to make it." The phone rang more frequently, registered letters arrived threatening penalties and ultimate foreclosure; and the patient, reporting the anxiety of the bank officers, repeated she wasn't sure she could make it and might lose the investment.

By the first of the following month another $3500 fell due and the patient continued to claim helplessness and uncertainty as she was formally threatened with legal action toward foreclosure. It was not clear why she was having all this difficulty. Promptly on the deadline day for a second monthly default, she carried to the bank, in her black handbag, money in small checks and cash collected over a six-week period. These had been stashed in a dresser drawer and apparently ignored. She reported the great feeling of mastery and relief with which she squared her accounts, and how she felt in control as she extracted the money from her bag, slowly counting out $7000 as the various bank officers hovered around.

Attempts to get the patient to discuss these events were not particularly productive although the symbolism seemed clear. The entire episode, which had happened over a five-week period, was recounted to the patient. She was asked what came to her mind.

She then told of how frightened she was when she felt the baby moving, how helpless she had felt. This had been a transient thought which was quickly dismissed. The idea of helplessness and fear brought up the following new material which came out in fragments over time, here summarized.

At age eighteen she had been married to a young fireman. Within a year of a highly emotional and stormy marriage, she had a baby. This child, a son, was born with a massive *spina bifida* and required institutionalization from birth. The husband left the marriage, disclaiming both economic and emotional responsibility for mother and child. The patient, then nineteen, got a job and spent over half of her income maintaining the child in a private institution, visiting him weekly until his death twenty-eight months later. Until she met her current husband she had not been in a committed relationship for eight or nine years.

With interventions, over the next block of sessions, the patient became sharply aware of how frightened she was at feeling out of control with the current pregnancy. She was terrorized that she would have another malformed child, and that she would have to wait helplessly for four months to know. The memory of the first child was closely bound up with a self-image of being basically damaged herself, and she feared that this would be manifested again with the coming baby. She did not trust me, either to want or to be able to help her. Her subjective sense of herself as damaged, and thus unworthy, intensified these feelings. She needed to keep a distance lest I see her flawed rejectability.

The patient described how whenever she had felt the baby move, she had felt strong surges of undefined fear and feelings of being over-whelmed, small and helpless. She had kept pushing the thoughts away by stepping up her already frantic pace of work. In this frame of mind she had begun to stash away the rents as she collected them, keeping the reality of the adequate amounts of money collected isolated from the iterated stance, "I don't know that I can make it." She had felt a great sense of mastery as she watched the gyrations of her creditors. This had culmi-nated in a sense of power and control as she had plunked down the $7000. The patient saw clearly how she had staged and enacted a drama around the fear of loss of control and the assertion of it around the money, in lieu of the fears about the pregnancy which were overwhelmingly frighten-ing. There were childhood antecedents for this type of enacted displace-ment. With fluctuations in her anxiety, the patient could deal with her fears and also her positive wishes more directly in the therapy. She had an uneventful delivery of a normal girl child.

This woman transformed her subjective sense of helplessness about her pregnancy into a creative pantomime in which the secreting of money in a dresser drawer represented the frightening pregnancy; and she paid the money, that is, delivered the baby with complete control. She brought her black bag to the delivery. The episode has a quality of children's play, combined with the use of her everyday reality in a creative way. I consider it a paradigm of acting out.

To the degree that the use of lexical thought as trial action is less available, narcissistic and borderline patients may have a greater propen-sity for the acted-out models of conflict expression since enactive and cognitive-affective modes are more available than lexical ones and are experienced as more real and more meaningful.

My patient's mortgage and J's spectacles illustrate the varying mean-ings with which humans can endow their products and how they can involve others in the solution of conflicts through such enacted meanings. Not only works of hand and mind, but interactions and relationships can be endowed with such meaningful significance. The apples of Cézanne are an entire image conceptual world of affect-laden ideas. From earliest times the infant begins to construe a sense of self and gradually of the world of others. Somaesthetic, kinesthetic, enactive, symbiotic, imagistic, and lexical forms for this cognitive-affective construal all succeed each other in the developmental sequence and continue operative on conscious and unconscious levels after they have been transcended. None of the earlier ways of construing the self and world are ever given up; they are layered over at some level. The obstetrician still images the stork. Such layering and interaction build an ambiguity and incongruence, a conflict potential, into the human developmental experience, which is at least as important as the tension of delayed or forbidden gratification of needs.

THE SELF AND PERFORMANCE ANXIETY

The following vignette serves as a clinical illustration of how creative activity is fostered or hampered by the preoedipal variations of the self-concept.

A patient who was a highly successful performing artist and whose performances achieved high creative levels described varying kinds of "stage fright." At times the performance anxiety was so overwhelming as to be close to paralyzing. The analyzed content of the anxiety was a sense of helplessness that what was expected was beyond his capacities. There was an unconscious expectation of being either laughed at or treated with cold indifference. At other times he felt "stage fright" but it was described as increasing his zest for playing and he expected to be warmly received and felt masterful.

The alternating experiences of performance anxiety might be understood as fluctuations in castration anxiety, oedipal guilt for actions having unconscious forbidden sexual meaning. The threat of breakthrough of the repressed unconscious meanings would then increase the performance anxiety to near paralysis levels.

The type of transference material argues against this as the basic interpretation. The patient had no sexual performance problems. The predominant unconscious meaning both sexuality and his playing had for him was a succoring one. They served as an antidote against a chronic fear of separation and desertion by a loving person, originally his mother.

The instrument sounded his cry for love which he expected to be heeded when he felt himself to be lovable and which became a near paralyzed cry of anguished despair when he felt unlovable. His own capacity for feeling masterful and loving were directly related to his feeling loved and cared for.

He manifested a similar alteration in performance anxiety in the transference. When he felt cared for by the analyst his material flowed smoothly. He remembered and associated to dreams. When he felt uncared for he became manifestly more anxious and the analytic process was correspondingly constricted. There could be ascertained over time a distinct shift in subjective self-feelings which in turn affected his manner of construal of all of his actions and a shift in his experience of the performance anxiety. These shifts could be initiated by external experiences which would play on his self-esteem. He had a relatively high vulnerability to such external influences. This was related to his childhood experience, in the individuation of his subjective self.

The vulnerability of the patient to external vicissitudes of praise and blame is a developmental lacuna for which I would like to coin a term and characterize it as the *poikilothymic* stage as contrasted to a *homeothymic* stage. (The prefix terms are appropriated from biology. Mammals are categorized as being homeothermic, that is, having a relatively uniform body temperature maintained nearly independent of the environmental temperature, while lower vertebrates are poikilothermic, or relatively dependent on the environment for their body temperature level.) Sometime in the preoedipal developmental stages, with individuation and the acquisition of relative autonomy, a qualitative shift should occur from relative dependence on continuing outside confirmation, positive reinforcement, etc., and from relative vulnerability to outside negative input to a relative level of independence and the maintenance of an internal sense of self not so exquisitely tuned to external influence.

As in J's case, performance had overdetermined meanings, and success in the analysis depended on the handling of the preoedipal meanings having to do with the development of the psychological self.

CREATION AND DESTRUCTION

Margaret Brenman-Gibson (1976), in her work on the creative process, mentions that contemporary painters speak of their successive creations, destructions, and recreations on canvas. She describes artistic creativity as reflecting on inner struggle in which the work of art is an outcome of opposing forces of annihilation as well as creation. She quotes a letter of Mondrian's: "My style of painting is this: First I had to annihilate the form by reducing it to lines, colors and circles. . . . Then I had to destroy the color. . . . Then I had to tear out the circles to leave only the planes and lines" (p. 345).

The artistic creation may still continue to be productive of anxiety because the conflict issues embedded in it continue unabated and induce further acts at attempting integration. A work too close to the threat defended against must be modified or destroyed. A forty-year-old chronic paranoid schizophrenic patient who has been in and out of institutions since age twenty-three lives a marginal, solitary existence. Except for weekly or biweekly dinners at his parents' home and weekly visits to his therapist, his life is a totally solipsistic and obsessionally routinized, mundane set of activities. Self-care is marginally minimalized. Any attempts at breaking out of this regressive state are frightening to him and conjure up the threat that he will have to go back to the hospital. Prior to his first hospitalization, the patient had demonstrated marked abilities in drawing and painting and had subordinated these to pursue a professional career. Halfway through professional school, he suffered his first break. Since then he has not been able to sustain any activity.

The patient recently bought a canvas and paints and proceeded to paint a painting which he intended for his father. It was not clear what had shifted, for previous attempts at drawing had made him exceedingly anxious. He finished the painting in about a week. It was a depiction of a pastoral scene in which a group of animals had gathered around a watering hole. Over a period of several days the patient became progressively more anxious, felt he was losing his mind, and was convinced he would have to return to the hospital. He finally destroyed the painting. He was not overtly enraged. He immediately felt in perfect control again, that is, his routine regressive marginal self. It was not possible to get much associative material from him. The entire episode is overdetermined, to be sure, by the significance of giving his father a gift, the rage against his father and mother, and the meaning of the subject matter. The hypothesis I would venture is that the painting represents an expression of the deep wish to be cared for but in a form which signifies a breakout from his regressive state since it is an act of mastery. It is this act of mastery and the powerful affective-cognitive reations it evokes that begat the destruction of the painting. In the face of such fragile vulnerability, the creative act carries threats of being overwhelming to the self. An act of assertion and of mastery is terrorizing in the face of such conflicts. The patient's entire existence has been modeled to defend against the awareness of unresolved self-conflicts. The mastery asserted by the painting threatens to bring these too sharply into focus, and threatens to fragment the subjective self.

Every construal in which incongruence is resolved, that is, all creative products, can, in turn, engender new conflict of meanings which for better or worse bring the need for further resolution to the subjective self.

UNCONSCIOUS ASPECTS OF CREATIVITY

The following may shed some light on aspects of the creative process. It is in the self-analytic tradition. Some years ago I became interested in psychological aspects of the Jewish Passover Seder ritual. I formulated a thesis that in the dim, prehistoric past, child sacrifice was a practice and that traces of this could be discerned in and inferred from the Seder ritual (Schlesinger 1976).

Prior to publication, I presented the paper in various places, among others at the mid-winter meeting of the American Psychoanalytic Association (1972) and to a lay audience in San Francisco. The latter meeting became extremely emotional since one of the audience discussants said that I was a self-hating Jew who was traducing the Jewish tradition and resurrecting blood-libel myths in the guise of psychological interpretations. I was quite upset by this response, despite a very positive reception from that audience. I was reasonably sure that this irate response was idiosyncratic, yet I felt anxious and discomforted.

That night I dreamed that I was confronting an audience. Their mood was quite hostile and I felt frightened and angry. I rose up. I faced them and said very emphatically and clearly, "I insist you call me brother Schlesinger."

As I thought about the dream the next day, my thoughts went to my brothers. I thought of my three brothers—two older and one younger—and how I was close to the next oldest and next youngest, but at greater distance from my oldest brother, Max. Sol, my next oldest brother, needed me more. My younger brother, Morrie, was closer in a self-sufficient way. I recalled a childhood memory in Leipzig when I was two and a half years old.

My two brothers, eight and nine years older, had taken me along to fetch the midwife as my mother went into labor with my younger brother. As I remembered alternately toddling along and being carried, there was excitement and mystery attached to the memory. Now I thought of them by the Yiddish names of our childhood—Meyer, Shulim, and myself as Yankel. There is warmth and closeness in those names. Shulim had lifted me up and I had with his urging pulled the handle which rang the midwife's bell. I helped Moisheh come into the world, I rang the bell for him. I was a promoter of life, a good brother. Ringing the bell—tolling the bell— brought into awareness Paul, my dead brother, whom I never knew. He had been born some three years before my birth and had died just short of his first birthday. Two years later I came into the world and was told by my mother that I was his replacement. There were really five of us, I thought: Meyer, Shulim, Paul, Yankel, Moisheh. Then came a reliving of the previous night's denunciation and my upset. The paper became in my mind the *Pesach* paper, the Yiddish word for Passover. Then I remembered that Paul's Yiddish name had been Pesach. It was my brother Pesach's paper. I had written a paper about the sacrifice of my brother, whose death was linked in my sense of myself with my being born. When I had made my hypothesis about the dim prehistoric past, a double meaning had been operative. The history a few years before I was born and the prehistoric Hebrew past I had hypothesized were condensed in my fantasy of child sacrifice. The angry discussant's comments had played on a partly unconscious, partly conscious, sense of myself as a profoundly guilty survivor, who would be punished by exclusion. The insistence on being called brother had overdetermined conflict meanings beyond the scope of this paper, involving sibling relations and membership in the Jewish and psychoanalytic communities.

My brother, Pesach, was long dead. A year before I started work on the paper my brother, Shulim, had died. Death dominated the associations that crowded in—my great grandfather, one hundred years old when the Nazis came to my birthplace, Czestochowa, and my three living grand-parents and scores of relatives all perished, while I survived.

It was out of the materials of this conflict, long dormant in the mind, that I had been led to construe with the help of historic and mythologic materials a tenable hypothesis about the origins of the Passover Seder in ritual sacrifice of children. The death of a child was thus endowed with meaning and had lost its helpless, unmastered, vulnerable guilt-ridden character. I could continue to call myself brother Schlesinger, a calling I had to reassert since my unconscious self-concept of guilt had broken through. I had to reassert my brotherhood, in response to one discussant who had threatened me with an exclusion I had long feared unconsciously and which the paper had been written to undo.

CREATIVE ASPECTS OF ANALYTIC THERAPY

Without violating any fundamental canon of psychoanalysis, psycho-analytic treatment can be conceptualized as creating a set of conditions in which a patient's belief system about himself and the world is understood in its infinite detail and application. The manner in which he construes himself and the world and, therefore, acts externally is related to the development of the self in earlier life experiences. The oedipal conflict and the vicissitudes of sexual and aggressive meanings are construed by the self in a variety of modes dependent on how the earlier preoedipal self and self-object stages have been integrated. Over the course of treatment the patient's belief system and mode of construing himself and the world will be reflected, in major ways, in how the psychoanalytic process and the psychoanalyst are construed. Through interpretation of these trans-ference manifestations and childhood reconstruction, the analysts' ability undermines the continuing ability of the patient to hold onto the infantile belief system and over time there arises the possibility of a new belief system and a new sense of self with new construal of object relations, sexuality, and aggression. In this emphasis on a psychology of meanings, human subjective construal and the concomitant necessity to resolve incongruence and behaviors are characterized as creative work.

Human psychological problems can be seen as botched creativity. Such a theory allows childhood genesis, later experiential, and innate creative integrative capacities full scope and obviates the positing of psychological energies. It does not abrogate the significance of sexuality, aggression and bodily experiential states but it focuses on the subjective meaning that such body feelings have for the individual in question. The imperious urging of such tensions in humans is more significantly a function of how they are perceived and construed than of some quantitative pressure for release (Klein 1976).

Postcript. Levitt and Rubenstein have used for their epigraph the soulsick Heine's attribution of his creativity to attempts at self-healing. So their money is on narcissism. My epigraph is of the apples of Cézanne and their meanings. My emphasis is on the human capacity to construe. There is, however, no reason to choose sides. We need one another. May I suggest as a joint logo: the gifted, convalescent, narcissistic Heine, munching on one of the meaningful apples of Cézanne.

REFERENCES

Basch, M. (1976). The concept of affect: a reexamination. *Journal of the American Psychoanalytic Association* 24:759–777.

Brenman-Gibson, M. (1976). Notes on the study of the creative process. In *Psychological Issues, Monograph 36*, ed. M. Gill and P. Holzman. New York: International Universities Press.

Erikson, E. (1972) *Toys and Reasons. Stages in the Ritualization of Experience.* New York: Norton and Norton.

Gill, M. (1976). Metapsychology is not psychology. In *Psychological Issues.* Monograph 36, ed. M. Gill and P. Holzman. New York: International Universities Press.

Horowitz, M. (1970). *Image Formation And Cognition.* New York: Appleton-Century Crofts.

Klein, G. (1976). Freud's two theories of sexuality. In *Psychological Issues,* Monograph 36, ed. M. Gill and P. Holzman. New York: International Universities Press.

Kohut, H. (1971). *The Analysis of the Self.* New York: International Universities Press.

Kris, E. (1952). *Psychoanalytic Explorations in Art.* New York: International Universities Press.

Mahler, M., Pine, F., and Bergman, A. (1975). *The Psychological Birth of the Human Infant.* New York: Basic Books.

Papini, G. (1952). *Michelangelo: His Life and His Era.* New York: E. P. Dutton.

Schapiro, M. (1979). The apples of Cézanne. In *Modern Art: Selected Papers of Meyer Schapiro.* New York: George Braziller.

Schlesinger, K. (1962). On acting out. Presented at West Coast Psychoanalytic Societies Meeting, Seattle.

——— (1976). Origins of the Passover Seder in ritual sacrifice. *Psychoanalytic Study of Society* 7.

——— (1979). Jewish humour as Jewish identity. *International Review of Psycho-Analysis* 6.

Spitz, R. (1965) *The First Year of Life.* New York: International Universities Press.

Steinberg, S. (1979). An artist's perception and her artistic style. Unpublished paper.

The Hysterical Personality Disorder: A Proposed Clarification of A Diagnostic Dilemma

GORDON BAUMBACHER, M.D.
FARIBORZ AMINI, M.D.

This paper reviews the marked confusion surrounding the diagnosis of the hysterical personality disorder, which has resulted from the use of vague and at times contradictory criteria in making this diagnosis. It is recommended that the diagnosis be based exclusively on psychodynamic characteristics, and a specific psychodynamic formulation is offered for this disorder. The formulation is examined from the perspectives of genetic development, drive organization, and ego and superego organization

The concept of the hysterical personality disorder (synonymous here with hysterical character disorder) has had a confusing history in psychiatry and to a large extent remains, at present, a source of ambiguity, confusion, and contradiction. There is no one disorder to which this concept refers, and the diagnosis is plagued by imprecision, changing diagnostic criteria, apparently unpredictable treatment results, and widespread disagreement over optimal treatment methods. "Repeated inconsistency", write Easser and Lesser (1965, p. 390), "in the ability of the [psychoanalytic] method to reverse the course of the hysterical symptoms has led to uncertainty, discouragement, disinterest, and in Freud's words, 'affords us a good reason for quitting such an unproductive field of enquiry without delay.'"

In this paper, we will address ourselves to the significant confusion that persists in the psychoanalytic and psychodynamic literature in regard to the hysterical personality disorder (Chodoff 1974, Guze 1975, Halleck 1967, Slavery 1974). This confusion will be clarified by suggesting criteria for this diagnosis and for distinguishing it from other difficulties that superficially look hysterical, but, we think, are otherwise dissimilar. We will specifically contrast the hysterical personality disorder with the hysterical character neurosis and the borderline personality organization with "hysterical features." A specific formulation will be suggested and will be illustrated with clinical examples. The formulation offered will be based on psychodynamic considerations which will include an examination of drive organization, ego and superego organization and genetic development.

HISTORICAL SURVEY

In a recent article, Lazare (1971) has provided an excellent review of the multiple uses of the concept of the hysterical character over time. He has pointed out that not only have different theoretical and conceptual frameworks within psychiatry as a whole given rise to different understandings of this disorder, but also that within a given theoretical framework, such as the psychoanalytic, the term has had different meanings and uses.

Early papers on hysteria in the psychoanalytic literature addressed themselves principally to conversion symptoms such as blindness, paralysis, convulsions, and disturbances of sensation and consciousness (Freud 1888, Breuer and Freud 1893-1895, Abraham 1908, 1910). Although character types associated with other disorders (oral and anal, for example) were discussed, the character traits later reputed to be seen frequently with conversion reactions, such as emotional instability, suggestability, and excitability, received minimal attention (Lazare 1971), and the hysterical character as such was not described until the 1930s.

Lazare cites three principal authors who dealt with the hysterical character during the 1930s. Frank Wittels (1930) provided the first psychoanalytic description and discussion of the hysterical character. In contrast to the earlier formulations of Abraham, who related hysterical symptoms to failures at the genital level of development, Wittels regarded the hysterical character as resulting from earlier development and as more severely disturbed. He "saw the developmental failures as 'pregenital'. . . . The ego and the id he saw as indissolubly bound. In addition, 'the boundaries between the ego and the external world, between body and soul, are blurred'" (Lazare 1971, p. 132).

Shortly after the publication of Wittels's work, Freud elaborated his views on character types. In "Libidinal Types," he discussed three character organizations in terms of his newly emerging structural model (Freud 1931). Of the three types—the erotic, the obsessional, and the narcissistic—the erotic is most related to the later descriptions of the hysterical character disorder. "Erotics are those whose main interest—the relatively largest part of whose libido—is turned towards love. Loving, but above all being loved, is the most important thing for them . . . this type represents the elementary instinctual demand of the id, to which the other psychical agencies have become compliant (p. 218). Freud goes on to add that if this type develops a neurosis, a hysteria is most likely to occur.

Without exploring the distinction, Freud also conceptualized psychological disorders as being at least two types, neurotic and characterological. "Experience shows that all these types can exist without any neurosis. The pure types, marked by the undisputed preponderance of a single mental agency, seem to have a better chance of manifesting themselves as pure characterological pictures, while we might expect that mixed types would provide a more favorable soil for conditions leading to neurosis" (Freud 1931, p. 219).

Lazare contrasts Freud's position at this time with the previous one of Abraham. By stating that all three types may exist with or without neurosis and that the likelihood of developing a neurosis in any type is unknown, Lazare suggests that Freud is rejecting Abraham's hierarchical model of personality. "He substitutes a horizontal one in which personality types are different but do not necessarily represent varying levels of health" (Lazare 1971, p. 132).

The approach Freud uses for assessing both neurosis and personality is an expansion of the one introduced in *Inhibitions, Symptoms* and *Anxiety* (Freud 1926), that is, a means of assessing psychological functioning from a structural perspective as well as from the previous descriptive and topographical views. He now applies this approach to character organization as well as to symptom formation.

The next major work on the hysterical character was that of Wilhelm Reich in 1933. Reich returned to Abraham's model with its emphasis on hierarchical organization in which the hysterical character resulted from fixations at the genital level of development. However, as Lazare correctly notes, "Abraham in fact, had referred to hysterical symptoms, not hysterical character" (Lazare 1971, p. 133). Nevertheless, Reich adapted Abraham's model to his own theory of character. He described "the hysterical character as having the following traits: obvious sexual behavior, a specific kind of body agility, and undisguised coquetry, an apprehensiveness when sexual behavior seems close to attaining its goal, an easy excitability, a strong suggestibility, a vivid imagination, and pathological lying" (Lazare 1971, p. 133).

To a large extent Reich's ideas have continued to the present, representing with only minimal alteration one major position. In this view, the hysterical character continues to be associated with traits similar to those described by Reich regarded as resulting from genital, oedipal difficulties. "In his comprehensive work, *The Psychoanalytic Theory of Neurosis* (1945), Fenichel restated Reich's formulation of the hysterical character, thereby acknowledging that Reich's position was becoming generally accepted" (Lazare 1971, p. 133).

In a 1953 paper, Marmor, however, took issue with Reich and Fenichel, and reexamined the assumption that difficulties at the genital level were of primary importance in the hysterical character. (Although Marmor uses the term hysterical personality, he is referring to the same disorder which other authors term hysterical character.) He concludes that, "(1) Oral fixations are of basic importance in the hysterical character. (2) These oral fixations give the subsequent oedipus complex of the hysteric a strong pregenital cast. (3) There is a close psychodynamic relationship between hysteria, addiction, certain types of depression, and schizophrenia" (Marmor 1953, p. 670). He also concludes that an orally fixated person may be either neurotic or psychotic depending on the balance between ego strengths and weaknesses. Presumably, therefore, a hysterical character could be either neurotic or psychotic or some intermediate state.

Thus, the literature up to and including Marmor's 1953 paper is contradictory in regard to both the etiology of the hysterical personality disorder and the assessment of the severity of the pathology found in this condition. It is seen by different authors as resulting from difficulties at almost opposite ends of the developmental process, and characterized by either relative health with a good response to treatment, or by more grave and pervasive difficulties with a variable but at best guarded response to treatment.

More recent papers (Zetzel 1968, Easser and Lesser 1965) have noted the conflicting views in the literature and have attempted to reconcile the various positions. In doing so the authors of these papers generally have taken the position that the hysterical disorders represent a continuum in which, "Hysterical character traits and manifest oedipal symptomatology" (Lazare 1971, p. 134) are associated with major difficulties from both pregenital and phallic-oedipal issues and ego organizations. For example, Zetzel (1968) states:

> In place of the earlier dichotomy [hysterical characters and hysterical neurotics] I would now like to suggest that women whose presenting symptomatology suggests a diagnosis of either hysterical character or hysterical neurosis tend to fall into one of four sub-groups. These may range from the most to the least analyzable on the basis of their response to therapeutic analysis.

The first subgroup, which responds well to analysis, is the healthiest and is comprised of individuals that Zetzel terms "true good hysterics," while her fourth subgroup is comprised of the least healthy individuals termed "so-called good hysterics." The second and third subgroups distribute themselves between these ends of the spectrum.

Easser and Lesser (1965) also include a wide range of disorders under the term hysteria. Within this large group they make an important distinction between the hysterical personality (which they use synonymously with hysterical character) and a group of hysterical appearing but much less healthy individuals. "We have reserved the term 'hysterical personality' for the more mature and better integrated and have termed the large group that extends from the pregenital to the psychotic as 'hysteroid'" (Easser and Lesser 1965, p. 405). Nevertheless they continue to place the hysterical character on a continuum with these much more severe disorders, the "hysteroid," and continue to link these groups together through the use of hysterical traits which they see as common to both.

Lazare (1971) has summarized the clinical picture and underlying psychodynamics seen in the hysterical character as described by the authors of the 1965 and 1968 papers. He views these authors as being in essential agreement. In regard to personality traits (the clinical picture) he presents the following composite:

Hysterical patients throughout the health-sickness continuum share traits in common, but the traits are apt to be more exaggerated and more sharply defined in the sicker group. In this respect, the sicker patients appear to be more hysterical than the healthier ones. The self-absorption becomes more blatant, insistent, and bizarre. There is an aggressiveness of the exhibitionism which has an inappropriate demanding nature and coldness which reflects primitive narcissistic needs. The sexual provocativeness tends to be more direct, more crude and often socially inappropriate. The impulsivity is generalized.... The emotional lability like the impulsivity is generalized....

The healthy hysteric is apt to be ambitious, competitive, buoyant, and energetic. She is more apt to have a strict punitive superego as well as other obsessional personality traits which are likely to be adaptive. (p. 134)

In summarizing the psychodynamics of the hysterical character, Lazare (1971) presents a mixture of issues related to oral and oedipal themes as being of significance. He suggests that it is the relative proportions of these themes in a given case that result in a "healthy hysteric" or a "sick hysteric."

In the healthy hysteric, there is a preponderance of oedipal conflicts over oral ones. The presenting problem revolves in the main around sexual behavior and the real or fantasized sexual object. . . . To avoid sexual issues however, there may be regression to orality. . . . The sick hysteric, in contrast, suffers from more infantile fixations with oral problems predominating. This may lead to a condensation of pregenital with genital aims under the overriding influence of aggressive needs. . . . The sick hysteric defends not against sexuality, but against passive and primitive orality. (p. 135).

In these papers (Zetzel 1968, Easser and Lesser 1965), the authors recognize that a wide range of psychopathology of varying severity has been included under the diagnostic term. They follow the position of Marmor (1953), that varying combinations of oedipal and preoedipal issues and ego organizations will result in a hysterical disorder of varying severity in which the individual is more or less disturbed. They do not offer, however, a specific formulation of the hysterical character disorder, nor do they provide an explanation (other than in general terms) of how the hysterical traits on which the diagnosis continues to be based result from either oedipal or preoedipal issues.

In his book, *Neurotic Styles* (1965), Shapiro has introduced a somewhat different perspective regarding the conceptualization of the development and functioning of the hysterical personality disorder. He associates a cognitive style with a neurotic disorder, and suggests that the cognitive style is a major factor in its etiology. While providing the very useful concept of cognitive style, this approach has tended to enhance the confusion surrounding the hysterical personality rather than to reduce it. Cognitive style refers to an individual's usual way of perceiving and organizing information. Shapiro (1965, pp. 13–14) quotes George Klein as saying "The cognitive attitudes . . . seem to reflect highly generalized forms of control, as likely to appear in a person's perceptual behavior as in his manner of recall and recollection." Shapiro adds, "Klein considers that a variety of such attitudes [cognitive attitudes] are available to an individual and has used the expression 'cognitive style' to refer to the total arrangement of them in a given person" (p. 14). The concept of cognitive style, however, is descriptive; in itself, it neither represents nor necessarily implies a form of psychopathology. Nevertheless, the cognitive style referred to as a hysterical style commonly has come to imply psychopathology, and more specifically a hysterical disorder. This cognitive style usually is characterized as global, impressionistic, more attuned to perceiving emotions and relationships than facts, and associated with the use of repression as a defense mechanism. Although it is true that this picture is frequently seen in the hysterical personality disorder, for reasons that we will discuss later, the style is neither the disorder itself nor its cause. Furthermore, it can be seen in a wide range of individuals other than ones with this difficulty, ranging from those who are normal to those who are severely disturbed.

The most recent major discussion of the hysterical personality disorder is found in the book, *Hysterical Personality* (1977), edited by Mardi Horowitz. This work represents an attempt to synthesize viewpoints covering historical, epidemiological, psychological, and developmental aspects of the illness, as well as issues of treatment.

The working definition employed by the authors is a descriptive one. Horowitz specifies three characteristic groups of behavior organized according to the interval of time observed that taken together are equated with the hysterical personality. The three groups are long-order patterns (interpersonal relationships), medium-order patterns (traits), and short-order patterns (information processing styles). Specific types of behavior are listed for each category. For example, long-order patterns show "repetitive, impulsive, stereotyped, interpersonal relationships often characterized by victim-aggressor, child-parent, and rescue or rape themes," and "drifting but possibly dramative lives with an existential sense that reality is not really real, frequent experience of self as not in control and not responsible." Under medium-order patterns are described attention-seeking behaviors including "demands for attention and/or the use of charm, vivacity, displays of sex appeal, childlikeness, passivity, or infirmity." Mood is characterized as labile, and suggestability may be notable. Information processing style (short-order patterns) is typified by a global deployment of attention (Horowitz 1977, p. 5).

In a later chapter, Blacker and Tupin (1977) propose a new structural model to account for not only the traits listed, but also for the varied character types that previously have been classified as hysterical personalities (p. 121). They consider failure of the formation of a firm sexual identity to be basic to hysterical difficulties in both men and women and to result from varied amounts of both preoedipal and oedipal conflicts occurring along a psychosexual continuum (pp. 121–122). Thus, these authors return to the formulation put forth in the previously discussed papers of Zetzel (1968), and Easser and Lesser (1965), in which hysterical personalities are divided into more healthy oedipally fixated groups and less healthy preoedipally fixated groups. For example, Blacker and Tupin write, "the more genitally fixated, less oral, less narcissistically vulnerable hysteric may be ambitious and successful with fairly good employment and educational records. . . . The more pregenitally fixated or more narcissistically vulnerable hysteric is characterized by ego weakness with poor integration of personality elements and poor differentiation of internal and external reality" (p. 126).

The authors attempt to include this broad range of difficulties under one diagnostic heading by making issues of sexual identity central to the behavior patterns by which they typify the disorder. They note that sex-role behavior may be learned at all developmental levels, and that coy, seductive behavior is rewarded with attention in the childhood of the future hysteric.

> For the female child, the mothering person, having been unable to deliver sufficient nurturance during infancy, continues to be found wanting as the child grows older, and the little girl turns to the parent of the opposite sex. . . . A young girl then looks to father to supply the missing nurturance and can only extract it on the basis of her coy, seductive flirtatious behavior which is, of course, rewarded with superficial focused interest. . . . (Blacker and Tupin 1977, p. 132)

We think, however, that this formulation continues to contain some of the same major difficulties previously encountered by including together on the basis of similar behavior patterns individuals with oedipal stage conflicts based on unconscious sexual and aggressive wishes with others who have troubles of sufficient severity that there is poor differentiation of internal and external reality. In their chapter, "Epidemiology of Hysterical Phenomenon: Evidence for a Psychosocial Theory," Temoshok and Attkinson (1977) note the lack of consensus regarding the definition of the hysterical personality and the difficulties that are thus created. They point out that hysterical phenomenon, so classified by behavior patterns, need not represent a disease at all and may have significance other than as manifestation of psychopathology.

Metcalf (1977), in the chapter, "Childhood: From Process to Structure," offers a developmental perspective on the disorder. He stresses the crucial nature of early parent-child interactions on later psychological organization. We consider the developmental approach an illuminating one which we also will address. Somewhat in contrast to Metcalf, we will focus more specifically on the psychological organization in childhood which we propose may lead to the later development of a hysterical personality disorder.

ASSESSMENT OF THE PROBLEM

Both historically and in current usage, the hysterical personality disorder is defined by a rarely stated mixture of criteria from different perspectives. In the formulation of this problem, particularly, descriptive and stylistic aspects of personality functioning have become blended implicitly with dynamic considerations and assumptions of psychopathology. "The terms hysteria, hysterical character, etc., are so loosely defined and applied so promiscuously that their application to diagnostic categories has become meaningless. The use of these labels for evaluation, analyzability, or prognosis has become tantamount to predicting a throw of the dice" (Easser and Lesser 1965, p. 392).

As a result, the understanding of the condition has remained confused, and no specific criteria have been developed on which to base a diagnosis. The diagnosis often is derived from features of personality and cognitive style with assumptions regarding psychopathology made with little attention to the specific psychodynamics involved or to whether the diagnostic criteria used really represents a psychopathology at all. Thus, although not necessarily so stated, the hysterical personality disorder has been defined principally by the use of descriptive, nondynamic considerations. The attempt has been made then to force psychodynamic features into alignment with diagnosis already made. Inevitably, this has resulted in very different types of difficulties being included together because of superficial, descriptive, stylistic similarities.

The difficulties raised by this manner of diagnosis would be akin to clarifying all medical illness in which an elevated temperature occurred as simply "fevers" without regard to other aspects of illness or to etiological factors. It would be no surprise to find varied, perplexing, and often disappointing response to treating all illnesses so diagnosed with a single agent.

PROPOSED APPROACH, AND CLARIFICATION OF TERMS

The hysterical personality disorder should be considered a type of psychopathology and the diagnosis should be based on psychodynamic considerations and criteria. As such, this syndrome should be distinguished from what is called the hysterical style or hysterical cognitive style. As previously suggested, these latter concepts refer to a way of perceiving and organizing information and are not themselves a pathology. For similar reasons, we will not consider conversion reactions and dissociation reactions. Although those disorders are classified as hysterical neurosis in *DSM II* (1968), they are seen in many diverse personality types (Guze et al. 1971) and are not unique to the hysterical personality (Rangell 1959).

Our use of the terms psychodynamic and psychopathology will be consistent with their general employment and meaning in the literature. We will define the concept of psychodynamics broadly to include not only the vicissistudes of the drives but also the functions of the psychological structures that mediate drive expression and the adaptation of the individual to his environment (Hartmann 1939). Thus, this term will correspond to the five metapsychological viewpoints outlined by Rapaport and Gill (1959) but our principle focus will be on dynamic, genetic, and structural issues. Therefore, regardless of the grounds on which the suspicion of the diagnosis of the hysterical personality disorder is raised, be it presenting symptoms, life style, or cognitive style, the diagnosis should be made only after consideration of the individual's psychodynamics, that is, drive organization, ego and superego characteristics and organizations, and genetic development. Clearly, examination of these aspects of psychological functioning will take into account the individual's conflicts and fantasies—both conscious and unconscious.

Psychopathology will be used here to refer to a consistent impairment or limitation of the individual's capacity to function resulting from internal psychological conflicts or early deprivations. The idea of intrapsychic conflict, of course, has long been central to the conceptualization of psychopathology. Engel wrote (1962, p. 311): "In general, it is the activation of old unresolved conflicts which constitutes the greatest obstacle to coping successfully with current demands, whether they arise from bodily changes or environmental pressures."

Markedly abnormal situations early in life that result in severe deprivation of basic needs also may result in psychological dysfunction that is based on deficit rather than conflict. This idea, for example, is implicit in Erikson's (1963) concept of basic trust and the difficulties that result from its absence or distortion, and in Kernberg's (1967) hypothesis in regard to the formation of the borderline personality.

The syndrome for which we are reserving the term *hysterical personality disorder* derives predominantly from phallic stage developmental issues. By that, we do not wish to imply a simple prospective one-to-one correspondence between childhood difficulties and adult psychopathology (Blos 1972), but rather that in adults the hysterical personality disorder presents with principle features and characteristic problems that retrospectively can be understood as resulting from a particular and faulty solution to phallic stage tasks. The decision to term the difficulty that we will describe as the hysterical personality disorder is to some extent an arbitrary one. As suggested by the earlier discussion, there is at present no one illness to which this diagnostic label refers, but rather a host of different illnesses. We think that careful differentiation should be made between these syndromes with significantly differing dynamic constellations and that the terminology employed should lend clarity not confusion to these distinctions.

For clarity of presentation, we will first trace the genetic development of the disorder, as reconstructed retrospectively, and then summarize the main clinical features found in the adult. We will distinguish, on the basis of the psychodynamics involved, this clinical entity from the other syndromes that, because of descriptive similarities, are presently associated with it. Although this difficulty may be found in both men and women, for reasons that are inherent in its dynamics, it is more likely to be found in women. Therefore, our major emphasis will be on its presentation in the female.

In defining the hysterical personality disorder as resulting predominantly from phallic stage issues, we do not wish to imply that other issues are irrelevant. On the contrary, as Marmor (1953) has pointed out, oral themes are significant. As we will discuss later, the presence of oral issues, but not major oral fixations, predisposes the individual to greater difficulty with the resolution of phallic stage tasks. Nevertheless, the principle features of the disorder derive from the later period. Where difficulties from the oral period predominate, the resultant clinical picture is quite different. Kernberg (1967) has drawn this distinction well in contrasting the hysterical personality with the infantile character in which oral issues do predominate. For example, he writes:

> The need to be loved, to be the center of attention and of attraction, has more of a sexual implication in the hysterical personality, in which oral-dependent needs are linked with direct genital exhibitionistic trends. In the infantile character the need to be the center of interest and attraction is less sexualized and it has a more helpless, mainly orally determined, inappropriately demanding nature, and the exhibitionism has a "cold" quality, reflecting more primitive narcissistic trends. (pp. 652–653)

The development of this disorder then, presupposes at least a relatively successful mastery of issues preceding the phallic stage of development. If there are present residual difficulties from preceding stages, these are not of such severity that they constitute the major psychopathology in the character structure. Thus, as children, the patients that we are describing entered the phallic phase with ego and drive organization having attained a post-ambivalent, post-anal sadistic level. In the usual devlopmental sequence, early in the phallic phase object relations continue to have a strong preoedipal organization to them, in that the dyadic relationship to the mother predominates over triadic, competitive issues (Brunswick 1940). This, too, is the case for the group that we are discussing. The child's relationship to his mother *per se* is still of greater concern to him than his anxiety over real or imagined rivals. Envy is still more of an issue than jealousy. We suggest that it is specifically difficulties with the developmental tasks of this initial phallic phase, in which object relationships are still predominantly dyadic, that provide the basis for the later development of the hysterical personality disorder.

GENETIC DEVELOPMENT

For both sexes the central developmental task of the phallic stage is that of dealing with increased genital awareness, and in a more general sense that of exploring and mastering drives and interpersonal relationships organized, symbolically, around a phallic mode. These phallic issues are characterized by drives that are still directed toward the mother as the primary love object and which have as their aim an intrusive and possessive relationship to her. Object relationships are not as yet predominantly competitive and triadic as would be the case in the later stages of development.

During this stage, the girl, even with the most optimal development, encounters a narcissistic injury. She is faced with the realization that genitally she and males are different and that to be phallic enough (in terms of genitalia) to maintain the wished-for exclusive relationship to her mother, she needs a penis. Boys, also, at this stage of development, face similar difficulties *vis-à-vis* the inadequacy of their penises.

In order to avoid confusion, it should be emphasized that we are not discussing the development of either gender identity or sexual identity *in toto*. These identities derive from a much broader developmental scope than just the phallic phase. As has been demonstrated in a series of recent articles and studies, sexual and gender identities begin to form, and in certain respects are established, in early preoedipal stages, but in other respects, they continue to be modified until the close of adolescence (Greenacre 1950, Kestenberg 1956, and Stoller 1968). As Stoller (1968, p. 30) has pointed out, such recognition does not minimize or eliminate the impact of phallic stage issues on personality development. "While the process of developing gender identity goes on intensively until at least the end of adolescence, the core gender identity is fully established before the fully developed phallic stage. This is not to say that castration anxiety or penis envy are not essential parts of the development of gender identity, but rather that these latter conflicts occur after core gender identity is well established."

Genitally the little girl cannot be phallic and she must come to terms with the failure of reality to support the fantasy that she could phallically love and possess her mother. In fantasy, however, she can retain, undiminished, the idea that her male counterpart can do so. The result is that she experiences an inevitable narcissistic injury in regard to the loss of both the wish for phallic capability (in terms of her genitalia) and, more importantly, the wish to be able to maintain exclusive posession of her mother in a phallic mode.

The issues of this developmental stage have been well described and verified in both clinical work and developmental research. Karen Horney (1920) summarized the material as follows:

> "Our empirical material with regard to the masculinity complex in women is derived from two sources of very different importance. The first is the direct observation of children, in which the subjective factor plays a relatively insignificant part. Every little girl who has not been intimidated displays penis envy frankly and without embarassment. We see that the presence of this envy is typical and understand well why this is so; we understand how the narcissistic mortification of possessing less than the boy is reinforced by a series of disadvantages arising out of the different pregenital cathexis: the manifest privileges of the boy in connection with urethral erotism, the scopophilic instinct, and onanism. (pp. 12–13)

Judith Kestenberg (1956) describes the impact of this period for the girl in somewhat greater detail.

> Soon the clitoris is singled out as a more sensitive and distinct organ which conveys the qualities of aliveness she had lost earlier in the discovery of the inanimateness of the doll. Frequent complaints about the flabby consistency and the undefined borders of the rest of the genital highlight the clitoris as a very special organ, which the girl hopes to enlarge by various manipulations. Fantasies about growing a penis (illusory penis [Rado, 1933]) seem to alternate with hopes to grow a baby externally. At the height of the phallic phase the girl cathects the clitoris in the sense of an active masculine organ. She develops a sense of organ belonging. Because this organ gives her a great deal of satisfaction she feels that it might satisfy her mother too. Both the baby and the penis which she wants to develop there are meant to be presented to the mother now. But the baby idea is mostly condensed with the penis representation, as the penis itself is valued as a baby-making organ. A frequent speculation of this time concerns impregnation with a penis which, deposited in a mother, transforms into a baby. This in turn leads to ideas of multiple penises, as many as necessary to produce a lot of babies. Such thoughts are used for consolation about the smallness of the clitoris, which "was big once and will grow back to make another baby." The girl eventually gives up her mother attachment and this libidinous zone because of her disappointment in the zone itself and in the mother who failed to give her an organ more suitable for satisfaction and baby-making. (pp. 281–282)

In a later paper (1968), Kestenberg elaborates on the contribution of genital awareness and sensation to the development of gender identity in both the male and female. Nevertheless, she notes phallic phase issues continue to have a significant psychological impact on the girl.

Most dramatic is the feeling of loss at the end of the early maternal phase (inner genital phase) at the age of four. In repudiating her femininity the girl denies the existence of her introitus and recognizes with sorrow that the "live doll" she had treated like a real baby is only an inanimate object. . . . She transfers all feelings to the clitoris which, in the phallic phase, becomes hypercathected at the expense of inner genital sensations. (p. 471)

Kestenberg emphasized that the narcissistic injury and disappointment are not only the result of the little girl's perceptions of her genitalia per se, but also the result of the necessity of giving up phallic strivings toward her mother and therefore of giving up her attachment to her mother via this mode. Never before has she had to do this. In normal development, the little girl relinquishes her libidinal phallic strivings toward her primary love object, her mother, and transfers her libidinal drives to her father and later to other males. With this shift, the little girl enters the positive oedipal phase in which a receptive mode of libidinal drive organization is substituted for the previous phallic one. While these events result in depression, in normal development this affect is tolerable and does not prevent the major shift of libidinal drives from the mother to the father.

In the female patient who develops a hysterical personality disorder, however, the core dynamics and psychopathology result from the girl's inability to make this shift, and from the pathological organization of defenses that she uses to manage the unresolved issues of this stage. Factors that increase the girl's vulnerability to depression and to narcissitic injury will make it more difficult for her to relinquish her phallic attachment to the primary love object, her mother. If she is either unusually strongly attracted to her mother or unusually fearful of her loss, she will be more vulnerable to the depression that accompanies this stage, and if the depression is too severe, the little girl will be unable to give up her phallic strivings toward her mother. Clinical observation has indicated that underlying oral needs are frequently present in the hysterical personality (Marmor 1953), and it is just the presence of such overly intense needs that would produce the predisposition to depression that complicates the solution of phallic stage tasks. While underlying oral problems may set the stage for the difficulties in the phallic stage that give rise to the hysterical personality, the oral needs themselves are not the predominant difficulty. If oral deprivation has been so severe that the reactions to it become the major feature in the personality, the resultant disorder would be better classified as one deriving from oral and not phallic issues.

In the case of unresolved phallic stage issues, drives remain focused on the mother, and the libidinal drive organization remains phallic. Thus, the positive oedipal stage is never truly entered, and all subsequent stages become distorted by continuing phallic stage issues. In regard to the characteristics of this situation, Humberto Nagera (1975) writes about the phallic or phallic-oedipal stage:

> It should be noted that a regression to the object mother of . . . [this] stage (with the attendant modifications in all the lines) or a move toward the mother of the inverted complex . . . may determine, in extreme cases, a homosexual outcome and a homosexual object choice in the adult, either in reality (leading to overt homosexuality) or only in fantasy, crippling the sexual life of the patient. In either case the homosexual position adopted will be in the case of regression to the first stage, an active-masculine one. . . . (p. 22)

In effect, the woman with a hysterical personality retains the core dynamics of a phallic stage girl. She remains in love with her mother (as the primary love object) and remains in constant need of warding off the narcissistic injury of her fantasized inadequacy and feared loss.

This defensive need frequently results in the particular stylistic features associated with the hysterical personality. The narcissistic injury may be defended against by displacing her phallic strivings from the genitals to her entire person. She then becomes not just feminine, but feminine in a manner reflecting both her phallic wishes and her feelings of inadequacy in regard to them. The result has often been referred to as a caricature of femininity or hyperfemininity. Such a woman often appears naive and childlike but at the same time she uses her body as a phallic object; she adorns her body, she makes herself and her presence intrusive, creates a stir wherever she goes, and in her childishness or naivety, she may be very aggressive.

Aggressive drives, in this disorder, are less at the core of the basic difficulty than are libidinal drives. The intense positive attachment to the mother at this stage normally results in a greatly reduced expression of aggression and markedly reduces the strong ambivalent feelings that characterize the previous anal phase.

> In normal (and abnormal cases), the usual ambivalent feelings present in the anal phase (especially toward the mother) are partly

resolved by the strong positive cathexis directed to her during the "first stage" of the phallic-oedipal phase of the girl. This intense cathexis is perhaps one of the factors behind the process of "fusion" that is observed with the move from the anal-sadistic into the phallic-oedipal phase. This view is supported, on the other hand, by the fact that girls that have shown extremely ambivalent feelings toward the mother during the anal phase find a great measure of relief in this respect at the time they move into the first stage of their phallic-oedipal phase. (Nagera 1975, p. 33)

Aggressive feelings, however, are mobilized by the intense disappointment that the girl experiences in her mother. In the girl's view of herself as phallically inadequate, the mother usually becomes the fantasized culprit. She blames her mother for not having made her differently and considers her mother to be defective also. The anger thus generated is highly unacceptable as it, too, stems from the underlying defended narcissistic mortification, and it is warded off by the powerful positive mother attachment. It creates an additional impediment to the normal movement to the next developmental stage (the oedipal or phallic oedipal second stage), in which among other things rivalrous and aggressive feelings toward the mother are prominent.

DRIVE ORGANIZATION

Regardless of the personality style or the specific mode of defense against the narcissistic injury, for the woman with this disorder, drive organization remains characteristically phallic. In later relationships, the essence of the phallic stage object relationship to the mother is the organizing principle. Her primary libidinal and sexual attachment remains to her mother, and later relationships embody the unconscious attempt to recreate this relationship. Thus, for a woman with a hysterical personality disorder, the unconscious love object is a homosexual one. Behaviorally, however, she is not homosexual. She may, and usually does, overtly seek relationships with men. Even so, other than superficially, she has little interest in men as men, since unconsciously her principle libidinal interest remains in women. She may fall "in love" with men quickly, often without really knowing them. Their specific characteristics may be relatively unimportant, as beneath her conscious involvement with men remains her unconscious wish to find, in loving and being loved by them, her mother, who continues to be the recipient of her phallically organized drives. Of course, no man can love her as the mother she wishes for, and each such attempt is doomed to failure. While the woman with a hysterical personality disorder may be seductive in the sense of being flirtatious or hyperfeminine, she is not comfortably sexual and she may be anorgasmic. If she is orgasmic, this is usually a split off function (genitality as a perversion). Sexual interest in her and a true sexual response on her part are frightening, as they represent for her homosexual and incestuous desires.

While the content of specific fantasies in individual patients will be highly varied, the form of the fantasies, nonetheless, will reflect this mode of drive organization. Thus, the fantasies involve dyadic rather than triadic or competitive relationships. The dyadic is between two women, and the mode of interaction is phallic.

A clinical example may help to illustrate the drive organization involved in this disorder. A relatively young woman, who was treated in psychoanalytic psychotherapy, provided a history of longstanding difficulties in her relationships with men. In the past, she had been involved with many different men, some only briefly, some for periods of several years. These relationships had all ended in disappointment and disillusionment, although in most cases the patient felt that she had wanted the relationships to succeed, and that she had worked hard to overcome the difficulties that developed. The men with whom she became involved all had certain features in common, and, as she later came to understand, these features were essential to her interest in them: they were either already married or involved with another woman.

Her attitude toward this situation, however, was not one of competition. Although the patient was intensely interested in these other women, she did not wish to defeat or displace them. Through the man that she was involved with, she wished to know about the other woman with whom he was involved, and a significant aspect of her relationship to the man became their discussion of the other involvement. While she experienced disappointment and sadness at the difficulties in her relationships, and intense frustration with the apparent hopelessness of them, she, nonetheless, did not experience jealousy toward the other women or attempt to induce the men to give them up. On the contrary, she regarded them as her companions in an unhappy and perplexing situation, and in some instances she developed with them a direct acquaintance which evolved into a warm relationship. These latter relationships were always platonic, but were often described with a greater sense of affection, depth, and interest than characterized her portrayal of her relationships with men. While she was very unhappy and often miserable in these situations, she usually did not experience her feelings as depression. With the breakup of each of the relationships, however, she would become quite depressed. She was remarkably blind to the inherent contradictions entailed in the pattern of her involvements, and initially blind to the pattern itself.

On the surface, a woman such as this would appear to be repeatedly involved in triadic relationships. Beneath the surface, however, the focus of her interests in these relationships was principally dyadic. Her conscious and active interest in a man provided her the means to both gratify and disguise her stronger unconscious and forbidden wish for involvement with a woman. The determinants to her behavior repeatedly proved to be these unconscious interests. Competition in these relationships was of minimal significance.

The patient was generally anorgasmic; however, she was able to experience orgasm under particular circumstances. Occasionally she would become drunk in a bar where she was unknown and become involved with a strange man for one night. In this situation she reached orgasm, but the next day she would feel great remorse and guilt. At first she felt the guilt was in response to her irresponsible and drunken behavior, but later she realized that a substantial cause of the guilt was the sexual excitement itself which for her was linked to prohibited incestuous and homosexual wishes.

This patient presented as a tastefully dressed, attractive woman. She had the pattern, however, of usually carrying with her a large handbag plus a large assortment of books and packages. Her entrance and exit from the office often was accompanied by a flurry of activity as she clutched at objects tumbling from her arms. Early in her treatment her deportment in the office was characterized by an almost constant motor activity. She squirmed and wriggled in her chair; from time to time buckles on her clothing would become entangled in the fabric of the upholstery and there would follow a series of contortions while she extricated herself. In social gatherings, too, she often made herself the center of attention as a result of a propensity to unwittingly involve herself in slapstick mistakes. Needless to say, these also were disruptive of whatever else was going on.

The patient was a capable and talented woman. She had achieved moderate success in a field related to theatrics; however, she was unable to rise above this level. Because of the quality of her work she had repeated opportunities to do so, but each time she experienced a feeling that she described as paralysis. Behind that feeling was the idea that she did not have what it would take and that to try would result in her failing, being found out as a fake, and exposed to ridicule.

In her therapy, the picture of the drive organization that lay behind the themes that characterized her relationships and her inhibitions unfolded gradually. Although she initially brought forth material in the therapy, she presented herself as incapable of working with it, and covertly invited the therapist to confirm her feared inadequacy by taking over. Behind this, there emerged a specific fear that she was incapable of doing the work required in therapy, and if she attempted it, she would only fail and be shown up to be an "inadequate mess."

She worried that the therapist would then agree that she was "hopeless" and give up on her. In response to this image of herself and the fear of abandonment, there was a prolonged period in which she felt extremely depressed and immobilized. When she was convinced of the therapist's consistency, she allowed herself to acknowledge the fury behind the fear that she would be rejected as inadequate and hopeless. These feelings related to the birth at age three and one-half of her younger sibling, a brother. At this time certain inconsistencies and deficiencies in the mother crystalized in the patient's mind around the decreased attention she then received and the partially real, partially imagined transfer of her mother's affection to her new sibling of the opposite sex.

Concomitantly in her current life, she experienced a substantial shift in her conscious interests. She lost all interest in men. Her relationship to them became clipped and businesslike. This did not represent a wish to snub men per se but rather reflected her lack of interest in them and her focus on the task rather than the person when working with her male colleagues. She became, however, more directly and intensely interested in women. One woman in particular came to occupy a central position in the fantasies that emerged during this period. This was a co-worker whom the patient thought much more capable and powerful than she. In comparison to her fantasies of this woman's capabilities, she felt herself to be hopelessly inept and unable to perform adequately. In fact, she found herself unable to perform work that she had previously mastered, and in her therapy she again experienced the conviction that she would not have what it would take to complete her treatment. Just as she fantasized herself remaining subservient to the admired and capable female co-worker whose power she could never match, she imagined herself remaining forever in therapy, a defective and incurable patient.

During the time that she was struggling with this image of herself, she was diagnosed as having an abdominal condition that required non-emergency surgery. In a session she described the surgical procedure (as she understood it) and the impending plans for hospitalization in the relatively near future in some detail, but in an unusually bland and affectless manner. Subsequently she reported a dream that occurred the night after that session. In the dream she entered the therapist's office and announced to him that she had been discovered to have cancer of the throat. This was accompanied by intense embarrassment. She continued by saying that she did not understand why she had been embarrassed. It had seemed that in telling the therapist of the cancer, she was revealing something too intimate. Perhaps, she thought, it had something to do with how she wanted him to respond. She wanted him to be interested and concerned, but that somehow seemed wrong. She was puzzled as to why. She added further thoughts having to do with the planned surgery. The therapist suggested to the patient that she was both excited and frightened by what she imagined the therapist's response would be to something that she wanted to show him in herself.

Several themes developed from this idea. Many of these were contained in the image of cancer. It represented the wish for something which would grow within her and the punishment for this wish. She wanted to excite the therapist with what she would show him but also feared that she would do so (the embarassment of the dream). In addition she felt that such a wish was very wrong. It was wrong not just because she wanted to be seductive, but she wanted to be exhibitionistically seductive with the therapist, and she wanted him to respond in a feminine way, to want to be captivated and excited by her. At the same time, she feared that what she fantasized inside her would be inadequate and unexciting, just as she imagined her outsides to be. This mobilized powerful, forbidden, vengeful, and sadistic feelings which further fueled the wish to be able to dominate the therapist.

She then permitted herself to explore further a persistent thought she had entertained regarding her surgery: that she would request permanent sterilization at the same time. This idea was in contrast to her conscious real desire for marriage, children, and a family. It proved to be related to her fantasy and fear of an internal growth. Pregnancy was associated with the wish for something inside of her to compensate for the imagined genital defect; however, she simultaneously was afraid that it, too, would be inadequate. She wished a pregnancy as a gift from her mother to make her complete and as a demonstration to her mother that she was complete. Although she imagined this as an addition to herself that would recapture her mother's lost interest in her, she also was frightened of both the wish to regain her mother in this way and the hope that she would be successful. The feelings embodied in these fantasies were mainly sexual, and she felt highly inappropriate in regard to her mother. She also experienced anger and contempt for her mother as inadequate, specifically in her capability to properly endow her in the first place. The thoughts of sterilization represented a punishment for both the libidinal and angry feelings, and an attempt to master these conflicts in a counterphobic way. These fantasies, and the feelings contained in the pregnancy idea, underlay and paralleled the dream and the feelings toward the therapist represented in it. Of course, there were other determinants to the dream and other meanings, but they were peripheral to the issues under discussion here and not central to the dynamics of the patient's major difficulties.

Over time, she extricated her real capacities and abilities from their crippling association with her fantasy of herself as a defective child who had lost her mother to her phallically endowed baby brother. Aggressive behavior, which she previously had needed to inhibit and disguise, became less threatening to her. She became more aggressive with both men and women, and recalled a significant but previously omitted portion of her development which had to do with a major aspect of her relationship to her mother. Throughout later childhood and adolescence, she had remained closely attached to her mother through the mode of arguing aggressively and provoking arguments. As an adult, this continued to be the case in an attenuated form in reality, but much less attenuated in fantasy. The patient was surprised to realize how much this manner of relating to her mother comprised the bond between them. It is worth emphasizing that although her father was important to her, the emotional impact for this patient of these issues was in relationship to her mother and not her father.

The drive organization of this patient is graphic and characteristic of the disorder that we are terming the hysterical personality disorder. Although she was superficially interested in men, her drive organization remained that of a phallic stage girl for whom the mother was still the primary object of her drives. In keeping with this, her drives reflected a phallic mode and their object unconsciously was associated with incestuous and homosexual wishes. As in this case, the severity of the narcissistic injury, associated with the fantasy of phallic inadequacy, prevented the substitution of the father for the mother and the substitution of a receptive mode for a phallic one. Because of this heightened narcissistic vulnerability, as a child she was unable to tolerate the depression that is entailed in this shift (from mother to father) and consequently remained bound to the mother.

The issue of the fantasy of phallic inadequacy in this disorder is a more complicated one than that of penis envy per se. Of greater significance is the consequence of the fantasy which necessitated the giving up of the mother, at least in terms of the phallic mode. The depression involved in this may be of greater degree and significance than that of penis envy, and this latter idea may all too readily be accepted as a defense against acknowledging the greater loss of the primary love object, the mother.

EGO AND SUPEREGO ORGANIZATION

We will not attempt a comprehensive outline of ego and superego functioning. Rather, we will limit ourselves to those characteristics that are relevant to the disorder in question. Many of these characteristics have been implicitly or explicitly covered in the previous discussion, and these will only be summarized here.

Ego Organization

In general, ego functions reflect at least a phallic stage of development. The capacities for reality sense and basic reality testing are intact. The ability for sublimation is present; self- and object boundaries are formed and object constancy has been attained. Disorders with severe distortion of the capacity for stable object representation, such as splitting, reflecting earlier pathology, are not present.

Self- and object representation, however, reflect the predominant difficulties of this disorder. Central to the self-representation is the belief in an inadequate or defective self. This, of course, is likely to be unconscious, with only the derivatives initially manifest. The patient already described played out themes based on this belief. For example, in her profession she repeatedly achieved a certain level of prominence only to experience panic that her imagined inadequacy would be discovered and that she would be shamed. As she said, "I feel like such a fraud when I'm doing well." She then would create, in reality, what she imagined in fantasy, by sabotaging herself and demonstrating herself as defective. This aspect of her object representations included an intense envy. It was essential to her that she attribute to certain others as much grandiosity as she assigned inadequacy to herself. In regard to people, especially women, who were confident, competent, and aggressive, she was prone to exaggerate inordinately their power and abilities. At times, this assumed almost magical proportions in which she admired their exaggerated abilities and fantasized a closeness with them in which she would partake of their powers. The essence of the fantasy was that only in this way would she be able to remedy her subjective feeling of inadequacy.

In the hysterical personality disorder, ego functions having to do with defenses are also likely to present a characteristic picture. In considering these aspects of ego activity, it is useful to view the defensive functions in terms that include more than the idea of defense mechanisms alone. Hoffer (1954) suggested the concept of defensive organization. "We may be justified in conceiving the defensive processes and the defence mechanisms as being part of and as operating within a defensive organization, which is itself a part of the total ego-organization, though not identical with it" (Hoffer 1954, p. 195). It represents that aspect of ego activity which "explores the possibilities for an adaptation to the disequilibrium of intrapsychic internal conflict and attempts to find the best solution in the given circumstances" (Lichtenberg and Slap 1972, p. 776.)

Viewed in this way, defensive operations in a given character or disorder are closely related to the overall level of ego development and to the particular defensive requirements, the vulnerabilities and conflicts that need protection, in the individual. In all likelihood the specific defense mechanisms and modes of handling conflicts that together comprise the defensive organization will be determined significantly, if not predominantly, by the developmental process in both its healthy and pathological aspects, including, in addition to the conflicts, "the vicissitudes of object relations" (Lichtenberg and Slap 1972, p. 781).

In the hysterical personality disorder, the principal necessity of the overall defensive organization is to guard against the reemergence of the phallic narcissistic injury. To accomplish this, the displacement of phallic strivings from the genitalia to the whole body (or its substitute) must be both facilitated and protected. Displacement is assisted by modes of perception and other defense mechanisms which avoid attention to specifics and avoid focus on details. The processes which are useful in this regard include repression, denial, rationalization, exaggeration, and a global, impressionistic type of perception.

Repression and denial, of course, traditionally have been associated with this disorder. These both function to obliterate the awareness of information (internal in the case of the former and external in the case of the latter) which the individual must now know. "Infantile development clarifies the connection between ego function and defence; when the child becomes aware of external reality, then it also realizes unpleasant facts and denies them; for instance, the differences of the sexes. As soon as it begins to remember, it also recalls painful experiences and represses them" (Van Der Leeuw 1971, p. 56).

In the patient previously described, these two defense mechanisms served an additional purpose. Her use of them, which for a long time was not under her control, left her with important gaps in her conscious knowledge of internal and external reality. The patient then experienced herself as confused, unable to plan and to predict events and, most important, unable to think. Thus, she used this as a confirmation of the unconscious fantasy that she was defective, although she expressed the idea in a disguised and displaced manner. Only after she had begun to deal with the underlying self-image, could she permit herself to think more effectively.

Rationalization and exaggeration also facilitate the avoidance of precise and detailed perceptions by making it easy to disregard them. In providing a false meaning or explanation to occurrences, rationalization renders the significant trivial and the trivial significant. Exaggeration can be used to amplify the meaning or impact of events to such an absurd degree that they appear make-believe and, therefore, discountable. Fenichel, in describing defenses in the hysterical character disorder writes: "perceptions one does not like to believe are intentionally made improbable by an absurd exaggeration" (1945, p. 529).

These defensive processes are likely to result in the global, impressionistic, cognitive style that frequently accompanies this disorder. The style itself may serve to obscure detail. While such a cognitive style may be, to a variable extent, the result of the psychopathology, it is not the pathology itself or the cause of the pathology. In other character organizations it also may be present and serve a less obligatory and nondefensive role; for example, as in creative individuals.

Superego Organization

Superego functioning represents that organization within the psychic apparatus which "becomes a systemic third dependent variable in the intrapsychic conflicts, and which exercises control over drives and some essential tendencies and functions of the ego, e.g., individual self interest and even self preservation" (Loewenstein 1966, p. 302). Loewenstein divides the activities of the system superego into two broad categories, those of the ego-ideal and those of conscience. The latter is synonymous with the term, prohibiting superego. While the functions of the prohibiting superego develop largely out of the resolution of the oedipus complex, the ego-ideal is conceptualized as resulting, to a greater extent, from preoedipal determinants. Most important of these are the idealized self- and object representations, which are "connected with ontogenesis of narcissism on the one hand and with idealization of the parents on the other . . ." (Loewenstein 1966, p. 304).

Attitudes and behaviors are influenced by the prohibiting superego predominantly in terms of restraint. Particular wishes and their expression in thought or action become forbidden for moral reasons. As a result, this aspect of superego functioning takes on the qualities of an ethical code limiting conduct, both real and imagined, from the more abstract perspective of principles of good and evil.

The ego-ideal affects the ego by directing interests toward valued goals and attitudes. It mobilizes the individual toward becoming what he feels he should be, and the specific content of the ideal self- and object representation will have much to do with the determination of particular goals and ambitions held by the individual. "The state of harmony between the ego ideal and the ego is experienced as narcissistic self-satisfaction and as a feeling of pride" (Kramer 1958, p. 39).

From the foregoing perspective, the superego found in the hysterical personality disorder has certain predictable, though not invariant, features. The prohibiting superego, relatively speaking, tends to be flexible regarding the specifics that are enjoined and the severity of the enjoinder. These values, rather than being fixed or rigid, are significantly dependent upon the attitudes found in the current love object. The continued phallic stage tie to the mother lessens the impact of the subsequent oedipal stage on superego formation, and the unconscious image of self as defective compromises the formation of an independent, self-sustaining value system. Strong convictions raise the danger of challenge and the fantasized fear of being unable to withstand the test. In relationships this "results in a projection of the superego (equated with the desired phallus) upon the love object which is thereby elevated to serve as superego. From then on the female anxiety of conscience becomes to a certain extent a secondary 'social anxiety'; above all, the opinions and judgments of the love object become decisive and—like his penis—can always be taken from him again" (Jacobson 1937, p. 535). This should not be misconstrued as a revival of the antiquated concept of superego impairment or "immorality" in the individual with a hysterical personality disorder. Rather it reflects the situation in which the functioning of the prohibiting superego is subject to the influence of important others, and to a significant extent is dependent on them. The results of the primary difficulty thus affect this aspect of the superego even though it is not one of the principal parties to the original conflict. By contrast though, since ego functions are essentially intact, there usually are not the harsh characteristics that frequently accompany disorders of preoedipal original, in which severe superego prohibitions are enlisted to support weak or absent ego mechanisms for the control of direct drive discharge.

The ego-ideal reflects distortions in the content of (not the capacity for) the self- and object representations. There may be great concern with issues that raise the potential, real or imagined, of injury or slight, as these threaten to evoke the underlying deprecatory self-image. The concern involves more than just the avoidance of anxiety producing situations. There is likely to be the need to demonstrate actively that such issues do not exist. Consequently, comparative themes, such as who has more, who is better provided for, whether situations are fair or inequities are present, produce worry, and often the need to minimize real discrepancies. Even if an inequity imposes added burdens and problems it may nonetheless be viewed with envy.

Another patient, a young woman, with a hysterical personality disorder, was particularly sensitive to these issues. At her work she was constantly attuned to the amount and type of work that her fellow employees were doing, especially if they were women. If she thought that others were asked to do more, or more complex work than she, she felt incensed and unjustly treated. During several periods when she, as well as her co-workers, were overloaded with work, she perceived her co-workers as being assigned more sensitive and difficult projects than she. She brought up with her supervisors her concern at being treated unjustly. The result was that she received even more to do. On many of these occasions, to keep up with this added load, she had to work at least one additional day per week; she did this readily without receiving overtime. She found being overworked preferable to feeling unequal with some of her fellow employees. The emphasis of her concern was less to obtain special favor with her superiors than to prevent discrepancies between her and her peers.

This patient also was made very uncomfortable by worry that she would appear inadequate. This discomfort, in addition to being based on themes already discussed, had a superego component to it. She worried that if, even in fantasy, she appeared inadequate, her mother would be very hurt, and in response to this idea she felt intensely guilty. Involved in the fear and guilt that she would hurt her mother was the strong wish to do so. She harbored the fantasy that her mother had inadequately provided the ability for her to pursue her phallic striving, and in response to this she felt for her mother both fury and contempt. Her fantasy of her mother as inadequate, like her image of herself, was most unacceptable to her.

ALTERNATIVE OUTCOMES

The usual stylistic presentation in the hysterical personality disorder is that of a hyperfeminine woman. As we have described, this pattern serves both as a defense against narcissistic injury and as a displacement of the phallic strivings. It should be noted, though, that in women an alternative pattern based on the same dynamics is possible, and that men also may demonstrate a hysterical personality. We raise these alternatives both for completeness and to emphasize the necessity of examining dynamics rather than stylistic features in arriving at a meaningful diagnosis. We will not discuss these alternatives comprehensively, as to do so would be beyond the scope of this paper.

Women with a hysterical personality disorder may present with a "masculine," aggressive style as well. If the narcissistic injury has been too severe, femininity or hyperfemininity itself may be too closely linked to the imagined phallic stage insult. It will then lose its use as a defense, and may be replaced by less disguised phallic behavior. In such an instance, the picture may be that of a woman with aggressive and "masculine" stylistic features. This, too, serves the purpose of displacing genital, phallic activity to the whole person and permits phallic activity at the same time that it defends against narcissistic injury. It does so by denying the differences between male and female.

Men also may show hysterical personality. Although the disorder is much less frequent in males than in females, the underlying psycho-dynamics derive from similar issues resulting from the phallic stage. In this case, the male also enters the phallic stage with an unusually strong maternal attachment, often based on underlying oral issues. For the male, of course, the problem is not the presence of a penis but rather of its adequacy. He may consider himself inadequate as a male in comparison to his fantasized or real perceptions of adult males. He will experience, to some degree, a narcissistic injury similar to that of the female. The more intense his imagined inadequacy and the more intense his attachment to his mother, the more severe will be the narcissistic injury. If the resultant narcissistic injury is too severe he will be unable to enter the competitive oedipal stage, and instead may defend against the injury by denying its source. Then masculinity itself will need to be denied, and in its place the male will need to show effeminate features. Although the man with such a disorder may be stylistically effeminate, the issue is not one primarily of homosexuality, as the underlying dynamics remain those of the hysterical personality.

The clinical picture resulting from the dynamics described is that of an effeminate appearing, but not homosexual male. His interest in women is largely motivated by the need to assuage unconscious fears of phallic inadequacy. As in the female hysterical personality disorder, relationships may tend to be relatively short-lived and sequential. Each new relation-ship temporarily assuages his unconscious fear—but only temporarily. No other woman is his mother, and his unconscious need is for the impossible reassurance from her.

DIFFERENTIAL DIAGNOSIS

Much of the confusion that exists in regard to the diagnosis of the hysterical personality disorder results from vague and unclear concep-tualization. By making the psychodynamic structure of this difficulty the critical factor in the diagnosis, more precision may be possible in the use of the term. It would seem appropriate to us that regardless of stylistic features, disorders characterized by psychodynamics other than those resulting from phallic stage issues, organized in the manner proposed, should not be grouped diagnostically with the hysterical personality disorder.

Two entities that frequently demonstrate descriptively hysterical traits, but which should, and can be distingusihed from the hysterical personality disorder, are the borderline characters and the hysterical character neurosis. Individuals, usually women, with borderline character organizations and conventional hysterical features, such as seductiveness, flirtatiousness, dependency, and emotional lability, are commonly diagnosed as hysterical personality disorders. Often such terms as the "sick hysteric" or the "oral hysteric" are applied to them. Classification in this way suggests that the underlying psychopathology is similar, in all the cases, even if more severe in some instances. Diagnosis based on psychodynamic considerations, however, may disclose fundamental differences. Central to the borderline character organization are significant deficits in ego structure and the capacity for whole, stable object representations (Kernberg 1975). These ego impairments include lack of anxiety tolerance, lack of impulse control, lack of developed sublimatory channels, and primitive mechanisms of defense. Distortions in the capacity for object representation are manifest by splitting and, under certain conditions, the loss of self-object boundaries (Kernberg 1975). As a result, in intensive treatment, patients with this character are prone to develop transference psychoses.

The psychopathology in the borderline seems to differ in kind rather than degree from the hysterical personality disorder as described. In the latter, failure of complete ego formation is not at issue, and because of these distinctions, prognosis would be expected to vary considerably between the two groups.

The hysterical character neurosis has a greater similarity to the hysterical personality disorder than has the borderline character. Nonetheless, there are significant psychodynamic differences. Character neurosis, in the model suggested by Anna Freud (1965), may develop as a solution to neurotic, oedipal conflicts. The conflicts are solved in the sense of avoidance by a regression in both drive and ego organization to a preoedipal position that was previously successfully outgrown. At this point, symptoms may develop or the underlying conflict and the regression may become woven into character structure, but "in any case, the result is unmistakably neurotic . . ." (A. Freud 1965, p. 131).

Nagera (1975) describes the situation, for the girl, in which regression occurs from attachment to father and rivalry with mother of second stage oedipal organization to the phallic stage. Intensely hostile and competitive, maternally directed feelings thus are avoided by reestablishing the positive phallic attachment to her. "Not infrequently, we have noticed that an inability to separate from the mother ensues at this point" (p. 34), with future distortion of subsequent development. For adult difficulties deriving from this condition, we would suggest the term hysterical character neurosis be applied. It differs from the hysterical personality disorder in that the underlying conflicts and ego organization are triadic oedipal ones, rather than dyadic, with only a secondary regression to a dyadic state.

CONCLUSION

The conceptualization and understanding of psychopathology can be enhanced by an approach that stresses the etiology and the underlying psychodynamic organization in a given disorder. The developmental perspective is central to such an endeavor, and psychiatric disorders conceptualized in terms of the vicissitudes of development could usefully supplant the perennially unsuccessful attempts to categorize psychopathological formulations in outmoded diagnostic terms (Clower, unpublished paper).

The developmental view is a hierarchical one. It is based upon the idea of a sequential unfolding of capacities and capabilities of increasing complexity in multiple areas of functioning, as Anna Freud describes in her concept of developmental lines (1965). Not only is there mutual interaction between the various functions, but new abilities emerge from the foundation of those already established. Failure to acquire or master stage-appropriate skills in an area distorts both the interaction with other lines of development, and the subsequent structure that would evolve from that level. Erikson (1963) has applied, from embryology, the idea of epigenecity to this phenomenon in psychological growth. As in embryology, epigenecity suggests that early disturbances are likely to cause greater and different difficulties than later ones.

"Basic categories of psychopathology," writes Clower, "such as psychosis, atypical ego development, borderline states, narcissistic disorder, character disorder, neurosis, situational reactions, and transient developmental disorders can be studied in terms of development of object relationship and attainment of object constancy" (p. 19). We would add in terms also of their relationship to the degree of development in all major lines.

From this model, the expectation would be that problems resulting from a given developmental period would differ in nature and in the possible range of severity from those of other periods. The particular characteristics of a difficulty would reflect the specific vulnerabilities inherent in the emerging but not yet established capacities of the stage.

A given problem would be unlikely to give rise to psychopathology potentially ranging from neurotic to psychotic, or even borderline. On the one hand, almost by definition, difficulties that give rise to failures of significant aspects of ego formation (failures of structure) occur pre-structurally, and therefore preconflictually, in the sense of internal conflicts. On the other hand, neurotic conflicts, occurring internally between intrapsychic structures, can take place only following relatively successful and complete structure formation.

By applying this view to the hysterical personality disorder, clarification and simplification of some of the confusion that has surrounded this illness is possible. It provides a rational basis for limiting the diagnosis to a particular psychodynamic formulation and classifying problems with other dynamics differently. We do not wish to imply, however, a schematic unidimensional approach to human behavior. While we recognize that in all individuals there is a complex interweaving of issues from all levels, we do not think that a specific disorder encompasses in its origin all stages of development. To argue differently runs the risk of blurring meaningful distinctions and making everything the same as everything else.

REFERENCES

Abraham, K. (1908). The psycho-sexual difference between hysteria and dementia praecox. In *Selected Papers of Karl Abraham*, pp. 64–79. London: Hogarth Press, 1948.

———— (1910). Hysterical dream-states. In *Selected Papers of Karl Abraham*, pp. 90–124. London: Hogarth Press, 1948.

American Psychiatric Association (1968). *Diagnostic and Statistical Manual of Mental Disorders*, 2nd ed. (DSM II). Washington, D.C..

Blacker, K., and Tupin, J. (1977). Hysteria and hysterical structures: developmental and social theories. In *Hysterical Personality*, ed. M. Horowitz, pp. 94–141. New York: Jason Aronson.

Blos, P. (1972). The epigenesis of the adult neurosis. *Psychoanalytic Study of the Child* 27:106–135.

Breuer, J., and Freud, S. (1893–1895). On the psychical mechanism of hysterical phenomena: preliminary communications. *Standard Edition* 2:1–17.

Brunswick, R. (1940). The preoedipal phase of libido development. *Psychoanalytic Quarterly* 9:293–319.

Chodoff, P. (1974). The diagnosis of hysteria: an overview. *American Journal of Psychiatry* 131:1073–1078.

Clower, V. (n.d.). A recapitulation of the major issues in the position paper of Preparatory Commission IX, child analysis. Unpublished.

Easser, B., and Lesser, S. (1965). Hysterical personality: a re-evaluation. *Psychoanalytic Quarterly* 34:390–405.

Engel, G. (1962). *Psychological Development in Health and Disease*. Philadelphia: Saunders.

Erikson, E. (1963). Eight ages of man. In *Childhood and Society*, pp. 247–274. New York: Norton.

Fenichel, O. (1945). *The Psychoanalytic Theory of Neurosis*. New York: Norton.

Freud, A. (1965). In *Normality and Pathology in Childhood*. New York: International Universities Press.

Freud, S. (1888). Hysteria. *Standard Edition* 1:39–58.

———— (1926). Inhibitions, symptoms and anxiety. *Standard Edition* 20:77–175.

———— (1931). Libidinal types. *Standard Edition* 21:215–220.

Greenacre, P. (1950). Special problems of early female sexual development. *Psychoanalytic Study of the Child* 5:122–138.

Guze, S. (1975). The validity and significance of the clinical diagnosis of hysteria (Briquet's syndrome). *American Journal of Psychiatry* 132:138–141.

Guze, S., Woodruff, R.A., and Clayton, P.J. (1971). A study of conversion symptoms in psychiatric outpatients. *American Journal of Psychiatry.* 128:643–646.

Halleck, S. (1967). Hysterical personality traits: psychological, social, iatrongenic determinants. *Archives of General Psychiatry* 16:750–757.

Hartmann, H. (1958). *Ego Psychology and the Problem of Adaptation.* New York: International Universities Press.

Hoffer, W. (1954). Defensive process and defensive organization: their place in psychoanalytic technique. *International Journal of Psycho-Analysis* 35:194–198.

Horney, K. (1920). The flight from womanhood. In *Psychoanalysis and Women,* ed. J. Miller, pp. 5–20. Baltimore: Penguin.

Horowitz, M. (1977). The core characteristics of hysterical personality. In *Hysterical Personality,* ed. M. Horowitz. pp. 3–6. New York: Jason Aronson.

Jacobson, E. (1937). Female superego and castration conflict. *Psychoanalytic Quarterly* 45:525–538.

——— (1964). *The Self and the Object World.* New York: International Universities Press.

Kernberg, O. (1967). Borderline personality organization. *Journal of the American Psychoanalytic Association* 15:641–685.

——— (1975). *Borderline Conditions and Pathological Narcissism.* New York: Jason Aronson.

Kestenberg, J. (1956). On the development of maternal feelings in early childhood. *Psychoanalytic Study of the Child* 11:257–291.

——— (1968). Outside and inside, male and female. *Journal of the American Psychoanalytic Association* 16:457–520.

Kramer, P. (1958). Note on one of the pre-oedipal roots of the superego. *Journal of the American Psychoanalytic Association* 6:38–46.

Lazare, A. (1971). The hysterical character in psychoanalytic theory: evaluation and confusion. *Archives of General Psychiatry* 25:131–137.

Lichtenberg, J., and Slap, J. (1972). On the defensive mechanism: a survey and synthesis. *Journal of the American Psychoanalytic Association* 20:776–792.

Loewenstein, R. (1966). On the theory of the superego. In *Psychoanalysis: A General Psychology,* ed. R. Loewenstein, L. Newman, M. Schur, and A. Solnit, pp. 298–314. New York: International Universities Press.

Marmor, J. (1953). Orality in the hysterical personality. *Journal of the American Psychoanalytic Association* 1:656–671.

Metcalf, A. (1977). Childhood: from process to structure. In *Hysterical Personality,* ed. M. Horowitz, pp. 223–281. New York: Jason Aronson.

Nagera, H. (1975). *Female Sexuality and the Oedipus Complex.* New York: Jason Aronson.

Rado, S. (1933). Fear of castration in women. *Psychoanalytic Quarterly* 2:425–475.

Rangell, L. (1959). The nature of conversion. *Journal of the American Psychoanalytic Association* 7:632–662.

Rapaport, D., and Gill, M. (1959). Points of view and assumptions of metapsychology. *International Journal of Psycho-Analysis* 40:153–162.

Reich, W. (1949). Some circumscribed character forms. In *Character Analysis,* pp. 189–207. New York: Orgone Institute Press.

Shapiro, D. (1965). *Neurotic Styles.* New York: Basic Books.

Slavery, P. (1974). The hysterical personality: a controlled study. *Archives of General Psychiatry* 30:325–330.

Stoller, R. (1968). *Sex and Gender.* New York: Jason Aronson.

Temoshok, L. and Attkinson, C. (1977). Epidemiology of hysterical phenomena: evidence for a psychosocial theory. In *Hysterical Personality*, ed. M. Horowitz, pp. 142–222. New York: Jason Aronson.

Van Der Leeuw, P. (1971). On the development of the concept of defense. *International Journal of Psycho-Analysis* 52:51–58.

Wittels, F. (1930). The hysterical character. *Medical Review of Reviews* 36:186–190.

Zetzel, E. (1968). The so-called good hysteric. *International Journal of Psycho-Analysis* 49:256–260.

Diagnosis Revisited (and Revisited): The Case of Hysteria and the Hysterical Personality

ROBERT S. WALLERSTEIN, M.D.

A discussion of "The Hysterical Personality Disorder," by Gordon Baumbacher, M.D., and Fariborz Amini, M.D. The effort of Baumbacher and Amini at clarification of the diagnostic meaning of the group they designate *hysterical personality disorder* is discussed within the context of all the difficult and problematic conceptual and definitional dilemmas that exist within psychiatric and psychoanalytic nomenclature. The following discussion presents the issues of psychologic-psychodynamic as opposed to medical-somatic nosology in general and the special problems inherent within the realm of hysteria. Among the issues considered are the oral hysteric of Marmor (1953), the "hysteroid" of Easser and Lesser (1965), and the "so-called good hysteric" of Zetzel (1968), and the additional issues that inhere in the distinctions among the varieties of neurotic (nonpsychotic) disorders: the symptom neuroses, the character neuroses, and the impulse neuroses (or character disorders). The extent of philosophic or aesthetic preference in current denominational designations is referred to.

Ilza Veith's comprehensive book, *Hysteria: The History of a Disease* (1965), begins with the sentence, "Hysteria, of all mental diseases," has occupied the interest of medical writers since medical writing began (p. vii). And in the most recent book in this domain, *Hysterical Personality* (1977), the editor, Mardi Horowitz, continues in this same vein. He states on the first page of the introduction that "many kinds of personality classification exist. . . . Of these psychiatric categories, hysterical personality is one of the most venerable . . . " (p. 3). Yet despite this long scientific attention, the concepts of hysteria and of hysterical personality are among the most confusing and problematic in dynamic psychiatry today—which is all the more reason to welcome the continued efforts at review and at clarification represented by Baumbacher and Amini, who focus on the diagnostic dilemmas inherent in the concept of "The Hysterical Personality Disor-

der." I welcome it, both for the illumination that such continued thoughtful study may bring to a murky field, and also the opportunity that it
affords a reader and critic to review, and hopefully clarify, his own
perspectives.

   The conceptual confusions surrounding the concepts *hysteria* and *hysteri-*
cal are in part those that confound the entire state of psychiatric and
psychoanalytic nomenclature and nosology. Additionally, these confusions seem peculiarly specific to hysteria, seemingly structurally the
simplest (or most transparent) of character organizations, but in actuality
one of the most complex and problematic. Let me briefly review the
nature of some of these abounding confusions. First of course, I refer to
the still primitive and inchoate state of our whole system of psychiatric
classification. As compared with that in somatic medicine, in psychological medicine we have a far less well articulated set of consistent principles
for our taxonomy of disease—with full acknowledgment of all the in-
completeness and inconsistencies still existing among medical taxonomy
as a whole. But in psychiatry, diagnostic categories are still almost totally
conceptually unorganized and we rely for our designations on a pragmatic
and, therefore, to a considerable extent haphazard admixture of considerations: behavioral-descriptive, stylistic, underlying (structurally)
etiological, innately developmental, environmentally or socially determined, and psychodynamic (or metapsychological). One can readily substantiate this sweeping categorization by a careful perusal of the
vicissitudes of the diagnostic categories and the changing conceptualizations that implicitly underlie as given in the three DSM[1] classifications,
adopted in the decades since World War II by the American Psychiatric
Association. This is quite apart from the confounding considerations,
further sources of distortion and confusion, that are created by political
motivations—actually coming in one instance to a vote of the membership
between alternative propositions on how to categorize the various patterns of sexual behaviors and manifestations. The point is that we are
beset by a confusing melange of nomenclatural principles, certainly in
DSM, that is, in psychiatric nosology, but also in psychoanalytic nosology,
which more often than we like to admit is a not much modified conceptual
transplant from the basic categories of psychiatry—hence, also contaminated by the same confusions. As a clarifying caveat, these "conceptual
confusions" are less a matter of the fuzziness of our knowledge than of its
burgeoning, unintegrated complexity. Psychiatry, an applied healing art
and clinical discipline of medicine, rests as a clinical application to the
problems of the mentally and emotionally ill, on knowledge from three

   1. Of the three, it is *DSM II* (1968) which is at this moment in current official use. DSM-III
is in the process of coming into official use.

basic realms of science: biological, psychological, and social. The clinical application of knowledge from three such conceptually and hierarchically separate realms makes inevitable the "confusions" of psychiatric conceptualization in general and psychiatric diagnostic nomenclature in particular. The word *inevitable* here is of course a reflection of our current state of knowledge, and is subject to revision and to being superseded as we proceed to effective overarching conceptualizations, perhaps general systems concepts, that can encompass the phenomena of these currently separate scientific realms in meaningful juxtapositions and appropriate hierarchical organization.

But there is another special problem of psychiatry and that is the concept, made so central to our thinking by Freud, of the active continuum between normal and pathological functioning. It was Freud whose studies of the mechanisms of the mind first made so clear that the same conceptualizations of conflict, defense, affect, meaning and motivation, operated across the entire spectrum of psychological health and illness, and that the psychopathological compromise or resolution is but an inappropriate exaggeration of the normal mental operations. In that sense, though the classical symptom neuroses, such as conversion hysteria or anxiety hysteria (i.e., hysterical phobic states) are clearly specifiable as mental illnesses by symptom manifestation, everyone has also some form of character structuring, character style, or "neurotic style" (Shapiro 1965). There is the question not only as to when the natural fears of everyday life are phobic illness, but the even more insidious (difficult) question as to when the hysterical character *style* is a hysterical character *neurosis* or a hysterical character *disorder*.

In his 1931 paper on "Libidinal Types," Freud gave early cognizance to just this issue. Among other types, he suggested an "erotic type" which most subsequent writers have taken, properly I think, to be a reference to what we today call the hysterical character type. "It seems easy to infer," Freud wrote, "that when people of the erotic type fall ill they will develop hysteria" (p. 220). He then said of the relationship of these "types" to illness: "But it must be required of all such types that they shall not coincide with clinical pictures. On the contrary, they must comprehend all the variations which according to our practical judgment fall within the limits of the normal. In their extreme developments, however, they may well approximate to clinical pictures and in that way help to bridge the gulf that is supposed to be between the normal and the pathological" (p. 217). In a major sense, Shapiro's whole book on *Neurotic Styles* (1965) is a discussion of just these issues of the border between normal character style and what is to be called character neurosis. Certainly, we have here another major basis for conceptual difficulties in establishing a taxonomy for "illness."

This in briefest compass is a statement of some of the *general* problems that plague our efforts at a systematic nosology of mental illness within a psychodynamic framework but within that, or rather, on top of that, the diagnosis of hysteria and of the meaning of hysterical character is beset with very particular difficulties of its own. These stem from the fact that hysterical phenomena are not as clumped around a nodal point as ought to be expected from a properly coherent diagnostic constellation but are spread along several spectra, which in many ways are orthogonal to, rather than congruent with, each other. Let me explain.

First, there is the familiar clinical axis of the spectrum from oral to phallic-oedipal to describe the predominant psychosexual developmental fixation levels in the hysterical personality. It was basically Abraham (1921, 1924) and Wilhelm Reich (1933) who first established solidly the linkages in psychoanalytic terms of the hysterical phenomena to the phallic-oedipal level—Abraham for the hysterical symptom neuroses and Reich for the hysterical character (rather than Freud, whose own few writings on character typology can be read, more ambiguously, as also emphasizing the orally dependent aspects of the hysterical character type). Reich, in the definitive psychoanalytic text on character to that point (1933) declared that "the hysterical character is determined by a fixation on the genital phase of infantile development, with its incestuous attachment" (p. 190) and a little further on, "As Ferenczi put it, the hysterical character *genitalizes everything . . .* " (p. 191, italics mine). He then went on to add as if in anticipation of the later arguments about the evident orality of the hysteric:

> To the extent to which other than genital mechanisms are found in the hysterical character they no longer belong specifically to this character type. For example, one often finds depressive mechanisms. In these cases one finds that the genital-incestuous fixation was in part replaced by a regression to oral mechanisms. The marked tendency of hysterics to oral regressions is explained by the sexual stasis at this zone and by the fact that the mouth, having assumed the role of the genital, absorbs much libido ('displacement from below upward'). (p. 192)

As is well-known, it was Marmor who in 1953 first challenged this one-to-one concordance, by focusing on what Reich had so emphatically disavowed, the *"orality* in the hysterical personality" (italics mine). He did this most persuasively along essentially three lines of argument: (1) by demonstrating the many orally-determined mechanisms and symptoms that are invariable parts of the presenting picture of the hysteric, even in hysterics of the classical literature before oral features were specifically highlighted as such, including Freud's famous case of Dora with her symptoms of nausea, anorexia, gastric pains, and her history of prolonged thumbsucking in childhood; (2) by pointing as well to the "immaturity and instability of its ego structure and its close relationship to addictions, depressions and schizophrenia—all, it seems to me, best explained on the basis of deep-seated oral fixations" (Marmor 1953, p. 661); and (3) by pointing to the refractoriness to therapy of the hysterical character organizations because of propensities for sweeping oral regressions, as against what he termed the "clinical myth" that the hysteric *should be* the easiest neurotic to treat because the prevailing fixation point is presumably at the highest infantile developmental level.

It is worth digressing a little to illustrate the extreme (at that time) to which Marmor pushed his argument:

> The clinical association of the hysterical personality with schizophrenic reactions, in particular, and the similarities in the underlying character structure of the hysteric and certain schizophrenics is in fact a rather striking one and probably more than coincidental. The borderline between hysterical introversion and schizophrenic autism, between hysterical fantasy and schizophrenic delusion, and between hysterical materialization and schizophrenic hallucination is often a narrow one; and quantitative factors may effect the qualitative transition from one to the other. (p. 660)

The further and well-known subsequent contributions are, in a major sense, only elaborations of the phallic-oral continuum or dichotomy between the views of Abraham and Reich and those of Marmor. Easser and Lesser in their 1965 "re-evaluation" described six analytic patients of their own in a composite, comprehensively detailed description of traits and behaviors. They separated them from a larger, phenomenologically similar group who also used hysterical mechanisms and they arrived at a bimodal distribution along a spectrum between their patients, whom they called "hysterical" (Reich's phallic-oedipal fixations) and what they chose to separately name the "hysteroid" (akin to Marmor's more primitive fixations). They made the phenomenological differential diagnostic point that "in many instances the hysteriod would appear to be a caricature of the hysteric much as the hysteric has been said to be a caricature of femininity" (pp. 398–399). They said that "in order to delimit the hysterical personality it is necessary to differentiate our group from other patients who also employ hysterical mechanisms. These patients range widely diagnostically from the infantile dependent to the borderline, and the psychotic. For the purposes of this discussion we shall designate these latter groups as 'hysteroid'" (p. 398). In terms of core problems, "In contrast to the hysteric, the core of the hysteroid's problem lies with the mother or maternal object" in the realm of major "affect deprivation," and with "more infantile fixation and the consequent weaker integration and synthesis of the ego" (p. 400). The problem rested, in their eyes, with the issue of the at times difficult differential diagnosis between these two groupings. "Unfortunately, despite careful clinical evaluation, differentiation may not be possible without clinical trial. The difficulty in diagnostic assessment is hardly surprising when one considers that there is no sharp differentiating line but rather a continuum, and that within this continuum, the hysteroid often shows the hysterical mechanism more clearly and dramatically" (p. 400). And in summation, "We feel that one can err as much in the direction of emphasizing early fixation as to assume that all hysteria is oedipal in origin. It is preferable to divide these patients into two separate diagnostic classifications for the purpose of improving therapeutic selectivity and validity. We have reserved the term 'hysterical personality' for the more mature and better integrated and have termed the large group that extends from the pregenital to the psychotic as 'hysteroid'" (pp. 404–405).

It is clear that Easser and Lesser advanced the overall arguments in a number of directions. They were the first to make the explicit separation as bimodal nodal points along a continuum of the two kinds of hysterics. They named one group hysterics (by implication, the true hysterics) and the other hysteroids (phenomenally similar but dynamically and structurally less well integrated), thus separating out as two kinds of individuals the predominant hysterical type, as differently emphasized by Reich and Marmor. They also concomitantly broadened the argument with the less explicit point, but shown clearly in their material, that they were making their typological differentiation along more than one continuum: not just the libidinal (phallic vs. oral) fixation points along the psychosexual developmental axis, but also along the various lines of development of ego (and superego) functions and of the parallel development of object relationships—all of these in all their interlocking complexity and their mutually interacting influences. What Easser and Lesser did not make at all clear was the extent to which they felt that unfolding drive development, ego development, and object relations ran along comparable and congruent tracks, or could take dissimilar lines, accounting in individual patterns of unevennesses for so much of the differential diagnostic difficulty in comfortably placing a particular individual in the right grouping.

Zetzel in 1968 carried matters to the further point of differentiating four nodal points along the regression, or the therapeutically good-bad spectrum, by differentiating (1) the true good hysterics who exhibit

genuine triangular conflicts and have a well-consolidated sense of differentiation between outer and inner reality (speaking of that anxiety-
hysteric (phobic) Little Hans, she said "Though a rival in terms of internal
reality, his father was a support and an object for identification as a real
person. This conflict, in brief, is the first really significant confrontation
to the child of the difference between external and internal reality" [p.
257]; (2) the potential good hysterics, who differ quantitatively from the
true good hysterics (the former are "often afraid of their dependent
wishes which are nearer the surface than is typically the case with the
true good hysteric" [p. 259]); (3) the depressive characters, with low self-
esteem and devalued femininity, "passive dependent transference reactions" (p. 259), and yet with some possibilities of treatability ("despite
these serious drawbacks, many of these patients have experienced some
genuine triangular conflict, often idealizing their fathers to an excessive
degree" [p. 259]); and (4) so-called good hysterics with "floridly hysterical"
symptom pictures, the least treatable (while "their symptoms may present a facade which looks genital, they prove in treatment to be incapable
of recognizing or tolerating a genuine triangular situation. . . . They are
genuinely incapable of the meaningful distinction between external and
internal reality . . . " [p. 259]).

We can see through all this how Zetzel not only expanded the array of
nodal constellations into four distinguishable types of people, but shifted
the main grounds for the distinction from the libidinal fixation points to
the level of ego organization, the orientation to reality, and the capacity
for whole-person more than dyadic object relations, all seen from the
clinical psychoanalytic perspective of amenability to therapeutic intervention, that is, treatability. She summarizes:

> The basic question I have posed in this paper may be stated quite
> simply. How far can we regard manifest oedipal or genital symp-
> tomatology, i.e., instinctual content, as acceptable evidence that the
> patient in question has achieved and/or maintained a level of ego
> development at which the capacity for identification, object relations,
> and affect-tolerance permits emergence and recognition of a *triangu-
> lar* situation which involves three whole individuals? This I regard as
> indispensable for the potential ability to distinguish between external
> and internal reality which is one major criterion of analyzability.
> (p. 260)

All of these differential diagnostic issues in the understanding of the
hysterical character—or in the meanings that we give to the concept—
that are involved in these considerations of instinctual development, ego
development, and of the development of object relations, are comprehen-

sively summarized in the 1971 article by Lazare who *in addition* particularly highlights another source of diagnostic complexity and confusion which Lazare calls the semantic area, (conceptual, I would add, as well as definitional). "Of the larger group of patients characterized by some common personality traits and manifest oedipal or genital symptomatology, the subgroup that appears most floridly hysterical is referred to as 'hysteroid,' 'infantile personality,'[2] or 'so-called good hysteric.' The subgroup in which the hysterical features are most subtle is referred to as 'good hysterics' or 'true hysterics.' In other words, the patients who appear most hysterical are not really hysterical while those that appear least hysterical are the true hysterics." (Lazare 1971, p. 136). Put somewhat differently, the usual behavioral criteria for the delineation of the hysterical character run differently than the semantic criteria to which the various authors seem to have rather uniformly repaired. Those who behaviorally look more hysterical in the sense of the dramatic or flamboyant hysterical character type are the very ones who look less hysterical in the sense of the dynamics of the "good" or "true" hysteric. And add to this a point of my own, quite neglected in all this literature: the flamboyant or histrionic hysteric seems quite generally to be taken as the behavioral epitome of what alerts us to the hysterical diagnosis and incidentally fulfills the lay stereotype, as when one popularly speaks of someone being or acting hysterical or when we say "Don't get hysterical."However, we also know, even though we don't seem to write about them in the same way, that there may be at least an equally large group of true or good hysterics in terms of the underlying phallic-oedipal fixations or the capacity for genuine triangular object relationships, or an advanced level of ego organization and a consolidated sense of distinction between inner and outer reality (or however one conceptualizes this) who behaviorally are not dramatic actors but rather constricted wall flowers, shy and even tongue-tied in interpersonal encounter, at extremes mousy and totally inhibited in demeanor and interaction. Here I speak of the behaviorally constricted (true) hysteric as against the behaviorally more flamboyant (true) hysteric, both opposite in manifest behavioral functioning (phenomenological opposites) but united in being equally expressions of underlying true hysterical "high level" dynamics. And just as the dramatic hysteric can be more the hysteroid (and tends to be so, the more dramatic the behaviors), so can the constricted hysteric also be more the hysteroid. Here the assessment of underlying structural-dynamic, of drive, ego, and object relations needs to be made separately from the phenomenological assessment of the overt behaviors.

2. This is Kernberg's term for this same group as described in his 1967 classificatory and descriptive paper on the borderline personality organization.

At this place I should turn to my last point concerning the conceptual confusions that beset our nomenclature as a whole and hysteria, hysterical behavior, and the hysterical character in special degree. This has to do with how we choose to make our major diagnostic groupings and I trust that I have by now adequately conveyed the extent to which I think that at this stage of the art, there is still much individual choice and personal aesthetics involved in taxonomic positioning. Staying now within the realm of neurotic illness, leaving aside, that is, the borderline conditions (with all the different descriptive terms coined to try to capture their psychological essence), many of the sicker narcissistic and also the "as if" characters, and the psychotic conditions, psychotic characters, and the frank psychoses—leaving all these aside there is still a broad realm of disorders characterized as neurotic, which I find it useful to categorize in threefold fashion.[3]

First there are the classical *symptom* neuroses, which is where psychoanalysis itself began and which achieved their major codification in 1945 in Fenichel's *The Psychoanalytic Theory of Neurosis*. Here we have traditionally placed the anxiety hysterias (phobias) and the conversion hysterias with the standard assumption that in these instances the typical "hysterical" level conflict situations could be readily demonstrated. All this, of course, is with full recognition that there are pregenital phobias and pregenital conversions and that phobic and conversion symptoms are not always engrafted upon, or rather do not always stem from, hysterical character formations—and incidentally Fenichel himself had sections in his book dealing with just these pregenital phobic and conversion phenomena. Second, there are then the *character* neuroses initially given proper form in Reich's *Character Analysis* (1933), in which he was the first to make psychoanalytically explicit that a neurotic character structure underlay every symptom neurosis. This at once broadened the scope of analytic work from just the resolution of symptoms to the concomitant unfolding and reconstruction of character. It is to the manifold problems of this broad realm of the character neuroses that the paper by Baumbacher and Amini (and this discussion) is addressed—at least to the problems of the hysterical segment of the broad realm of the character neuroses. And third, again to borrow a phrase from Fenichel, there are *impulse* neuroses, by which I mean the various behavioral pathologies or pathologies of impulse, usually called *character disorders* including problems of sexual

3. Nor do I want to discuss here the nature of the so-called hysterical psychosis, its relation to the transference psychosis, and to psychotic states in general on the one hand or its relation to the hysteroid state (put more precisely, its shading in to the hysteriod state) on the other hand. For some discussion of these issues but not specifically in these terms or in this framework, see Wallerstein (1967).

behavior and deviation, addiction and abuse, delinquency and klep-
tomania and pyromania and a host of other significant expressions of the
impulse-ridden character. It is this distinction between the *character neuroses*
(with the pathology evident in the fixed and exaggerated character traits)
and the impulse neuroses, or *character disorders* (with the pathology evident
in ego-dystonic or socially-dystonic behaviors), that I want to note since I
will come back to it when I discuss the perspectives offered for our
consideration by Baumbacher and Amini.

Which brings me to the question: Where in the developmental history
of these concepts of hysteria and hysterical character does this new paper
by Baumbacher and Amini, "The Hysterical Personality Disorder: A
Proposed Clarification of a Diagnostic Dilemma," fit in? Clearly these
authors' philosophic bent and their scientific interest is in the direction of
increasing specification and delimitation of the concept of the hysterical
character and its pathology. Unlike the disposition of others (among
whom I include myself) to emphasize the permeabilities of definitional
borders and the crystallization of nodal constellations of attributes out of
continuities and spectra, Baumbacher and Amini choose to focus as
narrowly as possible on a particularized and delimited universe that they
choose to call "the hysterical personality disorder" and to describe it in
terms of its essential attributes that mark it off as clearly as possible from
all other related, neighboring groupings. As I have indicated, that they
make this separatist choice, emphasizing distinctions rather than linkages, is a matter of taste and not of science—at least in the present state of
knowledge of the art/science of the taxonomy of mental disorder. They
recognize this same point of choice when they say: "The decision to term
the difficulty that we will describe as the hysterical personality disorder is
to some extent an arbitrary one." They go on to say in confirmation of
their intent and philosophic thrust, "As suggested by the earlier discussion, there is at present *no one illness* to which this diagnostic label refers,
but rather a host of different illnesses. We think that careful differentiation should be made between these syndromes with *significantly differing
dynamic constellations* and that the terminology employed should lend clarity
not confusion to these distinctions" (italics mine).

Having embarked on this course, Baumbacher and Amini have, I think,
wisely decided to eschew phenomenology and behavior as their central
organizing principles and have opted rather for psychodynamic configuration, albeit weighted somewhat more to the elements of drive organization that they deem centrally determinative to the concept, the early
phallic stage and still preoedipal intrusive and possessive relationship of
the young child (of either sex) to the mother as primary love object within

the context of an essentially still dyadic and not yet triadic object world[4] and weighted proportionately somewhat less (though still significantly) to the considerations of the usually achieved concomitant levels of ego and superego development, including orientation to reality, coherence of self- and object representations, and integrations of ego-ideal and prohibiting superego. Their central point is that the little girl is characteristically not able to live up to the fantasied requirements of this phallically intrusive phase and must then come to terms with the consequent disappointment and narcissistic injury—"the failure of reality to support the fantasy that she could phallically love and possess her mother." Let me follow now with a more extended direct quotation from the authors on how this dilemma is said to be either successfully navigated or not, the latter outcome laying the essential groundwork for the evolution of the hysterical character:

> In normal development, the little girl relinquishes her libidinal phallic strivings toward her primary love object, her mother, and transfers her libidinal drives to her father and later to other males. With this shift, the little girl enters the positive oedipal phase in which a receptive mode of libidinal drive organization is substituted for the previous phallic one. While these events result in depression, in normal development this affect is tolerable and does not prevent the major shift of libidinal drives from the mother to the father.
>
> In the female patient who develops a hysterical personality disorder, however, the core dynamics and psychopathology result from the girl's inability to make this shift, and from the pathological organization of defenses that she uses to manage the unresolved issues of this stage. Factors that increase the girl's vulnerability to depression and to narcissistic injury [that is, stemming from the incompletenesses of resolutions of the tasks of earlier developmental phases] will make it more difficult for her to relinquish her phallic attachment to the primary love object, her mother. If she is either unusually strongly attracted to her mother or unusually fearful of her loss, she will be more vulnerable to the depression that accompanies this stage, and if the depression is too severe, the little girl will be unable to give up her phallic strivings toward her mother. Clinical observation has indicated that underlying oral needs are frequently present in the hysterical personality (Marmor 1953), and it is just the presence of such overly intense needs that would provide the pre-

4. Though these dynamics apply in large part at this stage to children of either sex, the authors focus on the vicissitudes of the drives in the little girl because those who emerge as hysterics are most typically female and because little boys (faced with difficulties not of absence but of inadequacy of their penises) do then undergo the classical different developmental vicissitudes determined by their gender relationships.

disposition to depression that complicates the solution of phallic
stage tasks.

To Baumbacher and Amini, it is this developmental dynamic and the
failure of its appropriate resolution that defines and circumscribes the
hysterical character formation, and in the interests of diagnostic clarity
they ask that all other formations stemming from failures at other
developmental stages with their other central developmental tasks should
be differently named and conceptualized: the oral hysterics of Marmor
and the hysteroids of Easser and Lesser and the third and fourth groups,
of the so-called good hysterics of Zetzel. It is certainly legitimate to do
this. One can hardly quarrel with the delineation of the central developmental dynamics in that cohering subgroup out of all the individuals upon
whom the hysterical mantle gets cast since the authors have articulated as
clearly as anyone what is classically agreed to be the basic drive and ego
and object relation organization of those "true" hysterics or "best" hysterics. And they have illustrated their formulation well with carefully
documented and very apposite case material.

The question, however, is really this: Does one gain more than one
loses by thus separating related groupings that in fact flow indis-
tinguishably into one another, since human beings do not come neatly in
pure typologies but in the myriad configurations that make no two
human beings exactly alike? And by highlighting one (I think artificially)
separate group of true or best hysterics as the only hysterics worthy of
the name, are not the rest cast into a darker penumbra, unnamed and
therefore with lessened delineation, much as shining an intense beam of
light into one small sector of darkness makes it harder to see what is
outside the beam of light and certainly harder as well to see the many
connected strands between what is illuminated and what is not. By this I
do not at all propose that we fall into the opposite and equally extreme
position that the authors warn against in their final sentence, "of blurring
meaningful distinctions and making everything the same as everything
else."

All of this, as I have already said, is a matter of scientific taste and
preference as to where one feels it most potentially rewarding to place
one's bets. Is the greater gain to be achieved by emphasizing connected-
nesses and continuities with gradually shifting nodal emphases or, conversely, by emphasizing separatenesses and precise clarity of boundaries?
On two other counts, however, I feel that Baumbacher and Amini can be
properly taken to task: in the one instance for having carried the thrust to
distinctness too far, and in the other instance for having unwittingly, at
least in one area, added to the kinds of diagnostic confusions they are

trying so hard to dispel. Where I feel that they have gone too far and have burdened the data with more requirement than can adequately be fulfilled is in the very brief section at the end of their paper on differential diagnosis. This arises not in their distinguishing between the true hysterical character (they call this group hysterical character disorder or synonymously, hysterical personality disorder) and what they call the borderline character (or the sick hysteric or the oral hysteric or the hysteroid) because this distinction is clear enough—and well enough delineated in all the literature that I quote in this review—certainly at the nodal points (even though I prefer to see the hystericalness that connects them all because I feel that it enhances both my understandings and my interventions in regard to the clinical flux that I see across the patients who come to my consulting room). Rather, it arises in the much more precious attempt to separate the hysterical character *disorder* (the group they have spent their paper characterizing) from another group for which they suggest the name, hysterical character *neurosis*.

This latter group are those who have (presumably reasonably successfully) navigated with presumed reasonable success the early phallic stage dyadic attachment to the mother as as the still primary love object, have in fact entered the second stage oedipal organization with its triangular constellation of (receptive) attachment to the father and rivalry with the mother but who, in the face of the neurotic oedipal conflict of that next developmental phase, avoid by regression "in both drive and ego organization to a preoedipal position that was previously successfully outgrown."[5] "Intensely hostile and competitive, maternally directed feelings thus are avoided by reestablishing the positive phallic attachment to [mother]." The authors' summary of this posited distinction is that: "For adult difficulties deriving from this condition, we would suggest the term hysterical character neurosis be applied. It differs from the hysterical personality disorder in that the underlying conflicts and ego organization are triadic oedipal ones, rather than dyadic, with only a secondary regression to a dyadic state." My own summation would be that here is an effort at a differentiation beyond what the clinical material (that we see *in vivo* in our consulting rooms) can characteristically bear.

Where I feel that Baumbacher and Amini have unwittingly added to the very confusions that they are working so vigorously to undo is in this very last act. Their nomenclatural distinction is made between stage one phallic-oedipal fixations, which they call hysterical character disorder, and stage two phallic-oedipal fixations (with symptomatic regressions to the earlier stage), which they call hysterical character neurosis. Their

5. Again, this discussion is in terms of the developmental dynamics of little girls.

reasoning in this is clear. They want to reserve the designation of neurosis for the higher level conflicts in individuals of fully consolidated ego organizations with unconscious conflict between the fully established psychic structures, that is, fully formed intrapsychic conflict, while they then use the designation, *disorder*, to characterize lower or earlier failures of developmental mastery where the drives are struggling within the context of less fully consolidated psychic structures. I won't at this point try to go into what I think would be the wholesale assaults upon almost our total nosology if this principle of nomenclature were to be applied across the whole spectrum of psychopathology. I would rather advance the viewpoint that not only are the two, the hysterical character disorder *and* neurosis—as they characterize them—not at all that readily distinguishable in clinical encounter but that both are aspects of the hysterical character neurosis. I prefer to reserve the rubric of disorder for the clear behavior disorders or impulse neuroses marked by socially or ego-dystonic, uncontrolled, if not totally uncontrollable, *behaviors*. At least from my perspective, greater overall diagnostic clarity and distinction resides in the direction of that kind of tripartite division of neurotic difficulties: the symptom, the character, and the impulse neuroses (or synonymously with the last, character *disorders*). Is this again all a matter of scientific taste and preference as to where one wants to place one's conceptual and definitional bets?

At this concluding point, one should ask, what is the outcome of all this, the article by Baumbacher and Amini proposing a "clarification of a diagnostic dilemma" and my critical response, proposing what? Alternate forms of clarification? Actually, the whole is indeed a two-part exercise in attempted clarification, succeeding together, to the extent that they have succeeded, in further clarifying where the conceptual as well as semantic issues of diagnosis and of clinical understanding are that require such continuing efforts at clarification, and failing together, to the extent that they have failed, out of the inherent complexities and grave limitations of current understandings in our field.

REFERENCES

Abraham, K. (1921). Contribution to a discussion on tic. In *Selected Papers of Karl Abraham*, pp. 323–325. New York: Basic Books, 1953.

——— (1924). A short study of the development of the libido, viewed in the light of mental disorders. In *Selected Papers of Karl Abraham,*; pp. 418–501. New York: Basic Books, 1953.

American Psychiatric Association (1968). *Diagnostic and Statistical Manual of Mental Disorders*, 2nd ed. (DSM II). Washington, D.C.

Easser, B., and Lesser, S. (1965). Hysterical personality: a re-evaluation. *Psychoanal Quarterly* 34:390–405.

Fenichel, O. (1945). *The Psychoanalytic Theory of Neurosis*. New York: Norton.

Freud, S. (1931). Libidinal types. *Standard Edition* 21:215–220.

Horowitz, M. (1977). (ed.) *Hysterical Personality.* New York: Jason Aronson.

Kernberg, O. (1967). Borderline personality organization. *Journal of the American Psychoanalytic Association* 15:641–685.

Lazare, A. (1971). The hysterical character in personality theory. *Archives of General Psychiatry* 25:131–137.

Marmor, J. (1953). Orality in the hysterical personality. *Journal of the American Psychoanalytic Association* 1:656–671.

Reich, W. (1933). Some circumscribed character forms. In *Character Analysis*, pp. 189–207. New York: Orgone Institute Press, 1949.

Shapiro, D. (1965). *Neurotic Styles.* New York: Basic Books.

Veith, I. (1965). *Hysteria: The History of a Disease.* Chicago: University of Chicago Press.

Wallerstein, R. (1967). Reconstruction and mastery in the transference psychosis. *Journal of the American Psychoanalytic Association* 15:551–583.

Zetzel, E. (1968). The so-called good hysteric. *International Journal of Psycho-Analysis* 49:256–260.

REPLY BY GORDON BAUMBACHER, M.D. and FARIBORZ AMINI, M.D.

We appreciate the thoughtful and comprehensive review, "Diagnosis Visited (and Revisited): The Case of Hysteria and the Hysterical Personality," by Robert Wallerstein, and the opportunity to reply to it. Wallerstein aptly summarizes the current embryonic state of psychiatric nomenclature with its ambiguities, methodological uncertainties, ill-defined boundaries, and lack of an overall conceptual organization. He illustrates these problems well in his summary of the literature on hysteria, hysterical phenomena, and the hysterical character, and his discussion sets our paper in relationship to these problems of nomenclature and to the problems of theory behind them.

Wallerstein contrasts our more delimited view of the hysterical personality with his own more general one which, as he states, emphasizes "the permeabilities of definitional borders, and the crystalization of nodal constellations of attributes out of continuities and spectra. . . ." He points out that the choice between the positions is one of taste not of science. With this we would agree, with one addition. To the criteria of taste we would add that of utility. It is not only fair but also necessary to ask how useful a theory is, in what way it is useful and to compare its utility with that of other theories so assessed. Wallerstein himself raises this consideration when he asks, "is the greater gain to be achieved by emphasizing connectedness and continuities with gradually shifting nodal emphasis or conversely by emphasizing separatenesses and precise clarity of boundaries?" As with any theory or hypothesis, we think the answer to the question lies in exploring the avenues raised by the approach which hopefully would include some prospective criteria for validation or invalidation of the original idea.

The view we present should generate further specific hypotheses which can be tested in the clinical treatment setting. For example, where Wallerstein takes us to task for drawing too sharp a distinction between the hysterical personality disorder and the hysterical character neurosis—a distinction which he feels the data will not support—we think that such a division can be made. It results from a more specific delineation of these disorders, and from it important treatment considerations result. In the hysterical personality disorder, defenses protect mainly against the powerful feelings that accompany an injured self-image and depression. We stress "mainly" because obviously other issues will be present as well, but without the same intensity. In the hysterical character neurosis, defenses, including defensive regression to a phallic stage organization, protect mainly against the emergence of oedipal fears—that is, fears of retaliation and punishment that result from competitive, triadic fantasies involving both libidinal and aggressive wishes. Of course, depression and narcissistic issues will be present, and in treatment cannot be ignored, but again they would not be expected to be the central treatment or transference issues. Stated in psychosexual terms, in the hysterical character neurosis, as opposed to the personality disorder, the issues are more those of penis greed than penis envy, and fears of retaliation (castration), that is, being penetrated and torn apart rather than of depression. Treatment interventions in the former diagnostic category would need to be directed more toward fears of aggressive, competitive wishes and fantasies and the concomittant libidinal wishes, while in the latter diagnostic group, interventions would need to be directed more toward increasing tolerance of depression.

We would hope that our approach would lead to understanding not only the differences but also the valid similarities among different diagnostic groups. In defining diagnostic categories as specifically as possible and in postulating explicit etiologies to the disorders in them, the theories may be tested in the clinical setting. For the diagnoses that prove valid, comparison and contrast between them would permit arrangements in a variety of series or continuums designed for particular purposes. The perspective of other sciences then may shed further illumination on those disorders at their interface with the societal and biological realms.

Expiation as a Defense

RUTH RIESENBERG MALCOLM

This paper presents a specific defense mechanism that leads not only to the stagnation of the analysis but also makes it difficult to terminate analysis. The predominance of what I call "expiation" demands continual punishment of the self and of internal objects in contrast with reparation. It is essential for the patient to maintain the immobilization of the analyst and of the analytic work. This defensive constellation aims at protecting the patient from the pain that comes from the guilt brought from the realization that his good and loved object is the same one that he hates and has attacked. Expiation is to be distinguished from the negative therapeutic reaction as well as from other problems in psychoanalysis. A case is presented. There is also a discussion of the relevant psychopathology and of the technical problems expiation poses, with particular attention to countertransference.

I wish to deal in this paper with a specific type of defense which organizes itself in the analysis into tight, closed, and rigid behavior that creates an impasse which may make continuation of analysis, as well as termination, impossible. I am referring to those patients who use expiatory behavior as a form of self-punishment and suffering, avoiding what for them is feared as even greater suffering and danger, namely, their perception of the damaged state of their internal objects—a perception indispensable for any real reparatory work.

The patients I wish to discuss feel their internal world to be populated by damaged or destroyed objects. They are afraid of being responsible for this destruction and feel helpless and hopeless to do anything about it. They have often reached the point in the analysis in which some of the persecutory anxiety and schizoid defenses have diminished, they appear more integrated, and they have experienced relief. They are on the verge of coming closer to realizing how they perceive the state of their loved internal objects. But here they experience a pain of such intensity that it quickly becomes persecutory. They fear this pain to be unendurable and this makes them turn away with hatred from analytical work.

Turning away is achieved by leaning towards masochistic behavior, which in turn serves the purpose of preventing the emergence of any awareness of their feelings of guilt. Also, being in pain seems to alleviate the guilt. They feel they are making expiation—that they are being incessantly punished for what they believe is the damage they have done. This punishment takes the place of what instead should be reparation, that is, restoration of internal objects that have been attacked in fantasy. Through reparation, a modification of the internal world is achieved; it becomes more benign and therefore growth can take place.

In most analyses we get momentary or temporary expiatory reactions. But in this paper I am describing situations in which the whole analysis is being turned by the patient into a continual failure for the analyst, with its aim to produce punishment. In "Mourning and Melancholia," Freud (1917) described a similar type of condition and he pointed to the links with introjection and identification. In "The Ego and the Id" (1923) he referred to the polarity of life and death instincts, and suggested that the negative therapeutic reaction was related to the death instinct.

In her classic paper about the negative therapeutic reaction, Joan Riviere (1936) used the recent discovery by Melanie Klein of the depressive position, and she emphasized the role of manic defenses, particularly ominipotence and omnipotent denial of psychic reality. Riviere especially pointed to the need to recognize the positive feelings of the patient, suggesting that what the patient most fears is that the process of improvement would lead to suicide or disintegration.

Klein, in her paper, "Envy and Gratitude" (1954), added to Riviere's formulations. The hatred aroused by admiration and appreciation of the analyst's good capacities (and the internal objects represented by him) increases the tendency toward a negative therapeutic reaction and, in turn, increases the unconscious feelings of guilt. In the same paper Klein also spoke of the problem created by "the stifling of feelings of love and corresponding intensification of hate, because it is less painful than to bear the guilt arising from the combination of love, guilt and hate."

I have referred specifically to some points in the literature on negative therapeutic reaction, since I consider them to be closely connected with the type of analytic problem I am trying to describe. Nevertheless, I believe that there are some differences between the patients that react with a negative therapeutic reaction and those in whom expiation predominates. These latter patients react to the analysis with something that could be thought of as their motto: "no change provides safety from pain and disaster." Organizing their whole behavior in the analysis so as to create a static situation that consists of their own suffering and misery plus the analyst's immobilization, they feel that this static condition encapsulates or puts their dread within limits; it contains it in such a way that they do not have to actually face it. Bion (1963) refers to a phenomenon that is similar to what I am trying to describe here. In what he calls *reverse perspective*, the patient also tries to achieve a static condition, but does it secretly. The immobilization of expiation is not a secret. He clings to a situation of nonanalysis in a setting that is nominally analysis, and feels that this state of affairs should last for life. The patient's awareness of being able to produce the halt in the analysis also brings feelings of triumph, often linked with sexual excitation. This erotic satisfaction contributes, in part, to the perpetuation of this type of behavior. The patient believes that he avoids or denies his helplessness through keeping things as they are. He projects his helpless self into the analyst, and also his own potential for perceiving guilt. Through the use of those projective identification mechanisms, he not only feels that he has rid himself of those feelings and problems, but also avoids the responsibility; for now the analyst is the guilty one.

These dynamics, the belief in having succeeded in ridding himself of the dread of madness or death, together with the sexual gratification, both masochistic as well as sadistic, place this problem close to the area of perversion. Here I think it worth remembering Glover's paper, "The Relation of Perversion Formation to Reality Sense" (1933), in which he describes sexual perversions as defenses used by the patient against psychosis.

Along with the patient's fear of harboring damaging and accusing objects, the patient also has a relation to an idealized omnipotent primary object. The emergence in the analysis of contact with this ideal object (experienced in the transference as the analyst), and the patient's own good feeling toward the ideal object, sometimes permits a breach in the otherwise steel-like enclosure, and proper analytic work can take place. But the patient will generally react to this achievement in two ways. On the one hand he will feel pleased, sometimes relieved, and will be more generous. This encouragement makes the patient feel that the analyst has been sufficiently reassured, so that the patient feels he has removed any danger of the analysis coming to an end. On the other hand, progress fosters the patient's hatred because he feels quickly exposed to those very conflicts that he is trying to avoid, and thus he will reinforce his attacks on the analyst's competence. From the analyst's point of view, this type of encapsulation and the occasional breakthrough that permits a more hopeful view of the patient's loving and constructive capacities, undoubtedly complicates the whole range of countertransference responses.

The combination of these factors makes the analysis go in circles. The patient's interest is to prevent it from progressing, since the so-called "analysis" is perceived by him as confining his problems to the analytic sessions without further consequence. The analyst feels that he can neither help the patient nor terminate the analysis, because the patient's expiatory behavior presents a continuous danger of suicide or disintegration. Both analyst and patient are locked in a difficult, even impossible, situation. Should termination be contemplated, *both* patient and analyst are faced with a sense of absolute irreparability.

CLINICAL PRESENTATION

Mr. K came to analysis primarily with the desire to become an analyst, but also to get some help with his problems, the most important of which he felt to be indecisiveness. He described himself as a "compulsive doubter" and "the most successful failure." In his first interview he reported a profuse symptomatology. His aspirations were bizarre and he was intensely arrogant and incoherent. He was also obviously in considerable pain. He showed some warmth as well as a fine sense of humor. It was very difficult for him to leave the interview.

Previous diagnostic consultations with different psychiatrists had resulted in apparently different diagnoses, all along lines of psychosis or borderline conditions. A previous analysis had lasted three years, and turned into a three-times-a-week psychotherapy. The analyst ended it abruptly in a way that seemed to me to be very traumatic, but Mr. K spoke of this with both glee and triumph.

Mr. K was the only son of what appeared to be a very disturbed family. He described his mother as an "extremely good person": "She always wanted the best for me." From the beginning he repeated that she had used influence to get him into exclusive schools and other circles. But she worked full-time, and actually took no personal care of him because of what appeared to be excessive anxiety. Mr. K nonetheless always spoke of her with reverence. The little time she spent with him was spoken of as not merely good, but nearly perfect. He used to say this in a flat voice with no feeling. He also said that she worried very much about him, fearing that he did not grow, put on sufficient weight as a baby, or was not pretty enough. In the preliminary interview he communicated something that would recur frequently in the analysis, namely, that he had never told her that he loved her and that she died before he thought of doing so, when he was seventeen.

The father emerged from the patient's description as hard and indifferent, not sharing much of his life with the family. The parents were separated for approximately two years when the patient was two years old. Mr. K's father had died before the analysis began.

During Mr. K's first year of life he was looked after by a quick succession of nurses. Then a permanent nanny arrived, who stayed until he grew up.

Despite many problems in infancy and childhood, Mr. K finished school, studied at a university, and obtained a degree and a professional qualification. He emigrated to Australia partly because he could not get along with his father and also because his mother used to tell him that this would be "the best place in the world to live." In Sydney lived his mother's sister of whom he said he was very fond. He went to Melbourne and there suffered his first major breakdown and had to return to England. He spoke of his coming back in many ways. He stressed how besieged he was by doubts about returning but also said that he needed "to make it up with father before it was too late."

But when he returned, trouble with his father started again and during a very violent row, his father told him to go to his room. He stayed there, literally, doing nothing for a year. Finally, he made himself leave the room, studied his father's craft, making jewelry, and in spite of disliking it, worked at it part-time.

Phase 1: The Psychotic Transference

I want to divide the account of his analysis into three phases. In the first, the patient was highly disturbed. He often had flights of ideas, made many puns, constantly mocked everything, and he sometimes hallucinated. In the first week of his analysis he spoke of a dream and an incident with his father, both of which would bear considerable importance in his treatment. The dream occurred during the night before his first analytic session with me. He was in a village inside a ditch, and had to climb up to get to freedom. He had in his hand a kind of miner's pick, but when he proceeded to make his way up, an enormous amount of rocks, earth and all kinds of heavy things fell on his head. To his surprise, the first association that came into his mind was a very thin girl whom he knew. At that time she was about to leave London to go south.

As can be imagined, my interpretations of this material were very tentative. They were related to his fear of what the analysis might do to him or what he might do in it. I also mentioned that he might be worried about my strength: would I have to run away? (My accent as well as my appearence suggests that I might be native to a southern Latin country.)

The incident he told me about had occurred when he was ten years old, and he related it with a mixture of worry, satisfaction, and hatred. His father asked him to go and buy cigars for him. The patient provocatively asked "Where?" His father, irritated, said "Stanmore", the location of the jewelry workshop, some forty-five minutes from home. Mr. K did exactly that, going to Stanmore and coming back some two hours later. He spontaneously volunteered an explanation. He said that he had always been very passive and wanted to be told what to do. He said this in a strange, very flat voice, sneering at the same time. He also said that the actual place where his father wanted him to go was in fact opposite their home, but the patient did not like the place. He thought it was frequented by prostitutes and he felt ill at ease there. He said that he had always hoped that his parents or grown-ups would guess how he felt.

At the time, I noted how immensely heavy Mr. K felt and how despairingly he experienced the approach of the analytic task. I also noted that I felt uncomfortable about the way he spoke of the incident with his father. I wondered how much he would use sadistic sexual acting out.

From the beginning of the analysis Mr. K reacted very intensely to weekend separations. After the first analytic holiday he came back in a severe state of depression.

In this phase, as in the following one, he often communicated concretely through action rather than verbally. He used to wear ragged clothes, especially a pair of old trousers, full of holes, as a way of showing me how impoverished, miserable, and broken he felt. He usually came in a long coat, several sizes too large for him, that had belonged to his father, and he kept emphasizing that it was "his dead father's coat." (When we started the treatment, his father had been dead for several years.) In the sessions, he moved around the room, sat on the floor, or stood immobile near the door. He often felt that I suffered from delusions.

In this first phase there emerged material that threw light on his early infancy. For one thing, we learned about his severe feeding problems. He often reacted to my interpretations by turning them into a meaningless mash which he would let ooze out in the form of fragmented sentences, words, and mere sounds. I learned in what way disintegrative processes were in operation and also that he had to get rid of its products very quickly. In response to my interpretation of this material, he told me that he had been informed that he had suffered a severe diarrhea during most of his first year of life or a bit longer, and that this drove his mother frantic. We then were able to link his behavior in the transference to experiences in his early infancy.

In the transference, I stood for all kinds of part or whole objects. There emerged with great clarity a division of me as a very powerful mother (or breast), that could give him anything if I so wished, and as a nurse, I could make him normal—be his analyst or make him an analyst, that is, somehow let him become me. Or else I was felt to be rigid, just giving him interpretations, keeping set times, a harsh nurse determined to feed and clean him. Occasionally I was a more intermediate figure: not too bright, quite insensitive, just wanting him "to adjust," the nanny who wanted him to be a well-behaved child.

In a paternal transference, he perceived me as stronger and more aggressive, ready to criticize. He had to win me to his side, conquer me, or fight me. All this was done in a highly erotized and teasing way; and it felt very homosexual.

In spite of the severity of pathology, genuine progress took place. Mr. K's relation to me changed and his material became more coherent. He started again to report dreams (which had stopped for quite some time); he developed a passion for them because their analysis brought him great relief, as well as convincing understanding. He stopped hallucinating.

Phase Two: Extreme Control

Together with these positive changes, new aspects began to appear in the sessions; it is those which I refer to as the second phase. Mr. K began to control me more and more. He produced two or three repetitive themes with the aim of proving that I could do nothing; at the same time, he really expected me to provide an answer that would solve his problems at a stroke. For example, he would ask me a question, generally practical and referring to an actual situation in his everyday life—for instance, whether he should post a letter. I was ordered to answer in one of four ways: yes or no, "I don't know," or "I cannot answer because it is again the psycho-analytic technique." It was irrelevant what I interpreted or if I actually answered as he demanded, because when I did so he proceeded to find a flaw in the answer. Whatever I said, or if I said nothing, it always drove him to recite the alphabet again and again, sometimes for the duration of several sessions.

I initially tried to deal with this development as ordinary material to be interpreted in the whole of the transference context. Since I could not reach him this way, I would begin my intervention with "I don't know," and try to explain the reason why I was in no position of knowing, and how the problem seemed to go further than the realm of the question and answer. I added that he might be very determined to get an "answer" from me but that I thought he also might perceive my interpretation differently. He would answer that all that was irrelevant since I had spoiled "his orders" by going beyond the sentence, "I don't know." He would ask why could I not just say, "I don't know," or why could I not just say "that it was against the technique." My attempts to remind him that he knew (from his own statements in previous sessions) that the technique was no more than a part of a process would be interrupted.

At some point I managed to get across to him (and I wish to remind the reader that most of the time he was monotonously reciting the alphabet) that his questioning me, together with his need to make me obey orders, seemed to suggest other questions that might feel upsetting to him, which probably felt too painful and were related to the way he was treating me. Therefore, by turning me into a mechanical answering machine he believed he could avoid those potential upsets. Sometimes his whole manner would show that he was touched by my words. But the hatred of having been touched and therefore losing successful control would increase his anxiety, driving him to intensify the monotonous recitations.

On the occasions in which I would just say, "I don't know," he might speak about something else, but then promptly repeat the original question. He would say he was not sure if my response was "the answer" or just a "catch." I tried as far as I could to point out both his controlling behavior and also the fears I thought were underlying this control. I remarked that the dread he might be experiencing made him fear that everything was a trick. I also attempted to link this fear of guilt with the sadistic satisfaction he was getting from his behavior, and how this in turn made it more difficult for him to get out of his psychological state.

Another theme, his complaints about his life and work, also applied to the analysis. Mr. K would say in a very tormented way: "I drill holes and fill them up with silver; that is all I do." He drilled into all my attempts to interpret and filled the sessions with repetitions of the alphabet. In turn, I often felt as if my mind were a sieve. I could remember very little from the sessions, but was preoccupied with what was going on in them. My mind was not functioning during sessions, but it did not wander. The reason for this, I believe, is that he had a powerful hold on me, probably through a minute type of projective identification. I remember an occasion in which I was very preoccupied by a problem of my own, and it came fleetingly into my mind during a session. Mr. K stopped saying whatever he was saying, and sat up in a panic.

This behavior lasted for many months. I think that due to all the effort, very slowly one could see a mixed response. He tried to harden himself even more against my interpretations. He even brought a tape recorder into the sessions with the explanation that he had no memory.

With this new development, I felt very uncomfortable, but I accepted the machine at first, because I knew that should I refuse it, the likelihood was that I would not be able to enforce my refusal. I also thought that should I succeed, it was very probable that Mr. K would perceive it as an increased success: I would be doing what he had been demanding all the time: "giving direct orders." With him, I kept my instructions to an absolute minimum; the analysis took place in the consulting room at set times and the door would be closed. With the rest of his actions, I tried to deal with them through analytic interpretations.

I felt that the tape recorder, moreover, showed two main things: his behavior was leaving him without a memory, that is, without a mind, and that he also had a desire to remember. I oriented my interpretations from this second aspect. I emphasized the pains and difficulties arising from his continually trying to put out of his mind almost everything by question-ing and, even more, monotonous chanting of the alphabet. There was some positive explicit acknowledgment from him in the midst of his acting in.

Together with the appearance of the recorder there was, at first, increased bizarre behavior, I think probably as a response to how he perceived my feelings. But in spite of some mockery, his desire to remember was taking first priority, to the point of his genuinely stating, "I did not want to lose what you were saying." His recitations diminished and an increase of violence in his associations came to the fore.

Once, upon entering the room, he looked with horror at the couch, stood very still, and asked me if there was a four-poster bed where the couch used to be. He said that he saw it. I will try to summarize the content of many weeks of work on this issue. The main associative theme was prostitution and a pub called "The Blind Beggar." During this time, news reports were following a trial that was taking place. A criminal gang that used to terrorize the East End of London was being tried. It had just come to light that the gang's means for getting their objectives was torture. The gang operated from the Blind Beggar pub.

As I have mentioned before, Mr. K's main mode of communication was through actions or tone of voice. At this point I felt, from the way he was speaking, that something very dangerous was going on, and for the first time in this analysis I actually became frightened for my safety. I used my fears as an orientation of where to put the emphasis in the interpreta-tions. (I also took some practical measures of protection, such as having a nurse in the flat who would come should I ring an electric bell near my chair.) The content of the interpretations pointed mainly towards the operation of a torturing gang inside himself, directed against both me and the self who wanted "to remember," to learn, and to know so that he could feel better. This cruelty in him was so terrifying that he felt we had to submit to it to prevent further and worse consequences. I linked it to blindness—so as not to get insight, not to know, since the guilt of seeing what was going on was threatening the most intense pain. In that way, he felt better to be a beggar, to get nothing, rather than the awareness of this awful sight. I also, very slowly, emphasized that now, in spite of the torturing terror, he was now more able to look at what was going on in his mind. He could now bring it more into the open, speak about it and, though half-heartedly, try to remember the meaning it had for him. The half-heartedness came from the question: Who was remembering? himself? or a machine without responsibility?

While working in this area, my fears progressively diminished and I dispensed with the nurse. Mr. K made repetitive attempts to increase and harden his control, while at the same time his cruelty towards me became more vicious. Nevertheless, I felt that he could keep an increasingly continuous contact, mainly through interpretations that he could take and which allowed for an alternation between cruelty and genuine understanding. This allowed him to attempt to control the cruel behavior and he tried to work with me. Those attempts, however slight and short-lasting, had a real constructive quality, and marked changes occurred in the sessions. The recitation disappeared almost totally. He began again to bring dreams and work at them. Glimpses of changes in his external life emerged. He seemed less isolated, spoke about people, and resumed his original profession part-time (which he liked better than jewelry and which he had stopped practicing because of excessive anxiety). His relation to a girlfriend seemed to become less bizarre.

It seems to me that many factors had played a part in producing those modifications (I am speaking of work done over a period of years). The decrease of the need of such a sadistic control was partly due to his perceiving me as a strong analyst and thus able to contain his "horrors" without being completely overwhelmed by his anxieties and therefore more able to present them back to him (reintrojection) in a modified way (Bion 1962). He experienced gratitude and a desire to make good, which in turn brought new incentives towards further understanding which, in small quantities, could be used by him.

In other words, through the increase of introjective processes a more benign relationship was setting in which allowed for the possibility of structural modifications. His superego (internal objects and an internal analyst) became less cruel and punitive. His ego as well became stronger and therefore much less in need of resorting to extreme modes of defense. The following vignette might bring a clearer feeling of what I am trying to say. In one session, he said rather angrily that I was like one of the nurses he had as a baby: "She must have been a brutal beast." He had been told that she even sat him on top of a wardrobe to get him to eat. I said that this could be taken as beastly, but that I also wondered if he might not be saying, however angry it made him, that he recognized my efforts as like that of the nurses in childhood: not letting him starve or go hungry. I added that we might have been trying to get the baby in him to take something in, since food, mental food, is important for life and growth. He was moved by this and felt thankful. He said, "I have to give it to you, you do try and if something does not work you try something else, in spite of me being so beastly to you. Either you are not too frightened or you still go on in spite or whatever."

This improvement in the analysis lasted for some time, after which I began again to feel myself progressively more limited in my thinking (this time it felt differently—more oppressive) and in my capacity to reach him with my interpretations. A new repetitive theme started to establish itself in the material. He began to produce endless variations of one sentence: "I made a mistake"; "A mistake happened;" "It is all because of a mistake." The mistake to which he referred was that he came back to England instead of staying in the ideal place, Australia. As one may imagine, I tried to deal with this material from many angles—all to no avail; and then I realized that I was totally stuck. We were in what I call the third phase.

Phase Three: Stagnation

With phase three, Mr. K had reached the most difficult point in his analysis, for along with the improvement, feelings of guilt became paramount. However difficult the previous two phases were, for the patient this last one appeared to be insurmountable.

The themes were very repetitive, circling mainly around the same contents. For example, Mr. K would walk into the room, not looking at me. Once on the couch, instead of speaking directly, he would say something like, "Shall I talk to you or not?" Or he would recite a long rigmarole, always the same, which amounted to asking me whether he should write for an application to the Institute of Psycho-Analysis.

In spite of the immense repetitiveness of these sentences, the feeling they conveyed to me was far from being always the same. Sometimes it seemed to be a plea to give him a helping hand that would allow him to start. Sometimes he did accept the help and began to speak directly about the issues that were in his mind. But of course this did not always happen. There were very subtle nuances in how he said things that did allow me to sense different things.

On other occasions, he sounded more excited and whatever I said then was discarded. If I said nothing, this was taken as a hostile provocation or as proof that I had been put out of action. When I did speak, be it an interpretation or a description, Mr. K would meet it with great contempt. He would tear it to pieces and the "mistake" was brought to the fore, generally in a very plaintive, monotonous, nasal tone, immediately followed by a superior attitude to prove that, since the mistake took place twenty years ago, it was of no use for either of us to try to understand anything at all.

During this period, Mr. K suffered intensely, but according to him, I also had to suffer, so he had to "drill it into me." One of his fears was that otherwise I would not know how he felt. He again resorted to the use of massive projective methods and concrete behavior. Also he believed that this was sexually stimulating for me, that it must be exciting, "kept me on my toes," particularly if he could believe that he was hurting me. (My main feelings were very painful, and a couple of times I did actually get a very short-lasting, sharp stomach pain. He perceived the whole situation as turning into a flirtation, a sexual game.)

He also had the conviction that I had the power to put things right, but, of course, not through analysis. For him this meant putting the clock back twenty years, and turning him into an analyst. He believed firmly that a word of mine would make him accepted into the Institute of Psycho-Analysis. He felt that I was very cruel not to do this, and it stimulated him to further cruelty to prove how useless I was.

Through very careful listening to his way of talking, rather than its content, since what he said was usually very much the same, I could sense a possibility of making contact with his anxiety. It is possible that I must have felt him more receptive and myself less tied up. I tried to do something that I had done before, to produce just descriptive summaries. Generally, as also in most of my interpretations, I would start from his state of pain, his desire to draw me into attacking him, and therefore become actively "the punisher." On other occasions I could sense from the way he was speaking that he was actually aware of thinking something else—or was preoccupied by something—and I would try to point this out to him. He would show surprise at my noticing it, and would allow associations to flow and would listen to interpretations. For example, one day he was reciting his litany: "Oh! that terrible mistake, why, why did I do it?" I felt that in spite of his usual monotonous voice, which he called "tuned-down-flat," he was agitated. I also felt myself becoming more alert. I ventured a comment in which in fact I said that I thought that he was agitated, and that it might be that this monotonous litany might also refer to something else. He was startled, and started speaking about having been very worried because of something he said to a colleague, that he thought might have been very unkind.

This instance, as well as some others, allowed for some analytic work to take place. He could then take in some understanding about his unkindness to me—originally the nurse—and the fear it gave him to look at it. We also worked on the fact that the "not looking" made him feel that he lived *ad aeternum* in "a mistake." He became more depressed, his whole demeanor changed, and he would appear very worried. During these times he shrank from any interpretation of his positive qualities as a person, since this seemed to increase feelings of guilt as well as fears about his ability to sustain his good qualities. For example, if I would refer to his concern about someone at work, he would react with a mixture of pleasure and fear—fear that would often lead him to mock me and himself or try to prove the contrary. "Me, doing something good! You must suffer from excessive imagination!"

I believe that "the mistake" was also an attempt at encapsulation, though of course not exclusively that. But a mistake, just one, however badly it made him feel, also allowed him not to have to look at many things, "many so-called mistakes," in his behavior towards his objects. Furthermore, the mistake consisted in leaving the land felt ideal by his mother. He had behaved very nastily to many people in Australia; he did break down; he "was expelled from Paradise."

At other times, Mr. K was in a more receptive and sad frame of mind. He would puzzle about why he behaved towards me as he did. He would question whether he was a pervert. These questions were sometimes mocking, but more often they were serious and concerned. On occasion my interpretations were oriented toward how much he worried about this. In spite of trying to laugh it off or reassure himself that I was a masochist and that was the reason I put up with him, he had doubts. He felt that his behavior was not only hard on me but incomprehensible to him, that just to say that he was "a pervert" did not mean much, and that he needed to look into this cruel, grueling behavior that he called "perversion." I sometimes also pointed out to him how much he wanted me to call him a pervert; the word would then acquire a moralistic meaning and he could feel me as accusing and punishing. In other words, through projective identification, I would be the punisher, and he thought that then he could avoid his own anxieties. When I managed to get this across to him and he did not feel me punitive, he experienced intense pain that drove him into panic, which in turn prompted him to intensify the cruelty of his behavior by a total grinding of my interpretations, rendering everything—that is, what I had said and his own understanding—meaningless.

If he did not succeed in this, and my words had some impact on him, he would force himself to sleep in the session in order to cut off all contact. He would also force himself into sleep when he came with the desire to tell me something he felt important. This felt too dangerous to him.

One of my greatest difficulties with this patient was to avoid being too repetitive, and to try to be alert to any minimal change in his way of speaking or inflections that could be used for either a new approach or for a new way of addressing him.

I also felt more and more under internal pressure. The idea of the scarcity of time kept creeping into my mind. I often found myself thinking that "I had to do something," or it would become "too late." "I had to think of something." I think that I might have contributed to his own fears by "trying too hard," until I realized and became clearer about the projections into me of feelings of irreparability. I could then orient my interpretations, starting from my feelings of pressure and his feelings about time passing. (He spoke often about this, but I do not think that my reactions were due to actual, external reality.) I became more watchful so as not to overinterpret, and tried to increase my containment of the situation for longer stretches of time. During the whole analysis I had let him talk or act at length, but I felt at this point, maybe not sufficiently, that he needed even a longer time. In spite of his intense suffering he needed me to wait and wait, and only then to interpret. This projective identification was aimed at testing whether I could endure him without going out of my mind. But it required a careful balance, since if waiting was perceived just "a fraction too long," it also was a proof that my mind was out of action.

In spite of all these difficulties, he managed to convey something that made me feel slightly hopeful, and also very sorry for him. After a period in which the balance between a total paralysis of the analysis and some more sensitive understanding was tipped a bit towards the latter, Mr. K became very depressed. His external life deteriorated. He complained often that he could not cope any longer and he interrupted analysis for some time. Guilt became very prominent.

He warned about the possibility of his stopping, several weeks before he actually did so. I think that the idea might have been in his mind for a longer time, considering the intense pressure I kept experiencing of "having to do something."

He approached the subject of stopping the analysis in two ways: First, he said he had no money, that he was spending more than he was earning, and he could not afford it. Of course, I think what he could not afford were his depressive feelings. Second, he just had to stop. His explanations came out so muddled that I cannot reproduce them here. His language was almost incomprehensible. He moved as someone attacked by most intense pains that could not be described in words. He acted as if under a tormenting force that dragged him away from me. He could not "stand coming to analysis." I think I was then felt by him as an internal analyst (externally he could be more warm and friendly to me) pulling him to the struggles between love and hate, life or death. He maintained that he could not stand this, that he had more to lose than to gain, much like a baby who, as soon as it allows itself to be fed, gets bouts of colic and diarrhea. Mostly those feelings were projected into me—therefore, the conviction that stopping would bring relief and possibly freedom.

He broke away from analysis, kept telephone contact with me, and eventually asked to come back. During the interruption, he had pulled himself together. He had started working full-time. He felt triumphant and hypomanic. He felt that he had cured himself in the same way, whatever that was, that he had got himself out of the room in his father's house. He also reacted triumphantly to my taking him back.

Why did he come back? And why did I take him back? It soon appeared that the flight into so-called "health" couldn't be maintained and that he was in panicky fear of collapsing, of becoming very depressed and of falling to pieces. He acknowledged only some of this when he asked to be taken back, but he did agree that now he was not coming for analytical training but as a patient in need of treatment.

My reasons for taking him back into analysis were mixed. I was aware of the dangers of not doing so. But I think it was predominantly his capacity to stimulate hope in me about making some fundamental change, as well as the projection into me of the need to do something. Looking back, I think I felt trapped in the situation which I described at the beginning of this paper, which is what makes it impossible to terminate an analysis. I think that I, as well as he, found it impossible to face the idea that he might be beyond repair. Though I was doubtful about the wisdom of taking him back, I discussed it with a colleague; I think I was more inclined to cling to hope.

I would like for a moment to consider some aspects of what I have been saying about this patient.

I think Mr. K had achieved a relationship to an object, a whole object, but this relationship was never firmly established and developed. It is my opinion that his tendency to idealization when he was an infant was expressed in multiple associations and reactions to interpretations. "Mother was extraordinarily good," "kind to a superhuman degree, she rushed from her death bed to take a gift to a charitable society." In the analysis, when something really did satisfy him he used to have a very strange, blissful smile or he would praise an interpretation or my capacity of making it, in a way that had no basis at all, either in what I did or said. For instance, when I once made an ordinary, pedestrian interpretation, not new, but to which he had not listened before, he said, with a kind of radiance, "You are Shakespeare!"

The idealization, a normal factor in any infant development, was probably accentuated in Mr. K by constitutional weakness. The split was between the very bad mother (breast) and the extremely good mother as expressed in his analytic material. This split was much stronger than in ordinary patients and, I think, probably was also reinforced by his mother.

Not only could she not contain his anxieties but projected her own anxieties into the child and needed continuous reassurance from him. She was always worried that he might not be well and dragged him from doctor to doctor. This was to the intense annoyance of the patient's father, who found no sign of things going badly and contrary to the view of the pediatricians. He had also been told that, when little, as soon as he and mother were together, he laughed and made all kinds of "cute things for her." Whatever he told me about things that went on at home with his mother, some of which sounded either harsh or bizarre, there was never a note of criticism for her. Also, there was never any praise for a nurse or nanny,

In the analysis, when he felt me as the ideal mother, he invested me with omnipotent powers. I could turn him into someone else: a very successful analyst. I think that as an ideal mother I was to get him right inside me, through his being fused with me, becoming me. I was the mother who got him into "exclusive places" (the only child). He also felt compelled to tell me ever so often how intelligent I was or how my interpretations sounded poetic—often when these remarks were completely alien to the general feelings he was having at the moment.

The deep splitting between the ideal mother and the bad persecuting nurses and the difficulty of bringing those aspects closer together was, I think, also influenced by another factor. It is my impression that as soon as he would get close to mother physically he became very excited. This excitement seems to have spoilt the contact, confusing him as to what was the quality of the object he was in contact with.

This confusion was seen in ample transference manifestations; deeply hostile as well as friendly actions were so intermingled by excitement, that it was often impossible to discern what was going on. It required a very lengthy, patient, and minute observation while holding the situation.

This extreme idealization of his mother made it much more difficult for him to work through guilt. Since his perception of mother was of a perfect object, and therefore any damage to it made the guilt enormous. And he felt helpless to repair the damage unless he himself was omnipotently perfect.

The conjunction of these factors made his capacity to bear pain, which was probably constitutionally limited, almost nonexistent. Therefore, guilt was perceived as a horrible experience and had to be avoided at all costs.

Finally, the paralyzing of the analyst, together with the avoidance of guilt, seemed to express a passive early experience of an inadequate external object. His reliving this in the analysis appeared to have the aim of communicating the experience of a passive helpless mother; but, at the same time this communication was turned into something pleasurable in itself. This erotization, which in the analysis appears so perverse, may have stemmed from an early experience, probably perceived as very confusing by the child, in which he felt that if he could act sexually, he would enliven the object and make it less anxious. I think this explains, at least partially, his conviction that somewhere there was some pleasure for me in all this.

Once Mr. K was back in analysis, after the short period at the beginning in which he was hypomanic, he made a genuine effort to work in the analytic sessions. But soon he relapsed into the ways I have previously described, this time in a worse form. He sometimes reported dreams literally in only the last one or two minutes of the session. They were often of concern to me and contained elements indicating potential suicidal danger. When I tried to refer to them the following day, Mr. K would not let me talk, he would go to sleep, and so on.

Two dreams were the last ones he reported before a complete paralysis took over. Unusually early in the session, looking very depressed, he reported the following.

"I was walking through a very dangerous path, probably mined, full of barbed wire. It was surrounded by police, just standing there. It was in Connaught Square and I felt that if I managed to walk through, I would be free." This last remark was painfully sincere. Then his tone changed. He seemed to force himself to mock me. He said, "Well, we lived right next to that place. Nanny used to take me there for walks. All right, come on. What can you make out of this?"

I pointed out that perhaps Connaught Square might also refer to something else. To my surprise, this silenced him and after some thought he reported that when watching TV the previous night, he saw a program about the seige in Connaught Square. The provisionals of the IRA were holding a couple as prisoners in a flat. He added that in the dream, he did reach the other side and was safe. He looked very subdued.

My interpretation was that he seemed to be suffering a severe conflict that had been with him since childhood. He knew he had to go through something very difficult to reach safety and real freedom. These difficulties felt horrible to him, both internally and externally. If he attempted to walk, he feared that he would be torn into pieces (the wire), this probably having to do with separation from his objects, both me and the original one. His insides would explode like the mines. It is striking that no helping hand existed and so he surrendered to an aspect of himself that ordered him to freeze everything, including the transactions between the analytical couple. There is a connection here to the imprisoned couple in the flat.

The patient was extremely quiet. After a moment he went on to say that he had "a bit of a dream" following the previous one and with the same theme. He described it as follows: "I want to reach freedom and safety. To do so I have to dig a tunnel and go through it. While I am digging it, I see the gravel and rubbish piling up into a terrible mess that makes me feel that I will never be able to clear it up." He had awakened abruptly at 3:00 A.M., feeling extremely depressed. After this description he complained about becoming increasingly slow in whatever he did. He could not function.

This session was drawing to an end. I tried in my interpretation to link the two dreams. I said that if he functioned in the analysis and he used me properly, he would see such a mess that he feels hopeless to put it right. But that he also felt me to be helpless, as somebody held in a seige, paralyzed like the policemen, paralyzed by his behavior in the previous sessions. It is his perception of me as being helpless that added to his hopelessness. If I was allowed to help him, and also, if he was aware of the mess, then both of us would have to clean it up. He felt very badly about it—so badly that he became panic-stricken with the fear that he would not be able to bear it. So he had to stop everything, even the dream by waking himself. He left the session looking extremely depressed. The next session he slept the entire time. I tried to reach him by reminding him of the similarity between the dream he told last session and the one he dreamed at the very beginning of his analysis. He jerked, opened his eyes, and went back to sleep. I don't know how much he had listened, but I think that he heard something.

I waited. I tried now to link both dreams to the anecdote he also told in his first session (both of those memories from that first session came suddenly and spontaneously into my mind).

I pointed out that his fears of the consequences of his provocative and stubborn behavior made him not only feel awful but also made him perceive me as an internal father, impotent to help him with the gravel. So he had to shut himself in by going to sleep. Again he jerked opened his eyes, closed them, and started a rythmical breathing so as to induce sleep.

He slept the entire time as well as in many subsequent sessions. It was impossible to reestablish any contact with him until he could completely resume the old pattern of repetitiveness which made the analysis static.

I want to end this clinical presentation with these dreams, which I consider to be very revealing, because they express his hopelessness as well as his determination to paralyze and maintain the seige. As a result of his own determined effort, he returned to his usual mode of stultifying behavior. I was totally paralyzed, while he suffered, complained, and demanded, as an immediate omnipotent cure, that I should make him into an analyst.

The analysis went on in this manner for many months. It became progressively impossible to reach him. By now I was faced with a decision. Was it advisable to go on in a situation in which I was no more than a guardian-nursemaid or a perverse sexual partner? This, of course, in addition to its uselessness, increases the patient's guilt. Or does the analyst have to take steps to end the treatment, facing the consequences this may have?

I finally decided in favor of ending the analysis. I waited for some time before actually telling him, in order to see how this decision might influence my work with the patient. I felt freer, but things did not change at all.

I gave the patient slightly less than a term of notice (approximately two months, a considerably shorter time than is my usual practice). I decided on this shorter time to give him a chance to do some work toward termination but also to not make the termination time so distant that my announcement might appear to him as more threat than fact. Also, in my wording of the announcement I did not leave open the possibility of continuing with me.

DISCUSSION

I want to limit my discussion to four main points extracted from the vast range of problems that a patient such as the one I have spoken about presents: (a) specific difficulties in the contemplation of terminating an analysis with this type of patient; (b) some comments on the problem of expiation; (c) the impingement of this type of psychopathology on the analyst's emotional responses; and (d) some considerations about technique.

Early in the paper I mentioned that from the patient's point of view, stopping the analysis carries serious dangers of suicide or disintegration. As many authors have already pointed out, this danger underlies many of the problems that bring about a negative therapeutic reaction. I think that the specificity of suicidal danger in an expiatory defensive constellation consists in the patient's carrying his expiation to the last consequences, for himself as well as for his internal objects. These patients will reach the climax of suffering by dying, which is what they fear most. The other specific causation in this syndrome is that they disintegrate when they do not have an external container, in which to encapsulate, *ad eternum*, the problems. Those problems, when having to be kept in themselves, drive them to defensive fragmentation, which may end in a permanent state of disintegration.

Riviere (1936) said that what the patient fears most, should he make contact with his inner world, is suicide and disintegration. It is my belief that for the type of patient presented, it is the analyst who actually fears those two possible outcomes much more than the patient himself. This fear in the analyst, conscious or unconscious, creates a state of anxiety closely linked with guilt, which I think in turn is stimulated and increased by the patient's projective identifications.

My experience, both in directly treating patients as well as in supervising colleagues, has shown me that the sense of failure, the incapacity to effect reparation with these patients, makes the analyst react in an anxious way. I do not mean acute anxiety, which is easier to detect and therefore to attempt to understand, but a kind of diffuse anxious state that expresses itself in a "pressure to help to alleviate pain." This may explain the sometimes overextended length of the treatment, when the same analyst, with other patients, could have concluded either to interrupt or to suggest a change of therapist, with more clarity of judgment. He will experience the usual pain and difficulty but without the agonizing feeling that "one has to go on" or that the patient cannot be abandoned. I have seen the same type of response in different analysts with very different personalities, as well as some with different analytic theoretical backgrounds.

In dealing with this kind of problem, and especially in treating Mr. K, I often asked myself if the difficulty was something specific to the patient's mental make-up or whether it was due to something shared by the analysts that treat those patients. I do not think I can answer the question with any accuracy. My observations incline me to think that the reactions of the analyst are mainly caused by the specific problems of the patients, especially their use of projective identification. But I am also led to suspect, with not enough evidence at present to substantiate, that there may be a common factor in the therapists' reactions, probably related to their personal modes of dealing with depressive anxieties.

In relation to the psychopathology of "expiation," one aspect deserves emphasis. I have spoken of this expiatory defense as a perverse organization, or even a perversion. I have mentioned the frequent use of erotized and excited manifestations in the analytic relationship. What I have not spoken about is my belief that what is sexualized is "the pain" itself. I do not mean the suffering, which I think can be more easily deduced from the expiatory behavior and is a common character in masochistic pathology. What I mean is that the perception of any contact—physical at first in early infancy and mental later on—is perceived as painful. This pain is immediately sexualized. This sexualization of very elemental units of pain serves to facilitate a pervasive expanding of generalized erotization. How does this take place? I do not think I can give an answer at this point. I can only state that in my observation it does take place and it could be of interest to find out why.

During the exposition of Mr. K's analysis and of the problems that arose in it, I mentioned many examples of countertransference reactions, feelings, or acting out. In explaining the difficulties in terminating such an analysis, I expanded on some specific countertransference responses. I want to end the subject of countertransference by mentioning what I think was my greatest block in perception. This was not Mr. K's sadomasochistic behavior, but the fact just mentioned, namely, that most early contacts were perceived as painful, and this pain was immediately turned into sexual experience. When finally I could see this, my first reaction was a mixture of dismay and disgust. A colleague from another country, whom I supervised in the treatment of a similar patient, also went through the same difficulties and reactions. I wonder if this could express such a twist in the relation to the object that the predominance of destructive impulses—be they reactional or primary—is so intense that it becomes almost indigestible for the analyst.

While I realize that my comments on this last point are not sufficiently illustrated in the material I presented, they are very difficult to describe in an account of sessions. However speculative, they are worth consideration.

To finish, I want to make a brief reference to my technique. The patient's behavior in the consulting room at most times was very bizarre, to say the least. Still, I consider that what was going on was a classical analysis, inasmuch as my method did not deviate from the ordinary analytic technique. The patient behaved as did some psychotics and children that I have had in analysis. I took his behavior as analytic communications which I tried to understand and interpret in the framework of the transference relationship. My interpretations, whenever possible, were guided by what I felt to be the predominant anxiety. I did not interpret symbolic contents, but I worded my interpretations in such a way as to deal with what I believed to be preconscious expressions of his defenses, as well as of contents which I hoped would lead to my understanding of genetic explanations.

The idea of introducing what Eissler (1953) has called parameters crossed my mind several times. I concluded that such an action would only be a way of bypassing what I felt most difficult to bear. In reflecting on the patient's possible reaction to the introduction of parameters, I became convinced that they would not only be unhelpful but actually damaging, since they might make him perceive my behavior as an expression of my having been destroyed analytically. I also thought that it could increase his anxiety as well as his feelings of triumph. In fact, I hold the view that extra-analytic interventions are in no case of any use. In an analysis, if there is any chance of helping a patient it is only by analyzing (Riesenberg 1971).

As to whether patients with expiatory behavior can be helped, I do not have an answer. From my limited experience, I suggest that better results are possible in patients whose expiatory organization is not so impenetrable that it both prevents the analysis from continuing and also makes the analyst feel that it cannot be terminated.

REFERENCES

Bion, W. (1963). *Elements of Psycho-Analysis.* In W. Bion, *Seven Servants.* New York, Jason Aronson, 1977.

Eissler, K. R. (1953). The effect of the structure of the ego on psychoanalytic technique. *Journal of the American Psychoanalytic Association* 1:4-143.

Freud, S. (1917). Mourning and melancholia. *Standard Edition* 14:237-258.

——— (1923). The ego and the id. *Standard Edition* 19:3-59.

Glover, E. (1933). The relation of perversion formation to the development of reality sense. *International Journal of Psycho-Analysis* 14:486-504.

Klein, M. (1954). Envy and gratitude. In *Envy and Gratitude and Other Works*, pp. 176-235. London: Hogarth Press, 1957.

Riesenberg, R. (1971). *Das Werke von Melanie Klein.* In *Die Psychologie Des 20. Jahraunderts.* Zurich: Kindler Verlag.

Riviere, J. (1936). A contribution to the analysis of the negative therapeutic reaction. *International Journal of Psycho-Analysis* 17:304-320.

Segal, H. (1967). The curative factors of psycho-analysis. *International Journal of Psycho-Analysis* 43:212-217.

——— Melanie Klein's technique. *Psycho-Analytic Forum* 2:197-211.

A Note on Expiation as a Defense

BETTY JOSEPH

A discussion of "Expiation as a Defense," by Ruth Riesenberg Malcolm.

There are two points on which I particularly want to comment in connection with Mrs. Riesenberg Malcolm's paper. First, there is the case material itself and second, some aspects of the nature of the patient's suffering—his expiation—and its connection with perversion.

Such a case in analysis poses extraordinary difficulty and the need, well exemplified by the writer, not only for endless patience and resilience but for watchfulness of countertransference, since it is constantly played upon by such a patient, so that "acting" in the transference becomes central to one's understanding.

The area, however, that I should really like to pinpoint is the relationship of the type of defensive organization, indicated by Mrs. Riesenberg Malcolm, to perversion. She describes how the encapsulation "places this problem close to the area of perversion." Increasingly, we must see the ubiquity of perversion as a fundamental problem. We must be aware of the importance of this problem as a real sexual perversion, lived out as such, at one end of the spectrum and as a characterological perversion at the other end of the spectrum. What we seem to be up against is a particular delicate type of balance, indicated by the writer, between the defensive use of the perverse sadomasochistic tormenting behavior and the open sadistic pleasure in cruelty and domination—the latter being linked with a delight in a negative therapeutic reaction. It is my experience that in many of these patients the emotion that is particularly unbearable, and which helps to mobilize the patient's defensive organization, is guilt. These patients seem to show a particular way of protecting the self from guilt and inner self-reproach, that is, by taking over the role of the reproacher as well as living out the reproached self and thus swinging into a sadomasochistic circle: exciting, endless, and untouchable. One of the tasks, then, for the analyst is to distinguish between genuine self-reproach, where the patient wants to understand what has gone wrong, and beating-the-self self-reproach, where the patient wants the analyst to collude with him in the beating. One of the many troubles with these patients is that they do not dare to seek real understanding because understanding brings guilt. This problem, to my mind, needs most sensitive handling by the analyst because he has to tease out the causes for the guilt but work in such a way that he does not seem to increase it. He must also never lose sight of the tormenting that is going on toward the analyst, internal and external, and the resulting vicious circle.

I am interested in many other aspects of these perverse personality organizations, in particular, reparation. These patients despair that they cannot sufficiently make good for all the damage that they do but, on the other hand, they perversely mock themselves at their constructive and hopeful or helpful behavior, trying to enlist the analyst in not taking seriously their own positive behavior. But it is not, as Mrs. Riesenberg Malcolm points out, only reparation that is undermined but the development of warmth and real object relations of a positive kind. I am reminded of a dream that a perverse patient told me after many years of analysis, when he had made a great deal of progress. He was puzzled by an element in the dream in which an evil-seeming man turned and shot at a black girl. He could not think of what the black girl was doing in his dream. He only knew one or two such women—one, he reminded me, was called Hope X. It is indeed the destruction of their own hope that becomes so striking as these patients progress. Because hope brings them closer to an object which they have been avoiding and also to many of the early problems that they have been keeping at bay by their omnipotence, their cruelty, and their destructiveness, they prefer not to take the risk of hoping. Nor do they wish to allow hope for long in the analyst! Mrs. Malcolm's patient seems to have had little or no hope that he could recover. She feels that he fears too greatly his own and his analyst's helplessness and the unbearable emotions that it arouses. I find her description of many of the points that her patient raises of great importance in cases where actual or character perversions are predominant but where hope is more available even though it will again and again be destroyed.

I suspect that this is an area of psychoanalysis that is being opened up considerably at the present time and will continue to be, as we struggle to get a better understanding of the particular type of personality organization of such patients and the precarious balance that they are managing to maintain: avoiding going forward towards better object relationships and yet avoiding falling too far backward toward disintegration and actual psychosis.

Interminably a Patient

EDNA O'SHAUGHNESSY

A discussion of "Expiation as a Defense," by Ruth Riesenberg Malcolm.

As the clinical record shows, the analysis of Mr. K was conducted by Mrs. Riesenberg Malcolm with courage and persistence, ending painfully when still very ill, Mr. K could no longer use it beneficially. The author's main purpose in reporting the case was to focus on the handicapping effect of a particular type of masochistic defense which she names "expiation." She shows, too, how Mr. K's mode of functioning makes termination hazardous, since his defenses lead either to disintegration or to suicide. I think her paper throws light also on another problem, since there is another possible outcome for him; if Mr. K is neither to deteriorate nor to become suicidal, he must perpetually be, if not Mrs. Riesenberg Malcolm's patient, then somebody else's. It is this contingency that I should like briefly to discuss.

Mr. K, and patients like him, must of necessity continue to depend on therapeutic care because of the specific direction and disposition of *their activity and passivity.* Mr. K is actively destructive and sadistic but only passively connected to help and care. His ego is in alliance with his destructive forces while his constructive functioning is delegated to his object. This is his abnormal resolution of the primary instinctual conflict between his life instincts and his destructive instincts. In this short commentary, ignoring the complex and unfortunate interaction of innate impulses, infantile anxieties, and inadequate nurture that created such a resolution, I shall only try to describe in broadest outline Mr. K's active and passive functioning.

Mr. K has not been able to confront and deploy his instincts in the normal manner. In "The Economic Problem of Masochism," Freud (1924) postulated that in the service of the life instincts the essential first step must be the deflection of the death instinct outward. Later, Klein (1932) postulated further that fear of annihilation from the death instinct within —is— the factor that initiates this outward deflection. This original deflection sets in train several important aspects of development, one being the normal frightened relationship to a hostile external object—a relationship noticeably missing from Mr. K's world. He is not afraid to indulge his sadism, and he claims that the object is not hostile. On the contrary he insists the object likes his mocking, his paralyzing and destroying: "It keeps the analyst on her toes."

Instead of perceiving the death instinct with anxiety within and deflecting it outwards, Mr. K has embraced it within. His ego is in a perverse alliance with it, identified with its impulses in a way that is the reverse of normal, since normally the ego identifies at its core with the life instincts. Mr. K deflects instead—in the sense of allotment—his life instincts to his objects, on whom he then enacts excitedly and triumphantly his cruelty and destruction. His objects are to be corrupted and seduced into liking this arrangement; they are also to continue to care for and sustain the patient. Yet he does not feel identified with this care, but merely submits to it passively.

This constellation emerged clearly in the analysis. For long periods, Mr. K was actively destructive of the analytic work and setting and sadistic to his analyst, while only passively accepting her care of him. It was she who had to worry, struggle and endure, provide a nurse to ensure safety, etc. Indeed, in the first week of the analysis, Mr. K warned his analyst "that he has always been very passive and wants to be told what to do." In this respect, as the analysis verifies, Mr. K knows himself. To some extent the analysis did help him with his problems of activity and passivity. It enabled a part of him to emerge that could cooperate a little more actively with the analyst as a helpful figure: as Mrs. Riesenberg Malcolm reports, there were times when Mr. K dreamt and reported his dreams to her and brought his material coherently. Furthermore, the analysis also brought Mr. K nearer to the perception of the terrifying truth about the cruelty and destructiveness that he embraced, which he was able to express in his material about the torturing gang in the Blind Beggar pub. But Mr. K, having been taken thus far by his analyst, could not go further.

His predicament is communicated in his two last dreams before he paralyzed the analysis completely. The first dream was as follows: "I was walking through a very dangerous path, probably mined, full of barbed wire. It was surrounded by police, just standing there. It was in Connaught Square, and I felt that if I managed to walk through, I would be free." His dream says that the nodal moment has now come. If he is to reach freedom and safety, *he* must take an active step: "if I managed to walk through, I would be free." But his first association is ominous, containing an indication of his habitual underlying passive attitude to the analysis. "Well," he says, "we lived right next to that place. *Nanny used to take me there for walks . . .* " (my italics). That is, he has been passively taken by Nanny, the analyst, to the place he has reached; he has passively submitted to the analytic process rather than actively allying himself with it. Now he must walk along a dangerous path, and brave his persecutors, represented by the mines and the barbed wire, instead of allying himself internally with them. But he cannot. It is not too much to say that this is the moment of his tragedy. His ego is too weak, the attraction of the easier and habitual perverse solution is too strong, and he is unable to take a step for fundamental change. In despair, he retreats and puts himself to sleep; for the potentially developing part of himself the sleep is now to be permanent. When he makes contact with the analyst again it is in his old mode; he is inaccessible to progress, he is actively sadistic toward and paralyzing of the analyst, who is now, as the clinical record shows, the only one trying and caring, since Mr. K is again submitting merely passively to her efforts.

Mrs. Riesenberg Malcolm draws attention to the significant similarity between Mr. K's very first dream on the night before his first session, in which "he was in a village inside a ditch, and had to climb up to get to freedom. He had in his hand a kind of miner's pick. When he proceeded to make his way up, an enormous amount of rocks, earth and all kinds of heavy things fell on his head," and his very last dream before the complete stagnation of the analysis, "I want to reach freedom and safety. To do so I have to dig a tunnel and go through it. While I am digging it, I see the gravel and rubbish piling up into a terrible mess that makes me feel that I will never be able to clear it up." These dreams show how Mr. K ends back where he began. Having been taken by the analyst to a vision of the freedom and safety that he cannot attain, he now closes himself away completely. Instead of being in a ditch, which at least is open, he is now shut in a tunnel. The dream also tells us that he is in a tunnel accumulating psychic debris, with which, I think, he will continue to require therapeutic aid.

In fact, Mr. K has already communicated to his analyst that he cannot manage without treatment. He made an attempt to leave treatment but failed; he had to ask to be taken back because of his fears of collapsing, becoming very depressed, and falling to pieces. And indeed, before Mr. K started with Mrs. Riesenberg Malcolm he had already undergone previous treatment. Mr. K's life pattern is, I think, to be perpetually a patient.

This, then, is one more factor adding to the pain of terminating a case of this kind. Along with the admission that the patient is irreparable, and that it is wrong to continue, there is also the knowledge of the patient's interminable need of therapeutic care. The analyst knows he is passing on his case to someone else. At this point, in my view, analysis would no longer be the treatment of choice, since analysis is a treatment for change, which, it has now been established, is not possible for Mr. K. Better a therapy which is openly a treatment for maintenance. It would set limits on Mr. K's field for cruelty, since his immobilizations would no longer be thwarting hoped-for progress, and would provide a less suffering and guilt-inducing framework within which Mr. K could be once again sustained as a patient.

REFERENCES

Freud, S. (1924). The economic problem of masochism. *Standard Edition* 19:157–171.
Klein, M. (1932). *The Psycho-Analysis of Children*. London: Hogarth Press, 1949.

The Role of Primal Scene and Masochism in Asthma

CECILIA KAROL, M.D.

Early investigators, such as French (1939), observed that asthma patients need to repress their sexual and aggressive impulses in an attempt to retain their mother's love. Early traumatic experiences (Brown and Goitein 1946), illness, primal scene, death in the family, miscarriage or birth of a sibling have all been mentioned as precursors of asthmatic attacks. These factors are also of considerable relevance in the case material presented here. Emphasized in this presentation, in addition to the above mentioned factors, are critical aspects of primal scene traumatic experiences and their role in the subsequent development of sadomasochistic character formation. This sadomasochism plays a considerable role in the later eruption of asthmatic symptomatology. The crucial factor in the asthmatic symptomatology arises from the effect of the traumatic experiences which are associatively linked to these sadomasochistic fantasies. Clinical material of an asthmatic girl with learning inhibitions and sleeping difficulties is presented. She demonstrates a clownish sadomasochistic type of behavior reflecting a disturbance in her object relationships. During the course of analysis, it was revealed that specific unconscious fantasies, associated with early traumatic experiences, played a predominant role in the development of her sadomasochistic attitudes. These, in turn, were linked to her asthmatic attacks.

The word "asthma" comes from the Greek word for "panting," and the Greeks defined asthma as a difficulty in breathing, accompanied by sound (Peshkin 1963). According to Lieberman and Lipton (1963), Hippocrates recognized the psychogenic aspects of the illness when he stated that "asthmatics must guard against anger." Immunobiologists, pharmacologists, and pulmonary physiologists have all agreed that whether the etiology of asthma is primarily hereditary or allergenic, the final common pathway in asthma is the same (Austen and Lichtenstein 1973). In spite of

I would like to acknowledge my thanks to Ira Mintz, M.D., for his comments in the preparation of this paper.

the increased drug armamentarium, death from asthmatic illness has increased in the past years (Siegal 1967).

HISTORICAL REVIEW

According to Trenting and Ripley (1948), in 1926, Ziegler and Elliott studied asthmatics without a history of protein sensitivity and concluded that asthma attacks seemed to be induced by psychic stimuli.

Faulkner (1941) looking through a bronchoscope found that bronchi dilated when pleasurable topics were brought up and constricted with unpleasurable ones.

Freud postulated early in his work (1925) that fantasies played a major role in the etiology of mental illness. He wrote that "unconscious fantasies are the immediate precursors of a whole number of hysterical symptoms." He attributed the formation of symptoms to reactivated fantasies and he postulated that a fantasy could be used defensively to either decrease anxiety or engender it further.

In "A Child is Being Beaten" (1919), Freud described at length the psychological relevance of beating fantasies and showed how these fantasies were related to feelings of punishment for forbidden genital strivings representing, as well, a regressive substitute for sexual intercourse with father. The importance of these sadomasochistic fantasies are particularly relevant to the theme of my paper.

Bacon (1956) postulated that asthma is a response to unconscious fears of damage of the respiratory system.

Thomas French (1939) observed that each of his asthmatic patients was exposed to sexual temptation which threatened his relationship with a parental figure—usually the mother. These patients subsequently confessed their forbidden impulses in an attempt to regain their mother's love. French also emphasized how asthma may be an equivalent of repressed rage related to the fear of loss of maternal love. The asthmatic attack was used to regain this affection. Finally, he stressed the importance of the mother-child relationship, especially aspects of the mother's unconscious hostility, overprotectiveness and conflicts over separation anxiety.

Melitta Sperling (1949) emphasized specific parental relationships, not only between asthmatic children and their mothers, but in children with ulcerative colitis and other psychosomatic illnesses as well. The child is rejected by the mother when he is healthy and is rewarded by the mother when he is sick and helpless. She also stressed the continuum between asthma, phobias, and aggressive acting-out behavior. The aggressive behavior is unacceptable to the parents who by now catalog their child as a "bad" child instead of a "sick" one, so that aggression is often replaced by asthmatic symptomatology.

In 1944, Brown and Goitein pointed out how early traumas such as birth of siblings, miscarriages, serious illness, primal scene, and death within the family may precipitate an asthma attack. Later in life, every crisis and stress may reactivate the traumatic event of early childhood, "repeating a patterned response of the organism via its particular organic safety valve of release in the 'oral' subject, (the lung)."

Knapp et al. (1970) hypothesized that "the asthmatic state consists of conflicting fantasies, regressively mobilized, in which destructive urges and affects are inhibited by guilt and fear, while primitive urges to take in, retain, and eliminate through the respiratory apparatus, are accentuated."

Wilson (1968) reported the analysis of a woman whose dreams preceding her asthma attacks expressed primal scene and pregnancy fears.

These authors have all emphasized sadomasochistic fantasies, a disturbed mother-child relationship, primal scene experiences, and the importance of aggression in the development of psychopathology in asthma.

Through the presentation of the following detailed clinical case, I shall attempt to link these factors to the development of asthmatic attacks during the course of puberty and early adolescence.

CLINICAL EXAMPLE

Susan was a thirteen-year-old girl, slightly overweight, with fuzzy hair and glasses. She was referred because of considerable difficulties in completing homework assignments and her complaints about not having friends and being made fun of in school. She also acknowledged difficulties in falling asleep. Her parents reported that at one point, she had told them of a fantasy of wanting to hit and bite the penis of a neighborhood boy. On occasion, when angry, she would punch her thigh with her fist and wish that she were dead.

My impressions were that Susan had an obsessional neurosis with hysterical features. Shortly after her analysis began, her mother phoned and told me that Susan just had a mild asthmatic attack. It was then that I learned that she had been having asthmatic attacks since the age of four and a half, although this had not been presented during the initial evaluation.

Salient features in Susan's early history included the mother's recognition that she consciously rejected Susan when she was a baby and the birth of a sister when Susan was two years of age. The mother acknowledged the preference for her second child, who was so much less demanding. Susan was reported to be a "colicky" baby who sucked on a pacifier until the age of seven. Although the mother provided her with the pacifier, she simultaneously told Susan that she shouldn't use it. Whenever at night Susan used the pacifier, she confessed as much to her mother the following morning. This compulsion to confess, and then be forgiven and regaining parental approval, persisted throughout her analysis.

Although Susan's mother had graduated from college with honors, she had great difficulty in expressing herself. She appeared vague, guilty, and unsure of herself. The patient's identification with her mother was evident, she too suffered from an initial difficulty in communicating and establishing friends.

Susan's father was a brilliant academician, who suffered from a severe obsessive compulsive neurosis which played a role in his need to control and tyranically rule the family. Interestingly, Susan's initial complaint to me was that her frizzy hair, inherited from her father, was the cause of her lack of popularity in school.

During the interview, I commented about her asthmatic attack. She stated that she heard it was psychological and that she hated taking medication or receiving shots for it. An early development of a therapeutic alliance arose with our mutual agreement that we would work towards the resolution of the asthma as well as the elimination of the medication. Both Susan and her parents agreed to consider discontinuing the medication, and although she had asthmatic attacks during the course of the analysis, Susan made a conscious attempt to analyze the asthmatic attacks rather than use the medication.

Course of Treatment

The analysis ran for four and a half years. I will focus on the analysis of screen memories, fantasies, dreams, and the recovery of the memories directly connected with the initiation of her asthma and the triggering of subsequent attacks.

After Susan's initial visit, she had her first period and then was amenorrheic for a few months. At the time of the month when she was supposed to have her period, she was invariably euphoric and talked endlessly in an attempt to ward off intense castration anxiety. She felt that her body was falling apart, and she overate. She indulged with pleasure in displaced castration fantasies of breaking a leg or an arm, walking on crutches, or suffering an attack of appendicitis. In her fantasy, she attempted to arouse the desperation of her parents and the sympathy of her friends. She fantasized that something in her body would be broken or cut off, but only through an accident or an illness. By creating such a fantasy her ego was attempting to bind and control her anxiety, preventing the actualization of her fears in reality.

During the initial phase of her analysis, Susan, like a typical obsessional neurotic, talked endlessly about her school, classmates and teachers, describing *ad infinitum* each one of their characteristics, what they said, and how they looked. She was extremely vivid and sometimes brought drawings to illustrate her lengthy descriptions as well as her fantasies, in which she invariably ended up as the victim. During the first two years of her analysis, I had to interpret repeatedly, and make her aware of how provocative she was with her classmates and parents. She maintained a positive transference with me although she constantly tried to provoke me into either feeling sympathy or scolding her for not doing her homework and fighting with her sister. She gradually uncovered an increasing number of sadomasochistic fantasies which she slowly began to recognize as playing an intimate role in setting off her asthmatic attacks.

One of these fantasies emerged quite early in her analysis. At one point she reported that she had an asthmatic attack earlier in the day because she became short of breath from running home from school. Her subsequent associations, however, led to uncovering a fantasy which immediately had preceded her asthmatic attack.

There were two girls. They were Hawaiian slaves. There were also two men, one a slave and the other a master whose mistress was there. The male slave sexually attacked one of the Hawaiian girls, who promptly told the master about it. The attacker was punished by having a hot stone placed on his penis. He screamed and a girl threw water or mud at him. She in turn was punished for having helped him and a stone was placed on her genitals until steam came out. The girls by now were twins and one fell in love with the son of the owner of the farm. He was a white man, and therefore the master, and he did not allow her to go with him. The slave wanted to go to bed with her but did not, "although they were both naked."

Her associations led to the theme of oedipal rivalry. She remembered a book which her mother had forbidden her to read, *God's Little Acre*. She said that in the book, a girl went to bed with a man who was married and who said that he would get her when she was drugged. The wife came in and shot the man between his legs with his mother of pearl gun and hit the girl with a hairbrush.

Recounting this story filled her with disgust, because it reminded her of her feelings that sex was dirty unless the person was married.

This was the first time in the analysis that we had a direct link between an asthmatic attack and the conscious and unconscious fantasies that had immediately preceded it. The sadomasochistic fantasies associated with sexual relationships were so filled with recrimination and guilt that the patient felt the need for immediate punishment. Her harsh superego's attack was elucidated later in the analysis. In this case, the additional recounting of the story of the girl who went to bed with a married man mobilized Susan's own oedipal impulses and her guilt feelings to the degree that she experienced feelings of revulsion and disgust in the analytic session. The oedipal fantasy in which she competed with the mother for her father, mobilized regressive sadomasochistic conflicts in which she punished and was punished.

It was my impression at this time, and this impression was confirmed later in the analysis, that the fantasy about the hot stone on the genitals and the emergence of steam appeared to be a displacement of a body organ function from the genitals upwards to the lungs. That traumatic insult to the genitals and the noisy emission of steam was symbolically represented in the asthmatic attack.

Another conflict was revealed which provided a connection between her asthma and primal scene experience. This emerged after a boy had given her a ring as a gift. Interestingly enough, just as there were many manifestations of body language symptomatology associated with the sadomasochistic fantasies, for example, experiencing disgust in the session, on this occasion she reported feelings of nausea on her way to the session. She was aware of her desire to remain home and eat. Additionally, she developed a headache and thoughts of not wanting to remember things. Her associations had to do with hostile feelings toward me, including impulses to hit me on the head with an axe. It was clear that the intense anxiety associated with emerging material provided the impetus for the somatic symptoms and, in addition, masked hostile feelings toward me as a transference object and secondary manifestation of hostility as a result of feeling coerced about revealing anxiety-laden material in the treatment. In the same session, she revealed that she was afraid of boys, because once she heard her father make love to her mother and thought that he was hurting her. Additionally, she expressed the fear that if a boy was on top of her, he could smother her and she would not be able to breathe.

It seems plausible that the somatic symptoms are closely related to the inability to cope with primal scene conflict and particularly with the auditory aspects of the primal scene, since she reported hearing sounds of wheezing. It also seems plausible that the headache reflected feelings of guilt about her hostility toward me in wishing to damage my head, and also her identification with a sadistic father who penetrates the mother during coitus. Some aspects of her inability to accept the emergence of femininity, as manifested by her early adolescence and by feelings of smothering, were also clearly evident by her amenorrhea.

The comments about the primal scene experience were then followed by a series of memories which led to the description of her first asthmatic attack at age four. She was spending the summer at a beach resort in the company of her parents and sister. The sister had been ill, and while she was not clear as to what the circumstances were, she did remember having slept briefly in each parent's bed. At that time, she remembered seeing the parents having intercourse and also remembered that her parents discussed her mother's recent miscarriage. One day, at the beach, she was told not to go into the water above her knees. When father walked away and mother was not looking, she remembered falling under the water, looking up and being pulled out of the water by the father. He admonished mother for not looking after her. Shortly thereafter, Susan developed pneumonia and, subsequently, her first asthmatic attack. Susan associated it to her being under the water and being smothered by her asthma, and as she talked during the session of her mother's miscarriage, she again felt nauseated and had fantasies of being pregnant and of getting an artificial penis by means of an operation. Susan's comments about being smothered by the water seem to be related to her similar feelings about a boy being on top of her during intercourse. One might consider that the asthmatic's feeling of being smothered by exuding fluid in the bronchi during an asthmatic attack is closely related to fantasies of being smothered in the water and, in Susan's case, with the sensation of someone lying on top of her during sexual intercourse.

Just as many psychosomatic patients deny the realistic possibility of death from severe psychosomatic symptoms, asthmatic patients also do not accept death as a finality. They deny the realistic possibility of suffocation through smothering by fluid in the bronchi with an unconscious intrauterine fantasy of life under water and regaining of the long lost and still-desired reunion with the mother. It is fair to presume that one aspect of this fantasy is represented in the memory of being under the water, looking up, and being pulled out of the water. (Two years later in the analysis, when she again recalled this memory, she added, "It felt safe to be under water; it was like being in my mother's womb.") Her associations to the miscarriage seem to relate to feelings of sibling rivalry with her sister, as well as to the ambivalent feeling about the dead sibling and the miscarriage. The sibling rivalry was previously alluded to in the fantasies about the twin sister and the girl who was tortured by a hot stone placed on the genitals. This conflict was additionally overdetermined and evidenced by revived feelings of nausea, where she identified with her mother in her fantasies of pregnancy while also serving as the recipient of punishment for her hostile feelings toward mother and wishing that her babies would die. These conflicts additionally determined her anxieties about sexual relationships. The fantasy about obtaining an artificial penis by means of an operation seemed to reaffirm her continued ambivalence over accepting the emerging feminine role and an unconscious desire for masculine strivings.

The patient continued to provide additional clinical material in the same session, and it is my feeling that adolescents characteristically can provide tremendous outpourings of clinical material from time to time, because of the fluidity of their psychic structure and the momentary relaxation of defensive structures. This is not to suggest that the associations and the symptomatology are not molded by both unconscious drives and the defenses against these drives. She further recalled that when she was four, a neighbor's boy had shown her his penis, and she had wanted to expose herself also but felt unable to do so. The penis envy persisted and was now represented by regaining it through the fantasy of biting it off. Again we see persistence of the inability to accept her femininity and the continued envy which arose in childhood when she felt so depleted that she was unable to express herself. The conflict over her sexual identification seems therefore to serve as one of the determinants in the formation of her sadomasochistic character structure.

Additional associations led to the recovery of further memories while on vacation at the beach. "There were two old lesbian ladies who vacationed there. One went crazy and one died." Susan associated going crazy with pregnancy and death with asthma. Her going crazy was linked to her identification with the lesbian lady, her renunciation of her own femininity, and her unacceptable sadomasochistic fantasies of wanting the penis by biting it off, which set off attacks of asthma. The sadomasochism here seems to be intimately tied to feelings of guilt over masculine strivings, hostility towards siblings—both born and unborn—and toward her mother, and fears of retaliation through death for this aggression.

Susan reported having had two repetitive dreams whose analysis provided additional understanding of the relationship between her primal scene experiences and her athma attacks. In the first dream, "I used to go up a staircase and there were people, but instead of people, there were carrots or maybe balls with eyes in them." The second dream:"I dreamed of going to the eye doctor—into a dark room."

Her associations to these repetitive dreams were as follows: "I was scared of these dreams which kept repeating time and again. I still go to an old-fashioned eye doctor who has a long nose with a wart on it. He puts drops in my eyes which blur my vision. During summer vacation, I used to sleep with my parents in the same tent, and had to turn around so as not to see certain parts of their bodies when they undressed. At home sometimes, I lay in the dark on my bed and feared that I would hear my parents having sex or that I would see them through a crack in the closet door. Sometimes I felt that if I was blind I would be safe."

The patient appeared to be displacing conflicts from the genitals upwards to the eyes. The eyes, which were capable of penetrating the environment symbolically, stood for the phallus and her repressed masculine strivings. The fear of going blind represented displaced castration anxiety, already alluded to in previous fantasies and associations. In addition, the fear of the doctor who penetrates her eye with a long tube from which fluid is ejected, clearly appears to be sexual in nature and representative of her conflict over femininity. Her sadomasochistic interpretation of coitus is evident in her fears of seeing or hearing the activity, and the wish to be blind seems to reflect her defensive attempt to cope with these fearful sadomasochistic experiences. Further, her identification with both the victim and the attacker emerged more clearly in the analysis of an additional asthmatic attack. It occurred after her father screamed at her for not having helped her mother in the kitchen. In speaking about the asthmatic attack in the following session, she remembered that the night before, she had an apprehensive feeling that she could hear her parents having intercourse. She then commented about her desire to see the movie, *Oliver,* for a second time, because she was attracted to the episode where Jennie, the protagonist, made a peculiar sound when she was killed by her lover. "Oh! Oh!" Jennie screamed. The patient commented: "It sounded as if she were being raped."

It seemed clear from the associations that her preoccupation with parental intercourse viewed it as sadistic, and this concept was reaffirmed by the subsequent association of Jennie being killed, recognized by the patient as a rape. The sound that caught her attention was respiratory in nature and equated with breathing. This reflected thoughts of the parents' heavy breathing during coitus, where both killer and victim were present. It also reflected her own dyspnea, where she is ambivalently identifying with both: the sadist in her masculine strivings and the victim in her feminine identification. This interpretation achieves added validity from her comment in a previous session of the fantasy of growing a penis and the thought that she could then rape me. These sadomasochistic sexual fantasies evident in her oedipal conflicts, as well as in the transference toward me, were so distressing to her that she fantasized killing both parents, a hoped for solution to her torturing self-preoccupation.

Additional material which shed further light on her breathing difficulties followed the analysis of a dream. Susan's bedroom was separated from the parent's bedroom by a closet having two doors—essentially a corridor between the rooms. The door in the parent's room had no lock and could not be completely closed. In spite of Susan's repeated requests to the parents that the door be fixed, the parents either postponed or ignored doing something about it. This behavior in which the parents unconsciously play a role in traumatizing the child with sexual activities tends to confirm Melitta Sperling's (1949) comments about the role of the parents in activating psychosomatic symptomatology in their children. The dream was as follows: "A man or me or some people were running away. There were racks and closets. A person was hiding. I was breathing so hard that they found me."

Her associations to the dream were that on the previous day, she had a fearful fantasy that her father would attempt to rape her, and that she would refuse his overtures. Susan then commented about her fears of her headache and the fantasy that she might develop a brain tumor. She continued elaborating upon a whole series of hypochondriacal preoccupations. She was fearful of bleeding, of death, and of a deformity and bulge in her tooth. During this time in the analysis, she suddenly became amenorrheic, after having had normal regular periods. She became frightened and developed fantasies of something growing in her uterus, "maybe cancer." On one occasion, after a fight with her mother, she inadvertently licked the crayon that she had been using in her art sketches and immediately became fearful that she could be poisoned. Subsequent associations to the fantasy reverted back to memories, when she was six years old, of having given her sister a solution of chalk to drink, thinking that perhaps she might die.

The material seems to indicate a tremendous preoccupation with oedipal fantasies and their consequences. By leaving the door open between the rooms, the parents exposed the patient to the temptation to experience primal scene activity. The dream where a person was hiding seems to be the patient who was breathing hard when she was discovered. The breathing represents a coalescing of breathing from sexual excitement, from terror at witnessing what to her was sadistic behavior and identification with both the mother and father, and the asthmatic attack. The associations seem to confirm this supposition, in that she reported a fantasy that the father would attempt to rape her and she would then refuse him. However, the ambivalent attitudes about her refusal seem to be demonstrated in the subsequent associations and in her behavior in the following weeks. The sudden amenorrhea, the fantasies of something growing in her head, and the fears of bleeding and death and of a deformity and bulge, all seem to indicate pregnancy fantasies. She confirmed this with the fear of a cancer growing in her uterus. These sadomasochistic, primal scene conflicts played a major role in her asthmatic attacks, which grew worse during these weeks in the analysis. These conflicts were also supported by sadistic death wishes toward the sister. Susan's fear of being poisoned was linked to her childhood wishes to poison her sister. The aggression toward the sibling was also reported earlier in the analysis, and repeated itself during the subsequent analytic material.

These conflicts would characteristically erupt after violent arguments with the mother. She remembered thoughts of wanting to kill her mother which would then be followed by breath-holding. She also recalled an interesting warning that the mother used to mention. Her mother's father had died of cancer of the lung. She told the patient that she should not cough in front of her, because "a person could kill someone with one's breath." She was referring to the ability of a tuberculosis patient to infect an innocent victim by coughing in his face. This seems to clearly indicate a threat that the exhaling of air or coughing is destructive and could kill. In the asthmatic attack, when the patient is filled with violence, the outpouring of air and anger is strangled and retained by the asthmatic state and the difficulty in the slow exhaling of air.

When she felt the impulse to kill the mother, two major defenses were mobilized: identification with the mother and turning the aggression against the self. The asthmatic attack represented a defense against a desire to kill the mother through the outpouring of the infected, contaminated air, at the same time choking herself by not being able to breathe.

These psychosomatic patients with frequent obsessional mechanisms typically associate thinking with doing. The unconscious belief in magic and the omnipotence of thoughts engenders great anxiety and fears that the destructive thoughts would result in the actual death of the hated object. As the analysis proceeded, a great deal of pregenital material emerged, particularly related to intrauterine sadomasochistic fantasies having to do with herself and her sister. These fantasies were closely related to the development of her first asthmatic attack. She again recalled the experience at age four of falling into the water. This time, however, she emphasized memories about the mother's miscarriage, her having viewed the mother's bleeding, and her fears of her mother's death. The hostility toward the sister, and toward the mother who was trying to replace the patient with a sibling, as well as the fears of retaliation for this aggression, was evident in her anxious anticipation of her menstrual periods.

She recalled a movie about a snake eating a lion cub and a fish. She associated it to the fantasy that she had about being inside the mother's womb and of being hurt by the father's penis during parental intercourse. These pregenital intrauterine fantasies were frequently elicited following the asthmatic attacks. On one occasion, she reported: "When I was inside my mother, I was in her stomach, and that reminds me of eating and sex. . . . I am afraid of falling asleep in the dark for fear of going blind. A sperm could fly through the air and get in by the mouth, nose or even eyes, and you could go blind."

At another time, she read that in a prison a man introduced a rod into a woman's vagina, which went all the way up to the woman's lungs, and the woman died. After reading this, she developed a fantasy about a penis reaching all the way from the vagina into the lungs and she added: "At the time I fell under the water at the beach, I had seen my parents having sex. When I was inside of my mother's uterus, I was surrounded by fluid, and fluid has to do with fluids in your lungs and asthma."

The clinical material indicates a continued preoccupation with preoedipal intrauterine fantasies of a sadomasochistic nature, where death and destruction predominated. She identified with her intended victims, the siblings and the mother, and she was fearful of being destroyed by the paternal phallus in the very way she hoped to destroy the victims. The patient emphasized again the fear of going blind. At this point, however, she provided additional material having to do with a sperm that could fly through the air and penetrate all body cavities.

On another occasion, she recalled having seen her parents having intercourse in the dark. The fear of the dark became clearer. She commented that she feared the dark "because a needle could get into your eyes and blind you." She equated the eye to the vagina with a comment; "if a needle, a penis or a rod goes in there, I could get hurt."

It seems plausible that in her fantasies, the penis that attacks her vagina was the equivalent of the sperm that flies through the air and penetrates all body organs. The mother's injunction that it is dangerous to cough, because the tubercular bacillus could fly through the air, invade the lung of an innocent victim, and kill by tuberculosis, determined the unconscious meaning and fantasies surrounding this patient's perception of the asthmatic attack. The need to hold the air in was an attempt to avoid destroying hated objects by turning the aggression against herself.

These sadomasochistic fantasies, which often took place during masturbation, were analyzed repeatedly. At one point, she commented with some degree of sadness that as she attempted to continually fantasize, "they were no fun anymore." She complained that I had spoiled her fantasies, and now, instead of the tremendous response that she was used to experiencing, they just didn't work, and on occasion, because she couldn't enjoy them, she didn't bother to finish them anymore. She even tried to set off asthmatic attacks and at one point said that she tried to breathe deeply in order to induce wheezing. At another, after reading the book, *Candy*, she said: "What a stupid book. At the end, Candy has sex with her father. After I read it, I didn't have sex—I mean asthma—anymore." The analysis of the sadomasochistic fantasies, which were repeatedly brought into consciousness and interpreted, deprived them of the early impact that they had upon the patient. Characteristically, the satisfactions which accompanied the sadomasochistic fantasies and the asthma attacks were removed, and one sees the patient attempting to recreate these satisfactions in her apparently fruitless attempt to reinduce either the fantasies or the asthmatic attacks. Clinically, one recognizes that these fantasies and psychosomatic symptoms do provide these patients with sources of gratification in spite of the deadly reverberations which could also accompany these illnesses. It is of some relevance that Susan further reconfirmed the impact of the analytic treatment upon her previous conflicts with the comments about *Candy*. She made the slip that she didn't have sex anymore with her father and recognized that she meant to say asthma.

Repeated analysis of her oedipal and preoedipal conflicts with the parents and the associative linkages to the asthmatic attacks resulted in an attenuation of the conflict to the degree that she could now tolerate whatever residual fantasies were still present without the need for feeling overwhelmed by the fantasies or by the asthmatic attacks which they triggered. Just as an erotization of thoughts interfered with her innate abilities, Susan had a great asset: a tremendous sense of humor, which permitted her to reveal the most unpleasant aspects of her life in a jocular manner. As trust in me increased, she was able to work through her defenses against castration anxiety, her penis envy, and her bisexual identification.

The analysis of Susan was not limited to uncovering unconscious fantasies and repressed memories. One had to work through strong resistances which manifested themselves in several ways. She spent endless hours chattering about her school, constantly complaining about her teachers, classmates, parents, sister, and friends. Whatever interpretation was made at the beginning of treatment, she would express doubt by saying, "maybe," "I think," or "I guess." She rationalized, intellectualized, and dramatized. As the analysis progressed, more overt oedipal fantasies took the place of the previous sadomasochistic ones. She presented me with drawings of Victorian maidens who were seduced and abandoned, or virginal brides or nuns who were led to the altar after endless adventures.

TRANSFERENCE AND COUNTERTRANSFERENCE

It is important to point out that from the start, a therapeutic alliance was established which led to a positive transference. Susan developed strong positive feelings toward me, and as she gave up her symptoms at home, she reenacted them in the transference neurosis which gradually developed. For example, just before planned short trips away from home and the analysis, she developed sore throats, or minor asthma, which kept her home. It was interpreted to her that leaving home meant growing up and becoming independent from her mother and the analyst. These minor illnesses kept recurring and she finally understood how she wanted to punish me for leaving her and also how she attempted to keep me with her by being ill, just as she kept close to her mother.

It is interesting to note the countertransference aspects engendered by her asthma attacks and sore throats upon her separation from me. I became aware of my concern that my leaving resulted in her being ill. When I worked this through, she no longer reacted to minor separations with sore throats and or asthma.

At the beginning of treatment, her clownish behavior and her negativism provoked sadistic reactions from her parents, teachers, and classmates. On one occasion her classmates stamped the word "dog" on her arm. Early in the analysis, she was nagging me by asking questions which were not gratified but were in turn interpreted in the context of wishing to involve me in her sadomasochistic games so that I would scold her and reject her like the other people in her life.

The negative aspects of the transference appeared in her developing car sickness (just when she was driven to the sessions by her father) and headaches, described previously, related to her oedipal competition. When frightened about the intensity of her feelings for her father, a homosexual transference appeared. Fantasies of having an operation to acquire a penis were expressed, as well as rage that I could not give it to her. She finally was able to accept herself as a girl without feeling that she was inferior. The nature of her object relations improved and she now had good friends of both sexes. Still, this was an aspect of her analysis not totally resolved, due to her leaving for college.

When she was seen on a follow-up, after four years, she had graduated college *cum laude*, was a writer, and no longer had asthma. But she had been unable to establish a long-standing relationship to a man.

CONCLUSION

This paper tried to demonstrate the effect of primal scene shock upon the future psychosexual development of an adolescent girl. It has also focused upon emerging sadomasochistic conflicts arising out of primal scene trauma and from subsequent later childhood conflict. These sadomasochistic fantasies were repressed by the ego and retrieved as regressed somatized asthmatic attacks.

Genetic, developmental, and dynamic factors were discussed which contributed to the manner in which the ego reacted to a series of traumatic events that occurred at the height of Susan's phallic-oedipal stage of libidinal development. In addition, unresolved preoedipal conflicts and fixations were contributory and significant.

To further understand the affect of primal scene on Susan's future development, one has to consider her ego state at the time of the trauma. There was an increased narcissism, heightened by maternal rejection, coupled with overprotection. Identification facilitated the introjection of scenes such as parental intercourse. She conceptualized the sexual act as an attack and identified both with the attacker and the victim through heavy breathing. The birth of her sister and the witnessing of her being nursed by her mother provoked envy and hostility toward her. Later on, the illness of the sister, which followed her mother's miscarriage, reawakened her feelings of rage at her mother for being pregnant along with murderous feelings toward her sister. By identifying with her parents during parental intercourse, Susan's asthma represented an attempt to deal with her intense jealousy of her mother and with her rage at being excluded during the sexual act. Aggression was regressively discharged somatically. The murderous feelings towards the parents and the hated sibling were internalized, then masochistically acted out in fantasy through the asthmatic attack. When Susan had pneumonia, the lung developed a psychic vulnerability which later predisposed her to the subsequent development of asthma.

Susan's oedipal conflict was intensified by spending her vacation together with her parents in the same bedroom. Her difficulties in breathing coincided with the witnessing of parental intercourse. She both identified with her mother in being attacked masochistically as well as identifying sadistically with the attacking father; thus, both sides of her identifications, masculine and feminine, were represented in the asthmat ic wheezing.

The secondary gain from her illness resulted in separating her parents and regaining her mother in a regressive infantile relationship where the mother became oversolicitous of her during illness.

Susan's illness helped her establish an object relationship with a nonintruding, nonthreatening, nonhostile analyst. With increasing conscious recognition of an expanding series of sadomasochistic fantasies, she was able to exercise increased conscious control over the fantasies and their effects so that her ego was able to absorb the recognition of what had been earlier overwhelming impulses. As a consequence, these feelings no longer erupted explosively and regressively in a somatized asthma attack. Objects were no longer dealt with as tormentors or sources of torment and thoughts were no longer erotized. This permitted Susan to do well in school, to utilize her creative talents, and establish rewarding friendships.

REFERENCES

Austen, F., and Lichtenstein, L. (1973). *Asthma, Physiology, Immunopharmacology and Treatment*. New York: Academic Press.

Bacon, C. (1956). The role of aggression in the asthmatic attack. *Psychoanalytic Quarterly* 25:309–324.

Brown, E., and Goitein, L. (1946). The meaning of asthma. *Psychoanalytic Review* 15:544–545.

Faulkner, W. (1941). Influence of suggestion in the size of the bronchial lumen. *Northwest Medicine* 40:367–368.

French, T. (1939). Psychogenic factors in asthma. *American Journal of Psychiatry* 96:87–101.

Freud, S. (1919). A child is being beaten. *Standard Edition* 17:177–204.

——— (1925). Some psychological consequences of the anatomical distinctions between the sexes. *Standard Edition* 19:248–258.

Knapp, P., Mushatt, C., Nemetz, J., Constantine, H., and Friedman, S. (1970). The content of reported asthma during psychoanalysis. *Psychosomatic Medicine* 32:167–188.

Lamont, T. (1963). Which children outgrow asthma and which do not. In *The Asthmatic Child*, ed. H. Schneer, pp. 58–74. New York: Harper and Row.

Lieberman, M., and Lipton, E. (1963). Asthma in identical twins. In *The Asthmatic Child*, ed. H. I. Schneer, pp. 58–74. New York: Harper and Row.

Peshkin, M. (1963). Diagnosis of asthma in children, past and present. In *The Asthmatic Child*, ed. H. Schneer, pp. 1–15. New York: Harper and Row.

Siegal, S. (1967). Current trends in bronchial asthma. *New York State Journal of Medicine* 67:921–929.

Sperling, M. (1949). The role of the mother in psychosomatic disorders in children. *Psychosomatic Medicine* 11:377–385.

Trenting, T., and Ripley, H. (1948). Life situations, emotions and bronchial asthma. *Journal of Nervous and Mental Disease* 108:380–398.

Wilson, P. (1968). Psychosomatic asthma and acting out. A case of bronchial asthma that developed *de novo* in the terminal phase of analysis. *International Journal of Psycho-Analysis* 49:300–335.

Multideterminism in Asthmatic Disease

IRA L. MINTZ, M.D.

A discussion of "The Role of Primal Scene and Masochism in Asthma," by Cecilia Karol, M.D. Dr. Karol has described a relationship between primal scene experience, sadomasochism, and asthma. While her clinical material strongly supports the relationship that she is attempting to prove, other researchers have found different conflicts that appear equally convincing in relationship to asthma. The following discussion attempts to correlate these differing perspectives, along with data from the fields of allergy, immunology, and animal research, in an attempt to provide a more inclusive explanation for these divergent points of view.

Dr. Karol has presented a great deal of clinical material, richly detailed in fantasy, dreams, associations, memories, and behavior, from a four-year analysis of a thirteen-year-old girl with asthma. The clinical data and the dynamic formulations derived from it attempt to prove that childhood witness of the primal scene can play a major role in the predisposition to asthma. In addition, the misperception of the experience in the child's mind which is experienced both as attracting and stimulating, as well as violent and repelling, contributes to the development of sadomasochistic character traits. This sadomasochistic behavior and fantasy, fueled in part by primal scene experience and additionally layered by subsequent life experience and psychological sequelae, contribute further to the development of attacks of asthma.

In the process, Dr. Karol also provides additional material which reveals how this girl's sadomasochistic character traits are fed by her misinterpretation of coitus, by sibling rivalry, and by her inability to accept her own femininity. These sadomasochistic attitudes then serve as some of the driving forces behind her repressed fantasies, and these contribute to the development of self-destructive behavior, phobias, and asthma.

A vivid illustration is provided by one of the early fantasies that occurred in the analysis. The patient reported an asthmatic attack, ostensibly caused by becoming short of breath while running home from school. We know in general that running or exertion often sets off asthmatic attacks in vulnerable children. It is not just the running and exertion that is responsible for the attack. What is usually missing is the meaning and effect of the exertion: the repressed, crucial, intermediate links between the hyperventilation and the asthmatic attack. The patient was able to recover those repressed fantasies which were probably mobilized by the hypercathexis of the respiratory system during the exertion.

The fantasy of the Hawaiian slaves was one of sexual attack and punishment. Intercourse was violent, forbidden, and oedipally linked. Punishment was castration. In addition to the crucial sadomasochistic fantasies, there seemed to reside within the fantasies themselves additional specificity for the asthmatic attacks. The respiratory specificity was further alluded to in the steam, which was related to breathing and wheezing. The intolerable, guilt-laden, sadomasochistic fantasies, overdetermined by respiratory symbolism, were repressed, and the conflict displaced from the hollow vaginal vault to the lung, with the punishment from the noisy burning steam replaced by the punishing, noisy wheezing.

Displacement figures prominently in the defenses of these patients and was clearly evident in this patient, where in addition to the displacement to the lung in the asthma, we find displacement of sadistic coitus and conception to the head with the headaches and to the eyes with the blindness, and to the head and tooth with the tumors. In addition, the fear of pregnancy seemed related to the development of amenorrhea. The intolerable fantasies have the potential for promoting various phobias, as well as other psychosomatic symptomatology. This is evident in this patient's fear of sperm that can fly into your eyes and make you blind, or its reversal, the concern (contributed to in part by the mother) that the tubercle bacillus can fly out of the lungs and kill. In both cases the air serves as the vehicle by which hostile impulses are propagated, either from the patient, invading the hated objects, or by denial and projection, the experience of being invaded and destroyed by the hostile environment.

This sequence was also present in a seven-year-old boy whom I treated. He became increasingly preoccupied with his fiery destructive impulses, which took the form in his play, of drawing fires which spread out of the house, and, fanned by the wind, spread to destroy the town. He was also fearful of the retaliatory thunder and lightning storms, which were denied projections of his rage and would blow and consume and destroy him. The comment of the mother of Dr. Karol's patient implied that you can kill someone with your breath—with your exhaled air.

Another patient reported a similar fantasy. A young engineer in his thirties had been seriously depressed for many years and had kept potassium cyanide capsules in his pocket for over ten years. The fantasy was that if he swallowed the potassium cyanide, an attempt might be made to revive him with mouth to mouth resuscitation. He feared that the rescuer might be poisoned by inhaling cyanide gas, present in his expired air.

The asthmatic attack can represent the unconscious impulse to violently exhale air (and kill the mother), along with the unconscious punishment for it (choking), and the ambivalent conflict (whether to exhale the air freely or not). Again, the ambivalence of the sadomasochistic fantasy can be seen in the movie, *Oliver*, where the patient sees the death of Jennie as a sexual attack, and the heavy breathing, "Oh! Oh!" as linked to parental coitus, with the man killing the woman.

The asthmatic attack itself seems to contain additional conflict over masculine strivings, femininity, and destructive views of coitus. She associates to the hostile air, sperm, bacillus, phallus—that penetrates and destroys others and further links the asthma to the sadomasochistic fantasies and conflict over her psychosexual identifications. Additional fantasies, dreams, and behavior serve to further confirm the relationship between primal scene conflict, sadomasochistic fantasies, and asthmatic disease. Her preoccupations with sadomasochistic fantasies take the form of being the aggressor (masculine with a penis) or the victim (feminine). In true compromise formation, the asthmatic attack reflects the discharge of aggression in identification with the man and the simultaneous punishment for it by identifying with the woman.

FURTHER SUPPORTIVE CLINICAL DATA

A patient who had severe asthma at age three was in analysis at age thirteen because of self-destructive behavior, poor school work, and lack of friends. For many months he had been preoccupied with masturbation, and with coital fantasies. Some of these took the form of blowing up and deflating long balloons, concerns about how things rise and stay up, objects that appear and disappear, and comments about girl friends, bare breasts and pornographic magazines.

One afternoon he was lying quitely on the couch and speaking about needing a haircut for his friend's Bar Mitzvah the following morning. He said that he was getting too heavy and that he did not know whether he would be able to fit into his suit, especially into the vest; he was concerned that he would choke in it. As he spoke, he kept inserting the ball point of one pen into the opening of the other. He began to encourage me to guess which pen was inserted into the other as he moved them back and forth. After a few moments of my guessing he suddenly commented, "See this scar? What do you think it's from?" He pointed to a round, flat, quarter-inch scar on his inner forearm. As I wondered aloud with him about it, he added, "It looks like I was branded," and made the hissing sound of steam emitted from a branding iron applied to flesh. "It's like the dog food commercial," he said, referring to a commercial where a branding iron is used to burn a brand name into a dish of dog food. He continued associating, "It could be acid, but I don't think so. It's not chicken pox because I'm immune from birth. My mother said that she had such a terrible case that I probably would not get it. I was exposed three times."

He returned to his thoughts about his Bar Mitzvah suit. "I can't get into it . . . too fat. You know those operations where the surgeons cut the fat off." I feigned some ignorance, and he continued, "If I was rich, I'd have him cut the fat off, off my abdomen here, and off my chest here, and off my neck, and arms and legs. They could use novocaine—no, probably a general. They'd need to use gas." The repeating theme of inhaling air and air mixtures figured prominently in this child's treatment.

It seemed apparent that the anticipated cutting of the hair on his head with the scissors, and the general preoccupation with coitus, as symbolized by the movement of the pens, set off castration anxieties and a series of sadomasochistic fantasies having to do with flesh being branded and being cut with a metal instrument (scissors, branding iron, and scalpel). Present in the string of associations was the concern for the scar on his arm, a displacement from the genitals. His fantasy of its having been caused by a branding iron, with his verbalizing the hissing, steaming torture, seemed strikingly similar to the sadomasochistic fantasies of Dr. Karol's patient where the hot stone is placed upon the genitals, and the hissing steam resulted. In both cases the sound of steam was present, undoubtedly linked to the hissing sound of the trapped air as it passes through the congested bronchi during the asthmatic attack. This suggests that while sadomasochistic fantasies can be causally linked to the production of the asthmatic symptom, the physiologic symptomatology itself can reaccentuate, further reinforce, and fixate the fantasy in a symbolic manner.

The patient's sadomasochistic castration fantasies continued with his ruminations about dealing with feelings of suffocation around his chest from the tight vest by having the fat cut from his body. In some manner, the tight vest which restricted his respiratory movements seemed to trigger off memories of early respiratory distress during his fateful and severe asthmatic attacks in childhood. His current adolescent development, sexual preoccupations, and the sadomasochistic fantasies surrounding it, seem similar to the type of fantasies and conflict about sexual identity that were present in Dr. Karol's patient.

Discussion

The material from Dr. Karol's patient deals primarily with conflict over sadomasochistic fantasies which are somewhat different from the dependency and separation conflicts described by Alexander (1956). Alexander's "contention that a specific conflict configuration is operative in asthma is the target of increased criticism in recent years because it is too restrictive. No single set of personal conflicts could psychologically sensitize all individuals who are biologically predisposed to bronchial asthma to a single kind of initiating event" (Weiner 1977, p. 248).

Weiner continues: "Therefore it is not the nature of the conflict that plays the crucial role, but rather some factor other than the conflict. The factor may be a failure to contain the conflict, or the intense feeling the conflict engenders. The conflicts are currently considered to represent necessary (but not sufficient) conditions in the further explanation of some forms of the illness."

Additional work by Knapp and his co-workers (1970) offers, in part, further support for this point of view. While acknowledging that attacks may occur under a threat of separation, he emphasizes the failure of defenses that could have dealt with the destructive feelings. Knapp (1960) also attempts to clarify the seeming inconsistency that although separation seems to trigger asthmatic attacks on the one hand, hospitalizing asthmatic children and separating them from the parents seems in many cases to result in the attacks subsiding. He hypothesizes that if the unconscious fantasies were primarily destructive, then hospitalizing the patient and increasing the distance from the hated object would decrease the symptoms. On the other hand, if the fantasies had to do mainly with fear of loss, then reuniting the patient with the parent would decrease the anxiety and the symptoms would subside.

A report by Chessick (1960) and co-workers that 80 percent of a group of drug addicts developed asthma during their period of drug withdrawal is impressive.

Physiological studies tend to suggest a relationship between suggestion, with its psychological effect, and the measured observation of bronchial constriction and asthma. Luparello (1968) and his colleagues observed the narrowing of the airway in asthmatic subjects in response to suggestion. In a subsequent paper (1971), he reported on a study in which a group of forty asthmatic patients and thirty-one controls were told that they would be inhaling five different allergens previously associated with asthmatic attacks. Saline solution was used, however. Only the asthmatic patients developed respiratory difficulties, with twelve of the patients developing actual wheezing and dyspnea. These patients were then given another saline inhalation and told that it was isoproterenol. The attacks promptly subsided.

Weiner (1977) has discussed convincing evidence of immunological factors. A guinea pig injected with an antigen and sensitized is permitted to inhale the antigen; it then develops wheezing and respiratory signs of asthma. A dog that is given an injection of the blood from an asthmatic patient will develop asthmatic breathing. In addition, "IgE antibodies from humans can be passively transferred to monkeys. Once the passive transfer has occurred, bronchial asthma can be provoked by letting the animals inhale the allergen to which the human donor was sensitive" (Weiner 1977, p. 284).

It is clear then that many factors are involved in asthma. Dr. Karol has carefully and convincingly demonstrated those psychological features related to primal scene and sadomasochistic behavior. The perennial question is: To what degree are these psychological conflicts primarily—or contributorily—etiologic in the development of asthma? Dr. Karol has indicated that the childhood experience of almost drowning and the subsequent pneumonia were followed by the first attack of asthma. These may be viewed as traumatic experiences, with the choking and respiratory difficulties serving as one determinant of the ultimately overdetermined choice of asthma, with the lungs as the end organ for violent sadomasochistic conflict. However, even with this history, we cannot determine and predict in advance which patient will develop which psychosomatic disease. These factors appear to depend upon a unique combination of genetic, developmental, immunological, traumatic, and psychological factors. Each of these factors, and perhaps others, is required in a particular constellation and perhaps even in a specific sequence. The end product is the emergence of a definitive illness, or in some cases an alternating sequence of psychosomatic diseases. Specific interference, however, in any of the factors which are predisposing, initiating, or maintaining the illness may modify or ameliorate the severity of the illness.

With this in mind, Wilson (1968) reported a first attack of asthma in a patient in the terminal phase of analysis. One might consider that such circumstances would be viewed as ideal for being able to predict the illness. Unfortunately that was not possible, and Wilson reported that the onset of the first asthmatic attack was a surprise to him. Interestingly enough, his patient also had a history of pneumonia and a traumatic episode around drowning. It suggests the possibility that a number of alternative outlets for expression of conflict exist: that the composite determinants for the conflict contain genetic, immunologic, infectious, developmental and psychological elements; and that the conflicts themselves can be expressed through behavior, psychological symptom formation, or psychosomatic disease.

One patient of mine developed in sequence ulcerative colitis, asthma, depression, self-destructive acting out, migraine, noninfectious monoarthular arthritis of the knee, angioneurotic edema, eczema, and nasorhinitis. It seems reasonable to assume that the multiple elements that contribute to the conflict can be responded to by the ego with multiple responses, including different types of psychosomatic disease. The presence of many psychosomatic diseases may require the existence of multiple and defective organically damaged end organs, which can be explained by an underlying predisposition and common immunological substrate with fixation of IgE antibodies in the membranes of the cells in the colon, lung, nose, arterioles, and skin (Weiner 1977). Thus, the concept of multiple psychic and physiologic vulnerability can be preserved. With the variety of factors that can become activated in a specific, yet not fully recognized fashion, and the diverse alternatives that the ego has to represent the conflict at different points of time and under different levels of ego integration, it is not surprising that a more precise elucidation of the nature of these illnesses has eluded all researchers.

It seems plausible to consider that, with this background, changes in psychological symptoms and psychosomatic disease may result in part from changes in the level of stress or in defense patterns, in shifting intensity of drives, and in alternating levels of ego integration and regression. The underlying conflicts, fantasies, anxieties, identifications, and character traits remain the same. At different times, for reasons that are overdetermined and multidetermined, these conflicts are expressed in different illnesses. It is not uncommon to find an asthmatic patient develop anxiety, depression, or neurosis, or for these and other symptoms to precede the asthma. M. Sperling (1968, p. 250) comments upon the error that is made when a connection is not recognized between a behavior disorder and a psychosomatic illness: "They are not recognized as different aspects of the same personality disorder." Incomplete analysis of the psychosomatic symptoms and its associated conflicts can result in subsiding intensity of the symptom, not through a complete solution to the conflict but rather through a shift in the manner in which it is expressed.

An asthmatic patient can develop depression or destructive acting out to replace a subsiding asthma. The destructive drives, and other conflicts which are still powerful, are now expressed with depression and masochistic behavior instead of the somatic equivalent. In a profession that emphasizes that events are overdetermined, it should not be surprising if the etiology of the illness is equally complex. At the same time, however, the recognition of these complex variables is not meant to disparage or to minimize the importance of and the effect of psychoanalytic treatment. Dr. Karol and others have demonstrated that in spite of the existence of these other factors, analysis of the predominating conflicts of the patient can result in a subsiding of the asthmatic illness.

My discussion of Dr. Karol's paper has attempted to emphasize what I feel were crucial features in her clinical material and in her dynamic explanation of that material. I have included my own clinical data which tend to support and to validate her conclusions. Furthermore, I have attempted to provide some additional perspective in considering how psychoanalytic factors can be integrated with genetic, developmental, immunological, and traumatic data into a more inclusive view of a challenging, complex, and deadly disease.

REFERENCES

Alexander, F. (1950). *Psychosomatic Medicine*. New York: Norton.

Chessick R., Kuland, M., Husted, R., and Diamond, M. (1960). The asthmatic narcotic addict. *Psychosomatics* 1:36.

French, T., and Alexander, F. (1941). Psychogenic factors in bronchial asthma. *Psychosomatic Medicine Monograph*, 4. Washington, D.C.: National Research Council.

Knapp, P. (1960). Acute bronchial asthma: psychoanalytic observations on fantasy, emotional arousal, and partial discharge. *Psychosomatic Medicine* 22:88.

Knapp, P., Carr, H., Nemetz, S., Constantine, H., and Friedman, S. (1970). The content of reported asthma during psychoanalysis. *Psychosomatic Medicine* 32:167.

Luparello, T., Lyons, H., Bleeker, E., and McFadden, E., Jr. (1968). Influences of suggestion on airway reactivity in asthmatic subjects. *Psychosomatic Medicine* 30:819.

Luparello, T., McFadden, E., Jr., Lyons, H., and Bleeker, E. (1971). Psychologic factors and bronchial asthma. *New York State Journal of Medicine* 71:2161.

Sperling, M. (1968). Acting out behavior and psychosomatic symptoms. *International Journal of Psycho-Analysis* 49:250.

Weiner, H. (1977). *Psychobiology and Human Disease*. New York: Elsevier North-Holland.

Wilson, C. (1968). The relationship between psychosomatic asthma and acting out. *International Journal of Psycho-Analysis* 49:330.

Parental Overstimulation in Asthma

C. PHILIP WILSON, M.D.

A discussion of "The Role of Primal Scene and Masochism in Asthma," by Cecilia Karol, M.D. The author presents case material corroborating Dr. Karol's hypotheses about the role of primal scene exposure and sadomasochistic fantasies in asthma and which documents the thesis that primal scene is a part of a global pattern of parental overstimulation which in the pregenital maturational phases establishes the predisposition to develop asthma. He further confirms Melitta Sperling's hypothesis that unconscious conflicts of the mother or father predispose a child to the development of psychosomatic disease and that specific parental habits and fantasies involving the lungs determine the choice of the respiratory system for symptom formation.

While my clinical experience with the analysis of adult asthmatics corroborates and confirms Dr. Karol's hypothesis about the etiologic roles of primal scene shock and masochism in asthma, the main thrust of my discussion will be to emphasize that although primal scene is very important, it is only one aspect of global patterns of overstimulating parental behavior which in the pregenital maturational phases establish the predisposition to develop asthma and that in subsequent developmental phases, particularly the oedipal and adolescent years, play a major role in causing emotional conflict, symptom formation, disturbances in object relations and asthma. These findings are consonant with those reported by Melitta Sperling (1963) in her work with children and by myself (1967) in my research with adults.

In addition I will review from my clinical material and that of Dr. Karol, Sperling's hypothesis (1963) that asthma is a manifestation of a pregenital conversion neurosis and that the choice of the respiratory system for symptom development is determined by specific attitudes and fantasies of the mother.

CLINICAL PRESENTATIONS

Case One

A thirty-year-old compulsive architect came for analysis of his chronic asthma. He was a nail biter and extremely impatient. He had a childlike sense of humor and was interested in magic, having a magical number of his own that he "discovered" wherever he went. An only child, he was born and raised in Warsaw. At three months he had pertussis which frightened his mother. During the first year he developed eczema and pruritic rashes in the groin and anus. A bright, precocious child verbally, he was breast-fed until two and a half years and bowel trained with difficulty at the same time he was weaned. His first asthma attack was at three years when he was separated from his mother because she had an elective abortion. The mother was an obese, dependent, childish woman who doted on her only child and seldom left the home. The father, a compulsive, narcissistic businessman who dominated the household, took a mistress in the patient's early years. At six years of age the patient was sent under an assumed name to live with a Polish Catholic family to protect him from the Nazis who occupied Poland.

During the two years he lived with this family, he was free of asthma although he experienced many frightening situations when the Germans periodically came searching for Jewish children. The Catholic foster parents were courageous, kindly people who, however, made him fend for himself as they had a large family. At the age of eight, the war was over and he was returned to his parents whom at first he did not recognize. They did not ask him about his feelings or experiences with the Catholic family and his asthma recurred.

The father was noisy and exhibitionistic; nightly after dinner he visited his mistress, returning home late to fall into a deep sleep, "snoring like a horse." The patient, who in his memory was a deep sleeper, shared a room with his mother, his bed right next to hers. He "knew somehow" that his father, who occupied the adjoining room, did come in and have sex with his mother. The patient recalled many times being awakened and fearing his father would choke to death from snoring. Instead of using the communal bathroom shared by the apartment dwellers, the father used to urinate in the kitchen sink where he also bathed his genitals and buttocks. On a rare occasion the mother weakly argued with father about his behavior but she was afraid of him and did all she could to please him. The patient was a good boy, never argued with his father, and did all the chores. He did not masturbate and only dared have erections at school. Until adolescence he was overweight and inhibited with girls. He was an excellent student, particularly in mathematics. At seventeen he took off weight, dated girls, and became more assertive, traveling alone in the summer and socializing. He achieved his architect's degree and came to the United States where, after a number of relationships, he married a successful businesswoman.

Course of Analysis

The analysis paralleled that of a typical compulsive neurotic except that from the first his asthmatic attacks were kept in focus. The patient reported two fantasies that he said were always in the back of his mind in connection with asthma. In the first he had a great sword with which he was going to cut a person in front of him in two: in the second he had a rifle with telescopic sights aimed at a man's head.

Preoedipal fantasies, dreams, and associations showed that the sword in the first fantasy symbolized the patient's teeth and oral incorporative conflicts whereas comparable oedipal phase data revealed the sword to be his phallus. The rifle fantasy had primarily oedipal derivatives. It was the castrating father projected onto me in the transference neurois whom he wanted to shoot. He never argued with or defied his parents or me and it was a long time in analysis before this attitude changed.

Early memories emerged with the analytic lifting of his amnesia from childhood which showed that in attempting to resolve his oedipal conflict he identified with sadistic aspects of his father's personality and behavior. Moreover, he had solved the trauma of separation from his parents at six years of age by secretly identifying with the Nazis and in fantasy joined them in torturing and killing Jews who represented his parents. Furthermore, as his Jewish name and identity were covered by a Catholic Polish one when he was placed with the foster parents, he identified with them. He became an expert on Nazi concentration camp tortures. The following sadomasochistic fantasies reveal that, in his asthma, he tortured the internalized bad parents projected onto me in the transference neurosis.

Describing his asthma attacks he said he felt all blown up, that his stomach was like a balloon. He was all trapped with air. He brought this up in the transference neurosis when he was separated from me because he had the flu; what amazed him was that he got no asthma or lung symptoms with the flu. Instead he had a series of sadistic fantasies that he realized were aimed at controlling me as he felt controlled by me and by his parents as a child. In one fantasy, he has a man all harnessed up and puts catheters in the nose, anus, and penis. The one up the penis goes half way up to make it painful. Then he pours cold water into the catheters and shouts at his victim that he is not to urinate or have bowel movements. He reported a dream in which he tortures people by putting them in a harness around the chest. His associations were to wanting to invent a harness for asthmatics like a parachute jumper's by which he could squeeze or expand a victim's lungs. Another association was that he hoped that I, the analyst, would get flu or asthma. He said that in an asthma attack he could not breathe out dirty foul air; all air was flatus.

During the summer vacation break in the second year of analysis I received a phone call from the patient, who had been hospitalized for status asthmaticus. All I could hear was wheezing on the phone. I told him that he was choking me to death inside himself in rage at my leaving him. His wheezing lessened and he began to give details of his illness. The hospital physician later called to say the patient was much better and the next day he was discharged. The rest of the vacation he had no serious asthma, nor did he call me. In analysis in the fall, he said that in his asthma attack he would not cooperate; he fought using the respirator and other treatment; he wanted to die. When he had been able to get me and his internist on the phone, he felt he had control of us, and following my phone interpretation he became aware of a fantasy directed at me. He fantasied he was an Arab terrorist who hijacked an Israeli airplane. In his fantasy, because his demands for money and power were not met, he killed all the families on the plane by blowing it up. These families, he realized, represented me, my wife and children. Following his awareness of these fantasies and their transference meaning, he relaxed and cooperated in the therapy of his status asthmaticus. This was his only attack of status asthmaticus.

Analysis of the patient's allergies graphically documented their emotional cause (Sperling 1953). He was very allergic to dust which unconsciously was equated with feces and flatus, and his mother. Whereas his father was very clean, bathing daily, his mother rarely washed. She had a brown spot on her back that they laughingly called her tatoo which actually was dirt. The patient's sense of smell was acute—as is typical of asthmatics—but he could not smell his mother, which he confirmed when visiting his parents as an adult. When he married, he insisted that his wife always bathe before intercourse so that she would be the opposite of his unclean mother.

He recalled that October, the tenth month, and seven, the seventh day, constituted his magical number, 107, and that the number represented his parents whom he had left on that date to go to his foster home.

The patient identified with both the mother and father in intercourse as his catheter fantasies reveal. Oral, anal, and urinary fantasies and conflicts were masked by his asthma.

He confused ejaculation with urination and had fantasies of impregnating women by blowing them up with a urinary ejaculation. His compulsive defenses required long analysis before he was able to let himself experience affects, to cry, or to get angry.

In the terminal phase of analysis, when his wife was pregnant with their second child, more sadomasochistic material emerged. He dreamed he was putting a pipe with compressed air through the first and second floors of his house. It had a plastic nozzle so he could always have air. However, he reflected in the dream that if he ran it through the basement, air would come out moist and smelly because of the humidity.

His associations were that he had tried to explain to his five-year-old son about birth, telling him that the woman has an opening in her, but he realized the boy would think of the opening as an anus. A pipe reminded him of blowing things up. The first and second floor are like one and two babies and number one (urinating), number two (defecating). His pregnant wife passed gas the day before and said she now "farted as loud as a weight lifter." She complained that he snored loudly. He recalled that at twelve years of age he had fantasies of a baby being born through his penis, but feared it would hurt. He saw animal eggs but confused them with feces. His asthma, he thought, was like pipes with air coming out. As a child he used to stick straws in frogs' anuses and blow them full of air. Then he would either float the frogs in water or step on them, bursting them. Later he learned the Nazis had similar tortures for prisoners. In the middle ages a criminal punishment was pulling people apart with horses. The pipes reminded him of penises with which a man could blow a woman up with air or urine. He recalled that when his mother was pregnant (when he was three and his asthma began) he was warned not to punch her swollen stomach. He remembered thinking it would burst like a balloon. In subsequent sessions he had dreams of his wife being dead and of the movie *Clock Work Orange*, in which some boys kill a woman with a gigantic stone phallus that "bursts her." He also had death wishes toward me. Another memory of his third year returned: of his mother having typhus and his being separated from her for several weeks. He recalled an encopretic episode at nursery school when he was five. When he was able to experience emotions, his asthma attacks subsided in frequency and intensity. Another shift was from part to whole object relations.

Prior to analysis his preferred sexual position was to have his wife on top and his goal was to prolong the act as long as possible. Aspects of his early relations with his parents, particularly his mother, were recapitulated with his wife. Modest and inhibited in public, he tried to be "totally free" at home. He farted frequently and encouraged his wife to do likewise. When he came home from work he took off all his clothes, even eating dinner nude. When unexpected callers knocked on the door he had to rush to put on some clothes. He tried to get his wife to be nude with him but she insisted on wearing a sarong. He purchased a country property with six acres of land where it was his particular pleasure to urinate and defecate in the woods.

He never wanted to be separated from his wife; they did everything together. He liked to suddenly pinch her: "any round, soft area was suitable"; sometimes she got angry as he really hurt her. If he reached home before she did he'd often hide in a closet, enjoying it when he could surprise or frighten her. He bought a house within walking distance of his work and was furious when his company moved their offices to Manhattan. He reacted as if the move was a personal vendetta against him. As he worked through his sexual conflicts and assumed normal sexual relations with his wife, he also became able to separate from her, and developed healthy sublimations in photography and civic work. These changes resulted from the analysis of his separation conflicts in the transference neurosis. His asthma developed at the time his mother had an elective abortion when he was separated from her. His murderous rage at his mother and the baby *in utero* was repressed and internalized in his asthma. Also repressed in his symptom was guilt at his pleasure in the baby's death.

Examples of the oral, anal, and urethral fantasies and impulses that emerged in the transference neurosis have been cited. There was preoedipal and oedipal primal scene which was an aspect of a general atmosphere of overstimulation, which included his sleeping in the same room next to his mother where he was exposed to her oral and anal habits and her masochistic subservience to his father. His father's urinary, anal, and phallic exhibitionistic behavior intimidated and castrated the patient. However, both parents were controlling, conscientious people with strict superegos who denied any meaning to their overstimulating behavior. Extreme exhibitionism was coupled with denial. The major symptom that developed in the patient was asthma which internalized and repressed oral, anal, urinary and phallic conflicts, drives and impulses. Except for his asthma he was a "good boy."

Comparison with Dr. Karol's Case

In both cases we see (1) obsessive-compulsive controlling fathers and mothers lacking confidence in themselves who cling to their children: my patient's mother by delaying weaning and bowel training until two and a half years and sleeping next to the patient until his late adolescence; Karol's mother by giving her daughter a pacifier until she was seven. (2) Primal scene and other overstimulating parental behavior that is denied: my patient who slept next to his mother was exposed to parental intercourse from the earliest years. Moreover, the father's snoring after sex with his mistress was a source of sadomasochistic conflict and fantasy. Other overstimulation occurred through his proximity to the body of his "smelly" mother in bed next to him and through the anal, urinary, and genital exhibitionism of his father. In Karol's case we see primal scene exposure associated with her first asthma attack. However, Karol's patient's parents refused to put a lock on their bedroom door, and letting their daughter sleep with them suggests the strong possibility of preoedipal primal scene and other overstimulating parental sexual and bathroom behavior pointing to pregenital conversion as etiologic in her asthma. (3) Parental organ system fantasies about the air, breathing, and the lungs were present in both cases: my patient almost died of severe infantile pertussis which would have made the parents hypersensitive to the fear or wish that he choke to death. Thoughts of death by choking were repeatedly aroused in the mother and son when father snored after sex with his mistress. The mother's unconscious anal and genital exhibitionism expressed in her uncleanliness caused a selective repression of the sense of smell in the patient. Another factor augmenting respiratory incorporation was the father's farting and smoking. In my research on the Isakower phenomenon and sand symbolism (Wilson 1975, 1980), I emphasized the anal aspects of cigarette smoking, particularly that cigarette smoke can express impulses and fantasies that are masked by flatus. The patient's father was a chain smoker yet the patient was forbidden smoking and had never done so. He was contantly choked by his father's cigarette smoke which he hated. This conflict enhanced pregenital conversion and respiratory incorporation. This patient once referred to smoking as "the visual materialization of a fart," and his sadomasochistic fantasies reflect the copraphagic impulses and fantasies that were repressed and internalized in his asthma. Karol's patient's fear of being smothered in intercourse derived from her overhearing the heavy breathing of parental intercourse. Her mother had neurotic ideas about the breath, warning her daughter not to cough in front of people, that a person could kill someone with one's breath. The mother's father had died of lung cancer and she also had a fear of tubercular infections by the breath.

Case Two

The role of primal scene, overstimulation and masochism in asthma were highlighted in the case of an adolescent whom I will term the "Gothic Boy" because, although he was born and brought up in the New

York area, he talked, thought, and behaved like someone from a Gothic novel. The patient was a shy, effeminate fifteen-year-old boy with an intellectual, old maidish manner of speech. His asthma developed three months before consultation; at that time, his mother was hospitalized for an unexplained operation. Otherwise healthy in childhood, he was enuretic until his sixth year. The mother was an intelligent, rigid, moralistic woman who said that she was not affectionate and regretted having had her mother, who lived with the family, take care of her children "as she had spoiled them." The father was a religious, self-made, successful businessman who disciplined his children, forbidding them television and movies and demanding top scholastic performance. Fights about discipline were constant. The patient felt his parents were always watching and spying on him. He had no memory of erections or masturbation but had crushes on certain boys at school. His only friend had been his eleven-year-old sister until in puberty she became contemptuous of him, calling him a "fag." He remembered hitting his sister with a block in early childhood and being severely punished. Since early years he was overweight, at seven weighing a hundred pounds. When he was six his mother bought a stuffed turtle for him and subsequently, usually to make up for leaving him alone, she bought him other stuffed animal toys until he had a large collection. When the family moved to the city just prior to the onset of his asthma, he was permitted to have half of them; the others were put in storage for him. Into early adolescence the patient invented sadomasochistic games, that he and his sister played, with these stuffed animals in which the animals would behead, strangle, and torture tinker toy figures who represented various humans. Occasionally he made up sexual plays. He was an authority on those beheaded queens, Mary, Queen of Scots and Marie Antoinette, and an expert on female murderers like Lizzie Borden. Since early childhood he had been preoccupied with death, read the obituary column, and wanted to visit the city morgue. He preferred cats to people and had four of them as pets. For many years two of the cats slept the first part of the evening in the parental bed next to the mother. Late at night they left mother and came to sleep with the patient. The patient feared and hated his father and blamed him for the infectious death of one of his cats. The parental bedroom door was always open, reflecting the lack of privacy in the home. In early years the patient had nightmares and was frequently taken into the parental bed. There was no memory of his sister's birth or mother's pregnancy. In latency he played at being the victim of an aggressive boy next door who used to lock him in closets. He had a strong belief in black magic and tried to kill people he hated by secret voodoo. His one "sin" was secret cigarette smoking. He talked frequently of wanting to be a woman.

Inspite of the serious character pathology there was no evidence of psychosis and the patient had a capacity for insight. Unlike most cases, he had wanted to get asthma to be exempt from athletics as was the case with an asthmatic classmate. He had one activity in which he excelled aside from his studies. That was butterfly collecting. His problem was in mounting his specimens as he could not stand sticking pins in the butterflies.

Course of Analysis

As I have described in another paper (1970), the first months of analysis in psychosomatic cases is a crucial period and the analyst has to concentrate upon the masochism and then the repressed aggressive drive components, leaving libidinal material until later. In this case the patient readily brought up his resentment and anger with his mother, father, sister and teachers—showing, however, considerable resistance to feeling any resentment towards me in the transference until in the fifth month of analysis, when he reported the following dream: "The scene was a room that I could not place. Mrs. W was there and my sister was in the background. I was shrieking at Mrs. W saying: 'How dare you look through my drawers, you filthy whore!' I continued to scream and yell at her until I woke up. On awakening I felt remorse and also amazement that I'd think of saying something like that to her in the dream, because I'd never say that to her face."

Associations. "Mrs. W is our cleaning woman. She is basically nice, but in reality she did search my drawers and found a package of cigarettes that I had hidden. She told my mother who blamed me and I tried to put it off on my sister, saying they were hers." The patient said that his reputation for moral behavior is very good in the family, where as his sister's is ruined anyway, so it wouldn't hurt her to be blamed for one more thing. Mrs. W has been consistently anti-Catholic and has made some hostile remarks about the priests and the Pope. The patient had kept quiet although he felt like killing her for these remarks, as he has a strong wish to join the Catholic Church because his ideas about morality are the same as the church's. An interpretation was made to the patient that he was not only screaming at the cleaning woman in the dream but at his mother and at me; that his mother was opposed to the Catholic Church and he knew very well that I, as an analyst, would not agree basically with the doctrines of Catholicism. Likewise, he knew that I was not basically in favor of his smoking, as I had brought it up with him as a problem to analyze and also had suggested that he not smoke in analytic sessions which he, with his strict conscience, took as a prohibition. The patient confirmed the interpretation by in a partly questioning voice, saying: "I must have been shrieking worse in my dreams; before I would have gotten asthma. When the dream woke me up I had some trouble breathing, but it wasn't really asthma and I went back to sleep."

In analysis the patient made considerable progress: formerly obese, he dieted and brought his weight down fifteen pounds. He looked forward to going back to school with pleasure and interest for the first time and planned to take some extra courses in language, which he enjoyed. Whereas in the six months preceding analysis he had missed nineteen days of school because of asthma, since treatment began he missed one day because of his illness. He began to question why he wanted to be a woman, which he saw now as being a very peculiar wish in that it meant to him to be a hypermoral person like the aspects of his mother that he hates. This dream was a result of a long series of interpretations of defenses against hostile id impulses. The libidinal aspects of the dream did come up in the session as the patient was puzzled as to why he would call a proper married woman like Mrs. W a whore. His association to whore was that he first learned the word two years ago, reading a book about Henry the Eighth in which Ann Boleyn, when she was having an affair with Henry the Eighth, was derided as a whore by the English Catholics.

His asthma cleared as he began to get an understanding of the masochistic meanings of his symptoms and of the defenses he had against aggression.

Discussion

Psychosomatic symptoms, including asthma, frequently first appear in adolescence (M. Sperling 1978) because it is in this phase that the child must develop the capacity to be independent of the parents. The following conflicts appeared to be the crucial precipitants of his asthma.

1. His mother, who had seldom left him, went to the hospital for a fibroid operation which frightened him. He was not told what the operation was for and feared his mother had cancer, a disease his grandmother had died of six months before.

2. His sister, five years his junior, no longer would play with him constantly. She now wanted friends of her own outside the family, and was becoming critical of her brother, calling him a fag.

3. When the family had moved to the city, in his fourteenth year, he had been deprived of half of his fetishistic animals which were put in storage. Although he tried to continue his sadistic games with these stuffed toys, he could no longer get his sister to join him and he had begun to feel ashamed of "these games." They were becoming ego-alien to him.

4. With the increased biological development of adolescence, he was aware of intense homosexual yearnings for an effeminate classmate; however, his superego forbade him any active homosexual gratification.

5. Frank death wishes came to consciousness toward a crippled classmate whom he envied, and toward certain teachers who ridiculed him for his effeminate mannerisms. No effective sublimations were available for these sadistic fantasies.

6. For many years prior to the development of asthma, he had been fascinated by strangling, beheading, and death. Female murderers particularly interested him.

7. Also prior to the asthma onset, he had wished to get asthma like a classmate. The patient had already feigned illness at camp to get sent home.

8. A powerful preoccupation with black magic had taken hold of him and he had attempted to murder people he hated by stealing a piece of clothing from the hated person, usually a teacher, setting fire to the cloth and then repeating magic prayers that the person would die by fire. His wishes were never carried out and he was increasingly guilty for having such feelings.

9. The actual precipitation of asthma was his separation from his mother which forced death wishes (of an oral incorporative nature) to be powerfully repressed. He was strangled for wanting her to strangle. The asthma also served as a punishment for other sadistic fantasies and his homosexual wishes.

10. The asthma made him sick and dependent on his mother.

11. Perverse fantasies were masked by his asthma. He revealed that behind his wish to be a woman were transsexual fantasies of being castrated and by surgical operations, being turned into a female with a vagina and breasts. He became angry at the thought that he could not have a uterus, become pregnant and have children. The patient's parents were cautioned by me that the patient in the future might try to go through transsexual operations and that his transsexual wishes had serious psychological meaning. They minimized their son's condition, refused consultation which I requested, and withdrew him from therapy as his asthma had cleared and he was going away to college. A follow-up is not available.

This patient's transsexual wishes and fantasies psychodynamically correlate with and confirm observations of Socarides (1978–1979) in his paper on "Transsexualism and Psychosis." Socarides notes that his patient's wish for sexual transformation defended him against paranoid fears of aggression. The findings in this case fully substantiate Socardies' view that transsexualism is a serious psychological condition and that surgery for it should be considered with the greatest caution, if at all.

Comparison to Dr. Karol's Case

In this case, we see controlling parents who even could force their son, who got excellent marks, to read mathematics at night as a punishment for minor misbehavior. Primal scene exposure probably occurred because of the lack of privacy, with no locking of doors as well as the parent's taking the boy into their bed when he had nightmares. However, in this case, most striking was the unusual relationship of the mother and son. That she unconsciously wanted him to be a female and to infantilize him was clear in that he, rather than his more rebellious sister, was encouraged to do the housework and wash the dishes. Male aggression was legislated against. The mother prevented maturation and promoted the development of fetishism by giving her son the stuffed animals every time she left him. Even more confusing for his development were the cats who slept with the mother and with the patient. The short one year's analysis permitted only minimal exploration of the psychodynamic significance of the patient's cats. It did become evident that they represented babies the patient had by the mother. That the warm body of the cat came from mother's bed to the patient's expressed the mother's unresolved incestuous tie to her son.

Specific parental fantasies and preoccupations with air, breathing, or the lungs were not recovered. However, the mother herself said that she was emotionally cold and was inhibited about kissing and hugging. She, as well as the father, was aware of and had done nothing to discourage the patient's and his sister's sadomasochistic beheading and strangling games. We can suspect that such hypermoral compulsive parents might unconsciously share their son's sadomasochistic fantasies. They certainly provided the paraphernalia and opportunity for sadomasochistic play in buying the stuffed animals and tinker toys as well as the morbid books on such women as Lizzie Borden. Allergic studies in this case were negative. Sadomasochistic conflicts and fantasies were central in this boy's psychopathology and character structure.

Case Three

In 1968, I reported on a patient who, with no previous history of asthma, developed symptoms of bronchial asthma in the terminal phases of her analysis. The asthmatic attacks, some seventeen in all, responded to analysis; the patient terminated treatment successfully, free of asthma.

The patient, a twenty-five-year-old woman, came to analysis with intense oral conflicts. An alcoholic who drank herself into a stupor every evening after work, she was severely depressed and suicidal. She lost one job after another. Behind a facade of helpless, childlike behavior was overwhelming oral greed. Denial and exhibitionism characterized her neurotic parents' behavior as she grew up. The wealthy socialite mother was an alcoholic whose drinking was denied completely by the family. The father, a very successful businessman, insisted that the family was poor and they lived in a rent-controlled building in an impoverished area. A compulsive man, he did daily exercises in the nude in a ritualistic fashion in front of his wife, son, and daughter. These exercises, which were preceded by a large glass of water and followed by a copious urination, dated from the time of the patient's earliest memory. He also kept binoculars in the living room window sill so that he could look at certain exhibitionistic women in nearby apartments. A second analysis confirmed my 1968 hypothesis that transference caused by a precipitous superego formation played a significant role in the asthma *de novo*. Also demonstrated clearly was the pathological effect that perverse parental sexual and toilet behavior had upon the patient's psychosexual development.

Follow-Up History

Ten years after termination the patient returned because of marital conflicts. Although she had two healthy children, a boy and a girl, sexual intercourse was infrequent and there were many quarrels. Formerly messy and disorganized, she had become compulsively neat, doing all the housework herself because a cleaning woman might not do the job properly. A long battle for control went on with her husband about choices: what kind of car to buy, where to live, how much money to spend, and where to go on vacation.

She had developed healthy sublimations in music and art that she enjoyed, and she felt pride in her volunteer charity work and her children's development. Gradually, however, she had stopped doing things with her husband, such as playing tennis and bridge with other couples. She had rare asthmatic attacks which she had been able to control. An embarrassing symptom, dating from early years, required further analysis: a compulsion to look at men's crotches to see what their genitals looked like and if they had erections. On subways and buses the compulsion was hardly controllable.

Course of Analysis

Analysis centered on her compulsive neurosis and she reported dreams reflecting anal phase conflicts. The following example is illustrative. She dreamt that a man was going to make love to her, then she saw a lot of people's anuses with hemorrhoids, some of them very big. She was going to kiss her mother on the mouth but then did not want to. In her associations she thought of baboons having big red bottoms. One of her aunts always talked about manure and had hemorrhoids. In the dream some anuses had hemorrhoids, others didn't. Hemorrhoids reminded her of little penises. She herself had had hemorrhoids and she wondered if she wanted the hemorrhoidal swellings to be little penises. She remembered so many times seeing father's penis and his urinating, but he also spent lots of time reading on the toilet with the door partly open. When she first married she was afraid of smelling and avoided having a bowel movement when her husband was home. She had been reading *The Joy of Sex* and wondered what anal intercourse would be like. It seemed to her that men have more pleasure than women. She hated football games which her husband was always watching on television. An interpretation was made that she had confused her vagina with her anus as a child and that she thought both were dirty holes whereas she envied father his penis and wanted one herself. Her response was that she remembered seeing her mother's genitals as a girl and was frightened and disgusted. She felt that she must have thought intercourse was like having a bowel movement because her parents were so cold and matter of fact about sex. The kissing made her think of her mother's conflicts and fears about kissing, that you could get infections kissing people; that her mother must feel the mouth, like the anus, is dirty.

She now perceived that her compulsion to look at men's crotches involved the analyst, whom she said she observed coming into sessions. The particular fascination was with whether he had an erection. She realized that when she saw her father's penis she could be sure it was not erect, that she could not be certain of what was happening if he wore clothes. There had been a reversal of normal female development in that she was reassured seeing the male genitals nude and anxious if they were covered.

A major focus of analysis was upon the patient's strict superego and its periodic projection onto the analyst in the transference neurosis. She began to admit to her exhibitionistic behavior. At home she was moralistic and prudish while her husband and children were around; when alone, she wore a bra and panties or a bikini. She went to social gatherings in extremely sexually provocative dresses and was seductive in her behavior. Memories of her father's genital exhibitionism and his voyeurism emerged coupled with penis envy and transference anger with me. She thought again of her father's daily nude exercises and remembered stepping over his prone body to go to his bureau for her weekly allowance money. She realized that with his binoculars he must have been looking for nude women in nearby apartments and that he was exhibiting to them. She thought that secretly she must want her father or me to see her when she exhibits.

Interpretations were made that she had identified with her exhibitionistic voyeuristic father and was arousing and frustrating men in adult life just as father had "cock teased" her in childhood.

In subsequent sessions she began to face her identification with her father's perversions. Like her father, she was proud of her figure and careful of her weight. She wore extremely provocative dresses to social events, dresses that revealed her breasts and nipples and skirts slit high to her thigh. She wore bikinis both for swimming and in her home, frequently leaving the window shades up. She began to receive anonymous phone calls, which she realized she enjoyed and provoked. Socially she was the target of sexual teasing and was frequently surreptitiously touched or pinched, which she tacitly enjoyed.

As the perverse body-phallus identification was analyzed there was improved psychosexual functioning. She then recalled that the night she developed her first asthma she had had an impulse to fellate her lover who was gratifying her by cunnilingus. She wondered if she had been afraid of biting his penis or being hurt by it. The interpretation was made that she was punished in her asthma for her oral incorporative impulses.

Comparison with Dr. Karol's Case

In this case we see the following parallels to Karol's patient: (1) an obsessive compulsive controlling father and a weak dependent mother; (2) primal scene and other overstimulating parental behavior, particularly the father's genital toilet and voyeuristic habits; (3) parental fantasies about the breath, air and the lungs apparent in the patient's mother's inhibition and avoidance of kissing and hugging. The mother was overconcerned with disease transmission by saliva and the breath and she suffered from chronic bronchitis with its typical cough. (4) As with Karol's case there were sadomasochistic conflicts and fantasies.

Discussion

We are in debt to Dr. Karol for her rich and penetrating asthma paper. It is by the thorough review of clinical psychoanalytic case material that we will arrive at an understanding of the enigma of psychosomatic symptoms. In this we are in the direct tradition of Freud. Over a thirty-year period I have analyzed seven asthmatics as well as treating many more in psychotherapy and supervising the therapy of other cases. My clinical experiences are in agreement with the conclusions that Dr. Karol reaches and, like her, I find that my research correlates with and confirms the work of Melitta Sperling (1963, 1978).

Different patterns of parental overstimulation were found in each case. Characteristic was the finding that there had been no age-appropriate privacy permitted the child. There were no locks on bathroom or bedroom doors. The parents were typically compulsive, controlling people, unlike the parents of many psychotics who grossly neglect their children. The asthmatic parent's overstimulation coupled with its denial is comparable to the parent-child interactions in nonpsychosomatic patients described by Shengold (1978) in his studies on "Soul Murder."

In case one the boy slept next to his mother until late adolescence, witnessing primal scene and knowing about his father's sex with his mistress as well as being exposed to his father's toilet exhibitionism. In case two the Gothic boy's incestuous and symbiotic tie to his mother was expressed by the cats which slept with the mother and child, by the fetishistic toy animals given to the child, and by the child's being taken into the parental bed where he probably witnessed primal scene. In case three, the asthma *do novo*, in addition to probable primal scene viewing because of the characteristically open parental bedroom doors, we can see the pathological results of the father's perverse exhibitionism in the patient's voyeuristic symptoms and body-phallus identification. All three parent pairs show compulsive controlling fathers and dependent, clinging wives.

Melitta Sperling (1978) dissected out various unconscious parental conflicts that she felt predisposed a child to develop psychosomatic symptoms. In case one we can see a dependent mother who clung to her only son, using him to replace her husband whom she had lost to his mistress. She unconsciously gratified anal drives and fantasies in her dirtiness, sensitizing her son to olfactory conflict and respiratory incorporation. He could not smell his mother but on buses could identify women who were menstruating by his acute sense of smell.

In the Gothic boy, the mother's and probably the father's emasculation of their son was apparent in their intolerance of any aggression and strict discipline, in his being assigned female roles, cleaning and dishwashing, that his sister did not share, and by the mother's providing the boy replacements for herself by the fetishistic stuffed animals. In case three the father's perverse exhibitionism to his daughter caused her looking compulsion and body-phallus identification. Her mother was a dependent alcoholic and tried to infantilize her daughter.

The denial in all three families was extreme. In case one, except for an infrequent weak protest by the mother, any emotional conflict was denied. It was extraordinary the way the parents had their son return to live with them after an absence of two years without asking him how he felt: was he afraid? had he missed them? In case two, the parents denied the obvious effeminate development in their son as well as his bizarre sadomasochistic behavior and fetishism. They were only interested in the resolution of his asthma. In case three, there was complete denial of the mother's alcoholism and the father's perversions. The denial in Karol's case was highlighted by the parents' refusal to put a lock on their bedroom door even when asked by their daughter.

These findings are in agreement with the hypothesis of Dr. Karol about the role of primal scene and masochism in asthma and correlate with and confirm the work of Sperling as well as that of Langs (1974, p. 490) who noted the sadomasochistic fantasies in his asthmatic case.

For the resolution of Dr. Karol's patient's asthma, the analysis of the oedipus complex in the transference neurosis was sufficient with preoedipal material being secondary. In most of my cases the analysis of preoedipal material was essential for the resolution of their disturbance in object relations and sexual functioning. Whether more preoedipal conflicts will appear when Dr. Karol's patient attempts an adult heterosexual relationship remains to be seen.

I do know from my research (1967) on stone symbolism that Karol's patient's Hawaiian hot stone in the genital fantasy might be the little girl's anal phase idea that intercourse involves one person defecating on or in the other—the vagina and anus being confused, as well as the penis and bowel movement being equated. The hot stone can represent a fecal phallus and the steam flatus.

As concerns primal scene, I have for many years felt that we should have another term or terms for "preoedipal primal scene." When we use the term *primal scene* we unconsciously think in terms of oedipal or postoedipal primal scene events, whereas the experiences that our pregenitally fixated psychosomatic patients have been exposed to is very early primal scene and other exhibitionistic behavior, which provoke reactions that are experienced in the context of preoedipal sensory modalities and fantasies. For example, some patients' preoedipal primal scene experiences are largely auditory, visual, or olfactory. Their egos record the experience before there has been a well-developed coordination of vision with other sensory and cognitive ego functions.

In the majority of analyzed cases of asthma the primary fixations are at the anal level, which was true of my cases (Sperling 1963). However, as Sperling emphasizes, the fantasies repressed and internalized in asthma attacks are specific for the individual patient but not for asthma in general.

Relevant to preoedipal fixations and fantasies in respiratory symp-tomatology is Ira Mintz's (1975) important concept of the *internalized air mother*. He notes that the infant swallows air along with mother's milk and in this process the ambivalently loved mother comes to be symbolized by air. Asthma expresses an internalization of the air mother precipitated by separation conflicts at later maturational phases. Psychoanalytic research has focused more on bowel training and fantasies about the fecal product. The psychic meanings of intestinal gas have been relatively neglected. In recent papers on sand symbolism, the Isakower phenomenon, and smok-ing addictions (1975, 1980), I noted the paucity of analytic research on the anal meanings of smoking and that smoke often symbolizes flatus. The first asthmatic patient whose case I cited was a nonsmoker whose father chain smoked. He aptly described smoking as the "visual materialization of a fart." Smokers, like asthmatics, repetitiously internalize and exter-nalize objects (the air mother) in their habit.

The analysis of a hyperventilator showed the psychodynamic meanings of the internalized air mother. The patient, a compulsive businessman, came for the treatment of marital conflicts. On his first summer vacation separation from me he knocked himself out by hyperventilating and was taken to a physician as an emergency case. Dreams and associations revealed that he was killing me in himself by poisoning himself with air. He resisted strenuously admitting to conscious control of what he was doing; however, analysis revealed that he was an expert on breath holding and air swallowing. Fascinated by air, he had been an expert sky diver (parachute jumper). This man was a "sneaky farter." As president of a company he would let a "quiet one loose," his pleasure being in watching the reactions of his subordinates as they smelled the flatus. He revealed that when very frustrated and angry he would swallow air and save it up for farts. At times when repressing intense rage he would swallow such large quantitites of air that he was doubled up with cramps—that is, he internalized the object. He was an extremely polite, gentlemanly man whose behavior reflected an identification with his mother who was a "perfect lady." Analysis revealed that his mother and grandmother who adored him were passers of gas and he identified with them.

In the case of the asthmatic who was enuretic until five years of age (Wilson 1968), when the bedwetting was replaced by asthma, both symp-toms served the same purpose, which was to keep him tied to his mother in whose room he slept until twelve years of age. In adolescence his asthmatic attacks decreased in frequency but he developed another way of using air to terrify and control mother and others. He became an expert underwater swimmer, particularly adept at holding his breath. He would stay under water so long that he frightened people into diving to look for him. He experimented with hyperventilation, that is, the internalized air mother. Urinary fantasies were prominent in his case. He always used condoms in his sexual affairs. Following intercourse he would always go into the bathroom and urinate into the condom ostensibly to find out if there were any leaks in the rubber. Unconsciously, urine and ejaculation were equated and his repressed wish was to kill the woman by blowing her up with urine. The female was represented by the condom which was blown up like a balloon. This man's asthmatic attacks were a talion punishment for this wish to drown or blow up the mother.

I think it is important to realize that frequently the internalized air mother in an asthmatic attack is composed of flatus. The Warsaw ghetto asthmatic said that in an asthmatic attack he could not breath out dirty foul air, all air was flatus, *and to breathe was to fart.* That an asthmatic attack can express the displacement up, repression and internalization of impulses and fantasies about passing gas has not been described in the literature.

It was, of course, an inexact interpretation that aborted the status asthmaticus of the Warsaw ghetto patient. Years of experience with psychodynamic intervention in states of psychosomatic suicide such as status asthmaticus, acute ulcerative colitis, or the crises phase of the emaciated anorectic show that an interpretation of the masochistic meaning of the symptom in the transference may be life-saving. In this instance this line of interpretation had been made before when the patient had severe asthma.

I am also in agreement with Sperling (1963) that the psychosomatic object relationship originates in earliest infancy and that oral fixations and fantasies appear in every analyzed case. A careful psychiatric and psychodynamic evaluation has to be made and the diagnosis may range from psychotic (Fink and Schneer 1963) to neurotic. In the asthma *de novo* case, psychoticlike material emerged in dreams; for example, she dreamt of me as hamburger meat that she was eating. Primitive acting out occurred in the case of the male asthmatic whose urinary conflicts I detailed (Wilson 1968). When this patient's asthma cleared he became more assertive with women and took his girlfriend to a resort. At the end of the weekend he was angry at the poor service. Instead of registering his complaints with the management he defecated in a glass tumbler and left it on the bureau when he departed. His girlfriend was shocked and told him he was "nuts." Before analysis he would have had asthma in the same situation. This is an illustration of the analyzable acting out of preoedipal impulses and fantasies that replaces psychosomatic symptoms (Sperling 1968, Wilson 1968).

In a significant number of cases urinary fantasies and fixations predominate (Wilson 1968, Sperling 1963, Knapp 1963, Fink and Schneer 1963). In these cases enuresis is replaced by asthma or the reverse occurs, asthma is replaced by enuresis.

A graphic illustration of the clearing of asthma on separation from the mother, parentectomy (Peshkin 1959) occurred in case one when the patient was sent for two years to live with foster parents and was symptom-free. As regards allergies, case one was allergic to dust and chocolate, which symbolized feces and his mother. The other two cases were not allergic.

In conclusion, asthma, like other psychosomatic symptoms, is a pregenital conversion symptom (Sperling 1973). When it appears in the first years of life it develops in the context of primal repression and the precursors of the superego. The predisposition to develop asthma is established in the mother-infant relationship. As our cases show, the symptom may occur at any later phase in life when castration and separation anxieties are mobilized. In Karol's case it was the oedipal primal scene events; in the Gothic boy it occurred in mid-adolescence, and in the asthma *de novo* case, marriage and the termination of analysis.

I have attempted to document further the sadomasochistic fantasies of asthmatic patients as they surface in analysis when the asthma symptoms subside. Our technique of treatment I have detailed elsewhere (Wilson 1970) as has M. Sperling in her papers. In broad outline it is similar to the technique Boyer (1975) outlines in treating characterological and schizophrenic patients. Volkan (1975) and Kernberg (1975) likewise use parallel approaches, although their terminology differs somewhat. All of us begin with interpreting the masochism showing the patients their strict superego and its various manifestations, particularly in the transference. Preoedipal material and the defenses against aggressive drive derivatives are interpreted first, with libidinal and oedipal conflicts left until later. The outcome of analysis in my cases was favorable both in respect to clearing the asthma and resolving the underlying personality disorder. As Dr. Karol's excellent result shows, analysis is the treatment of choice for psychosomatic asthma.

REFERENCES

Boyer, B. (1975). Treatment of characterological and schizophrenic disorders. In *Tactics and Techniques in Psychoanalytic Therapy*, vol. II. *Countertransference*, ed. P. Giovacchini, pp. 361–362. New York: Jason Aronson.

Fink, G., and Schneer, J. (1963). Psychiatric evaluation of adolescent asthmatics. In *The Asthmatic Child: Psychosomatic Approach to Problems and Treatment*, ed. H. Schneer. New York: Harper and Row.

Kernberg, O. (1975). *Borderline Conditions and Pathological Narcissism*. New York: Jason Aronson.

Knapp, P. (1963). The asthmatic child and the psychosomatic problem of asthma: toward a general theory. In *The Asthmatic Child: Psychosomatic Approach to Problems and Treatment*, ed. H. Schneer, pp. 234–255. New York: Harper and Row.

Langs, R. (1974). *The Technique of Psychoanalytic Psychotherapy*, vol. 1. New York: Jason Aronson.

Mintz, I. (1975). Air symbolism in asthma and related states. Paper given at a meeting of the New Jersey Psychoanalytic Society.

Peshkin, M. (1959). Intractable asthma of childhood, rehabilitation at the institutional level with a follow up of 150 cases. *International Archives of Allergy* 15:91.

Shengold, L. (1978). The problem of soul murder. *International Review of Psycho-Analysis*. 5:457–476.

Socarides, C. (1978–1979). Transsexualism and psychosis. *International Journal of Psychoanalytic Psychotherapy* 7:373–383.

Sperling, M. (1953). Food allergies and conversion hysteria. *Psychoanalytic Quarterly* 22:525–538.

——— (1963). Psychoanalytic study of bronchial asthma in children. In *The Asthmatic Child: Psychosomatic Approach to Problems and Treatment*, ed. H. Schneer, pp. 138–165. New York: Harper and Row.

——— (1968). Acting out behavior and psychosomatic symptoms: clinical and theoretical aspects. *International Journal of Psycho-Analysis* 49:250–253.

——— (1973). Conversion hysteria and conversion symptoms: a revision of classification and concepts. *Journal of the American Psychoanalytic Association* 21:745–771.

——— (1978). *Psychosomatic Disorders in Childhood*, ed. O. Sperling. New York: Jason Aronson.

Volkan, V. (1975). *Primitive Internalized Object Relations*. New York: International Universities Press.

Wilson, C. (1967). Stone as a symbol of teeth. *Psychoanalytic Quarterly* 36:418–425.

——— (1968). Psychosomatic asthma and acting out. *International Journal of Psycho-Analysis* 49:330–333.

——— (1970). Theoretical and clinical considerations in the early phase of treatment of patients suffering from severe psychosomatic symptoms. *Bulletin of the Philadelphia Association of Psychoanalysis* 20:71–74.

——— (1975). Sand: the primary symbol of smoking addictions and of the Isakower phenomenon. *Bulletin of the Psychoanalytic Association of New York* 14:4–6.

——— (1980). Sand: the primary dream symbol of smoking addictions and the Isakower phenomenon. In *Lives, Events, and Other Players*, ed. S. Orgel and B. Fine. New York: Jason Aronson.

The Psychodynamics of a Beating Fantasy

WAYNE A. MYERS, M.D.

A case history of a woman is presented whose primary conscious masturbatory fantasy from age three until age forty was of her father beating her. Late in her lengthy treatment, the conscious fantasy was seen to screen off the underlying, unconscious fantasy of being beaten by her mother. Early traumata, surgery, and primal scene exposures led to profound separation-individuation problems, heightened preoedipal and oedipal castration anxiety, and a faulty genital schematization. Compulsive masturbation, duplicating genital arousal initiated by the mother's early enema assaults and later by primal scene exposures, allowed neutralization of the intense aggression aroused by separation and castration traumata. Preoedipal fantasies screened off from conscious awareness by the oedipal ones were influenced by the primal scene exposures. These consisted of the ideas of being hurt (castrated) and beaten by the father. In the lengthy therapy with this patient an erotized transference developed in which, again, a libidinal gratification was used defensively to maintain the threatened object relationship. The interaction between beating fantasies and reality events is also discussed.

In "A Child is Being Beaten" (1919), Freud describes the development of beating fantasies. In girls, the first phase is conscious: "My father is beating the child whom I hate" (p. 185). The fantasied beating, often of a sibling, is taken by the child as evidence that confirms the fantasy of the father's preference.

The second phase of the fantasy is unconscious: "I am being beaten by my father" (p. 185). Feelings of guilt have transformed the initial sadism into masochism. Freud sees the masochistic wish to be beaten as a regressive expression of the girl's genital wishes for sexual intercourse with the father. The form of the wish is determined by her conceptualization of coitus as a sadistic attack by the father. Freud notes that "this second phase is the most important and the most momentous of all. But we may say of it in a certain sense that it has never had a real existence. It is never remembered, it has never succeeded in becoming conscious. It is a construction of analysis" (p. 185).

One of the six cases reported in his paper, a male, was clearly able to recall the conscious masturbatory fantasy of being beaten by his mother. Freud suggests that in the male, the defensive substitution of passivity for activity may have saved the fantasy from repression.

Several other observations in the paper are relevant to this presentation. He states that in both sexes, "the beating phantasy has its origin in an incestuous attachment to the father" (p. 198). With respect to the fantasy in girls, he adds, "It is not with the girl's relation to her mother that the beating phantasy is connected" (p. 186). My own material differs considerably from that presented by Freud; for the moment, however, let us consider Freud's description of the third phase of the beating fantasy.

Freud observes that the third phase is once again conscious. The children being beaten are invariably boys and the person administering the beatings is never the father. In this third stage, the fantasy is accompanied by sexual excitation and used for masturbatory gratification. Freud comments that girls, in turning away here from genital, incestuous feelings for father, may easily abandon their femininity and wish to be boys.

I will now present a detailed clinical description of a woman with long-standing beating fantasies. This woman suffered from, and recently died of, chronic disseminated lupus erythematosus. Two findings in her case differ markedly from those described by Freud: (1) her early disclosure, in the course of twice weekly psychotherapy, that her lifelong, conscious masturbatory fantasy had been one of being beaten by her father and (2) her recognition, late in therapy, that the conscious father fantasy screened off an unconscious fantasy of being beaten by her mother.

After the case presentation, I will differentiate between my patient and those described by Freud and then review the literature on beating fantasies and related topics in order to compare and contrast prior genetic and dynamic formulations with my own. My major thrust will deal with the relationship between certain types of disturbance during the separation-individuation phase and the later development of beating fantasies. Specifically, I will consider how early pathological interactions between my patient and her mother led to intense preoedipal castration anxiety and the consequent formation of a faulty genital schematization.

In order to deal with the intense separation and castration anxiety aroused in her early years, my patient turned to compulsive masturbation for solace. The masturbation initially reduplicated the genital sensations aroused during anal assaults (enemas) by the mother. The patient achieved an identification with the phallic, aggressor mother which bound up a considerable increment of aggression and thereby helped her defend against the threat to her developing sense of self- and object-constancy. With the development of a faulty genital schematization influenced by primal scene exposures (the sense of herself as castrated), the compulsive masturbation allowed a libidinal gratification which helped neutralize the aggression associated with the ideas of being hurt (castrated) and beaten by both mother and father.

After presenting more detailed formulations about the evolution of my patient's beating fantasies, I will discuss a parallel process seen in this therapy—the development of an erotized transference. As in the original masturbatory fantasies, a libidinal gratification was used defensively to neutralize excessive aggression which threatened to disrupt an important object relationship. One final point touched upon is the interaction between reality events and the development of, and later vicissitudes involving, beating fantasies.

CASE HISTORY

Early History

Mrs. A was an only child from a lower-middle-class family. Her mother kept her physically close during her childhood and rarely allowed her to express her individuality. The father was seen as frustrated and "beaten down" by the mother. Rarely affectionate to the patient, he openly verbalized his wishes to have had a boy like an older neighbor child whose name and age were the same as those of the man the patient ultimately married. Mrs. A was frequently frightened by her father's angry outbursts toward her but never recalled actually being hit. Her sense of rejection by her parents was somewhat ameliorated by the feelings of warmth and love communicated by the maternal grandparents, in whose home her family lived until she was an adolescent. With her grandfather in particular, she felt she really "mattered as an individual."

Wearning and toilet training were accomplished before the patient was a year old. The mother vigorously dealt with constipation by administering suppositories and enemas. For most of her first two years, Mrs. A slept in the parental bedroom because her mother needed to keep her close to "protect her from harm." Shortly after obtaining her own room, she suffered from recurrent bouts of tonsillitis with high fevers until a tonsillectomy was performed in her third year. She was tricked into going to the doctor's office for the procedure, being told by her mother she was going for ice cream. After the surgery, the mother kept the patient in the parental bedroom for several more months.

The Onset of the Beating Fantasy

After the tonsillectomy, at approximately two and a half to three, the patient recalled stuffing part of her blanket (previously carried with her as a transitional object) between her legs, creating the illusion of "something hard" being there. With the remainder of the blanket, she would attempt to cover her entire body, engulfing herself in the maternal substitute, as she rubbed the blanket and her fingers against her clitoris.

Accompanying the masturbation were fantasies of being beaten on the buttocks and genitals by a thinly disguised representation of her father: "a father, never mine, though at the same time, I know he really is my father." From puberty on, this fantasy was the sole means of achieving orgastic gratification, both in masturbation and in intercourse. From the earliest days of the masturbatory practice until the advent of puberty, the patient conceptualized herself in bisexual terms in the fantasies. She visualized herself as both her usual female self and as a twin male self-representation, both being seen as beaten by the father. Utilization of the blanket continued until she was forty, when she gave up her compulsive masturbation.

Shortly before the patient's seventh birthday, the maternal grandfather died of his second myocardial infarction. Mrs. A was not allowed to attend the funeral and did not cry about his death, though she later experienced an episode of hysterical crying after dreaming of an uncle's death. This isolation of affect is reminiscent of the Wolf-Man's response when his sister died (Freud 1918). He, too, suffered from beating fantasies.

At twenty, after an affair with an older married man, Mrs. A had brief, supportive psychotherapy with an older male therapist to whom she did not mention the beating fantasies. Shortly after, she married a man whose powerful father was visualized as a substitute for her lost grandfather. Though her husband was warm and loving, she never experienced orgasm with him without recourse to the beating fantasy.

When she was thirty, after the birth of her third child, Mrs. A became depressed and sought therapy with an older, kindly female therapist, who encouraged the patient to call often. The therapist also provided the patient with a blanket in her office to keep her warm, and Mrs. A would often curl up on the therapist's couch and act out her wishes to be engulfed by this all loving mother. Again, she was unable to mention the beating fantasies during treatment. The reduplication on the psychotherapist's couch of the masturbatory situation and the intense anxiety aroused by the fear of realizing her wishes to merge with the idealized mother, led to a worsening of the patient's anxieties and depression. She

Beating as ident. to Mother ("strong") who beats (emot + mentally or needs to merge)

was hospitalized for several months in a psychiatric unit where she received supportive psychotherapy, but no medication, from a young male resident. Following her discharge with a diagnosis of a psychoneurotic depression, she began therapy with me at the age of thirty-one.

The Course of Therapy

In the nearly fifteen years of her analytically oriented psychotherapy with me prior to her death, Mrs. A was seen in well over one thousand treatment sessions, with an initial frequency of twice a week. The extreme length of the therapy was dictated both by the tenacity of her symptoms and by the inexorable progress of her somatic illnesses. Physical symptoms referrable to most major organ systems led to innumerable visits to her internist and to other specialists and to frequent medical and surgical hospitalization, with death the ever present spectre hanging over the treatment.

During the first eight months of therapy, Mrs. A spewed out material from a variety of psychosexual and ego developmental levels. Wishes to merge with the mother or with the former female therapist were prominent. In dreams, her mother was seen as a powerful woman with a penis. Intense homosexual longing for female friends emerged, along with prominent wishes to have a penis of her own. She verbalized angry feelings about her husband and father not being strong enough as men to compel her to give up her tie to her mother.

A powerful erotized transference toward me developed. I was the wished for strong man who would enable her to cut the cord with her mother. I would marry her, make love to her, and impregnate her. In essence, I would be the idealized father-grandfather her husband and father had not been. Failing this, I would magically grant her a penis, and she would finally become the acceptable boy-child her parents had wanted. With her own penis, she would be able to replace the father in intercourse with the mother and to be united with her.

Dreams and memories of confusing fights in the parental bedroom led me to inquire gingerly whether she had ever seen or heard the parents having intercourse as a child. She answered that it seemed likely but she could not recall it. I was wary of her answers, since I felt she would accept any suggestion of mine because of the erotized transference.

Throughout these early months, and for many years thereafter, the material spilling out was matched by a flood of tears. While her tears evidenced her basic depressive mood, they often seemed unrelated to the specific content of her utterances. Since somatic concomitants of depression were not present, I entertained the diagnoses of either schizophrenia or a borderline state.

The chaotic material just described and the emergence in the eighth month of the treatment of the oedipal version of the beating fantasy (being beaten by a father) seem related to several factors. One major determinant was the intensification of Mrs. A's sense of herself as castrated, concomitant with giving birth to a male child and passing the age of thirty. The rage aroused then had been initially neutralized by union with the idealized female therapist. When this relationship led to a near enactment in reality of the preoedipal masturbatory beating fantasy, the ensuing upsurge of aggression had been turned against the self in an effort to maintain the idealization and the patient had been hospitalized. When the male resident had enforced a separation from the previous therapist, her anger was briefly externalized and she improved sufficiently to be discharged. In this setting of object loss and heightened separation and castration anxiety, the transference with me was erotized as a defense against the threat to the object relationship posed by her inordinate rage. The appearance of the beating fantasy at this time is not surprising; it had served a similar defensive purpose at an earlier developmental epoch.

Early Manifestations of the Preoedipal Beating Fantasy

In the second year of therapy, in the context of verbalizing her desires to be like her mother, Mrs. A fleetingly referred to wishes to be assaulted by a woman. The mother was symbolically endowed with phallic qualities because of the patient's fantasies of her magical ability to produce a fecal column like a penis by the use of suppositories and enemas. She offered with little direct affect associations about having felt a sense of loss (castration) after her tonsillectomy.

The idea of being assaulted by women was quickly replaced by fears of having an orgasm with her husband without a beating fantasy, lest she lose control of bowel and bladder function or lose her sense of self and merge with her husband, whom she viewed as deficient and emasculated. Here we see a clearcut defensive utilization of the oedipal beating fantasy to guard against anxiety aroused by derivatives of the preoedipal beating fantasy.

Further details of the beating fantasy with "a father" emerged, including some elaborate adolescent and adult transformations, such as those involving obvious father surrogates. In one dream of an older male teacher, for example, Mrs. A saw herself as repeatedly attempting to provoke the man into punishing (beating) her by not doing her homework. The dream finally culminated in the teacher's spanking her on the buttocks. While the patient's associations concentrated on the similarities between the teacher and the father, I did have the thought that the patient was not producing something expected of her (homework, feces) and was punished with a spanking (enema). While for me this called to mind the earlier sadomasochistic relationship with the mother, I did not think in terms of a discrete beating fantasy involving being beaten by the mother. In the transference, I became the father beating her and was seen in dreams as a Nazi concentration camp commandant, beating the patient, depicted as a Jewish prisoner.

The Family Romance Theme

In the third year of treatment, a dream in which she wondered who her real father was led to associations which uncovered a long-standing fantasy that her real father was the maternal grandfather, who had been good and loving to her. The actual father was seen as adoptive. Through this family romance theme, she was partially able to rationalize the sexual relationship with the actual father in the beating fantasies as one which did not truly constitute incest. During this period, she was still functioning at a marginal level in her real life situation.

Early in the fourth year of the therapy, Mrs. A's husband was hospitalized, first with a bleeding ulcer and then with a myocardial infarction. His illness, in its similarity to that of the maternal grandfather's, revived her feelings at his death and she felt an increased sense of herself as "empty and valueless." She incessantly demanded a baby from me and intellectualized about getting a penis.

In response to her reaction to the husband's illness, I inquired about possible fears regarding her own life because of the lupus. She met my interventions with denial and an intensification of her conscious wishes for a penis or baby from me. When these wishes were frustrated, she would attempt to provoke me to be angry with her. She frequently telephoned my office late at night declaring a state of emergency. After my repeatedly questioning her about these calls and the late hours involved, she finally admitted that she had hoped to interrupt me during intercourse. Prior to this, I had found myself getting irritated with her. I recognized, fortunately, that this was what she wanted, hoping that I would respond by punishing (beating) her. She intellectually accepted my suggestion that as a child she had probably wished to interrupt the parents and grandparents in intercourse. In her intellectualization, she connected the primal scene exposures and the beating fantasies, but the fantasies themselves, however, remained immutable.

Fears of Death

In the fifth year of treatment, she had to be medically hospitalized for serious complications of her lupus. It appeared she had only a short time to live and she became intensely depressed and suicidal. Fleeting fantasies of beating her daughter emerged, in addition to prominent feelings of depersonalization and derealization. I understood the latter as defenses against intense feelings of rage toward me and her internist for not being able to keep her alive. We were seen as impotent and castrated, as the husband and father had been, and as she herself had felt before the overwhelming power of the mother. The idea of beating her daughter was understood, at that time, only as an identification with the all powerful mother, whom she felt could keep her alive, if she could fuse with her. She had to be psychiatrically hospitalized once more but miraculously managed to survive her medical and emotional crises and returned to treatment.

By the end of the seventh year of treatment, the patient had intellectually related her beating fantasy to early primal scene experiences but was unable to relinquish her need for it. In her real life situation, she continued to exist on a very marginal level, both physically and emotionally. Her husband had taken over many of the parental and household chores.

Physically, her life was being maintained with heavy doses of steroids and other medications, which, along with antidepressant and tranquillizing drugs, produced distortions of her body image: weight gains led to more intense ideas of being pregnant. There was never, however, any evidence of lupus involvement of the brain, and no signs of organic brain damage.

The chronic lupus fevers were intellectually associated by the patient to her early febrile tonsillitis episodes. Mrs. A equated the debilitation caused by her illness with the loss of some aspect of her self (castration). This, too, I interpreted as similar to her early feelings following the tonsillectomy. In this setting, we saw an upsurge of the wishes for a baby and a penis and the already pronounced erotized transference, which seemed clearly a defense against the sense of loss of self (a feeling of heightened castration) in her acute perception of herself as a dying woman. She expressed feelings of being entitled to have my baby or to be given a penis by me, much in the manner of patients who perceive themselves as exceptions to the oedipal rules because they have suffered enough. This material is similar to data described by Blum (1973) and by Norton (1963) in papers on erotized transference and on dying patients.

Overt Psychosis in the Middle Phase of Treatment

At this point in time, I married. On noticing my wedding band, Mrs. A felt an acute and enormous sense of depression, followed by a brief period of denial of what she had seen, and then by periods of confusion and disorientation. She also experienced disturbances in reality testing, most particularly regarding the boundaries of her body and the nature of her genitalia (whether she had male or female genitals). She had to be psychiatrically hospitalized once more for a number of months. Though this was her first gross break with reality, my diagnostic confusion had long been resolved. Descriptively, a diagnosis of a schizo-affective psychosis seems most in line with her problems.

During her hospitalization, the staff psychiatrist treated her primarily with tranquillizing medications and antidepressant drugs in higher dosage than she had received before. Psychotherapy was largely supportive in nature. She saw herself as less dependent upon me after this episode and more able to express her angry feelings. Later she would view her mood change and the modifications in her reality testing as related to surviving what she had most feared, the loss of the sense of self, a kind of mini-death.

The real barrier, erected by my marriage, to the realization of her transference wishes to fuse with me made it easier for her to relate to me more realistically and integrate what she had already learned in the therapy. The hospitalization interruption also afforded some relief from intense wishes to fuse with the "maternal husband" and with me, and she felt revitalized and whole once more. Despite this salutory change, the beating fantasies persisted.

Resolution of the Beating Fantasy

In the ninth year of the therapy, the husband died of a second myocardial infarction. The medical parallel between her husband and grandfather finally allowed Mrs. A to more thoroughly mourn the dead grandfather. She also recognized that, via the medium of the husband, she had been attempting to present herself to her father as the idealized neighbor boy-male self she felt he would find acceptable.

Over the next year, Mrs. A began to experience increasing anger toward her husband and grandfather for having "abandoned" her through death, and toward her father for having rejected her for being a girl. Whenever she verbalized these feelings, I pointed out the connections between the loss of these important male figures and her own sense of castration. I also connected her need to turn her anger toward her father upon herself (expressed in the beating fantasy about "a father") to the libidinal gratification experienced during the primal scene experiences. I stressed that she had overcome her rage at the father's rejection by identifying with the castrated mother in the regressive primal-scene representation of the beating fantasies.

Mrs. A initially responded to my interpretations by attempting to become dependent on her powerful father-in-law, but as we worked through some of this material, she achieved a healthy degree of separation from him and from her own parents. She blamed her husband for allowing her to become so dependent on him and for abetting her sense of "emptiness" and "lack of value." In her increasing anger toward her husband, she was also able to feel his loss more acutely and realistically. She spoke of having been "punished enough by fate." Probably at this juncture, she was giving up her need for the oedipal beating fantasy involving "a father." The fantasy, which had its inception in traumatic events in early childhood, began to subside under the influence of traumatic reality events.

Early in the tenth year of treatment, Mrs. A's husband's gravestone was unveiled. The night of the ceremony, she dreamt of being at a dinner and being tightly embraced by an older woman she associated to her mother. Though she had felt sexually aroused by the embrace in the dream, and felt a desire to lose herself in the body of the older woman, she had turned from the woman to her attractive male dinner partner. Six months later, after dating several men, Mrs. A had sexual intercourse with one and finally achieved multiple orgasms during intercourse without recourse to the beating fantasies.

The patient saw her husband to be as less capable of closeness than her late husband or her mother and, consequently, as less overwhelming. When he proposed marriage, however, she became anxious and verbally lambasted her daughter. She felt guilty about, and frightened by, the expressed intensity of this actual rage (previously she had only had angry fantasies about the daughter). She saw her anger as an identification with the all-powerful mother, and I pointed out its use as a defense against wishes to fuse with the new husband (mother).

After she married the second husband, in the eleventh year of the therapy, she continually experienced orgasms in intercourse without using a beating fantasy. The beating fantasy cropped up only on rare occasions, as when her new husband attempted anal intercourse. In retrospect, of course, its appearance here could be related to the early enema administrations and the underlying beating fantasy involving the mother.

In the twelfth, thirteenth, and fourteenth years of therapy, a number of important changes occurred. Her physical illness was temporarily manageable, though hardly stable; as she had developed sclerodermatous changes in her esophagus and needed frequent dilatations to eat properly. Her emotional life was at its most tranquil level ever. The showers of tears in session ceased and she seemed a completely different person.

I realized now that the major defense she had utilized in therapy and in her life, had not been simply an isolation of idea and affect, but rather a more complex situation involving a splitting within the ego. She both knew and did not know certain facts at the same time. Her capacity to organize and synthesize painful information had been impaired. Since her psychiatric hospitalization following my own marriage, in the seventh year of the therapy, this impairment had largely been ameliorated.

At this time, Mrs. A spontaneously became interested in understanding the genesis of her beating fantasy. I was wary, initially, of having her pursue this for two reasons: (1) I feared upsetting the obvious improvement in her psychic state. (2) I had the nagging feeling that I was being subtly coerced into a path which, in risking her peace of mind, might represent an acting out in the transference of the masturbatory beating fantasy. In this situation, I hedged my bets both by proceeding cautiously with analysis of material brought up and by concomitantly tapering off the frequency of sessions (first to once a week and then less often). I recognized that Mrs. A's interest in understanding and integrating her problems was, in part, based on her recognition that with the advent of the scleroderma, she was living on borrowed time. It was less anxiety provoking for her to look directly at her fears of death and to feel prepared for it, than to face the possibility of being overwhelmed by unknown forces. Both her internist and I responded to her wishes to master her death anxieties by dealing honestly and straightforwardly with whatever questions she raised about her physical and emotional problems.

I was also able to interpret as a need to keep my interest her bringing up "interesting" material. She saw termination as castration on one level and as tantamount to death. She understood this concept and very effectively worked it through.

Several clinical fragments from the final phase of Mrs. A's treatment provide some sense of the fascinating material she produced then which helped to elucidate the meaning of her beating fantasies. For years following her psychotic breakdown, she had rarely ever referred to my marriage; now in the twelfth and thirteenth years of treatment, Mrs. A began to express feelings of curiosity about my wife. She wondered what she looked like and about the nature of our sexual life together. Her initial curiosity was followed by a series of sexual dreams involving me directly with an indeterminate woman, presumed to be my wife. In these dreams, the patient was aware of looking at the exciting scene and then being awakened by what seemed to be sounds. These sounds were reminiscent of a horse drawn wagon or of a truck and she felt as if it were rushing toward her from a distance. This happened about four o'clock in the morning consistently.

Effects of the Primal Scene

In associating to the dreams just described, she intellectually harkened back to her primal scene observations. When I questioned her about the wagon and about the hour of her awakening, she was shocked to recall that when she was about two, her father had worked on such a wagon, delivering milk, after losing a previous job with regular hours. She thought that he must have risen about four o'clock to begin work, but wondered whether he had not left bed later for work and whether she had not, in reality, been wakened by the sounds of parental intercourse. The idea of the truck or wagon driving at her seemed an obvious representation of her wish to replace her mother (my wife in the dream) in the primal scenes.

On one occasion, she interrupted her associations to such a dream to ask if my wife and I had any children and if they were breast or bottle fed. When I inquired why she had asked this, she spoke of hoping that my children had been breast fed; she had not been, and recalled the sensation of milk bottles being rudely shoved into her mouth. There was an accompanying feeling of soreness in her throat and a brief moment of confusion as to which parent was thrusting the bottle into her mouth. She also recollected that she must have grasped her blanket to her for security in childhood when something frightening happened to her.

I suggested to her that the probable primal scene observations had occurred around the time of the tonsillectomy, and were more likely to have been concretely perceived by her after the return to the parental bedroom. I also interpreted that the early threats to her bodily integrity and genital schematization from the enemas, febrile episodes, and tonsillectomy had been organized in her thoughts under the influence of the primal scene exposures. I noted that the confusion about which parent was shoving the bottle into her mouth probably related to her questions during the primal scene observations about who possessed what genitalia and to what had happened during the tonsillectomy to her own body (had she lost her penis?). I also once more interpreted to her that the rage she had felt in connection with her perception of herself as castrated had been largely neutralized by the libidinal gratification received from masturbation with the beating fantasy.

Mrs. A agreed with my interpretations and felt certain that the advent of the beating fantasies involving the utilization of the blanket must have begun at approximately the time of the tonsillectomy. She also began to experience a genuine sense of conviction about having really witnessed the scenes of parental intercourse and, in the months that followed, she began to produce a number of confirmatory details, recalling facts about the arrangement of the furniture in the bedrooms in her grandparents' home and nuances of parental interaction that had never been spoken of before. These details were followed by a vague recollection of movements in the parents' bed, a sudden cessation of activity, and of her father jumping out of bed and shoving her out of the doorway and back into her own room. It was never totally clear to me whether this was an actual recall or whether our constructions had given birth to this scene. What was clear, however, was that it carried with it an enormous sense of conviction about what we had been speaking of for many years.

Along with this primal scene material, there were frequent expressions of longing for the lost grandfather. She recounted countless details of his warmth and love for her and of his having possessed an attitude toward her that could only be characterized as "the milk of human kindness." After verbalizing this, she was struck by the phrase and, briefly returning to the milk-truck idea, recalled that once having returned to her own bedroom after the tonsillectomy and sojourn in her parents' room, she was located between her parents' and grandparents' bedrooms: hence she could have observed either couple having intercourse.

Memories of her grandfather offering her the bands from his cigars emerged and the round shape of the bands called to mind the caps around a child's milk bottle. The bands had also signified for her being married to him. She was suddenly excited and said this must have been the reason she was so upset when she saw my wedding band. The old wishes to have been married to the grandfather, which had been reactivated in the transference, had been shattered by the fact that I was married to someone else.

Subsequent to the above associations, Mrs. A briefly fantasized that she was my child and voiced desires to be the only one of my children allowed to nurse at my wife's breasts. When I questioned her about this, she exclaimed that in her daydreams she was my only "real child." I commented to her that she was reactivating the fantasy of the grandfather being her real father and was dealing with her disappointments over my not having married her as the "real" father had not. She agreed and began to feel angry at me and at her grandfather and to verbalize this quite clearly.

Sometime later, during the latter part of the thirteenth year of the therapy, Mrs. A had two dreams in one evening. In the first, she again dreamt of a sexual scene involving me. This time, however, the woman in the dream with me had her hair fixed in a bun in back, in the manner in which her grandmother had worn her hair. In the dream, my face looked pained, as if I were sick or angry, and she was aware of having awakened from the dream feeling anxious. Finally she had gotten back to sleep and then dreamt about some neighbor children, an older boy and a younger girl. In the dream, both children seemed the same age and looked more alike than they actually did in reality. Neither child was clothed and the little girl was staring intently at the little boy's buttocks, which seemed reddened with welt marks, as if he had been struck repeatedly with a belt.

In her associations to these dreams, Mrs. A began to perceive her anger toward her grandfather for his having abandoned her more concretely. She equated his desertion through death with my own desertion of her through marriage. The pained or angry look initially seemed to her a projection of her own angry feelings. It was only when she began to think of the second dream, with its obvious reference to the early bisexual twin version of the beating fantasy, that she wondered if the twin representation had also had its inception in the confusion over which parent had what genitals during the primal scene. She further wondered if she had attributed her grandfather's death to his having had intercourse and not to his having been a heavy smoker who died of a coronary. She recalled her father's talk about wishing that she had been a boy and felt certain that there had been an upsurge of the twin masturbatory fantasies after the grandfather's death due to her sense of loss and castration. In the original fantasy, as in the dream, she also associated the boy twin being beaten as a way of expressing her anger toward both the father and the grandfather for their having rejected her. I commented that she seemed intent on clarifying much of the chaotic material which she had spewed out early in the treatment. She said she was quite aware of that fact and told me she had been making extensive notes on all we had been speaking about. She expressed the idea of "really knowing things now," whereas in the past she had only "known things without really looking at them or understanding them." We pursued the multiple ramifications of these statements (including her overriding wish to know and master her anxieties about her impending death). The quality of knowing and not knowing at the same time, in the manner of the fetishist with a split in the ego, was also quite apparent to me. When I inquired why she was making notes on the sessions, Mrs. A spoke of her fear that the lupus would interfere with her new found clarity; this she equated with another kind of dying.

The two dreams of that one evening were referred to on a number of

occasions in the working through of much of the aforementioned material during the fourteenth year of Mrs. A's therapy. On one such occasion,
she referred to the little girl staring at the boy's reddened buttocks as an
"onlooker" and then spoke of an older woman as being a "participant in
the beating." When I questioned her about what she meant, she seemed
surprised and confused and felt that she had spoken of all of this to me
before. She mentioned that she was certain that she had told me years
before that in a number of her beating fantasies, there was "a woman, a
mother, not really mine in the fantasy, though I'm sure she really is my
mother; she helps the father do the beating of me or the boy. Sometimes
she does the beating all by herself. Those are the worst times of all."

I knew that she had never directly told me this before, though the
quality of staring intently in the sexual dreams about me had had the
"onlooker" quality she was referring to. Fleeting reference to her wishes
to be assaulted by a woman (when speaking of her mother giving her
enemas and suppositories) had been verbalized some dozen years before
and had never come up again. I did not even recall this initial reference,
and it was only after reviewing my notes of the early course of the
treatment at this time, that I discovered this allusion to the idea of being
beaten by a woman. My understanding of the events at that time is that
with the working through of the oedipal version of the beating fantasy
with "a father," the underlying preoedipal fantasy involving "a mother"
was free to emerge.

In considering with me her feeling of having told me about the fantasies
involving "a mother," Mrs. A said, "I must have" and then began to cry in
the manner of old. After a few moments, she stopped crying and angrily
screamed out: "I hate you for making me talk of this. I hate her. It's
another one of those things I've always known and not known. I'm not all
better. As far back as I can remember, there's been the mother in the
fantasies. Sometimes she just hovers over me or the boy, just the way my
own mother always tries to. Sometimes she's red with rage and keeps
hitting me on my buttocks. Just like those horrible enemas. I hate her so
much for that. She beat the shit out of me all my life and wouldn't let me
be. I hate you, too. You think you're so goddam smart. You think you
know everything and I know nothing. You and your stupid wife. She was
in some of the fantasies, too, just like my mother. Why shouldn't she be,
she beat me to you." Following this outburst, she again cried for some
moments and I feared that she might be decompensating. Fortunately,
however, she grew calmer and the session ended.

Over our next few meetings, she spoke of how upset she had been to
realize that her problems with clarity of thought had not been fully
overcome. The unverbalized statement was that she had not (and would

not) achieve the mastery she wished over the anxieties concerning her own death. I told her that I doubted that the fantasies concerning her mother had ever been totally available to her conscious mind, that they had been buried because she feared her rage toward her mother and needed to turn it back upon herself in order to prevent the destruction of the person upon whom she felt her life depended. She agreed but still felt anxious about the lack of control over her thoughts (her impending death).

Following the partial working through of this material, Mrs. A felt ready to discuss a form of modified termination with me, and we cut down the frequency of our visits to once a month, a schedule we followed until her physical deterioration became progressively worse in the fifteenth year of the therapy. She was unable to walk and became depressed by her weakness and lack of control over her musculature (likened to the loss of control of the anal sphincter in the early enemas). She began a vigorous course of physiotherapy but her constitution was too debilitated to withstand this and she succumbed to a cardiac complication of her collagen disorder. She was resigned at our last visit together in the hospital a couple of days before her death, a woman bloodied by fate but unbowed.

DISCUSSION AND REVIEW OF THE LITERATURE

The beating fantasies described by my patient differ from those described by Freud (1919). The majority of Mrs. A's fantasies were of the type Freud ascribed to the second (unconscious) phase of the fantasy—one which he felt was never remembered, but was a construction of analysis. Though my patient would say that the beater was "a father, not my father," she would also add that she knew this father surrogate really represented her actual father.

One reason for the conscious awareness of this fantasy became apparent when she revealed the defensive idea of the maternal grandfather, being her real father and the actual father, being adoptive. By this mechanism, she mitigated her sense of guilt over incestuous wishes toward the actual father. Another reason for the fantasy's being conscious was the defensive split within Mrs. A's ego: she knew and did not know of its existence at the same time. The impairment of the synthetic ego function in this psychotic woman allowed her to be aware of the unconscious portion of the fantasy. Although Freud does not clearly so state, presumably his patients were not psychotic; hence repression, and not splitting, would have been utilized defensively to block out conscious awareness of this fantasy.

A final possible reason for the fantasy being conscious in my patient was that it may have served an important defensive function in screening off even more unacceptable wishes to be beaten by the mother. Even though the mother fantasy was probably always present, it is likely it was not so in the verbally organized manner of the father fantasy. Only after the rage toward the father had been expressed could the rage toward the mother be tolerated more fully. In addition, in an attempt to master anxieties associated with her imminent death, the patient had erotized the need to know and to understand all the circumstances about her past. Since gratification associated with knowing allowed for some neutralization of the emerging rage to the mother, the preoedipal beating fantasy could surface.

One of the major genetic factors underlying this development of beating fantasies involving the mother was the prominent disturbance during her separation-individuation phase. Parental (especially maternal) ambivalence toward the patient led to a hostile clinging to the mother, in turn fostered by the mother's concomitant need to keep the patient close to her (even for a prolonged stay in the parental bedroom) presumably to deny her own hostile feelings toward the patient. In this connection, the mother also had difficulty separating from her own parents as evidenced by her living with them against her husband's expressed wishes.

Premature weaning and toilet training and the mother's use of suppositories and enemas led to an increase in aggressive feelings toward the mother. These feelings were turned against the self to defend against the threat posed by them to the developing sense of object and self-constancy. Early primal scene exposure and bouts of tonsillitis accompanied by high fevers probably contributed to early genital arousal and to distortions of body image, particularly of the genital schemata. Mrs. A's sense of herself as castrated was apparently organized unconsciously under these influences. Aggression toward both parents was neutralized by libidinal gratification achieved through masturbation accompanied by ideas of being hurt (castrated) and beaten by both men and women.

Sometime after the patient became two years old, the blanket, which had theretofore been used as a transitional object, became what Roiphe and Galenson (1973a) would refer to as an *infantile fetish* and what Bak (1974) would refer to as a *prosthetic object*. In any case, the blanket served as the prototype of her later illusory penis fantasies. The interconnections between the beating fantasies and the transitional object, or infantile fetish, will be touched upon in more detail in the concluding section of this paper.

Separations during therapy aroused intense feelings of anxiety in Mrs. A, and she viewed them both as threats to her sense of herself and as castration. Historically, oedipal disappointment at the hands of her reject-ing father, augmented by the loss of the maternal grandfather, had forced her back upon the relationship with the ambivalent mother for emotional nourishment. This process intensified her rage toward the mother and heightened her difficulties in separation.

In this setting, the male-twin idea became an integral part of the beating fantasy. In one sense, the disturbance of early genital schematization derived from early primal scene exposures; in another, the male twin represented an idealized phallic self-representation and a defense against the sense of being castrated. In addition, aggressive feelings toward both parents could be displaced onto the beaten twin. Finally, by this duplica-tion of the self-representation, the threatened loss due to intense aggres-sive wishes of the self- and object representations could be warded off. Bach (1971), in writing of imaginary companions in two female adults he had analysed, speaks of unresolved conflicts with the preoedipal mother as leading to difficulties in the later acceptance of their feminine identity, the companion serving as an idealized phallic self-representation. This is consistent with my own findings (1976) in patients who had imaginary companions and fantasy twins.

Greenacre and Bak, in their dialogue in the analytic literature on perversions, implicate preoedipal and oedipal traumata. Greenacre (1953), for example, emphasizes disturbances in the first eighteen months of life, such as the high fevers seen in my patient's bouts of tonsillitis, as determinants of the body image distortions seen in fetishists. In her 1973 paper, "The Primal Scene and the Sense of Reality," Greenacre notes that in women illusory penis formation and distortions of the genital schemata are likely to occur as a result both of early primal scene exposure and of repeated enemas during the first two years of life.

Bak, while stressing oedipal castration anxiety, also sees perverse rituals as serving to undo early separation problems. In his paper on the phallic woman, Bak (1968) reemphasizes an earlier formulation (1956): "This uncertainty of body image may also be a factor in masochism, in which the search for feelings and the reality of pain could be explained as an attempt to demarcate the body boundaries" (p. 31). In his 1974 article, "Distortions of the Concept of Fetishism," Bak observes that "in the later phase of genital schematization, which seems to take place at about thirteen to twenty months, even a temporary absence of the maternal object may create the loss of genital sensations and even some sense of loss of the genital itself, as if the mother, by removing herself, takes along with her the infant's genital. In this I hypothesize the genetic core of the indissoluble' connection between object loss and castration anxiety" (p. 211). He further states that frantic masturbation serves to reinstate the presence and stimulation of the maternal object by clinging to the genital and reproducing the sensations provided by the object.

While Bak is primarily discussing a perversion seen in men, his formulations seem to apply very well to the linkage between separation and castration anxieties seen in Mrs. A. To be more specific, during periods of heightened separation anxiety or when she felt increasingly rejected by her father, Mrs. A perceived herself as castrated. This degraded self-image was accompanied by an upsurge of aggression turned upon the self and neutralized by the libidinal gratification associated with masturbation and her fantasies. In the masturbation itself, Mrs. A duplicated sensations originally aroused by the mother. In this identification with the mother, the object tie was maintained. I shall return to this concept shortly.

Roiphe (1968) correlates the early genital phase observable in children between fifteen and twenty-four months with consolidation of self- and object representations and with the establishment of primary schematization of the genital outline. Roiphe and Galenson (1972) note that some of the children observed showed castration anxiety reactions after observing the anatomical differences between the sexes. The only children so affected at this age (fifteen to twenty-four months) were either those who had had earlier experiences that interfered with stable body schematization, such as serious illness or surgery, or those who had had experiences that interfered with a stable object representation, such as parental loss or neglect. The authors related the observed castration reactions to the rapprochement crises observed by Mahler (1966).

In later articles, Roiphe and Galenson again correlate early object loss with later faulty genital schematization (1973b) and early castration reactions with disruption in the thrust for individuation and with intensification of ambivalence in developing object relations leading to a pathological splitting of the maternal image, with the projection of the bad object (1973a). In the latter paper, they also comment on the need to turn the aggression against the self, which they see as fostering an early sadomasochistic erotization.

The many factors already mentioned in Mrs. A's history, such as the use of enemas, the bouts of tonsillitis, the early surgery, the maternal ambivalence, and the exposure to the nude adult bodies of her parents in the primal scene exposures, are similar to those mentioned by Roiphe and Galenson. To state my findings in their terms, the factors just mentioned led to faulty genital schematization (seen in the male-twin fantasy) and to heightened castration anxiety, which in turn led to marked problems in separation-individuation (the rapprochement crises), straining the already difficult mother-child relationship, and thereby promulgating increasing degrees of separation and castration anxiety in a vicious circle.

All of this led to the need to turn the heightened aggression against the self and to neutralize it with the libidinal gratification found in masturbating. The further genital thrust of the oedipal phase and the concomitant conceptualization of coitus as a sadistic act, set the stage for the development of the beating fantasies to accompany the masturbation. Whether these were well-organized verbal fantasies of being beaten by the mother is difficult to assess. Probably some type of fantasies about being beaten by the mother did exist and were then screened off in the oedipal variant of the beating fantasy.

In the analytic literature on beating fantasies, we find that Anna Freud (1923) describes a woman whom an elaborate superstructure of daydreams enabled to feel excitation while refraining from masturbation. The case is discussed primarily in oedipal terms. Hunt (1973), in a case similar to that of Anna Freud's, follows Kohut's ideas (1971), and notes that both the beating fantasy and the associated daydream express the wish to be loved by the father, the fantasy expressing the sexual desires and the daydream the narcissistic aspects of the wish for the father's love. In the Kris Study Group monograph on beating fantasies (Fine, Joseph, and Waldhorn 1965), Kris relates the universality of beating fantasies to the child's conception of coitus as a sadistic act. Niederland (1958) also relates beating fantasies to traumatic pregenital auditory primal scene experiences which later became elaborated into oedipal beating fantasies.

The importance of preoedipal determinants of the beating fantasy, notably oral aggressive strivings toward the mother, is discussed by Bergler (1948). He describes how the boy's aggressive feelings directed against the breasts of the frustrating preoedipal mother arouse guilt, leading to a turning of the aggression on the self; the boy's own buttocks then are equated with the maternal breasts in the beating fantasy. Though he does not describe any fantasies with women doing the beating, there is a similarity between Bergler's finding and mine. The affect of guilt, however, would seem more likely to be associated with an oedipal masturbatory fantasy, and hence I feel that there is some confusion in his presentation about the level from which the date emanates.

Rubinfine (1965) sees beating fantasies as becoming fixed when the normal obsessional mechanisms of childhood fail to adequately inhibit aggressive drive derivatives because of the parents' inability to deal effectively with the child's sadistic feelings. Lester (1957), in writing of an unconscious beating fantasy in a woman, also emphasizes sadistic wishes toward the mother, as does Johnson (1930) in her analytic fragment of an adolescent boy with a beating fantasy.

Schmideberg (1948) perceives beating fantasies as derivatives of, and defenses against, pregenital anxieties and sadism. She emphasizes oral and anal elements and advances the idea that the child being beaten in the fantasy is really a substitute for the parent, the substitution occurring as a means of warding off guilt feelings. She feels that guilt arising because of the father's presence as the beater in the fantasies might lead to the substitution of the mother as the one doing the beating. She unfortunately offers no clinical material to support this idea.

Ferber and Gray (1966) emphasize that early narcissistic injuries (in the first eighteen months of life) resulting from early surgery, oral deprivations, and premature separations, lead to later beating fantasies which are utilized to control the primitive aggression which threatened the unstable self- and object representations. Their findings are similar to my own.

Novick and Novick (1973) studied the child analytic material from the Hampstead index in order to determine the role of beating fantasies in normal and pathological development. They found no beating fantasies in prelatency children. In discussing the development of beating fantasies, they see active discharge of aggressive anal impulses to beat, hit, or overpower becoming sexualized under the influence of the sadistic theory of intercourse and crystallized in final form under the impact of the discovery of the differences between the sexes. They regard beating fantasies as representing both oedipal strivings and the punishment for them. They also observe that the oedipal wish to be beaten is or can be made conscious at that time (contrary to Freud 1919). They note that the fantasies contain a portion illustrating the narcissistic tie to the mother and conclude: "Although it is clear from our material that the beating fantasy is not formed until the phallic oedipal stage is reached, the primary determinants of the beating wish . . . are preoedipal" (p. 241). They add, "The beating fantasy [is] rooted in an early sadomasochistic relationship to the mother" (p. 241) While their timetable differs from mine with respect to the appearance of the fantasy (this may relate to the later age at which they date the discovery of the difference between the sexes), the emphasis on the early sadomasochistic relationship with the mother is similar.

CONCLUSION

In delineating again what I see as the genesis of the beating fantasies in Mrs. A, I hope to underscore those issues which I consider crucial to the development of these fantasies. In so doing, I will note how my viewpoint differs from, and compares with, certain others I have included in this paper.

The basic difficulties for my patient began in the disturbed early relationship with her mother. Mrs. A's mother was a hostile, castrating woman who suffered from considerable difficulty in separating from her own parents. Her ambivalence to the patient led to difficulties in the separation-individuation phase (the rapprochement crises), which she attempted to compensate for by keeping the patient in her bedroom for an extended period of time. We may also presume that the mother allowed the patient's continued presence in the parental bedroom because of her own ambivalent attitudes about sexuality—attitudes which must have had a considerable influence on the patient's developing attitudes in that area. At any rate, the mother-child relationship was pervaded by an excessive amount of aggression, which led to a concomitant heightening of separation anxiety.

The excess aggression in the mother-child relationship was also intensified by premature weaning and toilet training and by the frequent use of enemas and suppositories. The pervasive degree of aggressive coloring to the relationship posed a severe threat to the development of object and self-constancy; hence the major problem for the patient was how to neutralize the extra aggression. Needless to say, I see beating fantasies as one method unconsciously chosen by the patient in order to bind the aggression. In what I have mentioned thus far, I am in accord with those authors who point up the role of pregenital aggression in the genesis of beating fantasies (Bergler 1948, Ferber and Gray 1966, Lester 1957, Johnson 1930, Novick and Novick 1973, Rubinfine 1965, and Schmideberg 1948). In stressing the importance of the separation-individuation period, my work underscores the important data contributed especially by Ferber and Gray (1966) in their paper on beating fantasies.

The frequent enemas and suppositories administered to the patient by her mother led to a premature genital arousal and to a concomitant confusion of anal-sadistic and genital sensations. Such a confusion would likely foster a premature sadomasochistic organization of the personality and a turning of the aggression upon the self. If we then add the high fevers and distortions of the sense of reality present during the bouts of tonsillitis, the early tonsillectomy, and the exposure to the nude adult bodies of the parents and/or grandparents in the primal scenes, we have a description of a number of factors which I see as correlated with intense experiences of preoedipal castration anxiety. While such ideas have been put forth in other contexts (Greenacre 1953, 1973, Bak 1956, 1968, 1974, Roiphe 1968, and Roiphe and Galenson 1972, 1973a,b), they have not been described previously in conjunction with beating fantasies.

A contribution of my own which I wish to underscore here, is the manner in which my patient neutralized the intense aggression she felt in conjunction with her perception of herself as castrated and with the separation crises already described. The primary resolution of her conflict was the utilization of masturbatory fantasies of being beaten. Masturbation initially served as a defense against the threatened loss of the mother, by virtue of evoking a stimulation originally associated with the mother during the premature genital arousal accompanying the enemas. This stimulation was, at least in some small part, pleasurable, hence its duplication by the patient. Under the organizing influence of the primal scene exposures, the patient identified with the castrated parent (alternately seen as the "beaten down" father and as the mother) and, in her masturbation, achieved a direct libidinal gratification associated with the idea of being hurt (castrated) and beaten by both men and women. The identification with the aggressor parents achieved in the masturbatory acts and fantasies also helped to bind a considerable amount of aggression.

It seems apparent that the beating fantasies in and of themselves were not always sufficient to relieve the anxiety aroused by the perception of herself (and her mother) as castrated. As a result of this insufficiency, the patient had to adopt the additional defenses of an illusory penis and an imaginary male twin and the adjunctive use of her blanket as both a transitional object and an infantile fetish/prosthetic object in her masturbation (Roiphe and Galenson 1973a, Bak 1974). She could thus affirm and deny the existence of feminine (maternal and self-) castration, at the same time she was experiencing a libidinal gratification. Under the repeated influence of the primal scene exposures and along with the increasing influence of the positive oedipal attachment to the father, the beating fantasy involving the mother became split off and inaccessible to consciousness and was replaced by the one involving the father.

As noted previously, the erotized transference, which emerged when Mrs. A turned thirty and gave birth to a male child, was utilized to ward off the upsurge of aggression aroused by her heightened perception of herself as castrated. This aggression was further stimulated by the loss of the idealized mother (the kindly female therapist) after the initial psychiatric hospitalization. In order for Mrs. A to protect the threatened object relationship with me (the father), the transference became erotized. This is seen as a recapitulation of the earlier erotization of the ideas of being hurt (castrated) and beaten by mother and father achieved by masturbatory gratification in the childhood beating fantasies. Hence when the meaning of the erotized transference was clear to the patient, the aggression could be expressed more directly. Concomitant with this, the displaced masturbatory gratification achieved in reality with me was diminished. With this diminution of the acting out of the displaced transference version of the oedipal beating fantasy, the unconscious idea of being beaten by the mother could rise into consciousness in a more organized fashion and be recalled.

I would like to note here, in closing, that traumatic events in reality had originally given rise to the intense aggression in the mother-child relationship which started the patient on the route to producing her beating fantasies. In adult life, a further series of reality traumas, accompanied by the maturation achieved in her lengthy therapy, allowed the patient to replace the more primitive sadomasochistic fantasy with a higher level one—albeit, one still masochistic in nature. In essence, the patient replaced her beating fantasy with a fantasy of being the exception who had "suffered enough" and who did not need to punish herself anymore. Thus there was a significant relationship to reality in both the inception of, and in the later vicissitudes accompanying, Mrs. A's beating fantasies.

REFERENCES

Bach, S. (1971). Notes on some imaginary companions. *Psychoanalytic Study of the Child* 26:159–171.

Bak, R. (1956). Aggression and perversion. In *Perversion*, ed. S. Lorand, pp. 231–240. New York: Random House.

—— (1968). The phallic woman. *Psychoanalytic Study of the Child* 23:15–37.

—— (1974). Distortions of the concept of fetishism. *Psychoanalytic Study of the Child* 29:191–215.

Bergler, E. (1948). Further studies on beating fantasies. *Psychoanalytic Quarterly* 22:480–486.

Blum, H. (1973). The concept of erotized transference. *Journal of the American Psychoanalytic Association* 21:61–76.

Ferber, L. and Gray, P. (1966). Beating fantasies, clinical and theoretical considerations. *Bulletin of the Philadelphia Association of Psychoanalysis* 16:186–206.

Fine, B., Joseph, E., and Waldhorn, H., eds. (1965). Beating fantasies and regressive ego phenomena in psychoanalysis. *Kris Study Group of the New York Psychoanalytic Institute, Monograph 1*. New York: International Universities Press.

Freud, A. (1923). The relation of beating phantasies to a daydream. *International Journal of Psycho-Analysis* 4:89–102.

Freud, S. (1918). From the history of an infantile neurosis. *Standard Edition* 17:7–122.

—— (1919). A child is being beaten. *Standard Edition* 17:175–204.

Greenacre, P. (1953). Certain relationships between fetishism and the faulty development of the body image. *Psychoanalytic Study of the Child* 8:79–98.

—— (1973). The primal scene and the sense of reality. *Psychoanalytic Quarterly* 42:10–41.

Hunt, W. (1973). Beating fantasies and daydreams revisited: presentation of a case. *Journal of the American Psychoanalytic Association* 21:817–833.

Johnson, L. (1930). A woman is being beaten: an analytic fragment. *Psychoanalytic Review* 17:259–267.

Kohut, H. (1971). *The Analysis of the Self*. New York: International Universities Press.

Lester, M. (1957). An unconscious beating fantasy. *International Journal of Psycho-Analysis* 38:22–31.

Mahler, M. (1966). Notes on the development of basic mood: the depressive mood. In, *Psychonalysis—A General Psychology: Essays in Honor of Heinz Hartmann*, ed. R. Loewenstein, L. Newman, M. Schur, and A. Solnit. New York: International Universities Press.

Myers, W. (1976). Imaginary companions, fantasy twins, mirror dreams and depersonalization. *Psychoanalytic Quarterly* 45:503–524.

Niederland, W. (1958). Early auditory experiences, beating fantasies and the primal scene. *Psychoanalytic Study of the Child* 13:471–504.

Norton, J. (1963). Treatment of a dying patient. *Psychoanalytic Study of the Child* 18:541–560.

Novick, J., and Novick, A. (1973). Beating fantasies in children. *International Journal of Psycho-Analysis* 53:237–242.

Roiphe, H. (1968). On an early genital phase. With an addendum on genesis. *Psychoanalytic Study of the Child* 23:348–365.

Roiphe, H., and Galenson, E. (1972). Early genital activity and the castration complex. *Psychoanalytic Quarterly* 41:334–348.

——— (1973a). The infantile fetish. *Psychoanalytic Study of the Child* 28:147–169.

——— (1973b). Object loss and early sexual development. *Psychoanalytic Quarterly* 42:73–91.

Rubinfine, D. (1965). On beating fantasies. *International Journal of Psycho-Analysis* 46:315–322.

Schmideberg, M. (1948). On fantasies of being beaten. *Psychoanalytic Review* 35:303–308.

Preoedipal Determinants of a Beating Fantasy

ELEANOR GALENSON, M.D.

A discussion of "The Psychodynamics of a Beating Fantasy," by Wayne Myers, M.D. This paper emphasizes the role of the parental ambivalence towards the patient in the formation of beating
fantasies described by Dr. Myers. It is postulated that excessive maternal ambivalence
interfered with the normal resolution of ambitendency during the patient's second year,
particularly with the impact of the discovery of sexual differences which takes place at that
time. Under such circumstances, a split in both self- and object representations occurs, with
a heightening of unbound aggression—the combination of which might well have led to the
formation of the maternal aspect of the beating fantasy. Subsequent primal scene exposure,
along with the excessively ambivalent paternal attitude toward the patient could only
intensify the aggression and the already faltering sense of self and object. Through
defensive identification with the aggressor in relation to both parents, the aggression was
warded off but also led to confusion in her sense of sexual identity and further problems of
self- and object constancy.

Dr. Myers' rich clinical paper describing a seriously ill patient, whose
treatment was carried out over so many years, offers valuable insights
into connections between early developmental vicissitudes and their
subsequent psychopathological sequelae. For it is precisely in such cases
that reflections of the earliest eras may be clearly and even dramatically
identified, although this may unfortunately not always contribute to a
more effective resolution, given therapeutic methods now generally
available to us.

Dr. Myers identified two findings in his patient which were unlike
those originally described by Freud. First was the lifelong conscious,
masturbatory fantasy of being beaten by a man whom the patient
recognized consciously as her father. Secondly, it was revealed during the
course of treatment that this conscious fantasy served as a screen for the
unconscious fantasy of being beaten by her mother. Dr. Myers attributes

these variations on Freud's material to the seriously disturbed preoedipal experience of his patient, a disturbance which began sometime during the separation-individuation phase and eventuated in intense preoedipal castration anxiety with consequent faulty genital schematization. Heightened aggression was neutralized in part through compulsive masturbation with the underlying fantasied identification with the aggressor, the phallic mother. Subsequently, primal scene exposure served to heighten and to organize the libidinal component of psychosexual development. But this exposure tended to promote sexual identification with father, as well as with mother, with serious consequences for many sectors of development.

I should like to begin my own discussion with a consideration of some aspects of the clinical material as it emerged during treatment. It would appear that the predominant quality of the object relationships of both parents was of a highly ambivalent nature—as evidenced by the mother's constant preoccupation with the patient's anal function and the father's characteristic rage outbursts. This lack of modulation or fusion of libidinal and aggressive affects in the parents fails to support the developmental task faced by every two- and three-year-old child—to unite the good and bad maternal and paternal images, thereby achieving a greater stability of the parental imagos. The splitting of these images impedes the establishment of reliable parental mental representation and enhances the vulnerability to anxiety in the face of separation. Paradoxically, the presence of emotionally available grandparents might aggravate, rather than ameliorate, the tendency toward splitting, merely by virtue of the constrast they offer.

The tendency towards lack of unification of the parental imagos is always accompanied by a similar split in the self-representation. Excessive fears of self-disintegration which ensue are only aggravated at the time of the discovery of the sexual anatomical differences, toward the end of the second year. In this patient, there was the history of confusion in sexual identification: she thought of herself both as a girl and as her male imaginary companion.

I believe the reconstruction outlined above is essentially in accord with Dr. Myers' views. However, I would lay greater emphasis upon the splits in both self- and object representations as constituting the core of the patient's psychopathology. Whenever her sense of self or her connection with the parents was jeopardized, panic and rage states ensued. I believe it was precisely in this connection that the beating fantasies had their origins. To be beaten by the mother in fantasy also satisfied the guilt of her rage at her mother; at the same time it affirmed the fact of her very existence. To be beaten by her father in fantasy was stimulated not only by his angry outbursts in reality, but also by the primal scene experiences, during which the tendency to merge with both parents could be counteracted by the fantasied beating by the father. In this connection, it is interesting to note that during the patient's fifth year of treatment, at a time when she was deeply depressed, she experienced feelings of depersonalization and derealization, accompanied by fleeting fantasies of beating her daughter. This could be viewed as an attempt to fortify her sense of self through identification with the daughter who is being beaten.

It is my impression that the defense of splitting is central in the psychopathology of this patient, and it appears to me of great significance that this defense could only come to the fore and be approached within the treatment situation after the patient learned of the therapist's marriage. Only then did she pursue the genesis of her beating fantasy. It was as if the patient's wish for merging with the analyst had become less threatening, because of the reality of the analyst's wife, who had "beaten" the patient in merging with him. In any event, the analyst was now a more reliable and dependable object, who would remain stable and firm in his own identity, and offer a parallel and concomitantly more dependable sense of her own stability as a person, separate and distinct from both parents.

How fascinating, then, that the patient could now recall early oral sensations of the milk bottle and her transitional object blanket—dim remembrances of what must have been a more favorable first year of life experience, later reflected in memories of her grandfather's attitude of the "milk of human kindness."

Although I agree with Dr. Myers's opinion that the working through of the oedipal version of the beating fantasy played a significant role in allowing the preoedipal maternal beating fantasy to emerge, I believe other factors were also of considerable significance. The patient's rage at the preoedipal mother could now emerge: the analyst was not available for "merging" (he had a wife in reality!) but in addition he had clearly demonstrated his steadfastness, immutability, and trustworthiness by many years withstanding the attack of the patient's psychological and physical illnesses.

In summary, I am inclined to agree with Dr. Myers's second explanation of the conscious appearance of the father in the beating fantasy, that is, the presence of a defensive split within the ego in his patient, unlike the situation in Freud's patients. However, I would like to add to his views concerning the preoedipal form of the beating fantasy involving the mother.

I believe these earlier forms of the beating fantasy, that is, the fantasy of being beaten by the mother, is a far more common, and perhaps even a universal development in girls during the anal phase of psychosexual development. While ambivalence is a feature of the anal phase object relationship of both boys and girls, the hostile component of the ambivalence is considerably more intense in girls, following their discovery of the genital anatomical differences. Roiphe and I have reported this in a series of publications (Roiphe 1968, Galenson and Roiphe 1971, 1976).

Prior experience of a disturbance in the mother-child relationship or body-image development during the first year increases the hostility that follows the girl's discovery of the genital difference sometime between sixteen and nineteen months of age. This often leads to splitting in the maternal mental representation, with projection of the "bad" object and an accompanying split in the self-representation. Problems in confusion of sexual identity and the development of infantile fetishistic attachment to inanimate objects, which serve to shore up the faltering sense of genital identity, frequently ensue. Where the attachment to the father does not offer a less ambivalent type of experience, these problems of defensive splitting are intensified.

In Dr. Myers' patient, where there was such ambivalence in relation to both parents, one would expect to find reflections of split parental as well as split self-representations. It would appear, then, that the beating fantasy might serve a dual purpose: to neutralize the rage toward both parents, and, as Bak (1956) has already pointed out, to affirm the existence of the patient's own body boundaries and her sense of self through the pain of the fantasied beatings, particularly at times of separation or rejection.

The fine clinical and theoretical work which Dr. Myers has given us will serve to clarify previously obscure aspects of adult psychopathology, particularly as he has attempted to connect various adult psychopathological features with their infantile precursors.

REFERENCES

Bak, R. (1956). Aggression and perversion. In *Perversion*, ed. S. Lorand, pp. 231–240. New York: Random House.

Galenson, E., and Roiphe, H. (1971). The impact of early sexual discovery on mood defensive organization and symbolization. *Psychoanalytic Study of the Child* 26:195–216.

——— (1976). Some suggested revisions concerning early female development. *Journal of the American Psychoanalytic Association* 24:29–57.

Roiphe, H. (1968). On an early genital phase: with an addendum on genesis. *Psychoanalytic Study of the Child* 23:348–365.

Beating Fantasies: Symbiosis and Child Battering

STUART ASCH, M. D.

A discussion of "The Psychodynamics of a Beating Fantasy," by Wayne Myers, M. D. Freud's concepts in "A Child is Being Beaten" (1919) require some revision. The fantasy may involve both parents, with the confusion of sexual identity as an additional significant element. Further, there are similarities between the phenomenon of child battering and the dynamics of Dr. Myers's patient. Also, a significant question is that while beating fantasies are probably universal among children, why do only a small number of adults have them occupy a central role in their psychosexual development and fantasy life?

Freud's classic (1919) paper is still used extensively as a basis for understanding beating fantasies. This is unfortunate since students tend to overlook that it is one of his more speculative discourses, generalized from too few cases. The paper was a premature attempt to explain the problem of masochism. Even with our present background of ego psychology, masochism is still inadequately understood today. Freud's paper was conceived too early in the development of analytic theory to be of more than historical interest now.

By describing a patient whose fantasies did not coincide with those that Freud specified, Myers highlights several inadequacies of the original study. Making use of Mahler's (1957) work on separation-individuation, Myers also emphasizes several new aspects of the problem: (1) the role of both the mother and father in the beating fantasy; (2) the confusion of sexual identity; (3) the adaptational discharge of aggression in the beating fantasy; and (4) the battered child (a theme on which I will elaborate).

The Role of Both the Mother and Father

Myers reminds us that Freud believed that the beating fantasy had its origin in an incestuous attachment to the father. This concept has persisted since the 1919 paper. In the 1957 Kris Study Group on "Beating Fantasies" (Joseph 1965), Kris himself underscored his belief in the central role of the father. As part of his suggestion that beating fantasies may well be universal (as are rescue fantasies and castration fantasies), Kris postulated that they are part of a normal oedipal constellation, the wish to be loved sexually by the father. In the young child, this is usually conceived as being beaten by him.

The study group was at a loss, however, to explain why the fantasy assumes prime importance in the psychosexual development of only certain patients. Myers offers a reasonable explanation by suggesting that the difference may derive from preoedipal problems, specifically, in the failure to separate and individuate from the mother.

Although it is true that the manifest content of such fantasies usually has father as the beater, I suspect that in those patients for whom beating is a persistent masturbatory fantasy, the father is a screen for the preoedipal object, the phallic mother. The ambivalent wishes to remain a symbiotic part of the preoedipal mother may create the differences in the vicissitudes of "normal" beating fantasies. It may be that this is the distinction between Kris's "normal" beating fantasies and those beating fantasies which are acted out, either on oneself or others. Myers's detailing of his patient's fantasy life and its genetic antecedents supports such a concept.

Confusion of Sexual Identity

An integral part of Myers's patient's pathology was her serious difficulty in accepting her self-representation as a woman, without a penis. Although there is not sufficient data in the report for corroboration, I offer some speculations on how several of her symptoms may have served to deny her defective self-representation.

The perplexing flood of tears that was so prominent during treatment, and apparently unrelated to any depressive content, may have been part of this sexual identity conflict. It is possible to consider the crying as a restitutive symptom of marked penis envy, the wish to urinate like a boy, to be a boy. Greenacre (1952) describes several forms of weeping, one of which she labels shower, stream, or flooding tearfulness. She believes this occurs "whenever the sensitive subject of penis envy arises almost to consciousness" (p.117).

The patient's fear of having an orgasm lest she lose control of her bowel and bladder functions is similarly a defense against revealing her castration. It would be evidence that she lacks the stop-cock control that boys

have. Stream weeping is controlled and steady. It combines the fantasy of
having a penis and urinating like a boy.

Myers has made it clear just how difficult it was for his patient to accept
the fact that she was not a person with a penis. Her twin fantasy was only
one of several ways that she maintained the illusion that some part of her
was a boy.[1]Similar conjecture might explain her ability to tolerate orgasm
in intercourse provided there was an associated beating fantasy. The
beating fantasy would be a restitutive phenomenon since it includes the
twin-boy part of a self-representation, the phallic mother. Actually all
men—father, husband, and grandfather—seem to represent narcissistic
object choices, in Freud's terminology, or the phallic mother part of her
unseparated mother-child self-object representation, using Mahler's concepts. The milk bottle linkage to father/grandfather can be understood
similarly as part of a girl-boy twinning unity.

Certainly the masturbatory ritual with the phallic blanket between her
legs seems to be an attempt to deny castration. But more broadly it may
represent the phallic mother as the transitional object. Castration for the
patient represented loss of mother as a phallus and the need to recapture
her. Myers quotes Bak's pertinent comment on "the indissoluble connection between object loss and castration anxiety" (1974, p. 211). This may
have served as an additional motivation for using a man to screen the
mother in the beating fantasy itself. In a curious way this patient may
have used her men as transitional objects, security blankets representing
mother. The cloaking of her genitals with a blanket is reminiscent of
Nunberg's (1947) discussion of the foreskin as an unconscious representation of the mother cloaking the boy's genitals.

The Adaptational Discharge of Aggression

One of the more serious problems that is the heritage of defective
separation-individuation is the diminished ability to deal with aggression.
An unreliable, overly ambivalent mothering object prevents the child
from developing useful ways of dealing with anger. In these pathological
mother-child interactions, the child is prevented from learning that the
mothering object can be constant despite the child's anger. At the same
time, inconstancy stimulates even more aggression in the child, and the
problem escalates. An additional complication has been raised by

---

1. This fantasy of twinning as a corrective for the fantasied loss of the penis often has
been remarked upon (e.g., Nunberg 1947 and Glenn 1966). Among the several specific
clinical examples he describes, Nunberg also includes the famous discussion from Plato's
Symposium on the splitting of the hermaphrodite precursor of man into male and female
halves that then search for each other to reunite.

Hartmann (1953). The failure to handle or neutralize aggression, in addition to a greater resevoir of aggression, may be a genetic characteristic, specifically typical of schizophrenics. Furthermore, such a pathological mother-child relationship may repeatedly reinforce the lesson that the way to be loved (as a symbiotic object) is to submit to the sadistic mother. Paradoxically, the aggression turned against the self in the masturbation fantasy also serves to establish one's separateness, to recathect the self-representation.

Myers's report seems to support his thesis that the patient discharged her aggression in masturbation, with the drives directed toward herself in the beating fantasy. This is a most valuable contribution to the understanding of these beating fantasies and leads us to an area briefly touched on by the author, the patient's intermittent impulse to beat her daughter. In this sequence we can find precursors of the battered child phenomenon.

The Battered Child

Battering is usually done by the mother; rarely does the father become involved. Although there are several different categories of battering, the most common involves a strong symbiotic tie between mother and child. One usually finds that these battering mothers have a history of difficulty in developing a self-representation separate from their own mothers in childhood. Grandmother, mother, and child remain unconsciously fused; the identities of the three generations are merged and confused. The battering mother is attacking herself, in her child, as she was attacked by her mother. The object and self-representations are inadequately separated and unstable (Asch 1974). These mothers have never developed consistent control over their impulses and characteristically are unable to control their paroxysms of rage. However, it is a mistake to assume that they hate their children; the relationships are ambivalent, with as much (symbiotic) love as rage. These battering mothers refuse to part with their children and are filled with remorse once the explosion of rage is over. Similarly, the battered child is deeply attached to the mother, often adopting a paradoxical mothering role with her. It is significant that usually only *one* child is selected to be beaten. It can almost always be documented that the chosen child is the one who is unconsciously identified with both the mother and the grandmother (Asch 1966).

Myers's patient began to decompensate after her third child was born. There were two boys and a girl. Her impulse to beat only the daughter could be explained by the fact that the same-sex child was the one most likely to be poorly separated from her own self-representation. The impulse first emerged when the lupus became exacerbated and the patient had to face realistic fears of dying. Myers's belief that these sadistic impulses were part of a magical attempt to reestablish fusion with the powerful mother, and thereby be protected from death, is consistent with our understanding of battering. When the second husband proposed, the patient's incapacity to contain her aggression in fantasy reappeared and she "verbally lambasted her daughter." One can speculate that this was now a response to the threatened separation from the mother, with a renewed attempt to recapture mother through fusion.

Myers's paper serves to correct some specific and long-standing confusions about beating fantasies. However, we are still unable to satisfactorily answer Kris's question: If beating fantasies are so common and perhaps even universal in children, what makes their role so different in different people? Why do they disappear in most adults? Why do they play such a central role in some patients' psychosexual development and fantasy life, as in Myers's case, and in still other patients are acted out in overt masochistic beating perversions?

The explanation offered by most writers, including Myers, that such patients have an early history of actual beatings, or frequent enemas, has not been substantiated clinically. The Kris Study Group could not agree on the significance of actual physical punishment in childhood, even though it could represent reality coinciding with the inner wishes of the child: "the absence of physical trauma need not influence or determine the form of the beating fantasy and conversely the presence of severe physical punishment need not play an important role" (Joseph 1965, p. 57).

We should note the therapist's dedication to this woman, who in addition to her complex and recalcitrant character and symptom pathology, was also seriously physically ill. His ability to maintain therapeutic zeal with a patient who repeatedly presented life-threatening crises, long before she finally succumbed, is admirable. Since the aim of this paper is quite different, it would be valuable if the author could provide us with another report dealing with the management of his own and also the patient's responses to the painful physical treatments which she endured and the escalating and finally fatal assaults on her body.

REFERENCES

Asch, S. (1966). Depression: three clinical variations. *Psychoanalytic Study of the Child* 21:150–171.

Asch, S. and Rubin, L. (1974). Postpartum reactions: some unrecognized variations. *American Journal of Psychiatry* 131:870–874.

Bak, R. (1974). Distortions of the concept of fetishism. *Psychoanalytic Study of the Child* 29:191–215.

Freud, S. (1919). A child is being beaten. *Standard Edition* 17:179–204.

Glenn, J. (1966). Opposite sex twins. *Journal of the American Psychoanalytic Association* 14:736–759.

Greenacre, P. (1952). *Trauma, Growth and Personality*. New York: Norton.

Hartmann, H. (1953). Contribution to the metapsychology of schizophrenia. *Psychoanalytic Study of the Child* 8:177–198.

Joseph, E., ed. (1965). Beating fantasies and regressive ego phenomena in psychoanalysis. *Kris Study Group, Monograph 1*. New York: International Universities Press.

Mahler, M. (1957). On two crucial phases of integration of the sense of identity: separation-individuation and bisexual identity. Abstr. in Panel on Problems of Identity, rep. D. Rubenfine. *Journal of the American Psychoanalytic Association* 6:121–142.

Nunberg, H. (1947). Circumcision and problems of bisexuality. *International Journal of Psycho-Analysis* 28:145–179.

REPLY BY WAYNE A. MYERS, M.D.

Both discussants reiterate some of the clinical and theoretical features in the presentation and then offer some original and stimulating formulations of their own. In addition, they raise certain questions germane to the subject of beating fantasies which I will attempt to answer briefly.

Dr. Asch notes the difficulty that my patient had in accepting the representation of herself as a woman without a penis. I am very much in accord with his formulation of her persistent weeping as being a derivative of an unconscious fantasy of urinating as a male with a penis. If this specific interpretation was not actually made to her, it was certainly in my mind at various times during her treatment. Dr. Asch has elaborated upon the patient's fantasy of an imaginary male twin self-representation, in terms of the phallic mother aspect of the patient's unseparated mother-child self-object. This is an excellent clarification of the material, as is his depiction of the patient's use of men as transitional objects. In this insightful description, Dr. Asch adds another dimension to Bak's (1974) description of the "indissoluble connection between object loss and castration anxiety" (p. 211).

The material presented by Dr. Asch about the battered child is a fascinating extension of my material which frankly never occurred to me. I see this as a highly original contribution in its own right. The three generational interrelationships described by him are quite consistent with the familial interaction seen between my patient, her mother and her daughter.

One of the most important questions raised by Dr. Asch about my paper centers about the issue of why masturbatory beating fantasies persist in certain patients and not in others. I would like to return to this thorny problem after directing my attention to some of the points raised by Dr. Galenson.

In her discussion, Dr. Galenson puts particular emphasis "upon the splits in both self- and object representations as constituting the core of the patient's psychopathology." Although I use the term *splitting* in a somewhat different sense in the paper than she does, I have no argument concerning the importance of the specific mechanism she is referring to in the early developmental difficulties faced by my patient. In whatever terms this is stated, we are both emphasizing the significance of heightened unbound aggression in the genesis of beating fantasies. She and I both see one function of the beating fantasy as being an affirmation of the body boundaries and of the sense of the self. This is in keeping with Bak's (1956) formulations concerning masochism: the reality of pain (in my paper, I have extended this to include the fantasies of painful beatings by the mother and later by the father) serves to affirm the child's feeling of its own existence as separate from that of the mother. *NOT merged —*

(However Fantasy only?)

Dr. Galenson makes the interesting observation that my marriage served the important function for my patient of insuring her sense of separateness from me. I would agree, but would add that the reality events and attendant fantasies concerning the patient's psychotic breakdown ("mini-death") episode also helped to accentuate her sense of separateness from me. Dr. Galenson's suggestion that my being able to withstand the attacks of the patient's psychological and physical illnesses was of considerable importance is also highly accurate. In the latter years of her therapy, similar comments were verbalized by the patient herself. *yes— advanced.*

I am especially gratified to note Dr. Galenson's suggestion, based on child observation, that the fantasy of being beaten by the mother, especially evident after the child's discovery of the anatomical differences, is probably a universal phenomenon in girls in the anal phase of psychosexual development. I had hoped to generate this kind of corroborative evidence by presenting my clinical material in this format.

Dr. Galenson sees beating fantasies as neutralizing the rage to the mother and as alleviating the guilt feelings engendered by such feelings of rage. In this regard, I would differ slightly with her ideas, inasmuch as I see guilt as an affect which develops later, at oedipal phase resolution.

At this juncture, I am left with the problem of answering Dr. Asch's question as to why certain patients persist in keeping the masturbatory fantasy of being beaten and why others do not. I do not know if I can offer a wholly satisfactory answer to his question, but essentially I would like to underscore my contention that chronic, *actual* (as opposed to fantasied) primal scene exposures play a strong part in the genesis of beating fantasies.

In my experience with ten patients, five women and five men who had spent their first three to twelve years in the parental bedroom exposed to the primal scene, nine of them had persistent masturbatory beating fantasies (Myers 1979). While it is obvious that many factors are of importance in the genesis of such fantasies, the organizing importance of *actual* primal scene exposure cannot be underestimated. Clearly, further work will be necessitated before this issue can more firmly be resolved.

REFERENCES

Bak, R. (1956). Aggression and perversion. In *Perversion,* ed. S. Lorand, pp. 231–240. New York: Random House.
——— (1974). Distortions of the concept of fetishism. *Psychoanalytic Study of the Child* 29:191–215.
Myers, W. (1979). Clinical consequences of chronic primal scene exposure. *Psychoanalytic Quarterly* 48.

Primitive Defenses: Cognitive Aspects and Therapeutic Handling

LESLIE S. GROH, Ph.D.

In this paper the primitive defenses first described by Melanie Klein under the label of "schizoid mechanisms" are examined. The defenses considered are splitting, the pathological uses of identification and projective identification, and the psychotic forms of denial. This examination is twofold: (1) the cognitive aspects of these defenses as described in terms of concepts developed by Jean Piaget; (2) concrete examples of the operation of these defenses during the treatment of schizophrenic patients are given and the effects of interventions based on the cognitive analysis are described. It is stressed that at times interventions, such as interpretation and confrontation, based on cognitive analysis, can temporarily and in some instances even permanently stop the operation of these defenses, allowing emotionally meaningful material to emerge which expedites the therapeutic process.

One of the important contributions of Melanie Klein was the introduction of the concept of schizoid mechanisms, for it shed a good deal of light on the dynamics of the more severe forms of psychopathology, notably the psychoses (Rosenfeld 1966) and the character disorders (Kernberg 1970, 1975).

In her original discussion of these mechanisms, Melanie Klein (1946) was somewhat tentative about how much importance she attributed to this contribution as a means of treating adult psychotics, and in answer to critics she emphasized that in her writings she concentrated on the emotional aspect of the phenomena. This deliberate disregard of cognitive events has been a characteristic of therapists with an object relations bias (Mendez and Fine 1976), probably as a reaction to what they have seen as the classical analysts' disregard for patients' feelings and their tendency not to deal with material which originates at the preverbal levels. Since at present the importance of material derived from the preverbal stages is widely accepted, it may be the time to ask whether coordinating the findings of Melanie Klein with facts derived from cognitive research may strengthen rather than weaken the Kleinian position. A good point to start such an endeavor is the schizoid mechanisms—particularly their primitive form in which they occur in psychotic patients—because of their obvious relation to thought disorder, undeniably a cognitive phenomenon. To differentiate the schizoid mechanisms which occur in the defensive structure of psychotic patients and are imbedded in severely regressed forms of thinking from those occuring in normal children and in less severe forms of psychopathology, the former will be referred to in this paper as *psychotic defenses*.

The purpose of the following is twofold. I shall argue, first, that the developmental theory which Mrs. Klein proposed to explain the origin of psychotic defenses is basically congruent with the developmental research of Piaget, and on the other hand I propose that an understanding of the cognitive mechanisms involved in the operation of these defenses helps the clinician to deal with them more effectively during therapy.

PIAGETIAN AND PSYCHOANALYTIC THEORY

Convergences and Divergences.

Piaget's study of the development of thinking from birth is clearly relevant for psychoanalytic theory, a fact recognized by a number of analysts (Sandler 1975, Silverman 1971). A more systematic work in this area was that of Décarie (1965), who studied the development of children during the first eighteen months of life, using both the methods which Spitz (1965) developed for the study of emotional growth, and those devised by Piaget (1954) for the study of the development of object concepts. Her findings leave little doubt that these two aspects of development are closely interrelated.

There are also significant areas of disagreement. Freud (1900) proposed two stages for the development of thinking, that is, the prelogical or primary process thinking stage followed by the stage of logical or secondary process thinking. In contrast, Piaget (1951) described four major developmental levels of thinking, which will be briefly given here.

The first, or sensorimotor, stage occupies the first eighteen months of life. During this period thought, perception, and action are one, and only at about nine months of age is there evidence that reproductive memory is present, that is, the child can conjure images of absent people and objects.

The next stage, which Piaget called the stage of the preconcept, occupies the period from eighteen months to five years of age. By this time the child has achieved the internal representation of the world. Concepts are, however, still primitive and based on partial similarities; symbolism is used extensively and the logical processes are very much like that in the primary process thinking of adults.

This is followed by the stage of concrete operations. Here logical reasoning in the adult sense appears, but it can only operate if the child can support his reasoning by the active physical manipulation of the subject of his reasoning. Around ten years, adult type of logic, which is purely mental, emerges. This final stage is called the stage of abstract operations.

The subdivision of the development of adult thinking into two stages has little significance for psychoanalytic theory; more important is the evidence for a period where thinking is more primitive than the primary process. In one of her early papers, Melanie Klein (1930) reported the observation that there was almost no symbolism produced by a severely psychotic child, suggesting that there may be a form of thinking even more primitive than the primary process. Collating this with Piaget's (1951) finding that there is no symbolism prior to nine months of age seems to clarify this issue.[1]

One of the controversies which developed about Melanie Klein's formulations was that she proposed that complex mechanisms were operating very early in life. Facts and concepts derived from Piaget's work strongly suggest that apart from a very primitive form of splitting and a forerunner of projective identification, no such mechanisms are possible prior to nine months. This issue will be discussed in more detail when splitting and projective identification are examined.

Another aspect of Piaget's work which has relevance for primitive defenses is the basic elements, or *schemas*, from which concepts are constructed. A concept is said to consist of a perceptual schema, a cognitive schema, and an emotional schema. These three aspects develop separately in early life but later combine to form a concept. For example, the look and feel of a baby bottle constitutes the perceptual schema; the activity of sucking it and holding it constitutes the cognitive schema (what it is for); and the satisfaction derived from it forms the emotional schema. The final meaning of the concept is always the emotional schema, for Piaget's research indicates that even in case of highly abstract concepts there is an emotional element without which the concept is meaningless. It will be suggested later that removing the emotional schema from concepts is the basis of some pathological defenses.

1. Bion (1957) distinguishes between alpha and beta type of object representations, the former being less fragmented than the latter.

The Theory of Splitting

Melanie Klein (1952) proposed that the infant splits the mother's breast, and later the whole mother, into "good" and "bad" objects.[2] This is done by organizing experiences along the lines of hedonic tone. The process involved seems to be a dim association of the parts of the mother and parts of the baby with the prevailing experience of gratification and frustration. This means that there is a "good" self corresponding to the "good" mother and a "bad" self corresponding to the "bad" mother—the splitting of the self being an outcome of the introjection of the split object. This is assumed to be the situation during the first three months of life, after which the child starts to achieve some continuity of experience and begins to integrate the split-off halves of his objects and of his self into unitary mental representations. This process of integration continues during the first few years of childhood. While this splitting occurs first passively, probably due to the primitive cognitive equipment of the infant, splitting is used later actively as an ego defense. At this later stage, feelings, relationships, and even time sequences are split-off from each other. These later splitting processes are based on the original splitting of the objects and of the self.

This formulation is based on observations during the treatment of older children and adults. Melanie Klein assumed that what she observed was a regressed state in which events that occurred normally at an earlier stage were simply repeated at an age where their recurrence is pathological. The question which is raised here is whether splitting in the infant and in the schizophrenic are the same, and at what age splitting normally occurs in the child.

Organization of experience about people into satisfying and frustrating images whose literal existence is accepted by the child was observed by Piaget (1951) during the second year of life. This research gives no evidence of splitting taking place prior to the appearance of internalized mental representations, which occur first around nine months of age. However, since Piaget is clear that, in his view, later mechanisms are always based on earlier, more primitive ones, it is not unreasonable to assume that a more primitive form of splitting occurs much earlier. In this earlier form of splitting the process would condense perception of the object, the child's body, and the prevailing experience of gratification or frustration into a single conceptual unit. This conceptual unit at this stage

2. For purposes of clarification I would like to add that the Kleinian concept of splitting, which is seen as a pathological defense in adults, should not be confused with the term splitting as used by others in the analytical literature, such as splitting of the ego into an observing and an experiencing part.

is not capable of being recalled but can function as a recognitive memory in the presence of a similar object and a similar affective state. Nor is identification which transcends mere fusion in the here and now possible until reproductive memories can be established, at the ninth month. All this suggests a stage prior to nine months where the fusion of the child, the mother, and the affect forms a concept—which can act as a basis for the experience of familiarity but which cannot be actively recalled—and a second stage where an active splitting of object and self-representations occur. It is suggested that it is this second stage to which patients regress.[3]

Since the integration of "good" and "bad" objects and selves must depend on reproductive memories of experiences, the depressive position cannot begin until this age. This means that while Piaget's research supports the theory of splitting, it suggests that Melanie Klein mistimed the beginning of the depressive position at three months when it cannot occur before the ninth month.

The conceptual structure of splitting can be defined as follows. The experiences in which pleasure and love form the emotional schema of the concept are combined into one representation of the mother while the experiences in which pain and hate constitute the emotional schema of the concept are combined into another mental representation of the same person. The same thing happens with the self-representation, a happy and loving self-image as well as a frustrated and hating self-image are formed. This occurs when the child first develops the capacity to form reproductive memories.

It is the presence of reproductive memory which starts to interfere with splitting, for the child starts to recognize that the perceptual schema of both the "good" and the "bad" object concept is the same even though the emotional schema differs. This recognition ushers in what Melanie Klein (1952) called the depressive position, that is, the "good" and "bad" mother images merge to form the realistic mother concept and the "good" and "bad" self-representations also merge to produce a unitary self-image, and so a perfectly happy self and a perfectly satisfying love object cease to exist.

ACTIVE SPLITTING AS A PATHOLOGICAL DEFENSE

In severely disturbed patients the merging of the split-off aspects of the self and its objects did not occur, or only a partial integration took place which was then undone under stress in later life. Melanie Klein (1955) thought that when the unpleasant experiences outweigh the positive

3. This early fusion is probably what psychotic patients regress to in the transference, when the patient fuses with the therapist (Kernberg 1975).

experiences, the subjective pain during integration is too great to be tolerated. This means that pleasant experiences act as a kind of "glue" during early ego development.

My approach during treatment for patients with split self- and object representations is to bring the hate into the open in therapy and even encourage the patient to indulge in daydreaming aloud during the session about how he would like to get even with his "bad" objects. Artistic expression (drawing and painting) of these feelings is also encouraged. Repetition of expression of anger over a period of time seems to erode its intensity (David Rapaport called this process "entropy"), and at this point the patient becomes able to utilize interpretations of the splitting.

I shall describe now two examples of what, after careful scrutiny during psychotherapy, turned out to be cases of ego splitting similar to those seen in young children, as well as the response which therapeutic intervention elicited. Such processes can be seen in many psychotic and borderline patients, but the underlying dynamics are more apparent in these case vignettes than in others.

Splitting Verbal from Nonverbal Communication

The patient chosen to illustrate this mechanism was a fourteen-year-old institutionalized boy. When first seen, he was hebephenic and very resistant. He was finally persuaded to paint pictures, and while painting he kept up a more or less incomprehensible soliloquy. In his pictures he depicted happy scenes in which his mother loved him, bought him things, and so forth. What could be understood from the verbal content concerned the poisoning of people, chewing them up, etc.—in other words, all that violent pregenital aggression can suggest. For example, during the first therapy hour, he painted a picture of a woman handing a boy a giftwrapped box. He labeled the woman MUMMY and the boy ME. While painting, he talked constantly in a dead monotone, of which I could understand only two sentences which he repeated several times. These sentences were: "the cook poisoned the pie" and "the dog bites the cook." After this pattern became clear to the therapist, the disparity between the happy pictures and the violent content of his speech was pointed out to him. (You paint love, you talk hate). This type of interpretation was repeated during every session over a period of three months, as a result of which the patient became increasingly more coherent, his fixed stare disappeared, and he would dart a glance toward the therapist from time to time. His voice also became quite expressive. He then stopped painting and started to talk about himself. The story which emerged was the reality of his life: a drunken father who sexually abused the mother and the two sons, and a cold and distant mother who abandoned the patient years ago. Only after he told the therapist about his sad past did he realize the emotional implications—and then he became depressed. The content of his depression was that his former belief, that his mother loved him and was waiting for him to get well, was sheer fantasy. In other words he entered the depressive position; he experienced the loss of the idealized mother.

In this case the verbal and nonverbal levels of communication were expressing, respectively, the split-off destructive and loving aspects of the patient's self and their relations to their object representations, a step which was taken to escape depression. The dynamics were similar, therefore, to the active form of splitting during infancy. Interpreting the disparity between the two modes of communication disrupted the splitting process and led to significant therapeutic gains. The interpretation achieved this because it tied both love and hate to his self (you paint love, you talk hate), uniting the loving and hating self-concepts into a complete self-representation.[4] He next developed an intensely dependent and possessive relation to the therapist. He started to resent bitterly my other patients, complained about how my "fickleness" caused him intense pain and, finally, indulged in elaborate sadistic fantasies about how he would torture me to death. All this turned out to be a mother transference, which was interpreted to him in detail.

The splitting off of the verbal and nonverbal aspects of communication was also observed in several teenage patients with borderline ego organization. In these cases the verbal communication showed pure love for everyone, while the drawings and paintings depicted raw violence. Incidentally, all these patients thought that words expressed "real" attitudes, while artistic productions were meaningless figments of the imagination. Repeated interpretation of the disparity of their words and drawings led to the realizations of their ambivalence, and the splitting of the loving and hating aspects of the self was eliminated.

Splitting the Continuity of Experience

I have seen a number of cases, not necessarily psychotic, who exhibit a marked lack of ability to experience their lives as a continuum. A good example of this occurred in a woman patient at the beginning of the third year of her therapy. When first seen, she defined her problem as twofold. The first problem was that "a monster is living inside me who tells me to

---

4. Piaget (1951) believes that the word can act as a matrix which unites two or more nonverbal concepts into a more inclusive one.

kill my children and then commit suicide." The second problem was that she felt compelled to imitate the voice and the gestures of anyone she was talking to; and if more than one person was present she could not move or say anything for she could not imitate more than one person at a time. It also transpired early in her treatment that she experienced only one emotion—fear. She was convinced that everyone would eventually turn against her and kill her, although she did not know why. In her therapy, a variety of primitive defenses were dealt with and she eventually came to experience her emotions, hate, then guilt, and finally love. Each time she recovered the ability to experience an emotion, she would be over-whelmed by it and feel it intensely and continuously for three or four days. This frightened her. She also became severely depressed after she started to experience hate and love. Although these depressive episodes lasted only a few days, they frightened her, for she thought they would lead to rehospitalization. She finally started dating and became involved with a man. After a few disappointments she showed evidence of splitting the image of her boyfriend by organizing her pleasant and unpleasant experiences with him into separate systems. This showed in her switch-ing back and forth between idealizing and despising him. These switches were in no way related to the way he treated her at the time. While she idealized him she found it difficult to remember his hostile acts towards her in the past. Similarly, when she despised him, she plainly forgot his good points, such as his obvious devotion in providing her with entertain-ment whether he could afford it or not, his remodeling her house, and so forth. Repeated interpretation of the split brought forth only despair concerning her illness and the need for treatment ("you will only get me depressed again"), and in general turned out to be nonproductive.

The differences in the effects of the interpretation of splitting in the two case vignettes are quite striking. In the first one, the interpretations were given to a severely disorganized patient who functioned on an oral sadistic level and exhibited a blatant thought disorder. Here the repeated interpretation of the splitting precipitated his growth to a higher level, that is, he entered the depressive position. He then chose a real person, the therapist, to whom he attached his severe ambivalence and eventually he worked it through in the transference. In the second case, where interpretation of the splitting only led to conscious resistance, the patient was functioning adequately on her job, and a formal thought disorder could not be demonstrated in either interviews or psychological tests for a period of six months prior to the episode described. The sequel in the treatment of this patient was that several months later she broke up with her boyfriend, became depressed, and then started to split the therapist as she had done with her boyfriend. This time the interpretation of the splitting produced the desired results and she became aware of her intense ambivalence. Further material indicated that the "good" part of the split-off image derived from her childhood relation to a kindly grandfather and that the "bad" part derived from her interaction with her brutal and sadistic father who used to beat her for no reason.

The sequence of events in this case is similar to the therapeutic response of splitting in the case of a borderline patient described by Kernberg (1975). What I refer to is the fact that the splitting could be effectively dealt with in both cases when it was brought into the transference. Neither of these two women were psychotic when this occurred. Such a maneuver is not recommended with schizophrenics, with whom an almost constant interpretation of the transference should be done from the very first session in order to prevent the development of a delusional distortion of the therapist.

PATHOLOGICAL USE OF IDENTIFICATION.

Imitation in childhood and the related psychoanalytic mechanism of identification have for many years been recognized as playing an important role for the normal development of both the ego and the superego. It is also generally agreed in the clinical literature that identification can be used as a pathological defense by both neurotic and psychotic patients.

From the conceptual point of view, true identification depends on the presence of reproductive memory, which is a prerequisite for representation of the self and of the objects. Prior to this time (ninth month) the infant experiences fusion with the object while in emotional interaction, but this cannot occur in the absence of the object. The cognitive mechanism of identification is the bringing into one unified concept the representation of the self and that of the object. This can occur on a conscious, temporary basis when someone is imitated. In such cases, Piaget (1951) found that the perceptual schema in the concept temporarily dominated the rest of the concept, that is, behavior is largely determined by environmental cues. When, however, an identification is acted out, the perceptual aspect of the concept is largely suppressed by the cognitive and emotional schemas. This means that some degree of overt or covert imitation is necessary to establish an adequate mental representation of the object before sufficient internalization allows for identification. This is the vehicle of the acquisition of language and a variety of social skills.

Identification can also be used as a defense and when this occurs it may underlie bizarre symptom formation. One of these pathological uses of identification was described by Melanie Klein (1934), who found that some patients, whose basic self-identity is riddled by "bad" objects, intensify the process of introjection of admired persons to a pathological degree in order to avoid self-hatred. In such cases the introjects are not integrated into the self, or with each other, but act as temporary self-identities. Although such patients are not aware of the multiple identities they contain, they complain of not knowing who they really are and show signs of poor integration. In my clinical experience such discontinuity in self-identity can be quite blatant in some psychotics. Other psychotics are quite aware of the drastic changes in their self-identities but are unaware of the reason for this baffling experience. Because of the obvious discontinuity in their identities, such patients are sometimes erroneously described as suffering from ego splits, although, as will be seen, this is a primitive defense quite distinct from splitting.

Rapid Shifts in Identity Not Recognized by the Patient

One of my ex-patients, a school teacher, came into treatment for a catastrophic level of anxiety and his worry concerning a bizarre sexual deviation—he had no tactile sensation in his genitals but he could get an erection and ejaculate if the woman sucked his nipples. He had a history of several episodes of psychotic depression followed by confusional states. When treatment started, some brief periods of confusional states were seen during the sessions. Although it was summer, he complained of being cold and wore a heavy overcoat with a red rose pinned to his lapel. He was extremely dependent in his relation to the therapist and kept asking for extra hours. At this stage he saw himself quite literally as a little boy who tried to make his way in a hostile adult world. In therapy his facial expression, general bearing, and voice changed two or three times every session. When this was pointed out to him he was amazed and asked for a description of his behavior. After a while he was able to positively identify an uncle, a former teacher, and a previous supervisor at work, all of whom he greatly admired. After this was clear, the therapist would inform him which identity he was acting out. This was repeated for some months until he finally ceased changing his identity, became severely depressed, and reported that he experienced himself as a replica of his mother, whom he hated and despised. When the full impact of this reached him, he sat on the floor and retched. He then asked for sympathy and said he was so disgusted with himself that he wanted to vomit himself out. In the next session, he said that he realized now that his identification with his mother was a stupid, childish fantasy, and that he was really a better person than she. From this point on, his self-respect started to improve, his clothing became more appropriate. Still later on in his therapy it transpired that in his bizarre sex act he acted out the introjected "good" mother who could feed others.

In considering the various aspects of this case history, it appears that discontinuity in self-identity was adopted to cope with a very poor self-image based on identification with a split-off "bad" mother image. After this was discovered, the patient went on to bring forth the positive, feeding aspect of the mother. Only then was he able to unite the "good" and the "bad" aspects of his self and of his object.

Rapid Shifts in Identity as Experienced by the Patient

The patient who was chosen to illustrate this form of pathological distortion in the experience of the self was an eighteen-year-old male who was severely psychotic from the age of seven. The most obvious symptom was his immobility: he spent six to eight hours a day sitting in his chair, quite motionless. He also went through a very elaborate ceremonial putting on his pajamas every evening, the purpose of which was to prevent his anger during the night from localizing in the middle of his forehead and then leaving his body in the form of a death ray that would kill his father while he slept. He also believed that he controlled the minds of everyone around him; he even put all the words into their mouths when they spoke to him. The first intervention consisted of the repeated interpretation that he identified his body with his penis, that the "death ray" represented his poisonous urine with which he wanted to destroy his father. He ignored the interpretation at first, but kept on giving details of his evening ceremony. After the interpretation was repeated during several sessions he said that he started to doubt whether he could control what everyone said, for he did not want to hear my interpretation.

He then chose to talk of some of the daily events in his life, his interaction with his parents and his younger brother. This went on for some weeks when he suddenly reported that he turned into a boy called Bill. The therapist was quite stupified by this and asked what the patient meant. He said he experienced a literal physical transformation. Bill was a real person who lived in the same block. During the next several sessions he reported similar experiences of being transformed into John and Mike, both young men about his age. While these transformations were experienced as total changes in his body, his voice, and his habits, an observer could not detect anything. This was very mysterious to the therapist, and to try to solve the mystery a double-barreled approach was adopted. First, careful note was taken of the material that preceded each transformation; and second, the patient was carefully questioned as to the physical and personal characteristics of the three boys into whom he became transformed. As therapy progressed it slowly transpired that he felt he became John when he described some annoying experience, that he felt he was

Mike when he talked about something sad, and that he experienced himself as Bill when he talked of something frightening. He revealed that the real John was a bully, the real Mike was mourning his mother, and that the real Bill was known to the others as a coward. It also transpired that the patient did not experience anger, sadness, or fear. The therapist then told him that when he was angry he imagined himself to be John, that when he was sad he imagined himself to be Mike, and when he was afraid he imagined himself to be Bill. The patient's immediate reaction was that all this puzzled him. The therapist then asked why he did not want to be angry. He said he was afraid he would lose control and do something terrible. In a similar manner he thought sadness was unpleasant and that he was ashamed of being afraid.

For several sessions after this, when he reported a change in his identity, the therapist told him that he was really angry, or sad or scared, and pointed out that the material preceeding the change of identity would have called for that particular emotion. In a few weeks' time these changes in his identity stopped and he started to experience affect appropriate to the content of his communications. He then returned to the discussion of his nightly ceremonies, which lead into material about his oedipus complex which was severely distorted by pregenital sadism.[5]

The events in this vignette are unusual in my experience, and when the first identity changes occurred I found it quite confusing. In retrospect its basis seems to have been a defensive regression of thinking to the level of the preconcept, which allowed him to assume the identity of others when he experienced an emotion, of which they were a symbol. The motivation for activating such violent defensive measures was elicited by my interpretation of his nightly ceremony, which focused attention on his destructive wish. Several months later he spontaneously discussed his identity changes again and came to the conclusion: "I did it to stop myself from killing my father."

PROJECTIVE IDENTIFICATION

This mechanism is a special, primitive form of projection which differs from the usual form of projection in that instead of an impulse, such as sexual excitement, split-off parts of the self are projected (Klein 1946). What is projected can also be an introject or some special ability or skill personified as an introject. The dynamic reasons for this are that the person feels he cannot contain and control his sadism within his ego, so he splits off the part of his self containing his sadism and projects it onto

5. For the discussion of such a primitive oedipus complex see Melanie Klein (1945) and Kernberg (1975).

some other person. This reduces the inner tension but produces persecu- .
tion anxiety for the person who is the recipient of this projection becomes
the bearer of the patient's dangerous impulses. This may precipitate
splitting off a "good" section of the self and projecting it into the now
dangerous object in order to counteract and control the destructiveness in
it. In some patients it is carried to the point that they feel there is nothing
inside them.

As Kernberg (1975) has pointed out, another consequence of projective
identification is that since the patient feels he has parts of his self in the
other person, he has gained some degree of control over that person.

Another situation in which projective identification is used is when the
patient is exposed to a realistically dangerous situation. Since he cannot
assimilate his fear he projects the kind and loving aspect of his self to
escape from his terror. This results, of course, in a significant distortion of
reality, which could easily get the patient into serious trouble.

To understand the conceptual basis of projective identification, one has
to consider the conceptual structure of the self, which is a conglomeration
of mental representations of the person engaged in various activities,
acting under the influence of various emotions, as well as the mental
representation of other people which were structured into the self-
concept.[6] In small children and disturbed adults these constituent parts of
the self-concept are not firmly integrated and under stress can be dissociated from it. If such a detached component of the self is then combined
with the image of another person, the conceptual act corresponding to
projective identification takes place.

Projecting the "Bad" Self

The patient selected to illustrate this mechanism was a divorcee in her
late twenties. She had an acute psychotic break about a year and a half
before seeing me, the precipitating factor being her discovery that her
husband had had a mistress. At that time she was confused, incoherent,
and exhibited bizarre posturing. She was hospitalized briefly and then
placed in the day center of the facility, where her treatment consisted of
structured activities (mainly painting) and psychotherapy. A year later,
her therapist left and she was then transferred to me for therapy. When
first seen, she exhibited a clearcut thought disorder and some delusional
material. The episode described below occurred twenty-three months
after the transfer, starting with her 239th therapy hour. At that time, no
thought disorder could be demonstrated for several months, and she had

6. See also the discussion of cognitive mechanisms relating to identification as discussed
above.

been employed full-time for some six weeks. In her therapy, her struggle with her envy and her fear that she might hurt people she loved were the dominant themes.

The patient arrived looking very upset. She said she was bothered by a dream of the previous night. In this dream, she saw a small, catlike animal. It was a beautiful creature with soft velvet fur and beautiful expressive eyes. She then saw it turn into an ugly, disgusting creature, like a big spider, and she decided to kill it. She wanted to beat its head with a hammer. She could not find a hammer, so she used a shoe. The animal collapsed, did not try to fight or run away, just looked at her with her sad, hurt eyes. She wanted to kill her, put her out of her misery, but could not. She then woke up, upset and depressed. A little later her depression turned into anger.

The therapist interpreted that the beautiful catlike creature represented a beautiful woman whom the patient's envy turned into a disgusting creature.[7] The rest of the sequence expressed her struggle with her envy and destructiveness.

The patient offered an alternative interpretation. She thought that in the dream her aggressive part attacked her kind part.

The therapist pointed out that during the last few sessions she became increasingly more disturbed over her envy of a woman who gave her considerable help in obtaining and keeping her recently acquired job.[8]

The patient arrived punctually for the next session, sat down but stayed silent. When asked what the trouble was, she said she had nothing to say. This behavior continued for two more sessions. In the next session she informed the therapist in a tense, angry tone that she felt humiliated by the way the therapist had interpreted her dream. She thought that the

7. In formulating the interpretation, the following material obtained in earlier sessions was considered. In her preschool years the patient was very much attached to a cat, which was her only playmate. During her childhood she enjoyed walking barefoot so she could move around silently. She often stood motionless beside doors, startling members of the family when they passed her. Her mother would liken her to a wild animal, ready to pounce on its prey. She also produced two cat dreams prior to the one reported here. In one of them she and her fellow patients were represented by cats, while in the other her mother and herself were represented by a cat and her kitten. The spiderlike ugly creature occurred several times in previous sessions as a *conscious* self-representation, especially while under the sway of her guilt over her sexual urges.

8. In my practice, interpretation of the dreams of psychotic and borderline patients differs from the interpretation of the dreams of neurotics. With the more disturbed group, I stress the current object-relation aspects, while with neurotics the unconscious symbolism is emphasized. This practice is based on the assumption that with the severely disturbed the past and the present are not differentiated and that the object relations represent the deeper (oral sadistic) material, while the symbolic aspect of the content comes from the more superficial (oedipal) level. This idea is similar to the views of Segal (1977). A higher level symbolism, as it appears in fantasy and dreams, and a lower level of symbolism, which is used in projective identification is distinguished.

meaning was so obvious that she should have seen it herself, and the therapist's explaining it to her must have been motivated by a wish to expose her stupidity. She then called the therapist a "self-satisfied pompous ass" and ran out of the office. Shortly after she arrived for her next session, she reported being afraid of me. She felt she was like a frightened little mouse while the therapist was like a huge, savage cat that was ready to pounce on her and devour her. "Say something so I know you won't attack me," she said. It was interpreted to her that she put her wildcat-self, a symbol of her envy and greed evoked by the successful interpretation of her dream, into the therapist. She then said she could never accept presents or help of any value, for it made her feel cheap and worthless.

(oral sadistic) material, while the symbolic aspect of the content comes

These events can be analyzed in the following terms. During childhood, the relationship to her cat resulted in the splitting of this object into a soft, loving creature and into a silent, menacing wild animal. These object representations were then introjected, that is, connected to her self-representation without being integrated. Her facility to detach either of them from her self-representation and unite them with the representation of another person is typical of people who have not come to integrate their "good" and "bad" self- and object representations.

Projecting the "Good" Self

A school teacher, despite excellent academic credentials, found it difficult to keep jobs because of his periodic bizarre actions in class. He finally accepted a position in a school located in a tough slum area. After his first day on his new job, he told the therapist that most members of his ninth grade class carried switchblades. He then started to praise them in an exaggerated manner, commenting on their great potential, and finished his evaluation by asserting that they were kind and would not even harm a fly. These enthusiastic reports about his students continued for several sessions. He also reported that he became irritable with his girlfriend and lost his affection for her for no good reason. It was interpreted to him that since his class terrified him, he put his own kindness into them to escape his fear of thirty unruly, switchblade-carrying ghetto children. He responded by describing some threatening behavior on the part of one of the boys. Next, he was flooded by terror and quit the job the following day.

PSYCHOTIC DENIAL

The kind of denial one sees from time to time in psychotic patients is quite different from that observed in better integrated people. The neurotic version is an often verbal disclaimer of an unpleasant fact or feeling, while in the psychotic either *all* feelings are denied or the patient fails to experience affect which he expresses—often quite dramatically—in behavior.

Scotomization

The denial of all experience of affect was termed *scotomization* by Melanie Klein (1934, p. 282), "the *denial of psychic reality;* this may result in . . . the denial of external reality, and forms the basis of the most severe psychoses." This can be paraphrased by saying that if a patient denies experiencing all emotions, all concepts become meaningless.

One of my patients, a twenty-six-year-old housewife suffering from a multiplicity of delusions and cognitive impairment, came to a session somewhat upset after a rather unpleasant meeting with her mother. She described the event in a flat voice and then added that she could almost hate her mother when the latter was so derisive and unreasonable. She then added in a surprised manner: "I feel nothing." After a few second's silence she said: "Everything is strange. Nothing has a meaning any more." She then pointed at the bookcase and asked, "What's that?" The therapist told her then that she could not face her murderous hate of her mother so she denied she felt anything. The patient became rigid, brought her hands up to her face, started to cry violently and said: "My feelings are crazy, they are not real, people don't want to kill their mother." "You do." She answered: "Leave me alone, let me die, I'm rotten." She continued to sob for a while, and when this subsided the therapist asked her whether she had any feelings now. She responded in the affirmative and added that everything looked normal once more.

This scene was repeated with minor modifications fourteen times during the following three months.[9] During this period what she meant by her feelings not being real was clarified. She said that when something was right, it represented a sane idea, but when something was wrong, it was the product of a deranged mind and therefore not real. It was repeatedly explained to her that moral right or wrong and the reality of either subjective or objective events were quite distinct and unrelated. After this, scotomization did not recur in this patient, and her sadistic fantasies became available in treatment.

An examination of scotomization in terms of cognitive mechanisms appears to be helpful in that it sheds light on why a blanket denial of affect leads to a loss of meaning of all perception. Piaget (1951) concluded that all

---

9. One variation involved the denial of the reality of her unhappy childhood memories of being mistreated by her parents.

concepts consist of a perceptual schema, a cognitive schema and an emotional schema, which together constitute the concept. The final meaning of all concepts is the emotional schema, for nobody can comprehend anything unless he can relate it somehow to his inner, emotional experiences. In applying this analysis, when the schizophrenic denies *all* feeling, he dissociates the emotional part of the conceptual structure, which results in the decomposition of the inner representation of the world.

This was conceptualized by Melanie Klein (1934) as the denial of psychic reality, that is, decathecting the internal objects, or depriving self- and object representations from their emotional meaning. In Piagetian terms, the larger schemata which mediate the representations of the world are broken up, with the emotional schemata being dissociated from their perceptual ("sensory") and cognitive aspects.

Denial of the Emotional Significance of Behavior

Another patient, a twenty-one-year-old woman, was hospitalized after she piled the living room furniture in her home in the middle of the room and set fire to it. In the hospital, she was silent, morose, and periodically attacked staff members for no apparent reason. When several months of drug and ward treatment failed to produce any change in her condition, she was referred for psychotherapy. In the first session she described the events which led to her hospitalization. She was married only a few months at the time of her breakdown, and found that when her husband was at work she felt lonely and abandoned. Her clinging resulted in his spending more and more time at a local tavern. The day of the burning incident he was more than an hour late for dinner, so she became agitated and started to worry about a possible accident. Suddenly she stopped worrying, became calm and collected, and then set fire to the furniture. She assured me that not for a moment had she felt angry at her husband. The therapist then suggested that she may have expressed her latent anger by burning the furniture, to which she replied screaming: "Shut up, you s.o.b., I'm never angry!" The therapist then explained that although she had not experienced anger, she had acted angry. She denied that her shouting had meant anything, and the session was then terminated. Further treatment occurred in a therapy group, where the therapist instructed all patients to tell her when she acted angry, shouted obscenities, or threatened them with her fists. After three months of treatment, she stopped denying her anger, and her helpless rage then could be taken up and explored.

The observations described above indicate that this woman was unable to perceive and comprehend the emotional meaning of her own behavior, that is, experiencing emotions was completely dissociated from their behavioral expression. To explain this, I would like to invoke the mechanisms of assimilation and accommodation which, according to Piaget (1951), occur in a partially dissociated manner in the reasoning of young children and in the dreams and daydreams of adults. Assimilation gives control of behavior to internal cues, such as emotions, memory, and the self, while in accommodation behavior is controlled almost entirely by external cues. When the patient expressed her anger behaviorally at what she reacted to as an insult but did not experience her affect, it is not unreasonable to assume that the two mechanisms were dissociated.[10]

DISCUSSION

Developmental theory

The focus of this paper is on the cognitive aspects of some of the primitive defenses originally described by Melanie Klein (1934, 1946) under the label of "schizoid mechanisms." Kernberg (1975) more recently called these primitive, splitting-related defenses, in contrast to higher level, repression-related defenses. Since these defenses express the primitiveness of the cognitive organization of the patient, while also occurring in the context of strong, primitive emotions, a cognitive analysis of them is a logical extension of their study.

Primitive defenses are believed to be part of the normal development of the infant, and so Melanie Klein's developmental theory (1952) was examined in the light of Piaget's research findings (1951, 1954). For this purpose, two of Piaget's basic concepts were stressed, the mental representation of the self and its objects and the structure of conceptual schemata. As Decarie (1965) pointed out, the concept of representation as employed by Piaget is not very precise, and his terminology is at times also quite cumbersome. For this reason the terms "recognitive memory" (the subject acts toward the object only when he can see it), and "reproductive memory" (the subject act toward the object even when he cannot see it) were borrowed from general psychology. The transition from recognitive to reproductive memory was shown by Piaget (1955) and by Décarie (1965) to occur at eight to ten months in normal children living with their own families. That this is a crucial finding for psychoanalytic theory is suggested by the fact that the first object of which the child has a

---

10. An alternative formulation would be that the behaviorally expressed anger represented the sensorimotor mechanisms of this woman, while her lack of experiencing it expressed the operation of the verbal logic of her cognitive structure. This latter explanation does not seem to be acceptable, however, for part of the angry behavior consisted of verbal abuses.

reproducible mental image is *always* a person (Piaget 1973). Another important finding of Décarie (1965) was that this transition is not rigidly fixed; in disturbed children it may take place much later, and, as Anthony (1956) found, in autistic children it does not take place at all. Another finding of Piaget (1951), that splitting-like processes can be demonstrated in normal children, seems to corroborate some of Melanie Klein's ideas.

The conclusion was offered that the sequence of the development of object relations from primitive, fusion-like processes (during the paranoid-schizoid position) to one where the self- and object representations are at least partially differentiated (during the derpressive position) is supported by Piaget's research. This transition, however, generally occurs between the eighth and tenth months, and not three months as postulated by Melanie Klein (1952). It was also argued that since the mechanisms of projection and introjection are based on reproducible self- and object representations, they cannot operate before the transition to reproductive memory.

It was suggested that prior to age nine months, object relations take the form of the baby experiencing fusion with the object, the gratifying or frustrating affective reaction coloring the perception of both the baby and the object. This is very similar to the theoretical analysis of Ross (1975), who sees such experiences as primarily affective even though these experiences are often mistakenly taken for cognitive processes.

My conclusions clash, however, with those of Sandler (1975), who argues on the basis of Piaget's work that the child cannot manipulate mental images until after the sensorimotor stage, that is, after about eighteen months. In arriving at this conclusion, Sandler used the observations reported in *Play, Dreams and Imitation* (Piaget 1951), which I interpreted as showing the operation of splitting processes in the child. Furthermore, she ignored material in the same book which illustrated the use of play symbolism as early as the fifteenth month. A good example of the latter is when the little girl pretends to go to sleep, while using a fringed cloth or her mother's fur collar, to symbolize her pillow. This is clearly a manipulation of images.

In order to put the clinical examples discussed in the text above into perspective, a short description of the therapy I use when treating psychotics may be helpful. When I deal with psychotics, I use an expressive, exploratory form of face-to-face therapy with a considerable emphasis on obtaining fantasies, dreams, examples of artistic expression, as well as material concerning the patient's interpersonal relations, past and present. Development of a psychotic transference is prevented by a constant examination and immediate interpretation of all transference manifestations. Deep interpretation of instinctual material is given as soon as the information is clear enough, and if this stirs up various defenses, they are dealt with as they appear. Primitive defenses are handled, whenever this is possible, in terms of the unconscious fantasies in which they are embedded. When there is not enough material for this, a cognitive analysis is made. How this last technique is applied is illustrated in the clinical vignettes given above.

The disruption of primitive defenses is considered crucial, for it allows the emergence of emotionally charged material of primarily an aggressive nature, which is interpreted and the patient is given ample opportunity to ventillate.[11] The fact that schizophrenic patients produce much more destructive urges is explained by Melanie Klein's (1955) observation that patient's with a predominantly pregenital fixation tend to be more aggressive than others, an observation corroborated by Kernberg (1977) and my own experience.

When I use interventions based on a cognitive analysis, the patient must help by describing the subjective experience as clearly as possible, and observe what preceded the operation of the defense. My experience also suggests that when the defense occurs during the session, intervention based on cognitive analysis is most likely to get good results. There are also times when one could focus on several aspects of the patient's material, including cognitive aspects. In general, if the patient shows emotions, I prefer to interpret symbolic content. If, however, the affect is very flat, I find that dealing with the cognitive material is more likely to expose the affect.

Cognitive Aspects of Primitive Defenses

As mentioned earlier, Piaget's work suggests two levels of primary process thinking: one based on mental processes involving recognitive memory originating from the first nine months of life, and another developed during the later part of infancy and corresponding to thinking usually found in fantasies and dreams. A clinical parallel to this appears in one of Melanie Klein's (1930) earlier papers, where she described a severely psychotic child who showed hardly any ability to use symbols.

More recently, Bion (1962) suggested we distinguish between so-called beta elements of thinking, which are concrete and only suitable for projective identification, and alpha elements, which underlie fantasy and

11. The use of an expressive form of psychotherapy in the treatment of psychotics is controversial. Besides my obvious theoretical preference, I can offer the research findings of Karon and VandenBos (1972), who found that such a method is clearly superior to supportive therapy, with or without phenothiazines, for eliminating thought disorder.

dream thought and which can be stored, repressed, and elaborated. In a similar vein, Hanna Segal (1977) distinguished between symbols which are concrete and equated with the object they symbolize, and others which are experienced as symbols of the object rather than the object itself. Segal also thinks that projective identification can occur on two different levels: (1) the total equation of a part of the self with the object (this would be called fusion by other authors); and (2) a more tentative kind of projective identification not unlike the kind described by Kernberg (1975) as occurring in borderline personalities. This seems to represent some kind of consensus between leading Kleinian analysts about the existence of two kinds of primary process, and since this appears to be a parallel to the two levels of prelogical thinking, it may serve as a basis for the discussion of the clinical examples given in this paper.

1. *Splitting.* The cognitive mechanism of splitting in the two vignettes above differ markedly. In the first case splitting was based on a fragmentation of basic cognitive mechanisms, which were acting as vehicles for the expression of the patient's libidinal and destructive urges. In the other case splitting was based on the splitting of the self- and object representations along traditional Kleinian lines.

2. *The pathological use of identifications.* Again the examples given appear to reflect two different levels of cognitive organization. The first case, where the patient was not aware of his identity changes, reflects the defensive use of introjects, which were, in Kernberg's (1965) terminology, not "metabolized." Here we can see no lack of proper self- and object representation, only severe emotional disturbance. In the second case there seems to be fusion between parts of the patient's self and external objects into whom he first projected various emotions and then introjected them, indicating highly distorted self- and object representations.

3. *Projective identification.* These two patients also differed in cognitive level. The first example appeared in a woman who, at the time of the episode, was free of formal thought disorder but produced it defensively in response to a violent negative transference reaction. The segment of her self that she projected was a highly elaborate fantasy image developed during her childhood. The second patient had a formal thought disorder when the defense appeared, and it was accompanied by the actual disappearance of the projected aspect from his behavior, which suggests fusion.

4. *Psychotic denial.* Here both examples are clearcut cases of the fragmentation of the cognitive apparatus. In one case, the components of the patient's conceptual schemata were broken down into their constituent elements; in the other case major components of the cognitive apparatus were dissociated.

This reexamination of the examples suggests that it may be useful to distinguish between primitive defenses which are found in patients with formal thought disorder and other patients functioning at the borderline level. It would also appear that in psychotic patients, these defenses are based on the fragmentation of the cognitive apparatus, while in borderline patients their structure follows traditional psychodynamic lines. It is also obvious that while both the cognitive and the dynamic structure of these defenses in borderline cases can be readily understood, the cognitive aspect of these defenses as they occur in psychotics is more obscure.

There is no information in my clinical data on how psychotic patients fragment or dissociate major portions of their cognitive mechanisms. In view of the fact that such dissociations can be eliminated by verbal interventions, it is safe to conclude that such dissociations are psychological rather than neuropathological in nature. In the absence of positive evidence several hypotheses could be entertained: (a) Such fragmentation of cognitive structures could represent a regression to a very early stage of infancy where no organization except the so-called circular reactions exist, that is, the first three months of life (Piaget 1954). (b) They could be a variety of the "segmental set" caused by chronic, unbearable tension (Shakow 1977). (c) They could be the result of emotional exhaustion which the patient tries to correct by disrupting his thinking. Which alternative, if any, is correct is a question that will have to wait for an answer.

REFERENCES

Anthony, E. (1956). The significance of Jean Piaget for child psychiatry. *British Journal of Medical Psychology* 29:20–34.

Bion, W. (1957). Differentiation of psychotic from nonpsychotic personalities. In *Second Thoughts*, pp. 43–64. New York: Jason Aronson, 1977.

—— (1962). *Learning from Experience*. In W. Bion, *Seven Servants*. New York: Jason Aronson, 1977.

Décarie, T. (1965). *Intelligence and Affectivity in Early Childhood*. New York: International Universities Press.

Freud, S. (1900). *The interpretation of dreams. Standard Edition* 4 and 5.

Karon, B. and VandenBos, G. (1972). The consequences of psychotherapy for schizophrenic patients. *Psychotherapy: Theory, Research and Practice* 9:111–119.

Kernberg, O. (1965). Structural derivations of object relations. *International Journal of Psycho-Analysis* 47:236–253.

—— (1970). A psychoanalytic classification of character pathology. *Journal of the American Psychoanalytic Association* 18:800–822.

—— (1975). *Borderline Conditions and Pathological Narcissism*. New York: Jason Aronson.

Klein, M. (1930). The importance of symbol formation in the development of the ego. In *Contributions to Psycho-Analysis 1921-1945*, pp. 236–250. London: Hogarth, 1948.

—— (1934). A contribution to the psychogenesis of manic–depressive states. In *Contributions to Psycho-Analysis 1921-1945*, pp. 282–310. London: Hogarth, 1948.

———— (1945). The oedipus complex in the light of early anxieties. In *Contributions to Psycho-Analysis 1921–1945*, pp. 377–390. London: Hogarth, 1948.

———— (1946). Notes on some schizoid mechanisms. *International Journal of Psycho-Analysis* 27:99–110.

———— (1952). Some theoretical conclusions regarding the emotional life of the infant. In *Development in Psycho-Analysis*, ed. J. Riviere, pp. 198–236. London: Hogarth.

———— (1955). On identification. In *New Directions in Psycho-Analysis*. ed. M. Klein, P. Heimann, and R. Money-Kyrle, pp. 309–345. London: Tavistock.

Mendez, A., and Fine, H. (1976). A short history of the British school of object relations. *Bulletin of the Menninger Clinic* 40:357–382.

Piaget, J. (1951). *Play, Dreams and Imitation in Childhood.* London: Heinemann.

———— (1954). *The Child's Construction of Reality.* London: Kegan Paul.

———— (1973). The affective unconscious and the cognitive unconscious. *Journal of the American Psychoanalytic Association* 21:249–261.

Rosenfeld, H. (1966). *Psychotic States.* New York: International Universities Press.

Ross, N. (1975). Affect as cognition: with observations on the meaning of mystical states. *The International Review of Psycho-Analysis* 2:79–93.

Sandler, A. (1975). Comments on the significance of Piaget's work for psychoanalysis. *The International Review of Psycho-Analysis* 2:365–377.

Segal, H. (1977). Psychoanalytic dialogue: Kleinian theory today. *Journal of the American Psychoanalytic Association* 25:363–370.

Shakow, D. (1977). Segmental set: the adaptive process in schizophrenia. *American Psychologist* 32:129–139.

Silverman, M. (1971). The growth of logical thinking. Piaget's contribution to ego psychology. *Psychoanalytic Quarterly* 40:317–341.

Spitz, R. (1965). *The First Year of Life.* New York: International Universities Press.

Primitive Defenses: Cognitive Aspects and Therapeutic Handling

SUSANNA ISAACS ELMHIRST, F.R.C.P.

A discussion of "Primitive Defenses: Cognitive Aspects and Therapeutic Handling," by Leslie S. Groh, Ph.D.
One of Dr. Groh's explicit aims in this interesting and thought-provoking paper is to show that Melanie Klein's concept of schizoid mechanisms is therapeutically applicable by a psychologist. This aim he does indeed achieve, using very interesting and convincing clinical examples. However, his other aim, to provide evidence in support of Piaget's view that only at about nine months of age is abstract concept formation possible, is definitely not proven. Actually, he offers additional clinical support to the claim of Klein's followers that adult psychoses are accessible to the interpretive, psychoanalytic approach. This suggests that Klein's dating of the onset of mental mechanisms should not be lightly dismissed because observational methods do not reveal what is perceived by the psychoanalytic method.

Dr. Groh's interesting and thought-provoking paper appears at an opportune time in the history of psychoanalysis in America. Kohut and his followers are making it increasingly clear that they do not consider the psychoses amenable to the psychoanalytic method. They also imply, or actually state, that no significant psychoanalytic investigation of the psychoses has been done so far; as though the work of Abraham, Klein, Rosenfeld, Bion, and Kernberg (among others) had never been done. Further, there is among that group of analysts an increasing tendency to claim that projective mechanisms do not exist, or appear to be relevant to the narcissistic problems responding best to "self psychology."

Here comes Dr. Groh with a paper containing many convincing clinical examples of the application of Kleinian ideas and technique, particularly as developed by Rosenfeld with adult psychotics. Undoubtedly the work of Abraham and his successors does, and will, stand on its own and cannot be denied. Nevertheless, Dr. Groh's findings, from a very different background of training and environment, are a valuable support for a theoretical approach which has been both widely neglected and widely misunderstood in this country.

Further acquaintance with Bion's work, and of the way in which his findings can increase our understanding of the normal developmental use of projective identification, might have helped Dr. Groh with an area of theory which perplexes him and on which his results really throw no light. I refer to his wish to retain as proven scientific fact Piaget's claim that there is no symbolism before nine months of age. Dr. Groh's own clinical work shows clearly how the mind retains the capacity for symbolization in one aspect of the personality and has lost that capacity, or not yet gained it, in any other area. In particular, the patient Dr. Groh uses to illustrate rapid shifts in identity shows with great clarity and conviction that a patient can have extremely varied experiences of the self, actually amounting to a sense of changed identity, without giving any behavioral clue, even to the psychoanalytically experienced observer. Yet Dr. Groh continues to prefer Piaget's observations as decisive rather than those made first by Melanie Klein when she was psychoanalyzing very young children.

There are various reasons why this preference for the observation of behavior from outside, rather than looking inward, matters. Primarily, and in the long run, it is of concern because of the implicit claim that the psychoanalytic method does not truly offer a new vantage point for scientific study. Throughout history humans have had to concede that their observations were inadequate, because the tools with which they studied phenomena were not sophisticated enough. Such relegation is likely to be the fate of our present psychoanalytic techniques, though how and when remains obscure. Meanwhile, neither the observations of Piaget nor of Kohut need cause us to discard as no longer valid the notion that the capacity for symbolization is initiated whenever an infant is capable of awareness of an object, that is, perhaps even before birth.

I do not mean to imply that the majority of an infant's experiences are truly symbolic, accessible for abstract thinking. Being unable to distinguish the object and its internal representation— what Hanna Segal calls symbolic equation—appears to be the predominant experience of normal babies. The normal use of projective identification consists of the infant's concrete experiences (particularly at first the painful ones) being projected into the primary part object (usually of course the mother). In Bion's view, and terminology, these beta-elements are received by the breast (the container) which, by a process he calls reverie or alpha-function, renders them into x-elements, which are returned to the infant by the mother's care and attention, her smiles, and her speech. These alpha-elements are capable of being thought about, dreamed, remembered, and repressed. They are therefore the part-object precursors of fully developed abstract mental processes.

Bion postulates that this is an essential stage of the development of mentation and that a container which cannot sufficiently apply alpha-function to the infant's projections will distress the infant and disturb its development. Furthermore, Bion suggests, and it has been confirmed by others, that there are innate variations in the use that infants can make even of "good enough" containing part objects, some infants using projective identification more as a hostile assault on the breast than as a normal way of asking of it "what is going on inside me."

The successful psychoanalyst performs alpha-function on the patient's communications, whether or not he or she is aware of doing so. This is one of the main meanings of formulating an interpretation, verbalization of which is then the exact equivalent of the mother returning the baby's projected beta-elements in manageable form. In the more disturbed patient a simple description of what is observed may have a profound effect, as Dr. Groh has observed. Of course in paranoid states patients can perceive such observations as dangerous assaults.

Interesting and convincing support for the idea that abstract thinking begins very early, and gradually plays a larger and larger part in even very young children's mentation, comes from psychologists observing very young infant's responses to the people in its world. Fantz showed that babies under seven days preferred patterns to plain colors, preferred curved to angulated patterns, and preferred to have their visual images in focus. Carpenter's more recent work on the relationship of babies to the attributes of people is even more fascinating from our point of view. From three weeks of age a healthy baby living with its own family gives much more attention to its mother's face when she is speaking than to a stranger's face and voice, with attention clearly perceived as showing preference while eye and head aversion is recognized as revealing dislike and distrust, even distress. Least attention of all is given to the mother's face if a stranger speaks simultaneously. In these filmed experiments the babies do not cry, but they show distress in more subtle, nevertheless unmistakable ways. The experiments could not be conducted if the babies were crying at the onset. It is not clear whether the experiment is interrupted if the baby shows great distress by crying, or whether the unfamiliar surroundings mean that most babies dare not cry.

This type of work has not yet been done on babies developing abnormally, or in institutions, because a base of normal variation is still being established. So far as it goes, though, the work already supplies beautiful proof that babies remember the mother's face and her voice *and* a relationship between the two.

So we need next to consider what is the mental basis of memory. I agree with Bion that memory is impossible without alpha-elements and alpha-function. I also think, as he does, that these are related to, or equivalent to, abstract symbolic representation in the mind. So there must be the rudiments of a mind by the age of three weeks in a normal baby.

Karl Popper is explicitly opposed to what he conceived as the Freudian approach. Nevertheless, in his view "there is no such thing as passive experience: no passively impressed association of impressed ideas." He is evidently in agreement with a fundamental principle of the Kleinian approach as developed by Susan Isaacs and Bion, whether he knows it or not.

In conclusion, I would like to raise the question whether all mental experiences and mechanisms are defensive, as Groh seems to imply. Helplessness is so central to the fact and experience of an infant's life that all mental mechanisms, normal and abnormal, can be conceived of as defenses against what Bion has called "un-nameable dread." Why some babies prefer "normal" defenses and others "abnormal" is a vast and interesting question relating to the whole problem of the balance of normal and abnormal mental mechanisms throughout life. There is no period in anyone's lifetime when they could justifiably be judged as functioning normally in every area of their mental life. Recognition of this fact can increase people's empathy—be they therapists, parents, or planners of infant care—by diminishing their fear of primitive mental processes and thus their need to deny their very existence.

Reply to Dr. Frank's Discussion of "Introjection and the Idealizing Transference"

THEODORE L. DORPAT, M. D.

These comments are a continuation of a dialogue with Dr. Alvin Frank concerning Dr. Dorpat's original contribution, "Introjection and the Idealizing Transference," in the *International Journal of Psychoanalytic Psychotherapy*, volume 7, 1978–1979. Dr. Dorpat's reply was inadvertently omitted from volume 7.

IDEALIZING TRANSFERENCE OR
MIRROR TRANSFERENCE

After reviewing Dr. Frank's thought-provoking arguments and my process notes on the patient, I decided to stay with my conclusion that the patient had an idealizing transference. At most times she endowed the analyst, not herself, with attributes of omnipotence and perfection. The aggrandizement of the analyst was the most intense and enduring manifestation of her analysis. The terms *awe, admiration,* and *adulation,* noted by Frank as typical attitudes of patients with an idealizing transference, describe accurately this patient's feelings for the analyst.

One sentence in my paper was quoted by Dr. Frank in support of his argument: "Her attention was directed more to her fantasies and feelings and less consciously to the analyst." I did not mean to imply, as Dr. Frank has indicated, that the patient shifted her attention from the analyst to herself. What I meant to convey was that the patient shifted her attention from a kind of defensive and vigilant attentiveness toward the analyst to fantasies, dreams, and illusions about the analyst and herself. This change marked the beginning of the transference regression, and it occurred at the time that she "cured" herself of insomnia with the fantasy of the analyst listening to her.

It is possibly true that the patient developed a twinship transference, or some type of mirror transference in addition to the idealizing transference. Since I kept process notes on only the phase of the analysis reported in the paper, and since the analysis was ended over ten years ago, I do not have sufficient data to determine whether the patient manifested one of the mirror transferences. In my more recent analytic experiences with patients with narcissistic personality disorders, I have found that most of them develop both the idealizing transference and, at other times, one or several of the mirror transferences.

THE "REAL OBJECT" AND THE "SELF-OBJECT"

Dr. Frank's apparent disagreement on the issue of the "real object" versus the "self-object" comes from his misunderstanding of my explanations of the therapeutic process in patients with narcissistic personality disorders. I do not know to what extent his misunderstanding derives from my communication failures or to factors within Dr. Frank. It is not a matter of the real object *versus* the self-object but of *both* the real object and the self-object. Both the real object and the self-object concepts were used in my clinical descriptions and in my formulations on the introjection process. Under the self-object concept are considered the patient's need to fuse her self-representation with the representation of the analyst and her use of the analyst as an auxiliary ego and as a transitional object.

Something new—her introjection of the real object—was being added at the same time that something old, the self-object transference, was being revived. For example, the sleep-inducing power of the iris hedge fantasy came from the patient's creative fusion of what was real and new in the patient-analyst relationship with what was old and previously repressed. One may analyze the patient's analyst introject fantasies from both the self-object and real object perspectives. These fantasies were formed in part from her memories of what was new and real for her in her analytic experience. The other aspect of her analyst introject fantasies was the imagined perfection and omnipotent power of the analyst. This archaic aspect may be explained, as Frank noted, by the emergence and unfolding of the self-object transference. The formation of her analyst introject fantasies marked an intermediary stage between the kind of global fusion with the analyst which occurred during the first phase of the analysis, and the more nearly complete kind of separateness she attained at the end of the analysis.

The terms *real object* and *self-object* should not be used to refer to discrete and separable entities. It is both more accurate and useful to use them, and other object relations terms such as *new object, transference object, part object*, as words which refer to aspects of the subject's experience rather than as terms denoting separable entities. One can be tricked by the unvarying, discrete, thinglike quality of words in our language into thinking that they all must stand for unvarying, discrete, thinglike entities of some sort.

INTERNALIZATION PROCESSES IN ANALYSIS

Dr. Frank asks, "How are we to know that what is proposed is not merely an arbitrary superimposition of analytic functions and qualities onto similar characteristics newly demonstrated in the improving patient?" His question should be answered, of course, on the basis of the clinical evidence. A previous paper presented evidence of the internalization of patient-analyst relations in five patients who used analyst introject fantasies for strengthening and modifying various defective ego and superego functions (Dorpat 1974). The evidence in the present paper for the significance of patient-analyst internalization processes was derived from observing the transformations of the patient's bedtime iris hedge fantasy. She first used the fantasy of the listening analyst to put herself to sleep. Later, elements of this and other analyst introject fantasies were employed in developing her capacities for listening to herself (self-reflection) and to others.

Perhaps I did not adduce sufficient clinical evidence to confirm the hypothesis proposed in the paper on introjection and internalization processes. My aim was not to systematically test these hypotheses but to use the clinical data for investigating the various dynamic factors within both the patient and the analytic situation, which are necessary for the therapeutic introjection of patient-analyst relations. The psychoanalytic literature contains abundant clinical evidence attesting to the therapeutic significance of internalization processes in psychoanalysis (Dewald 1976, Lampl-de Groot 1956, Langs 1976, Loewald 1960, Rangell 1968, Reich 1960, and Searles 1965).

The important question is not whether such internalization processes occur but how they occur. My formulations about how they occur are congruent not only with the psychoanalytic studies cited above but also, as I indicated in the paper, with the internalization theories of Piaget and Mead.

REFERENCES

Dewald, P. (1976). Transference regression and real experience in the psychoanalytic process. *Psychoanalytic Quarterly* 45:213–230.

Dorpat, T. (1974). Internalization of the patient-analyst relationship in patients with narcissistic disorders. *International Journal of Psycho-Analysis* 55:183–188.

Lampl-de Groot, J. (1956). The role of identification in psycho-analytic procedure. *International Journal of Psycho-Analysis* 37:456–499.

Langs, R. (1976). *The Bipersonal Field.* New York: Jason Aronson.

Loewald, H. (1960). The therapeutic action of psycho-analysis. *International Journal of Psycho-Analysis* 41:16–33.

Rangell, L. (1968). The psychoanalytic process. *International Journal of Psycho-Analysis* 49:19–26.

Reich, A. (1960). Further remarks on counter-transference. *International Journal of Psycho-Analysis* 41:389–395.

Searles, H. (1965). *Collected Papers on Schizophrenia and Related Subjects.* New York: International Universities Press.

Name Index

Subject Index